I shall lift up mine eyes unto the hills
From whence cometh my help.

Psalms: cxxi, 1.

IN REMEMBRANCE

JOHN PUTNAM

1940–1962

Foreword

Professor William Clement Putnam, the author of this book, was stricken and died on March 16, 1963, at the age of fifty-four. He had taught geology for thirty-two years. This book is the result of his experience as a teacher, and of his love of teaching beginning students, especially those for whom a single elementary course would be their sole contact with the science of geology.

At the time of his death Professor Putnam had completed this manuscript, prepared the drawings, and gathered the photographs. He had not made a final selection from his collection of pictures, and he had not written the commentary to accompany the illustrations. Ten of his colleagues in the Geology Department of the University of California, Los Angeles, with the devoted assistance of Mrs. Evelyn Putnam and Mrs. Genny Schumacher, have completed his work, endeavoring, to the best of their ability, to do it as he would have liked it done.

Cordell Durrell

June 1963

Preface

An interested reader of textbooks of geology discovers that no common pattern exists in the order in which topics are presented. Talking the problem over with other instructors leads to the conclusion that here is an area of the widest divergence of opinion. The order adopted for this book is one developed in the course of thirty years of teaching and is a sequence that appeals to me, although I should be the last to claim infallibility for it. For this reason, each chapter is as self-contained as I could make it, and can be taught in nearly any sequence an instructor may desire. It does seem logical to me to proceed from the materials, such as minerals and rocks, which make up the visible Earth, through their geometric arrangement within the crust, to the various processes responsible for shaping the landscape, and to conclude with a panorama of the development of life. This arrangement, I find, gives the basic terminology, which is essential for an understanding of the science, very early in the semester. I am also convinced that an exposure to the concept of the immensity of time and to the evolutionary story as it is interpreted from the fossil record can be worked into a one-semester course. The pattern of former decades of a semester of physical geology followed by a semester of historical geology appears to be a thing of the past, and for the general student this trend toward a single course in geology is likely to persist because of the increasing number of prerequisites required of students today.

It is my hope that this book will provide more than a crutch to help pass a first course in geology, but will help in opening the door to an understanding and an appreciation of what a truly wonderful thing the world is that lies outside the classroom walls. We are one of the more footloose people on Earth, and in travels of even limited extent one inevitably encounters geology. This is especially true of a vacation trip which includes some of the national and state parks, particularly the western ones. Nearly all of them are dedicated to the preservation of some unique geologic phenomenon. I hope very much that this book may serve as a catalyst to spark an interest, which, when once aroused, can become a source of pleasure and satisfaction all the rest of one's life. Because this has been the goal I had in view in writing the book, a strong emphasis has been put on the meaning of landscape.

I have included a list of references at the end of each chapter. I tried to make this bibliography more extensive than is customary, and I also tried to make it a wide-ranging one. Included are references to popular articles as well as to research publications. The wary student may avoid the latter, but they should fire the interest of the gifted. My chief intention, though, in providing such a spread of references is to show that geology is a rapidly growing science characterized by a score of flourishing controversies, and that many of the problems with which its disciples wrestle are still unsolved.

It is my pleasant task to acknowledge the help that I received from many people, among whom are a number to whom I am delighted to express my gratitude publicly. The illustrations are the joint effort of Mrs. Peter Kurtz and myself, with her gifted draftsmanship being largely responsible for the artistic merit they may possess. The manuscript profited immeasurably from a reading by Dr. Ronald Shreve, who read it in its entirety, and by Dr. John C. Crowell, who read Chapter VI. My debt is great to Mrs. Genny Schumacher for her editing of the text. Few pages survived unscathed.

The photographs are credited in the text, but this is a most inadequate means of acknowledging my obligation to the many people and organizations that took a vital and enthusiastic part in helping me tell in pictures what can never adequately be told in words. There are far too many contributors for me to list their names individually without unduly extending the preface, but to each and all of them I wish to express my enduring gratitude. [Photographs and drawings without credit are the author's. C.D.]

To my friends and counselors at Oxford University Press I am greatly obligated for the interest, assistance, patience, and sympathetic understanding of the problems that were faced in carrying this book through to completion. I am especially grateful to John Begg, William C. Halpin, Herbert Mann, and James E. Zarbock.

I am greatly obliged to Miss Eleanor Roberts for the final typing.

My greatest debt of all is to my family for their forbearance, understanding, and shared determination in seeing the task of writing through to completion. In this regard, no words could possibly describe my indebtedness to my wife, Evelyn, or to my daughter, Margaret, or to my son, John, who while he lived was a devoted mountaineer and a good companion.

W.C.P.

Los Angeles, California
November 1962

To the Student

While my hope in writing this book is that it may help you in your course in geology, it is by no means the only source to turn to during the semester, or in later life, if you would know more of the Earth about you.

For this reason I have included a list of references at the end of each chapter. However, I have not included references to other beginning texts there; not from any desire on my part to conceal their existence but simply to avoid repetition in each list. My advice would be to consult several of these books during the course of the term, should you have an opportunity to do so, and compare their resemblances, differences, and emphases with mine. Among the texts in geology that I believe are especially helpful are:

Emmons, W. H., I. S. Allison, C. R. Stauffer, and G. A. Thiel, *Geology, Principles and Processes,* McGraw-Hill Book Co., Inc., New York, 1960.

Gilluly, James, A. C. Waters, and A. O. Woodford, *Principles of Geology,* W. H. Freeman and Co., San Francisco, 1959.

Holmes, Arthur, *Principles of Physical Geology,* Ronald Press Co., New York, 1945.

Leet, D. J., and Sheldon Judson, *Physical Geology,* Prentice-Hall, Inc., Englewood Cliffs, N. J., 1958.

Longwell, C. R., and R. F. Flint, *Introduction to Physical Geology,* John Wiley and Sons, Inc., New York, 1962.

Spencer, E. W., *Basic Concepts of Physical Geology,* Thomas Y. Crowell Co., New York, 1962.

In addition to textbooks there are other sources to turn to for assistance. Should you wish to know the precise meaning of a term, the definitions in the *Merriam-Webster International Dictionary* are very good. Another specialized dictionary which is useful is *A Dictionary of Geology,* by John Challinor, Oxford University Press, 1962. The American Geological Institute, 2101 Constitution Ave., Washington 25, D. C., publishes an excellent *Glossary of Geology and Related Sciences.* The same organization also issues a semi-monthly magazine, *GeoTimes,* which is a most helpful source for learning of the latest publications, films, and discoveries in the earth sciences. The Institute has also prepared an *Earth Sciences Sourcebook* which is published by Holt, Rinehart, and Winston, Inc., New York. This is a good place to look for material for projects, for outside reading, and for the names and addresses of each of the state geological surveys. Many of these state agencies maintain libraries and mineral collections and exhibits, or issue publications describing the local geology.

The largest single repository of geologic information in this country is the U. S. Geological Survey, an agency of the Department of the Interior, whose headquarters are in Washington, D. C. This bureau was established in 1879 and it has issued several thousand maps and documents since then. Most of these are highly specialized, but some are not, and some may describe the geologic pattern of the area in which you live. The list of publications is free and may be obtained by writing the Director, Geological Survey, U. S. Department of the Interior, Washington 25, D. C.

Nearly all the national parks issue guidebooks, and for some of the more geologically interesting ones, such as Yosemite and Grand Canyon, these publications are outstanding. Many of the larger cities have natural history sections in their museums, and these are excellent places to see fossil and mineral collections and other geologic phenomena that can be described only imperfectly in words. Outstanding in this country, as well as the world, are the American Museum of Natural History in New York, the Smithsonian Institution, U. S. National Museum in Washington, D. C., and the Chicago Museum of Natural History.

Increasingly this is becoming the age of the paperback, and the shelves of college bookstores are enlivened by their bright colors and attractive designs. A number of contemporary titles are listed in the chapter-end references, and in years to come there are certain to be many more. Some of these are reprints of classical papers, others cover particular aspects of the earth sciences, nearly all make interesting collateral reading. Several helpful paperbacks not included in the chapter reading lists because, like textbooks, they cover the entire range of geology are *The World of Geology,* edited by L. Don Leet and Florence J. Leet, McGraw-Hill Book Co., Inc., New York, 1961, *Study of the Earth, Readings in Geological Science,* edited by J. F. White, Prentice-Hall, Inc., Englewood Cliffs, N. J., 1962, and *The Birth and Development of the Geological Sciences,* by F. D. Adams, Dover Publications, Inc., New York, 1954.

Articles of geological interest appear in a wide diversity of magazines, some of general interest, others of more specialized appeal. Outstanding among these are the *Scientific American* and *Natural History*—the latter a publication of the American Museum of Natural History.

Contents

GEOLOGY

The Earth as seen from a Viking rocket at an altitude of 143 miles above White Sands, New Mexico. The view is toward the west and includes the northern parts of the Gulf of California and the peninsula of Baja California at the left, the Salton Sea at right center, and the San Joaquin Valley in the distance on the right. Cultivated fields near Phoenix, Arizona, are visible at the lower right. (Official U. S. Navy photograph.)

The Earth

We are small, and so to us the Earth seems large. Even in this day of greatly accelerated long distance flight, a transcontinental or transoceanic journey is still a tremendously impressive experience in terms of the distance covered and the ever-changing patterns to be seen. Strangely enough, air travel, now so commonplace, also leads to a greater appreciation of the vastness of the sea which was less fully grasped by most of us in a day when ship travel was a relatively rare event.

There are a number of fundamental things we should know about the planet Earth before we take up such lesser details as minerals, rocks, mountain building, and the work of such agencies as wind, waves, streams, and ice—all of which are the proper concern of geology.

SIZE

Many races of men are conscious that the world about them is large, but how large is a question without relevance if their horizons are limited to a tribal territory, the confines of a mountain valley, a short stretch of the coast line, or the congested blocks of a large city. However, a number of the earlier (and nearly successful) attempts at estimating the size of the Earth are of very great antiquity indeed, and one of them is worth citing here because it is so ingeniously argued, and because it shows a remarkable comprehension of the size and shape of the Earth as well as an understanding of part of its relationship to the sun.

Eratosthenes (c. 275-195 B.C.), when he was librarian at Alexandria, learned, in about 250 B.C., that at noon of the summer solstice the image of the midday sun was reflected from the water surface of a deep well at Syene—now called Aswan—yet at the same time at Alexandria, 480 miles to the north, a shadow was cast at the base of an obelisk. In fact, when the angle made by the shadow from the apex of the obelisk to the ground was actually measured, it turned out to be 7° 12′. Another quantity that was known to Eratosthenes was the distance from Syene to Alexandria, and this was thought in those days to be 500 stadia. Although there is uncertainty about the true value of this unit of measure, one interpretation is that Eratosthenes believed there was a distance very nearly equivalent to 480 miles between the two places (Hamilton, 1854).

By means of the geometry of that time the Greeks knew that a diagonal line cutting two parallel lines makes an equal angle with both of them. The diagram (Figure 1-1) shows that on the basis of this simple theorem Eratosthenes knew that the angle from Syene to the center of the Earth and then to Alexandria also would be 7° 12′. Since this was one fiftieth of 360°, this means the total circumference of the Earth would be 50 times the 480-mile distance from Syene to Alexandria, or 24,000 miles—a surprisingly close estimate to be made in a day so far removed from ours. A further, and less obvious, assumption that had to be made was that the sun was an immensely distant object.

This whole set of observations and conclu-

FIG. 1-1 *Eratosthenes' determination of the circumference of the Earth. By measuring the inclination from the vertical of the sun at Alexandria, and by knowing the distance from Alexandria to Syene, Eratosthenes was able to calculate the Earth's circumference.*

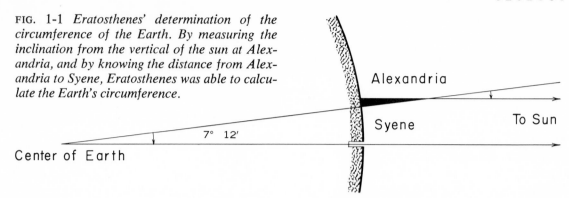

sions makes another point with which scientists are familiar, and that is the distressing number of times the same discovery may have been repeated, only to be forgotten and then long years after be rediscovered anew.

Others who made estimates in the centuries after Eratosthenes reported the Earth to be much smaller than it actually is, and this error, still current in Columbus's time, led him into the gross miscalculation still honored today in our using the name Indians for the pre-European inhabitants of the Americas.

Throughout Europe a tremendous surge of interest in the Earth followed Magellan's ill-starred (for him) world-encompassing expedition. Not only was the Earth's roundness convincingly demonstrated but an appreciation of its great size dawned on a skeptical world. Means of measuring the Earth's dimensions are enormously more effective now than they were in their primitive state of development during the Age of Exploration. For one thing there then existed no accurate way of determining differences of longitude, or east-west distances, on the surface of the globe.

Today, much greater precision is possible through the methods of *geodesy*. This is a branch of surveying that is concerned with, among other things, precisely locating the positions of places on the surface of the Earth, as well as the determination of the shape and size of the Earth itself. Through patient, devoted work over the past centuries an immense amount of data has been accumulated, chiefly through the building up of elaborate triangulation networks on all continents. Even in this age of exact timing devices and the adaptation of electronic instruments to surveying, much work remains to be done before the true size and configuration of the Earth are accurately known.

The dimensions generally accepted today, although their values unquestionably will be modified with time, are those derived by the American geodesist, Hayford, around 1910, which were adopted in 1924 by the International Union of Geodesy and Geophysics.

Equatorial Diameter	7,926.68 miles
Polar Diameter	7,899.98 miles
Difference	26.70 miles

SHAPE

These figures are tangible expressions of the fact, known to most persons, that the Earth is flattened at the poles, with the consequence that the equatorial diameter is nearly 27 miles longer than a similar line would be should it be drawn through the center of the Earth to connect one pole with the other.

That the Earth departs from a truly spherical form has a number of interesting side effects. In the first place, it affected the length of the meter, which was initially established in France in 1795—an unusual intellectual achievement to be accomplished during such an emotionally disturbed time as the French Revolution—and was supposed to be one ten-millionth of the distance from the equator to the pole. When it was finally determined that the Earth was not a perfect sphere, this destroyed the assumption upon which this unit of measure was to be established, with the result that an arbitrary standard —the distance between the end points of a platinum bar—was utilized as practical and reproducible. In 1889, under the Treaty of the Meter, a standard meter defined as the distance between two lines engraved on a platinum-iridium bar (which in the English system are spaced 39.37 inches apart) was adopted and preserved in the International Bureau of Weights and Measures near Paris. In 1960, a new standard was established and is now based on the orange-red radiation of the krypton isotope 86 and is defined as 1,650,763.73 wavelengths of this light in a vacuum.

The fact that the Earth is not a perfect sphere also affects one of the familiar geographic co-ordinates—the length of a degree of latitude. The question that might be posed in this regard—is the length of a degree of latitude greater or less near the pole when compared to the length of a degree near the equator?—is not as simply answered as it might at first appear. The question was debated for many years around the middle of the eighteenth century, and the correct answer, as perhaps might be expected, was deduced by Sir Isaac Newton (1642-1727). He recognized that centrifugal force would be strongest at the equator, where the speed of rotation times the distance from the axis would be greatest, and that it would be least at the poles. Newton pointed out that there should be a bulge near the equator where the inward pull of gravity is partially compensated by the outward thrust of centrifugal force. Therefore, he argued, the length of a degree of latitude would be greater at the equator and would be less at the poles, as is demonstrated in the accompanying diagram (Fig. 1-2) which shows that the lengths of arc on an ellipsoid intercepted by two equal angles—one at the equator, the other at the pole—are not identical.

However, the debate was not silenced by Newton's statement, and in fact was firmly contested by Jacques Cassini (1677-1756), Astronomer Royal of France, and his adherents. Cassini held the belief that although the Earth was admittedly a spheroid rather than a perfect sphere, it was elongated at the poles and compressed at the equator.

With feelings high, and with national prestige at stake, the French Academy launched two expeditions in 1734; one to Lapland under Maupertuis, the other to Ecuador under La Condamine and Bouguer. These parties were to measure the length of degrees of latitude at these widely separated places in order to determine which would be the longer, the near-polar or the equatorial arc, and thus it was hoped to humble the Newtonians. The two expeditions endured extraordinary hardships and difficulties, especially the South American enterprise. Its members made many of the first ascents of the forbidding Andean peaks, endured torments of thirst on the parched coastal desert, participated in bull fights, and for some death came in a variety of violent forms. Others conducted feuds of heroic proportions, and, as a final ordeal, two members, La Condamine in one party and Mme. Godin, sole survivor of

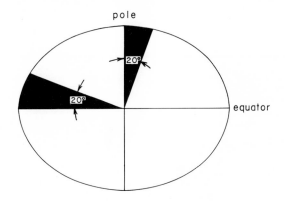

FIG. 1-2 *On an ellipsoidal Earth the lengths of arc of latitude that are cut by equal angles from the center of the Earth are greater at the equator than at the pole. (Earth's eccentricity is highly exaggerated.)*

another, returned to France by traversing the entire width of the South American continent, crossing the Andean crest and descending the uncharted Amazon.

Unfortunately for Cassini, in spite of these redoubtable undertakings, it was Newton and his vocal supporter, Voltaire, who were vindicated. The Earth does bulge at the equator and is diminished at the poles, and instead of being a perfect sphere is an oblate *ellipsoid of revolution* or, as it is also known, an *oblate spheroid.* Since it has other irregularities which give it a unique configuration the shape is known as a *geoid,* from the Greek, *geoeides,* or Earthlike. Actually, the geoid is a mathematical surface that coincides with mean sea level over the sea and with its extension beneath the land.

In practical reality latitude is measured at the surface of the Earth, rather than by reading angles from the center, as appears to be the way it is done in the diagram illustrating the Newtonian hypothesis (Fig. 1-2). On a ship at sea, to select an illustrative example, very commonly latitude is measured by determining the altitude at noon of the sun above the horizon. The accompanying diagram (Fig. 1-3) shows that the sun at the equator stands 90° above the horizon, yet the latitude there is 0°; while at the pole, if the day chosen is the equinox, the

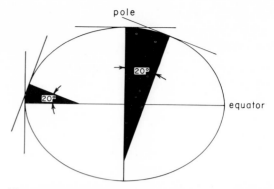

After B. F. Howell, Jr., *Introduction to Geophysics,* Copyright © 1959 McGraw-Hill Book Co., Inc. By permission.

FIG. 1-4 *On an ellipsoidal Earth the lengths of arc of latitude that are determined astronomically are greater at the pole than at the equator. (Earth's eccentricity is highly exaggerated.)*

sun's altitude is 0°, yet the latitude is 90°. From this example it is apparent that the latitude if measured in this way $= 90° - \phi$, where ϕ is the angle between the sun and the horizon. The intermediate case illustrated in the diagram (Fig. 1-3) serves to make the point; here the altitude of the sun above the horizon is 60°, and thus the latitude is 30°; $90° - 60° = 30°$.

This diagram also indicates that in reality this angle is measured from the horizon, which to a navigator appears as a plane which is tangent to the sphere. The following diagram (Fig. 1-4) also shows that the length of a degree of latitude (measured this way on the surface of the Earth) would be greater near the pole because the plane of reference is tangent to a circle of apparently greater diameter—the result of the Earth's rotational flattening—than at the equator where the apparent diameter of the geoid is less than the true diameter. This explanation is given to make the point that the length of a degree of latitude, were it to be measured from the center of the Earth (*geocentric latitude*), is longer at the equator and shorter at the pole; while conversely, the length of a degree (*astronomical latitude*) determined on the Earth's surface is shorter at the equator and longer at the pole.

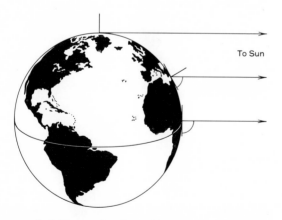

FIG. 1-3 *Determination of latitude by measurement of the altitude of the sun at noon on the day of the Equinox (March 21 or September 23) at latitudes 0°, 30°, and 90°.*

MASS

The land part of the Earth's surface consists of rocks, or of soil derived from the breakdown of solid rock. Such materials are heavier than water; in fact, a cubic foot of water weighs about 62.5 pounds while a cubic foot of granite weighs around 168 pounds, or 2.7 times as much. We say granite has a specific gravity of 2.7, or to put it another way, a block of granite weighs 2.7 times as much as an equal volume of water.

Very early in Newton's development of the Universal Law of Gravitation (1687) he pointed out in a brilliantly intuitive generalization that the density of the Earth would be five or six times as great as if the sphere consisted of water. He was not able to determine this value himself, but marked the way for others by showing that it could be found by measuring how much a mountain of known mass deflected a plumb line from the vertical. This measure would yield a value for the amount of the mountain's attraction for the plumb bob as compared to the far stronger pull of the vastly greater Earth.

A simple statement of the law of gravitation is, $F = G (M_1 M_2 / d^2)$, where G is the gravitational constant (with a value of 6.673×10^{-8} in the c.g.s. system—an almost infinitesimally small number, 0.0000000667), F is the attractive force between two bodies with masses of M_1 and M_2, respectively, and d is the distance separating them. One factor making the determination more difficult then than it is for us today is that the value of the gravitational constant was not known in the seventeenth century.

Knowing the mass of a mountain from its size (volume) and the assumed density of the rocks, it then appeared to be a comparatively simple matter to solve the equation for the mass of the Earth. Observations to test this hypothesis by measuring the deflection of the plumb bob were made in the Andes by Pierre Bouguer in 1783 and by Nevil Maskelyne, the Astronomer Royal, in Scotland in 1776. Maskelyne obtained a value of about 5 for the specific gravity of the Earth; a notable achievement considering the primitive instruments of his day. Using the same methods of comparing the attractive force of a nearby mountain range with the attractive force of the Earth, a surprising departure from the expected value was found by the so-called Trigonometrical Survey of India under the leadership of Sir George Everest. The surveyors found that the Himalayas, high as they are, failed to deflect the plumb bob from the vertical by the calculated amount that theoretically they should.

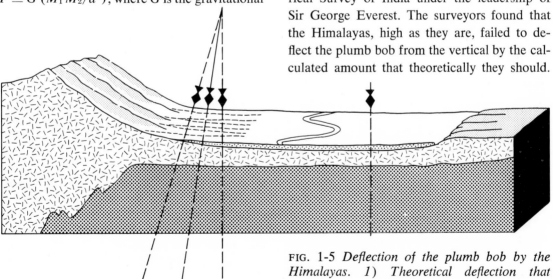

FIG. 1-5 *Deflection of the plumb bob by the Himalayas. 1) Theoretical deflection that should be caused by the mountains. 2) Observed deflection (the discrepancy from the theoretical one arises from the presence of the mountain "root"). 3) Undeflected position.*

The significance of this is that these immense mountains have "roots" consisting of rock that is lighter (of lower density) than the average beneath the low-lying plains of India to the south; therefore, their attractive force is not as great as if uniform density prevailed throughout. This seemingly insignificant discrepancy actually had a profound effect in shaping the theories of mountain building that are widely held today, as we shall see in a later discussion (Chapter XV).

Turning to the laboratory, efforts were also made at an early date to see if a value for the Earth's mass might be determined. The first valid experiment was made by Henry Cavendish (1731-1810) in 1797, using two large and two small lead balls—one pair being 12 inches in diameter, the other 2 inches. The small spheres were suspended from the ends of a rod, which in turn was suspended from a wire in the center. When the large spheres were brought near the small, the amount of twist (torque) in the wire could be measured. From this tiny displacement Cavendish determined the gravitational constant and also by means of this ingenious experiment he arrived at a value of 5.448 for the density of the Earth. In 1878, Phillip von Jolly made the first accurate determination of the gravitational constant (which can be defined as the attraction for each other of two masses of 1 gram each, spaced 1 centimeter apart). He achieved this by measuring the increase in weight of a carefully balanced 5 kilogram flask of mercury when it was brought close to a sphere of lead blocks about a meter in diameter (the sphere is still in existence and is exhibited in the Deutsches Museum, Munich). He found that the mercury flask showed an increase of 0.589 milligrams. Having determined the gravitational constant, he was then able to take the next step and compute the Earth's weight (W). This figure, refined since his day, turns out to be about 6.6×10^{21} tons (which is the figure 66 followed by 20 zeros). Since the size, or volume (V), of the Earth was

already known, the simple relationship W/V gave Jolly a density for the Earth of 5.692. More accurate determinations in modern times yield a value of 5.519.

This immediately poses a problem of fundamental importance, because typical rocks, such as granite, making up the dry land surface of the Earth have a density of 2.7. Where is this additional heavy material to be found to give such a high average value for the whole Earth? Does the density of the Earth increase at a constant rate from the surface to the center? Or does the Earth have lighter material in its surface layers and then have extremely heavy material concentrated in some kind of central core?

The last possibility appears to be more likely, and part of the evidence for this comes from the way the Earth responds to the tidal attraction of the moon. Because of the flattened shape of the Earth, the axis of spin shifts slightly when the Earth is subjected to such an external force, much as though the Earth wob-

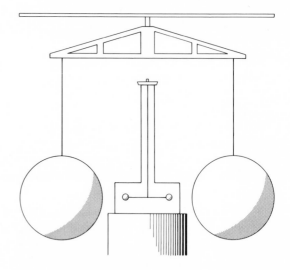

FIG. 1-6 *Schematic diagram of the equipment used by Cavendish to determine the density of the Earth. The small balls are free to rotate about the thin vertical wire supporting them.*

bled like a top. This shift is known as the *precession of the equinox,* and takes about 26,000 years to make a complete swing around a circle. When its nature is carefully calculated it turns out that it better fits the pattern of a planet with a dense central core. Another way of putting it is to say the Earth has a smaller moment of inertia than a sphere of similar size would have with a uniformly increasing density from the surface down to the center rather than with a concentration of denser materials near the center. In fact, other lines of evidence indicate that the specific gravity near the center of the Earth may be 15 and possibly as much as 18.

GRAVITY

In this section the term gravity is used for the property of acceleration which the Earth produces in a freely falling body. This property is one that Galileo (1564-1642) established about the year 1590 despite the opposition of his contemporaries, the disbelief of onlookers who were convinced that sorcery was involved, and the prestigious authority of the immortal Aristotle (384-322 B.C.) who had taught that an object ten times as heavy as another would fall ten times as fast.

Through observations made in the many years since Galileo's day we know that in a vacuum such diverse bodies as lead and feathers accelerate at the same rate because there is no air resistance to slow down the feathers, with their large surface area and light weight. However, the rate of acceleration is not the same at all places on the Earth's surface. At the equator the acceleration due to gravity is 32.09 feet per second per second, while at the pole it is 32.26. The reason for this difference is twofold: (1) the greater distance from the center of the Earth at the equator, and (2) the greater centrifugal force which opposes the force of gravity there.

We are concerned with an enormous force here; the Earth is so vastly greater than any single thing on its surface that the force with which it pulls objects towards itself is almost overpowering for large and heavy bodies. A little thought reminds us of the immense amount of energy we expend in lifting weights, in climbing mountains, or in flying airplanes, all in opposition to the force of gravity. All of us who have dropped rocks down wells or from the edges of cliffs marvel at how fast they disappear. Gravity is the force that does this; it is also the force that requires hundreds of thousands of pounds of thrust to be overcome when launching rockets into space.

How can the acceleration due to gravity actually be measured? For example, not too many of us are likely to drop iron balls from a leaning tower and time their short-lived flight with stop watches. A more practical way of determining the acceleration of gravity was discovered long ago, and also more importantly it was discovered that the acceleration varies locally over the face of the Earth. Since this last factor is of the greatest geologic significance, we will discuss this in some detail. The simple device that can be used to measure the acceleration due to gravity is the pendulum. The period of oscillation (the length of time required to swing to and fro) depends upon two factors: the local acceleration of gravity and the length of the pendulum. The discovery had been made very early, by Galileo in fact, that a given pendulum makes each swing in the same length of time. By using this principle, Christiaan Huygens (1629-95) finally succeeded in perfecting a dependable pendulum-regulated clock in 1673.

During this same critical period of scientific advances, a French scientist, Jean Richer, was sent by Jacques Cassini to French Guiana to make observations of Mars at the same moment that Cassini would be making them in Paris. By making such a simultaneous observation it would be possible to use the distance from Paris to Cayenne as a base line to triangulate from Earth to Mars in order to establish the distance separating the two bodies. Even considering the imperfections of such a clock in 1671, Richer was surprised to find that his pendulum clock, which was needed for keeping the time for his astronomical observations, consistently lost 2.5 minutes per day. Only when he shortened the pendulum length by 1/12 inch was the clock's accuracy restored.

Curiously enough, both Newton and Huygens, quite independently of one another, had deduced that the force of gravity would be diminished at the equator because of the Earth's equatorial bulge as well as the centrifugal force set up by its rotation. In other words, the acceleration due to gravity is greater at the poles, which are 13 miles closer to the center of the Earth (which is also the center of gravity) than the equator, and thus a pendulum-actuated clock gains time at the poles and loses time at the equator.

Bouguer, whom we encountered before in the Andes surveying an arc of the Earth's surface in order to establish the length of a degree of latitude, knew of the relationship deduced from Richer's pendulum clock and the variations in the force of gravity. Using the same principle, he, too, found the acceleration due to gravity decreased with altitude, which is to say with the increase in distance from the Earth's center which he reached on the Andean heights, the force of gravity grew less.

Since those days of the seventeenth and eighteenth centuries, the pendulum as a device for determining the force of gravity has been increasingly refined, until today gravity pendulums, torsion balances, and gravity meters are models of precision and can determine minute variations in the force of gravity over the Earth's surface as well as at sea. The use of the gravity pendulum and these related instruments brings out a third reason, in addition to the first two of (1) oblateness of the Earth and (2) differences in altitude, for variations in the force of gravity over the Earth's surface. This third reason is the relatively slight difference in

the density from place to place of the materials making up the surface layers of the Earth. Here another factor entering into the equation for the Universal Law of Gravitation is important, and this is the mass of the body involved. Thus, if the density of the rocky material in a localized part of the Earth's crust is less than the average for its surroundings, then the local value for the acceleration due to gravity will be diminished because the attractive force is not so great, and we say the area is characterized by a deficiency of mass, or shows a *negative anomaly*. This means it has an observed value for gravity which is less than the one that has been computed for the general region.

It became apparent during World War I that here was a powerful tool for detecting slight differences in the composition of the Earth's crust that may be hidden by soil or vegetation from an observer standing on the surface. By use of the gravimeter, exploration parties for oil companies can discover some of the structures, such as salt domes, that trap petroleum far below the ground surface. We shall learn more about the origin of these curious plug-like bodies of rock salt deep in the Earth's crust in Chapter VII.

SUBDIVISIONS OF THE EARTH

Most of us are well aware of the commonly accepted natural division of the Earth into land, sea, and air, and this tripartite separation is acknowledged scientifically by such terms as: (1) the *atmosphere,* or the gaseous envelope that surrounds the planet; (2) the *hydrosphere,* or the liquid mantle which is chiefly the sea, but that includes lakes and streams as well; and (3) the *lithosphere,* or the solid earth consisting not only of the rocky outer shell, familiar to us as the dry land on which we live, but also the deep interior. Although we are getting slightly ahead of the story, for each of these domains there are a number of generalized relationships that may appropriately be discussed in this introductory chapter rather than being deferred to a more specialized treatment later on. For this reason a synopsis of their general characteristics is given in the sections to follow.

The Hydrosphere

The statement has been made in some of the articles on space travel that, seen from afar, the Earth would appear as a pale blue sphere shimmering in space. Very likely this is true, and of all the planets, the Earth seen close at hand possibly would be the most beautiful, with its dominantly blue color varied by the dazzling white of the upper surface of the discontinuous cloud canopy.

How much of its surface is actually blanketed by the blue waters of the sea surprises most persons. Most of us are landsmen, and the sea is remote from our daily affairs. However, even those whose livelihood is won on it actually have little awareness of its enormous extent since most ships follow as direct and as short a route as possible from one seaport to another. Broad reaches of the ocean, once frequented by that wanderer of distant seas, the New Bedford whaler, are seldom visited now, and where seas were once whitened by the sails of clipper ships on such popular runs as the Cape Horn route, almost no vessels follow these lonely paths today. Our landlocked view of the Earth is further accentuated by the fact that most of the northern lands encircle the North Pacific, the North Atlantic, and the Arctic oceans. Here in the so-called land hemisphere, which is of chief concern to the peoples of North America and Europe, is found 80 per cent of the dry surface of the Earth, while 90 per cent of the water surface is in the far-distant Indian, the South Pacific, and the South Atlantic oceans.

A knowledge of the actual extent of the land and sea is useful in making comparative studies of the Earth, and also in developing a sense of their relative proportions. The figures cited here are reasonably accurate in light of our present knowledge and give a quantitative impression of the relative percentage of sea and land.

Area of the sea	(70.78%)	139,400,000 sq. mi.
Area of the lands	(29.22%)	57,500,000 sq. mi.
Total surface area of the Earth		196,900,000 sq. mi.

Considering the average depth of the sea to be about 12,500 feet, this means that the oceans of the world hold an enormous quantity of water—more than 300,000,000 cubic miles of it. From this vast storehouse close to 80,000 cubic miles are lifted by evaporation each year, in addition to about 15,000 cubic miles evaporated from lakes and from the land surface of the Earth. Of this total, approximately 24,000 cubic miles are believed to fall on land, which is another way of demonstrating that the oceans of the world cover an immensely larger area than the lands do.

The accompanying profile (Fig. 1-7) shows the relative distribution, by percentage of areas, of the various altitudes on the Earth's surface. It is apparent at once that the extremely high points, such as Mount Everest (29,000+ feet), and the great depths of the sea, such as the Mariana Trench (nearly 36,000 feet deep), occupy only a minute percentage of the total surface of the Earth. The diagram also demonstrates that there are two major levels on the Earth's surface; one above sea level at around 2,800 feet, the other below sea level at about 13,000 feet. Were the irregularities of the land to be completely leveled and a uniform, world-girdling ocean of constant depth to take their place, then all of us would drown beneath a universal sea whose depth would average about 1.5 miles. This would be a world we should not enjoy very much—even if we could live to experience it—because it would be unbearably cold and dark and the submarine pressures would exceed anything we could tolerate. Since a water depth of around 33 feet equals the weight of the entire column of air standing above the Earth, we speak of this depth of water as exerting a pressure of one atmosphere

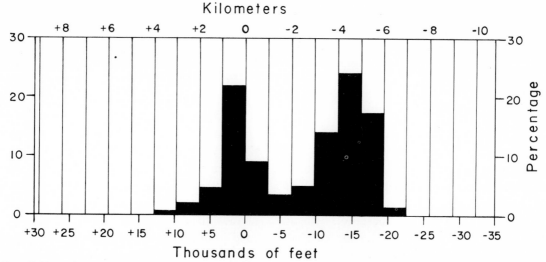

FIG. 1-7 *Distribution of elevation of the Earth's surface. Bars represent percentage of surface having altitude within indicated interval.*

—about 15 pounds to the square inch or slightly more than a ton to the square foot.

With the much greater density of water than air there should be little surprise that pressures in the sea increase rapidly with depth. At a depth of 6,000 feet (about one nautical mile) the pressure is roughly one ton to the square inch; at 30,000 feet it is about 5 tons to the square inch or 720 tons to the square foot—which gives the incomprehensibly large value of 1,440,000 pounds as compared to 2,000 pounds to the square foot for the pressure at the base of the atmosphere at sea level.

Thus far we have discussed the hydrosphere as though it were only the sea, and in truth it very largely is, as the figures below indicate (after Field):

WATER	CUBIC MILES
in the oceans	329,000,000
in the atmosphere	3,600
in glaciers and ice fields	3,250,000
in lakes and rivers	55,000
in the Earth's crust	20,780,000
TOTAL	353,088,600

From these figures it is apparent that the seas of the world make up close to 95 per cent of the total amount of water and existing snowfields and glaciers are only about 1 per cent. Nonetheless there is a constant going and coming of water on the Earth's surface, and thus a continuous interchange of water by evaporation from the sea to the air to fall as rain or snow on the land and thence by rivers and streams back to the sea again. Much of it simply falls back into the sea as rain.

Our present knowledge of the solar system indicates that liquid water in any large quantities is unique to the Earth. In fact, it is nearly alone even among the constituents of the Earth's surface since it can exist in the solid, liquid, or gaseous state at the pressures and temperatures ordinarily encountered in our worldly environment. What are some of the properties of this truly remarkable substance? In the first place its composition is simplicity itself compared with that of many other compounds since it consists of only two elements, hydrogen and oxygen. However, water is so unlike either of the gases as to make it seem incredible that it can in any way be related to them. These gases unite in such a way that two atoms of hydrogen when linked with one of oxygen are arranged as H-O-H, and written chemically as H_2O. When these two gases combine to form water, as is frequently done for a laboratory demonstration, a most impressive explosion results. Certainly a most spectacular illustration of this forcible union was the explosion of the German zeppelin *Hindenburg* at Lakehurst, New Jersey, in 1937.

Pure water freezes at a temperature of 0°C., or 32°F., but shortly before it reaches the freezing point it attains its maximum density at a temperature of 3.94°C., and as the temperature drops between 4°C. and 0°C. water expands by about 9 per cent. This remarkable property of expansion on cooling explains why ice floats—it has become less dense than water upon freezing—and also why it is that lakes freeze on the surface instead of upward from the bottom. In fact, this property of water, of slow contraction until the maximum density is reached and then relatively sudden expansion, is what causes the so-called overturn in lakes just before freezing. Surface water sinks to the bottom as it is chilled, until the whole lake reaches a temperature of 4°C. Then as the temperature continues to drop, only the surface layers freeze since they are now lighter and thus cannot sink through the denser layers of the lake. Biologically, this overturning of the water in a lake is of the greatest importance because surface water whose density has been increased through chilling carries oxygen down with it as it sinks. This aeration of the bottom layers of the lake makes it possible for fish and many other forms of life to survive in deep water. When surface water melts in the spring, the water in the lake is overturned again.

Sea water behaves in a markedly different fashion from fresh. It does not expand before cooling but shrinks steadily until freezing occurs, which for sea water of normal salinity is around −2°C. The geologically significant result of this behavior is a steady drift of cold water from the polar regions into the depths of the sea. There it likely remains for a long time since there is virtually no way to warm it up to be replaced by surface water, as in an overturning lake.

Among the important roles that water plays is its part as a universal solvent. Given enough time, almost all the common minerals in the Earth's crust are soluble in water. It is this invisible burden of solids dissolved from rocks and soil, amounting to something like 2¾ billion tons a year, transported by rivers to the final repository, the sea, that is responsible for its saltiness. The salt of the sea, however, consists of much more than sodium chloride (NaCl), familiar table salt, since about fifty of the elements found in the Earth's crust have been identified in sea water, too.

The salinity of the sea is remarkably constant over the world, and this is a powerful testimonial to the complete degree of mixing in its waters and to the freedom of interchange from one ocean to another. There are slight differences in its salinity from place to place, though. These differences are most conspicuous in the surface layers, and are the result of (1) local above-average evaporation which makes the water more saline than usual, as in land-girt seas such as the Mediterranean, the Red Sea, and the Persian Gulf, or (2) of increased precipitation and consequent dilution of sea water in the equatorial parts of the world with a resultant lowering of salinity, (3) the inflow of large rivers, such as the Amazon, and (4) the addition of large volumes of fresh water through the melting of ice in such seas as the Arctic Ocean and the Baltic.

The dissolved solids in average sea water amount to about 3.5 per cent of the total amount, or, as it is more commonly written, 35 parts per 1,000, and of this quantity sodium chloride is by far the leading constituent since it makes up 77.70 per cent of the solids present, or about 2.71 per cent of the composition of typical sea water. This is a strong contrast to the composition of river water where only a trace of NaCl is encountered as a rule. Similar reversals between the composition of river water and sea water are characteristic of such geologically significant compounds as the sulphates,

0.378 per cent in the sea but 0.057 per cent in rivers; or carbonates, 0.288 per cent in rivers but 0.00105 per cent in the sea; while silica, a most important constituent of the rocks of the Earth's crust, shows the following relationships: 0.05 per cent in rivers versus a mere 0.0004 per cent in the sea (Fox, 1951).

The reversal between the more abundant dissolved materials in rivers and the sea, as shown in the schematic statement below, is indeed a curious circumstance at first glance.

	SEA	RIVERS
MOST	$NaCl$	$CaCO_3$
LEAST	$CaCO_3$	$NaCl$

Where has the lime ($CaCO_3$) in river water disappeared, and why should salt dominate in the sea, especially when river waters which are the chief source of supply contain such a minute percentage? Lime is less soluble than salt and thus comes out of solution more readily. It is also extracted from the sea in enormous quantities by organisms whose achievements in construction range from making shells scarcely visible under powerful microscopes to building coral reefs. The steep outer slopes of these reefs rise as ramparts from the depths of the sea and their length may be as great as a thousand miles, as in the peerless example of the Great Barrier Reef of Australia. Silica is also withdrawn from sea water by such microscopic but marvelously ornamented plants as *diatoms* or such single-celled animals as *radiolaria,* whose remains sift down in a ceaseless rain from the surface waters to accumulate as broad plains of ooze in the deep parts of the ocean.

Salt, on the other hand, is useless to organisms as an ingredient in skeletons or teeth since it goes back into solution almost immediately with any drop in concentration. The salinity necessary to bring it out of solution requires a brine many times more concentrated than sea water, and such water is so saline that it can support only relatively specialized forms of life. The primary source of much of the sodium in the sea is probably the wastage through weathering and erosion of the rocky material of the lithosphere. The origin of the chlorine in the ocean is a more vexing problem, but this gas may very well have been added to it from volcanoes, fumaroles, hot springs, and geysers throughout the span of geologic time. Even more puzzling is the question of where the immense quantity of the Earth's water came from. No answer is known, but one likely supposition is that it too came from the Earth's interior, reaching the surface through volcanic activity.

There are a number of additional properties of water that merit consideration in a general discussion of the hydrosphere. For one thing, contrary to popular belief, water is slightly compressible and its density thus increases with depth and increasing pressure. For example, water at a temperature of 20°C. at the surface has a density of 0.9980, and at a depth of 2,000 meters, and the same temperature, the density will have increased to 1.0064 (Hutchinson, 1957). As a matter of fact, if water maintained the same density all the way to the bottom, the sea level would be 100 feet higher than it actually is (Kuenen, 1955).

A final property which is of the utmost importance in controlling climates and influencing many phases of life is the great heat-absorbing and heat-transmitting capacity of water. This is the property that keeps hot-water bottles hot, keeps our cup of coffee from congealing on a cold day, and makes water a reasonably effective coolant when circulated through an automobile engine. One of the most significant effects of water's enormous thermal capacity is the control the oceans exercise over the Earth's climates. The oceans have a strong effect in moderating what might otherwise be extreme temperature fluctuations over the bordering lands, and more importantly they transfer a prodigious amount of heat from warmer to colder areas by means of currents such as the Gulf Stream. The flow of heat northward by the Stream has tempered the climate of Scandinavia and Great Britain, which otherwise might be more like that of Labrador.

From almost every point of view water is a truly remarkable substance, and without it there could be no life as we know it on Earth. Among these properties of such crucial importance are (1) its heat capacity which enables it to store up solar energy, (2) its ability to act as a universal solvent, and (3) its extraordinary state of aggregation which permits its existence as a gas, solid, and liquid in the range of temperatures and pressures found on the Earth's surface.

The Atmosphere

A virtually invisible sea of air encompasses the Earth, and upon the delicate balance of its temperature, density, and composition our lives depend. Although we do not actually see the air, a wholly colorless gas that is a mixture chiefly of nitrogen and oxygen, nonetheless we are reminded of its presence in a multitude of ways. It imposes an ever-present frictional brake against missiles, airplanes, and even such earth-bound creations as automobiles. Furthermore, the atmosphere is responsible for the weather, and for such familiar phenomena as fog, snow, rain, hail, cloud, wind, and the like, as well as being the carrier of the all-pervasive smog, the bane of urban living today.

The existence of the air as an entity was recognized in ancient times, and the Greeks assigned a status to it equal to that of the other "elements" of their cosmos—fire, water, and earth. Recognition of air as a physical mixture and not a kind of chemical compound was not made until the eighteenth century, after the identification of carbon dioxide in 1754, nitrogen in 1772, and oxygen about 1773. That something else beside nitrogen was an inert constituent of the air was suspected in 1785 by Henry Cavendish, pioneer in the density determination of the Earth, but was not actually substantiated until 1892 through the discovery of argon by Lord Rayleigh.

Today we know the composition of dry air is essentially (Bates, 1957):

nitrogen	78.08%
oxygen	20.95
argon	0.93
carbon dioxide	0.03
rare gases	0.01

Water vapor is a most important constituent from the point of view of our welfare, and it is distributed unevenly throughout the atmosphere; the quantity may range from nearly zero up to a maximum of around 5 per cent. It is this modest concentration of water vapor that is responsible, upon condensation, for all the liquid or solid water that we see in the atmosphere or on the ground in such varied guises as dew, fog, rain, hail, or snow.

Another minor constituent of the atmosphere is carbon dioxide, which is such a vital link in the process of photosynthesis. The quantity present is minute compared to the total bulk of the atmosphere, as the table shows it to be only 0.03 per cent. A rather surprising thing about its abundance in the air is that between the years 1900 and 1935 the amount present apparently increased by around 9 per cent, which corresponds to an actual added quantity of about 200,000 million tons (Bates, 1957). This increase may reflect in part the staggering amount of coal and oil burned since the advent of the Industrial Revolution.

The tremendous weight of the atmosphere is astonishing. Everywhere on the Earth's surface at sea level it exerts a downward pressure of 14.7 pounds to the square inch, which is equal to 2,016 pounds to the square foot. That we are not flattened at once under this immensely heavy burden is only due to the fact that our body fluids and their dissolved gases are in equilibrium with it. Some of us are aware of the anguish we experience when we are taken out of our narrow band of tolerance to be exposed, through skin diving, for example, to higher pressures in the sea, or to the drastically diminished pressures encountered in high-altitude flight. Such sudden changes in pressure as the failure of the pressurized cabin of an airplane, at an altitude of over 20,000 feet, may cause total destruction of the aircraft and the loss of all the lives aboard. This is a dramatic reminder of how significant even a slight pressure difference in the atmosphere can be if a large enough surface area is involved.

The rapid decrease of pressure with altitude is shown on the accompanying diagram (Fig. 1-8). The pressure as recorded by a barometer is essentially zero at an altitude of 22 miles, as compared to nearly 30 inches at sea level. (This means that the total weight of a column of the atmosphere is counterbalanced by the weight of a column of mercury 30 inches high and with the same cross-sectional area.) Because of the thinness of the air on high mountains, breathing

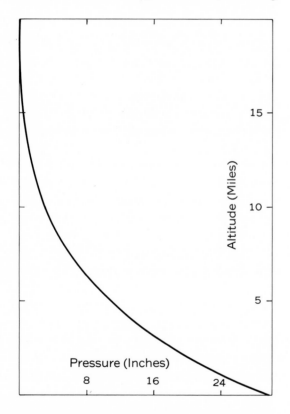

After Strahler, *Physical Geography,* 1951. By permission of John Wiley & Sons, Inc.

FIG. 1-8 *The average atmospheric pressure above the Earth's surface.*

is difficult and we are depressed at how enfeebled our efforts become. Potatoes remain hard as rocks when we boil them in water that remains tepid even though seething furiously. Automobiles labor ineffectively and airplanes respond sluggishly to their controls.

The marked increase of density near the base of the atmosphere is a strong verification of the fact that air is a highly compressible substance, especially when compared with such a liquid as water. The temperature changes that air undergoes when it compresses or expands are familiar to nearly everyone. On being compressed, air heats up, and, to use an extreme example, this is the principle used in the diesel engine. Air is compressed in the cylinders to a pressure of around 500 pounds to the square inch, the temperature rises to about 900°F., and this ignites the fuel without the necessity of using spark plugs. Conversely, air cools rapidly when it expands, and we are aware of this when we feel the stream of air escaping from either the valve in a tire or involuntarily and suddenly from a hole in its side.

The pressure/temperature relationship of air is of the highest importance in controlling the water-vapor content, and thus determining whether or not air can pick up more water or whether it will be compelled to drop what it holds. In general the water-holding capacity of warm air is greater than that of cold. Air that is being compressed picks up moisture rather than losing it. A good example is a wind descending a steep mountain slope, because such an air stream is being compressed as it moves from rarer into denser air. Thus, as its temperature increases, so also does its water-retaining ability, with the result that it will be a hot, dry wind, even though it be blowing downslope from the peaks of a snow-crested range. An instance of such a wind is the so-called *Chinook,* which almost overnight may whisk the snow off the high plains east of the Colorado Rockies, or the *Föhn* wind of the Alps. Conversely, rising air expands with the continuing reduction of pressure with increasing altitude, and thus cools as it rises. For dry air, the temperature drops around 5.5°F. for every 1,000 feet of rise, and this is termed the *adiabatic rate*. If the water vapor in the air condenses, the adiabatic rate is diminished to around 3°F. per 1,000 feet because of the addition of the heat of condensation of the water.

Even should the air be perfectly still, the temperature drops with increasing altitude. This effect is called the *lapse rate,* and is familiar to anyone with mountain experience. This cooling of air with increasing altitude is made visible for us in such a familiar scene as the plains at the base of a mountain range parching under the summer sun while the distant peaks rising above them shimmer beneath their blanket of sempiternal snow. Between these extremes the mountain slopes are clothed by a forest whose composition in part reflects the decrease of temperature with the gain in altitude. Near the base of the mountain, to select a typical example in the western United States, the forest is mostly broad-leafed trees that shed their leaves in winter; at higher altitudes the forest will be mostly pines, firs, and other needle-bearing, evergreen trees. Near the summit all that survive are stunted, wind-stripped trees and arctic shrubs.

All these striking changes are expressions of a combination usually of the adiabatic rate and the lapse rate. The accompanying diagram (Fig. 1-9) shows the effect of the latter, and this decrease amounts to around 3.3°F. for each 1,000-foot gain of altitude above sea level.

An impressive result of this drop of temperature with altitude are the snows of Kilimanjaro in equatorial Africa as well as on the slopes of the Ecuadorian Andes, but in these tropical lands it is necessary to climb to altitudes of 15,000 feet or more to reach the snow line. In mid-latitudes—on such mountain ranges as the Alps or the Colorado Rockies—the snow line stands at 9,000 or 10,000 feet, and in Alaska

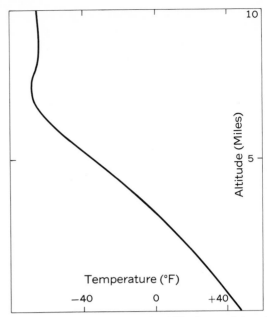

After Strahler, *Physical Geography*, 1951. By permission of John Wiley & Sons, Inc.

FIG. 1-9 *The average temperature above the Earth's surface. The boundary between the stratosphere and the troposphere is at 7 miles.*

or southern Greenland it has reached sea level at latitudes between 60° and 70° N.

The lapse rate diagram (Fig. 1-9) shows that at an altitude of around 35,000 feet the temperature no longer decreases with increasing height above sea level, but actually may rise slightly. The sharp temperature discontinuity is the *tropopause;* the atmosphere below it, or the part in which we live, is the *troposphere,* and the part of the atmosphere standing above the tropopause is the *stratosphere.*

The altitude of the tropopause varies with the geographic location on the Earth in much the same fashion as the poleward decline in the altitude of the regional snow line. The tropopause stands at around 10 miles above sea level in the tropics, in mid-latitudes it is about 7 miles high, and in the polar regions it has dropped down to about 5 miles. Because the lapse rate decrease of temperature is characteristic of the troposphere, regardless of its thickness, this produces the result that the temperature at the tropopause in the tropics is around —110°F., as contrasted to about —50°F. near the pole.

The tropopause marks the practical upper limit of turbulence in the Earth's atmosphere; the troposphere below it is a zone of changeable winds, of cyclonic storms, of snow, and of rain. It is also the part of the atmosphere that contains nearly all the dust and water vapor. The air in the stratosphere is cold, clear, and extremely dry; no cyclonic storms disturb it and there are no true clouds except in the basal part which is marked by the feathery traces of cirrus clouds—consisting of minute suspended ice spicules—and the "contrails" of high-flying jets.

How high does the upper atmosphere go? What is the nature of its boundary with space? The answer to these questions is simple: no one knows yet. Part of the difficulty here is the virtual impossibility of setting an upper limit to an incredibly diffuse pattern of widely separated gaseous molecules of such elements as hydrogen, helium, and oxygen—some of which are escaping to outer space while others are being pulled back into the Earth's atmosphere by gravity. So thin does this upper "air" become that at a height of 60 miles it is only one one-millionth as dense as at sea level.

A tremendously expensive amount of research has been carried on by the United States and the Soviet Union since World War II, probing the upper levels of the atmosphere with rockets. It has been discovered already that there is a vastly more complex pattern in the internal structure of the higher atmosphere than was indicated by the relatively simple concepts of a few years ago. Judging from the heights attained by auroras, an atmosphere of a sort may extend out to a distance of 750 miles, although so rarefied as to be imperceptible to our senses. To cite a single example of these upper atmosphere complexities, the temperature beyond the stratosphere seems not to decline at a constant rate but varies irregularly, depending in part on the dominant composition of the attentuated atmosphere. Much more information needs to be acquired before the actual range and distribution of these high-altitude temperature zones is established with certainty, although enough evidence has been accumulated to show that above the stratosphere the temperature seemingly increases to around 32°F. and decreases to around —80°F. at the top of the so-called mesosphere at an altitude of about 50 miles, which is also the upper limit of presumed accuracy of measurement. Then the temperature is believed to increase to as much as 2,000°F. at a height of 350 miles, on the basis of very fragmentary and uncertain information (Bates, 1957).

Few of these upper-air phenomena are of direct concern to geology, but some do have a bearing on the nature and even survival of life on Earth. The atmosphere acts as a thermal blanket to keep heat received from the sun from being radiated back into space almost immediately. The atmosphere shields us from destructive short-wave emissions from the sun, such as ultraviolet and X-radiation, yet fortunately from our point of view it permits the passage of the visible radiation which is so much a part of our life. It also acts as a powerful barricade against cosmic ray particles and the rain of meteoric fragments which otherwise would maintain a ceaseless fusillade upon the Earth.

In geology, our primary concern with the atmosphere obviously is with the part in direct contact with the sea or with the land. This is the part that brings rain and drought, heat and cold, wind and calm, and all the infinite variety of the day-to-day patterns of sky and cloud that we call the weather. Many of these changes are controlled by movements of air within the troposphere. In this first chapter, however, the atmosphere has been described as though it were essentially static, and the chief emphasis has been on its layered structure with regard to temperature and pressure.

The Lithosphere

Third of the three domains constituting the accessible parts of the Earth is its rocky shell. Its material constitutes the dry land upon which we live, and this is also the realm which provides the pattern of landscapes that make the Earth the uniquely wonderful thing it is.

Every observant person is aware of obvious differences in the material of which the Earth is made, and it is the physical nature of these differences, their meaning, and as far as we can determine, what their origin may be, that are among the major problems to which geology seeks an answer. One has only to visit a large museum and casually examine its collection of minerals, ores, fossils, and rocks to realize what a great diversity of wholly unlike substances constitutes the upper levels of the Earth's crust. A monumental edifice, such as a state capitol, a city hall, a court house, or a large bank, usually incorporates several kinds of building stones in its façade, lobby, or halls—white marble, red granite, green serpentine, buff travertine, and variegated breccias of all kinds. All these building stones are impressive in their multitude of textures and colors, and are an indication by themselves of the heterogeneous nature of the Earth's crust. Some of the explanations for this diversity of form and substance of the materials making up the solid Earth are given in the next chapter, as well as in the succeeding one on rocks, and telling the story of their origin will take us on a far journey indeed.

Before becoming immersed in a sea of details concerning different rock types, it is reassuring to know that all the diversity of rocks, which are the essential substance of the lithosphere, can be grouped into three major categories. This threefold subdivision is what we call a genetic classification and is based on the origin, or *genesis,* of the thing described. Thus, allowing for the inevitable exceptions, borderline cases and overlapping occurrences, the rocks of the world are placed in the following broad categories—igneous, sedimentary, and metamorphic.

IGNEOUS ROCKS.—These are rocks that have solidified from a silicate melt to which the name of *magma* (to knead) is given. A comparatively familiar variety of such material is *lava,* and most of us have seen photographs of this material in the craters of volcanoes or issuing as fluid streams from their flanks. Because of the high temperatures and accompanying lurid scenes associated with volcanic activity in the minds of most people, the word igneous, from the Latin *igneus,* having to do with fire, is used for rocks crystallized from the cooling lava. We use the same root in everyday language when we speak of the ignition system of a car. The varieties of igneous rocks that crystallize at or near the surface of the Earth from lava when it solidifies commonly are called volcanic rocks.

Other igneous rocks, such as granite, crystallize at depths far below the surface of the Earth, and because of the deep, inaccessible domain in which they form, such igneous rocks very often are known as plutonic rocks, after Pluto, Greek god of the lower world.

Granite, too, may have formed from magma, but how much or how little this may resemble lava is hard to say. After 160 years of controversy a spirited debate still flourishes as to the source of granite. But there does appear to be reasonably general agreement that the magma from which granite formed is molten, that its temperatures are high—high enough on occasion to recrystallize the enclosing wall rocks—and that although a "noteworthy part" of it is fluid, it may contain a considerable percentage of early crystallizing minerals floating in it. All are agreed that magma underground cools more slowly than magma at the surface, and for this reason the mineral crystals in the resulting plutonic rock are much larger in a granite, say, than in a typical, fine-grained, surface-cooled volcanic rock, such as basalt.

SEDIMENTARY ROCKS.—Of the three rock families, these rocks are perhaps the most readily comprehended, because many of them bear a close resemblance to the materials from which they are made and because many of the processes responsible for their formation occur before our eyes or else take place in environments that are reasonably accessible.

If igneous rocks are to be construed as primary, many sedimentary rocks can be thought of as secondary, or derived rocks, in the sense that they are fragments of pre-existing rocks. Examples of sedimentary rocks of this type are (1) sandstone, which consists of sand grains cemented together; (2) conglomerate,. which consists of rounded fragments the size of pebbles, cobbles, or boulders; and (3) shale, which consists of very small particles that may be comminuted down to the size of clay.

A concentration of such residues as rock salt, gypsum, Chilean nitrate, or some kinds of limestone, to name but a few of the many possibilities, may result from chemical precipitation in sea or lake water, and other sedimentary rocks of a kindred sort may result from the accumulation of a variety of organic remains.

In general, sedimentary rocks accumulate on the surface of the Earth, either on land or on the floors of lakes or of the sea. Thus, they form in environments which are more susceptible to observation or to study than the depths where plutonic rocks solidify or metamorphic rocks recrystallize. Since sedimentary rocks are built up through the slow deposition of material, they typically are formed in layers. These are called *strata;* a single layer is a *stratum* (directly from the Latin—a blanket or pavement, derived from *stratus,* p.p. of *sternere,* to spread out). Individual layers may range from paper-thin sheets up to massive beds a hundred feet or more thick.

METAMORPHIC ROCKS.—These are the rocks that most puzzled the first geologists, as well they might, because they do not form on the surface but appear instead to be products of the action of heat, pressure, and chemical activity operating upon rocks within the Earth through long periods of time—at least long when judged by our time standards. These factors operate to produce recrystallization, either partial or complete, of the minerals of the rock. New minerals appear and they may develop a wholly new fabric or orientation with respect to each other. Instead of having a random orientation and heading every which way, as is true of many igneous rocks, in the making of some metamorphic rocks the minerals under directed stress may realign themselves parallel to one another as in a stack of silver dollars.

In some types of metamorphism, the rock may undergo little or no change in chemical composition as its minerals recrystallize. The chemical elements already present regroup themselves under these conditions of higher temperatures and pressures to form new minerals which are stable in the new subsurface environment. In other cases new minerals are formed because new material has been introduced by heated, highly charged gases and fluids circulating within the Earth, very often associated with plutonic igneous activity.

The metamorphic rocks are almost certain to be complex because they have no single mode of origin but have a great diversity of origins. They can be made from all manner of rocks: igneous, sedimentary, or even from previously metamorphosed rocks. If they have any factor in common, it is crystallinity, and like the igneous rocks they consist of a fabric of interlocking crystalline minerals. Unlike many of the igneous rocks, some have a strongly banded appearance which superficially resembles the stratification of sedimentary rocks, but these bands consist of interlocking crystals segregated into layers of different colors—some light, some dark—rather than discrete granules deposited in laminae. Closer inspection will show that the banding, or layering, which is called *foliation* in metamorphic rocks, may be related to the parallelism of the minerals. This foliation, if only moderately well-developed, is characteristic of the rock we call *gneiss,* which may look very much like streaked granite. If the foliation is better developed, then it constitutes planes of weakness running through the rock because of the parallel alignment of flat, flake-like minerals, such as mica. Because the rock splits readily along such planes as these we say it has rock cleavage, and such a rock as *slate* is a prime example.

These three families of rocks making up the lithosphere by no means have an equal distribution over the face of the Earth. The two graphs (Fig. 1-10) show that only 5 per cent by volume of the Earth's crust consists of sedimentary rocks, while 95 per cent are igneous and metamorphic rocks. On the other hand, about 75 per cent of the total land surface of the Earth is covered with sediments. This simply means that the sedimentary rocks make a discontinuous blanket which is spread thinly over the much more abundant crystalline rocks, which are the true foundations of the continents.

Suggested References

Barnett, Lincoln, and the Editorial Staff of Life, 1955, The world we live in, Time, Inc., New York.

Bates, D. R., and others, 1957, The earth and its atmosphere, Basic Books, Inc., New York.

Buswell, A. M., and Rodebush, W. H., 1956, Water, Scientific American, April.

Carson, Rachel, 1950, The sea around us, Oxford Univ. Press, Inc., New York.

Davis, K. S., and Day, J. A., 1961, Water, The mirror of science, Doubleday and Co., New York.

Editors of the Scientific American, 1950-1957, The planet earth, Simon and Schuster, Inc., New York.

Field, W. O., 1957, Glaciers, *in* The planet earth, Simon and Schuster, Inc., New York.

Fox, Sir Cyril S., 1951, Water, A study of its properties, its constitution, its circulation in the earth, and its utilization by man, The Technical Press, Ltd., London.

Gamow, George, 1958, Earth, matter, and sky, Prentice-Hall, Inc., Englewood Cliffs, N. J.

————, 1960, Gravity, Anchor Books, Doubleday and Co., Garden City, N. Y.

Hamilton, H. C., 1854, The geography of Strabo, Henry G. Bohn, London.

Heiskanen, W. A., and Meinesz, Vening, 1958, The earth and its gravity field, McGraw-Hill Book Co., Inc., New York.

Hutchinson, G. E., 1957, A treatise on limnology, Vol. I, Geography, physics, and chemistry, John Wiley and Sons, Inc., New York.

King, Thomson, 1953, Water, Miracle of nature, The Macmillan Co., New York.

Krauskopf, K. B., and Beiser, Arthur, 1960, The physical universe, McGraw-Hill Book Co., Inc., New York.

Kuenen, Ph. H., 1955, Realms of water, John Wiley and Sons, Inc., New York.

Kuiper, G. P., and others, 1954, The solar system, Vol. II, The earth as a planet, Univ. Chicago Press, Chicago, Ill.

Mason, Brian, 1958, Principles of geochemistry, John Wiley and Sons, Inc., New York.

Singer, Charles, 1959, A short history of scientific ideas, Oxford Univ. Press, London.

Strahler, A. N., 1951, Physical geography, John Wiley and Sons, Inc., New York.

Sverdrup, H. U., Johnson, M. W., and Fleming, R. H., 1942, The oceans, Prentice-Hall, Inc., New York.

Yearbook of Agriculture, 1955, Water, U. S. Dept. of Agriculture, Washington, D. C.

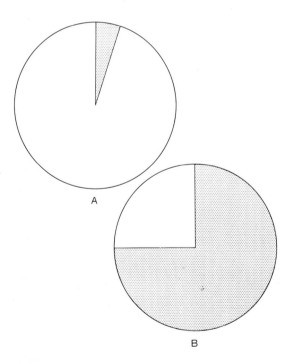

From F. J. Pettijohn, *Sedimentary Rocks*, 1958. By permission of Harper and Row, Publishers.

FIG. 1-10 *Relative abundance of igneous and metamorphic (blank) and sedimentary (stippled) rocks.* A, *by volume;* B, *by area.*

Dark hornblende crystals and white calcite, from Franklin, New Jersey. (Courtesy of the Smithsonian Institution.)

II

Rock-Forming Minerals

The rocks which make up the solid surface of the Earth and that are directly accessible to us, or which can be seen to a moderate depth in deep wells and mines, show almost as many colors, patterns, and textures as there are named varieties, approximately 2,000. Most rocks—granite is an especially apt example—consist of more than one kind of material. Granite (see Fig. 3-7) characteristically has a speckled appearance, and although most of the surface is light gray, the rock is mottled by scores of black spots sprinkled across it. The different colored substances that make up granite are minerals; the light gray areas are mostly quartz and feldspar, while the dark specks very likely are biotite (black mica). This points up a most important distinction to keep in mind: *Rocks are made of minerals, while with only a few exceptions minerals are not rocks.* Phrased more elegantly, rocks for the most part are heterogeneous aggregates of minerals, while minerals have an essentially uniform composition.

A quartz crystal (Fig. 2-1), although as hard and inorganic as a piece of granite, obviously has a wholly different appearance. Much of this chapter and the ones to follow are concerned with the natures and differences of minerals and rocks, but the important thing to remember is that, in general, minerals are the building blocks of which rocks are made.

Before launching into a discussion of the details, we should briefly consider what are the properties of these materials of the Earth's crust. Here the problem essentially is one of inorganic

FIG. 2-1 *Cluster of quartz crystals from Crystal Springs, Arkansas. These natural crystals are transparent and are characterized by numerous relatively smooth, flat surfaces. (Courtesy of the Smithsonian Institution.)*

chemistry, and the elements involved are surprisingly few; out of the approximately ninety that have been identified in the Earth's crust, eight are so much more abundant than all the others combined as to comprise practically 99 per cent of the whole. The most abundant elements are (Clark, 1924):

ELEMENT	CHEMICAL SYMBOL	PERCENTAGE BY WEIGHT
oxygen	O	46.59 ⎫ 74.31
silicon	Si	27.72 ⎭
aluminum	Al	8.13
iron	Fe	5.01
calcium	Ca	3.63
sodium	Na	2.85
potassium	K	2.60
magnesium	Mg	2.09

This table shows very clearly that three-fourths of the lithosphere consists of silicon and oxygen. In fact, one of the more abundant minerals is quartz, whose chemical composition is SiO_2 (one atom of silicon for every two of oxygen). When these elements are combined, the resulting compound, quartz (Fig. 2-1), is about as unlike its two components, when they are considered individually, as it could be. One,

oxygen, is an invisible and highly inflammatory gas; the other, silicon, is a silvery-gray, rather metallic looking element that is never found free, or uncombined, in nature. Quartz, the compound resulting from the union of these two elements, is harder than steel; when free of impurities it is as clear as glass, and, in fact, it is the limpid material commonly called rock crystal, which, if not interfered with during its growing stage, forms beautiful, six-sided crystals.

Definitions of a Mineral

Considering the table above, it is scarcely surprising that most of the minerals that are the chief ingredients of rocks should be composed of oxygen and silicon in combination with the remaining six most abundant elements: aluminum, iron, calcium, sodium, potassium, and magnesium. Such compounds are called silicates. The feldspars are typical, and $KAlSi_3O_8$, the mineral orthoclase, is representative (Fig. 2-2). The combination of oxygen and silicon alone is called silica, and quartz (SiO_2) is an example.

Most minerals are chemical compounds; that is, they consist of two or more elements in combination. Of course there are exceptions, such as gold, copper, sulphur, and carbon (which by itself makes such dissimilar substances as diamonds and graphite), which may occur as elements by themselves as well as in chemical

FIG. 2-2 *Cleavage fragments of the minerals calcite ($CaCO_3$), on the left, and orthoclase ($KAlSi_3O_8$), on the right. Because of the characteristic regular arrangements of the atoms in these minerals the calcite breaks, or cleaves, along smooth plane surfaces in three directions. The orthoclase breaks similarly in two directions, one being the front face of the piece and the other the two sides. Quartz (Fig. 2-1), which has a different internal arrangement of atoms, has no direction of cleavage. (Courtesy of the Smithsonian Institution.)*

compounds. Minerals are naturally occurring substances. This statement rules out laboratory creations (although some, such as synthetic rubies and sapphires, are virtually impossible to tell from the natural gem stone). Minerals have a reasonably definite chemical composition. Since they are naturally occurring substances, and not laboratory products, only rarely are they chemically pure compounds. For this reason, such properties as color may vary over a range as wide as from black to white, depending on the percentage of elements present for any mineral. Then, too, some minerals belong to isomorphous series. That is, they may preserve about the same appearance and nearly the same crystal form even though their chemical composition may vary systematically. One variety of feldspar, known as plagioclase, is an example, and chemically every gradation exists in this particular mineral between a composition of $NaAlSi_3O_8$ and $CaAl_2Si_2O_8$. In this mineral both sodium and calcium ions exist simultaneously, but as the amount of one increases, the other decreases. Minerals also have certain

FIG. 2-3 *Crystals of ice in the form of snow-flakes. Note the high degree of symmetry manifested in the forms of these crystals. During the complete rotation of any individual about an axis normal to the page, there would be six positions at equal angles with respect to one another ($60°$) at which the appearance of the particular crystal would be essentially indistinguishable from that at any other position. This six-fold axial symmetry is a characteristic property of ice that grows in a liquid or gaseous medium. The growth forms and shapes of cleavage fragments of almost all minerals have diagnostic properties of symmetry that depend on an orderly arrangement of the atoms and groups of atoms in an array that is periodic (i.e. repetitive) in three dimensions in much the same way that most varieties of wallpaper (especially the cheaper kinds!) are periodic in two dimensions. (Courtesy of Moody Institute of Science.)*

physical properties, determined by their chemical composition and by the geometric arrangement of the atoms composing them. It is this atomic arrangement that determines the crystal form of a mineral. Other properties include such things as color, hardness, and specific gravity.

From these statements it might seem that water could be a mineral. There is little question about ice, the crystalline phase of H_2O, although whether or not liquid water is or is not a mineral is a topic to stir up a mild debate. Few mineralogists would subscribe to this usage of the term mineral, since such substances are commonly held to be crystalline. That is, the atoms which make up a mineral are arrayed in ordered, repetitive ranks that have fixed average positions within which they are free to vibrate. Atoms in a liquid lack the orderly arrangement characteristic of an authentic crystalline solid, and although some repetitive order exists, individual atoms are able to glide past one another in constantly changing patterns. In a gas, disorder is the ruling principle, and atoms move with nearly complete freedom on widely spaced paths. It is their frequent collisions with such a confining surface as the inner tube of a tire that produces the effect we speak of as pressure. In light of its extraordinary ability to exist in all three physical states—liquid as water, solid as ice (Fig. 2-3), gaseous as steam—water as such would lie outside the pale of any reasonable concept of what is meant by the word mineral.

In summary, then, a mineral may be defined as (1) a naturally occurring substance with (2) a fairly definite chemical composition and (3) characteristic physical properties by which it may be identified. In short, a typical mineral is a crystalline solid and is an inorganic substance. Most are chemical compounds, but a few, such as the diamond, may consist of a single element.

Before we discuss the characteristics of individual minerals we should learn of the essential properties which are the chief means of their identification. Physical properties are the things we can see, or feel, or, for such minerals as halite (rock salt), taste. True enough, the chemical composition is possibly the most diagnostic property a mineral possesses, but few of us are going to pack along a fully equipped chemical laboratory to be used for mineral iden-

tification on a field trip. Since one of the critical differences between minerals and rocks is that minerals are approximately homogeneous substances, and most rocks are not, this means that one piece of quartz will be about as hard as another piece, that it will have the same specific gravity, and if formed in a similar environment, it will have about the same crystal form.

Physical Properties of Minerals

The significant properties of minerals that are readily observable in the field are listed below, and a judicious use of these, together with one of the standard mineral handbooks, should enable you to identify many of the common minerals. Their collection and identification is a rewarding activity that can take you to many interesting and unfrequented places.

1. COLOR.—This is the most obvious property that minerals possess, and for some of them it is diagnostic. An illustrative example is amethyst, which is the name given to a characteristically purple or pale violet form of quartz. The color of quartz ranges through a spectrum from absolutely colorless, glass-clear rock crystal to coal black varieties, depending for one thing on the nature and amount of impurities that are included. In short, color is an important property; for some minerals it is diagnostic, for others it is almost without significance. Unfortunately, colors cannot be used with the same confidence in identifying minerals that they can in naming birds and flowers. A considerable amount of experience has to be acquired before one learns which colors are meaningful and which are so variable as to be without significance.

2. HARDNESS.—This is a purely relative property, but its recognition has considerable antiquity since the scale which is still used was devised over a century ago in 1820 in the provincial Austrian city of Graz by the mineralogist Friedrich Mohs. It is an easy property to determine, and is one of the first to be deter-

mined in identifying an unknown mineral in the field. A harder mineral will scratch a softer one, and minerals of equal hardness commonly will barely scratch one another.

It certainly is common knowledge that diamonds are harder than almost all other substances, and for this reason Mohs placed it at the top of his hardness scale and assigned to it an arbitrary value of 10. Other softer minerals he ranked in a descending hierarchy, perhaps without realizing that unequal degrees of hardness separate the various ranks. For example, the interval between diamond and corundum is more than all the rest of the scale combined, and if absolute values were assigned to the actual intervals on the scale, diamond would be about 42 (Hurlbut, 1952).

diamond	10	
corundum	9	
topaz	8	
quartz	7	
orthoclase feldspar	6	glass
		knife blade
apatite	5	
fluorite	4	
calcite	3	
gypsum	2	finger nail
talc	1	

3. LUSTER.—This property is a measure of a mineral's behavior toward ordinary light, and is a measure of the amount and character of the light reflected. A diamond crystal has nearly total reflection, and for this reason we say that it flashes fire. The term *adamantine* is used to describe its brilliant luster. Sulphur is a slightly more common substance with the same luster, and its small, brilliant yellow crystals sparkle almost as brilliantly as diamonds do.

The two most common lusters are *metallic* and *nonmetallic*. The first of these terms means that the surface of the mineral reflects light in about the same way that a metal such as brass, iron, or lead would. Minerals with a metallic luster commonly are opaque, even along thin edges held up against the light. Nonmetallic lusters range over about every other type. If a

mineral reflects light to about the same degree as glass, it has a *vitreous luster*. Quartz is an excellent example. Among other terms that commonly are employed and are essentially self-explanatory are earthy, waxy, dull, resinous, pearly, and silky.

4. SPECIFIC GRAVITY.—A measure of the weight of a mineral compared to the weight of an equal volume of water taken at its maximum density at a temperature of 39.2°F. (4°C.) is its specific gravity. At this temperature the weight of any volume of water is considered to have a value of 1. Thus, quartz with a specific gravity of 2.7 is a substance that weighs 2.7 times as much as an equal volume of such water would weigh.

The specific gravity is usually determined by weighing a mineral in the air and then weighing it fully immersed in water, then:

$$\text{Specific Gravity} = \frac{W_a}{W_a - W_w}$$

where, W_a = weight of the mineral in air, and W_w = weight of the mineral in water.

This is a property that can be estimated with surprisingly high accuracy in an entirely subjective way, after experience has been acquired, simply by hefting the mineral by hand. Pyrite (FeS_2), with a specific gravity of 5, and galena (PbS), about 7.5, are perhaps typical of metallic minerals, while the range 2.6 to 2.8 covers representative rock-forming minerals, such as quartz, feldspar, and calcite ($CaCO_3$).

5. CRYSTAL FORM.—With the obvious exception of mercury and other less familiar minerals, such as opal which is an amorphous variety of silica, nearly all minerals are crystalline substances. The crystalline state of matter is a property which has excited wonder and engendered speculation for tens of centuries. Ancient and medieval literature is filled with references to minerals, their imagined magical or curative properties, and with conjectures over their origin and nature. By many it was believed that minerals grew from seeds, or that there were

mineral-generating fluids within the Earth, or that sex might enliven things even within this crystalline world and that there were such entities as male and female minerals.

Interesting as these surmises of our ancestors were, we know today that they are not so. We know that the crystal form of a mineral is not a chance vagary of nature, but that its surface is the reflection of an inward orderly arrangement of the elements that constitute the chemical substance of the mineral. Nicolaus Steno (1638-1686), a Dane and a true son of the Renaissance, during a life that included training as a physician, a sojourn in Paris, service in the court of Grand Duke Ferdinand II at Florence, and conversion from the Lutheran to the Roman Catholic Church in which he rose to become a prelate, found time to make remarkably perceptive observations on the geological structure and origin of the mountains of Tuscany and, most significantly for the immediate problem of crystal form, clearly demonstrated the fact that the faces of a quartz crystal

FIG. 2-4 *Cleavage fragment of the mineral halite* (*common rock salt*). *The three directions of cleavage are at right angles to one another. In halite the growth forms are commonly parallel to the cleavage forms.* (*Courtesy of the Smithsonian Institution.*)

always intersect at the same angle regardless of the size of the crystal (Fig. 2-1). From this beginning stems the branch of mineralogy known as crystallography.

Steno's original observation that the interfacial angles on a crystal hold constant, plus the fact that all crystals (no matter how complex their geometry may appear to be) can be placed in one of six major crystal systems is a testimonial to the orderly arrangement of their internal structure. Snowflakes (Fig. 2-3) are a familiar example of this generalization. In spite of the nearly infinite variety of forms which they may assume (it is a little too much to expect that no two are ever alike), most are some variant of a six-sided figure, and thus are placed in what is known as the hexagonal crystal system. This is the same system to which quartz belongs.

What is the mechanism that operates in nature to cause such unlike elements as sodium (Na), a metal, and chlorine (Cl), a gas, to combine to form a clear, crystalline mineral, halite (Fig. 2-4), whose faces intersect to produce nearly perfect cubic crystals? Such an orderly three-dimensional pattern of crystals is determined by the geometric internal arrangement or packing of the atoms of the elements of which they are made. How these building blocks of matter are assembled is important, because their internal structure is the fundamental pattern in the geometry of the lithosphere.

The basic unit of matter is the atom, and most of us are familiar with pictures of a multicolored sphere surrounded by a host of rings, each with its own planetary sphere, and all of these circling around the central sphere like tiny planets in a minute solar system. This is a model, or a stylized concept, of how the particles that make up an element are arranged. Very probably they do not look like this at all, but this is the so-called planetary model developed by Lord Rutherford in 1911, refined and amended to the present complex concept.

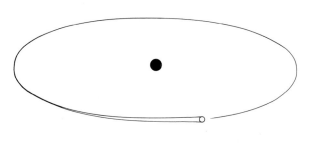

Hydrogen

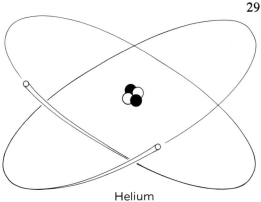

Helium

After L. D. Leet and S. Judson, *Physical Geology,* © 1958 by Prentice-Hall, Inc. By permission.

FIG. 2-5 *Structures of atoms of hydrogen and helium. The large solid circles represent protons; the large open circles neutrons; and the small open circles electrons. Because a chemical element is characterized by the number of protons in the central nucleus, hydrogen is given the atomic number 1, and helium is assigned the atomic number 2.*

The large sphere or group shown at the center of the atomic universe (Fig. 2-5) is the nucleus, and it can be visualized as consisting of two major kinds of particles—protons which carry a positive electrical charge, and neutrons which are electrically neutral. Most of the *mass* of an atom is packed in the nucleus; in fact, 99 per cent of it or better, but most of the *volume* is in the surrounding sphere. This outer space is very thinly occupied by a cloud of negatively-charged electrons circling around the nucleus in orbits somewhat analogous to those of the planets in the solar system. The electrons are infinitesimally small compared to the nucleus of the atom; an electron is only 1/1840th of the mass of the hydrogen nucleus—which is the simplest atom since it consists of only one proton as a nucleus with a lone electron whirling around it.

Most atomic structures are vastly more complex than this simple beginning. There are 102 recognized elements, and each of these is given a *name,* such as chlorine; a *symbol,* such as Cl; and an *atomic number,* such as 17. This number means that chlorine has 17 positively charged protons in its nucleus and in the surrounding electron cloud are 17 negatively charged electrons. Incidentally, the number of neutrons in the nucleus may vary; one *isotope* of chlorine has 18, the other, 20. Since the atomic weight of an element is the total number of neutrons and protons, this means there are two isotopes of chlorine: one with an atomic weight of 35 (17+18); the other, 37 (17+20).

The number of neutrons present in the nucleus seems to vary with the different elements, but there usually are about as many neutrons as there are protons in the nucleus.

The electron orbits are not scattered indiscriminately throughout the space surrounding the nucleus, but are arranged in separate, unequally spaced layers, or *shells.* Since a certain amount of energy is needed to keep an electron at a prescribed distance from the nucleus, these properly are termed *energy-level shells.* The thing to remember here is that the outermost of these energy-level shells is the most significant feature of the atom from the point of view of the formation of chemical compounds, of which minerals are typical inorganic compounds. For some reason, not fully understood as yet, if there are eight electrons in the outer shell of an element it is almost completely stable and rarely combines with others.

An atom is in equilibrium when the number of negatively charged electrons circling in their orbits is exactly the same as the number of positively charged protons in the nucleus. Should the atom lose an electron in the outer shell, then no longer are the electrons and protons in balance, but the atom has an excess of one proton and thus carries a positive charge. The element sodium (Fig. 2-6) is an excellent illustration because it is especially prone to lose an outer electron in view of the fact that its outermost shell contains but one. Its 11 electrons are grouped in three shells outward from the nucleus, as follows: 2, 8, and 1. When the outermost electron is lost and the whole structure is carrying a positive charge, we speak of it as a *sodium ion,* written Na^+. Chlorine has its electrons ranged in three shells: 2, 8, 7. If the chlorine atom can pick up an extra electron it will have achieved the goal of the maximum stability that comes from having eight electrons in the outer shell. It will then have an excess of negatively charged electrons over the positively charged protons in the nucleus, and thus it constitutes a *chlorine ion,* written Cl^-.

From this very brief discussion we learn that an electrically unbalanced atom is an *ion,* and that it may carry either a positive or negative charge. In this submicroscopic world, perhaps unlike ours, like repels like and unlikes are strongly attracted to each other. Thus a powerful affinity can develop between a Na^+ and a Cl^- ion. The excess electron of the outer sodium shell is transferred to the chlorine shell, and added to the seven already there, it gives the eight that are needed for maximum stability. The two resulting ions are now united by an ionic bond to form a completely new compound, NaCl, which is the mineral *halite* (Fig. 2-4), or the substance we call rock salt. Such a chemical compound, produced by the transfer of electrons, is called an *ionic compound.*

The important point is the relationship between atomic structure and the crystal form of minerals. Because of the rapidity with which electrons revolve around their nucleus, their orbits on each of the various energy levels might be considered as forming complete spheres. This is true even for the lone hydrogen electron. It does not revolve in a path that continuously lies in very nearly the same plane, but whirls vigorously around the nucleus at the rate of 7 million billion times each second. At this incredible velocity it spins a skein of successively occupied paths, and from a practical point of

---

FIG. 2-6 *Formation of sodium ion $(+)$ and chlorine ion $(-)$ by transfer of an electron (solid circle) from the outermost shell of a neutral sodium to the outermost shell of the neutral chlorine atom. The process of transfer is illustrated above, and the resulting ions with the stable outer shells of eight electrons each are shown below.*

After K. Krauskopf, *Fundamentals of Physical Science,* Copyright © 1959 McGraw-Hill Book Co., Inc. By permission.

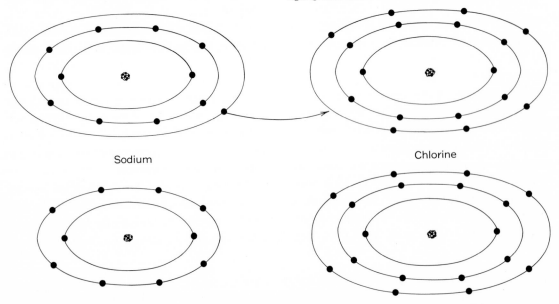

Sodium   Chlorine

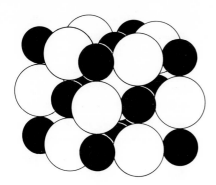

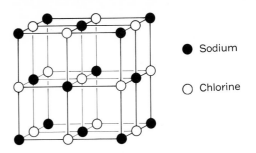

● Sodium

○ Chlorine

view it might be thought of as forming a spherical shell enclosing the nucleus. By comparison the shells and electron orbits for the calcium and iron atoms, with 20 and 26 electrons respectively, are much more dense.

For this reason, Fig. 2-7, illustrating the internal arrangement of a salt crystal, shows the individual sodium and chlorine atoms as spheres that perhaps look like tennis balls or marbles. This is unrealistic, but the device does enable us to (1) convey an idea of the spherical form of the electron shell generated by the orbiting electrons of the outermost shell, (2) show the relative size of the different atoms (in this case sodium has an ionic radius of 0.98 Ångstroms, a unit that equals 0.00000001 centimeter, and the ionic radius of chlorine is 1.8 Å), and (3) most important of all, illustrate the way these atoms are arranged to make a crystal of halite. The tennis-ball diagram, as well as the skeletonized lattice diagram resembling a wire cage, show that the sodium and chlorine ions are packed together in a remarkably strong, rigid arrangement, with each sodium ion surrounded by six, equidistant chlorine ions. The wire diagram, more obviously than the tennis balls, brings out the relationship that all the lines shown connecting the atomic centers intersect at right angles.

No wonder, then, that a halite crystal, newly formed from a strong brine, should be a cube. This mineral is indeed an outstanding illustration of the principle that the crystalline form of a mineral reflects the design of the ordered

FIG. 2-7 *Two representations of the structural arrangements of the ions of sodium (solid circles) and chlorine (open circles) in the mineral halite (Fig. 2-4). An actual visible crystal of halite would consist of a many-thousandfold repetition of the three-dimensional pattern illustrated here. The crystal structure depicted was one of the first to be determined rigorously by the use of X-rays. This development, which took place during the early part of this century, and the subsequent discovery of the structures of a myriad of other crystals, is part of one of the still unfolding heroic epochs in man's assault on the unknown, and led to the recent discovery of the structure of a large molecule in the living cell, called DNA (deoxyribonucleic acid), the carrier of heredity.*

ranks of the atoms within. Regardless of the size, or the imperfections of the external configuration of the crystal form that we see, the internal disciplined pattern of rigidly arranged atoms is invariant. Thus, the crystal form of a mineral is probably the most fundamental of its visible properties because for us it is the outward expression of the internal structure which is determined in part by the chemical composition.

The most convincing demonstration of the marvellously repetitive regularity of the internal geometry of crystals came about, as is so often the case, as the result of an extraordinarily fortunate and essentially intuitive experiment made in 1912 in Munich by Max von Laue and his associates. It established in one stroke the wave nature of X-rays, as well as the existence of the systematic internal arrangement of the atoms in a crystal. Laue was actually trying to find a diffraction grating (a glass plate with finely spaced parallel lines engraved on it) suitable for determining the nature of the X-ray. A diffraction grating serves to make visible light passing through the slits on its surface break up into colored spectra because the waves passing through the grating tend to reinforce or neutralize one another. Laue and his companions were convinced (correctly) that the wave length of X-rays was extremely short, and they all despaired of ever scribing a grating with slits closely enough spaced to diffract such finely structured waves. Finally, the thought occurred to them that the unknown particles in a crystal might be systematically arranged and might also be closely enough spaced that they would serve as a diffraction grating.

After the usual false starts and mishaps with their apparatus, they were successful in sending an X-ray beam first through a crystal of copper sulphate ($CuSO_4 \cdot 5H_2O$), and in a later experiment through a crystal of zinc sulphide (ZnS), discovering that an image could be obtained on a photographic plate placed behind the crystal, which in turn had been mounted between the photographic plate and the X-ray source. To their gratification the light-sensitive plate showed a pattern of dots. These were reflections from electrons that form the outer shells of the regularly arrayed atoms in the crystal. The experiment showed beyond doubt that (1) rather than being composed of rapidly moving particles, X-rays not only are wave-like in the same way that ordinary light is but have a much shorter wave length, and (2) that if the waves strike individual atoms in the crystal, the X-rays are diffracted by them in much the same fashion that light rays are diffracted by a grating. X-rays proved to be the magic key that unlocked the door to the unseen, yet ordered, world whose very existence could only be inferred as recently as half a century ago from surface measurements of interfacial angles and the geometry of crystal faces.

Deciphering the atomic structure of minerals proved to be no easy task, because, by the very nature of the evidence, mineralogists have had to work backward. If the characteristic arrangement of the atoms in a crystal were known in advance, it would be relatively easy to predict how the scattering of dots in an X-ray diffraction photograph would be patterned. However, not knowing the structure of the crystal and having to deduce it from the patterned dots involves elaborate calculations and the application of abstruse theories of wave motion. It can be done, but an immense amount of trial and error is called for in gradually constructing a model that finally fits the indirect evidence provided by the internal reflections of the atoms in a crystal. The deciphering of the labyrinthine structure of the protein molecule by this method stands as one of the great intellectual triumphs of our age.

6. CLEAVAGE.—This is the most distinctive property for some minerals and is quite unlike any that is used in the identification of other solid substances. Cleavage is the ability of a mineral to break, or cleave, along rather definite planes paralleling one another, usually on a fairly close spacing (Figs. 2-2, 2-4).

The most familiar example of nearly perfect cleavage in a single direction is that of mica, especially in the light-colored variety, *muscovite*. This mineral splits in successively thinner and thinner layers until only the finest transparent sheets are left. In earlier days these were used for windows on the Franklin stove, and today this sheet-like habit of mica, together with its nonconductivity, makes this mineral ideal for use in many varieties of electrical equipment.

Orthoclase feldspar ($KAlSi_3O_8$) is an excellent example of a mineral with two directions of cleavage—one nearly perfect, the other less so—with both intersecting at an angle of 90° (Fig. 2-2).

Calcite ($CaCO_3$) is an example of a mineral cut by three cleavage planes. These intersect at a high angle (74° 55′) to form nearly perfect rhombohedrons (a solid figure each of whose sides is an oblique-angled parallelogram with only the opposite sides being equal).

The geometrically repetitive nature of cleavage, its planar character, and the distinctive orientation of cleavage planes for many minerals are strong evidence that cleavage, like the crystal form of minerals, is a property determined by the packing, or geometric arrangement, of the atoms in a mineral.

One of the more dramatic illustrations supporting this statement is the dual expression of the carbon atom in the two wholly dissimilar guises of graphite and diamond. Both substances are composed solely of the element carbon in combination with nothing else, and for this reason they are called *atomic crystals* in contrast to *ionic crystals,* of which you may recall halite (NaCl) was used as an illustration. Graphite is a black, greasy substance that separates into flaky scales, and thus makes an ideal lubricant. Nothing could be more unlike this than the diamond, which is a most effective abrasive and, in addition, has such highly prized properties as brilliant luster, ability to take and hold a polish, and sharply defined, angular cleavages.

The reason for these profound differences in what is chemically the same substance lies in the completely unlike arrangement of the carbon atoms in the two minerals. In a diamond crystal the linkage between the carbon atoms is about as strong as it possibly can be. Each atom is in direct contact with 4 others, and in fact shares the 4 electrons in its outer shell with them. This arrangement produces a structure that is astonishingly close-knit (the centers of the carbon atoms are only 1.5 Å apart), as well as being one that stands up to stresses so well that the carbon atoms in a diamond can cut their way through any other substance. Nonetheless, there are planes of weakness in the diamond wherever centers of the carbon atoms are lined up properly. In fact, the perfect cleavage the diamond possesses gives it initially an oc-

tahedral (eight-sided) figure, which is the pattern that is employed by diamond cutters in exploiting cleavage planes.

Graphite crystallizes in thin, parallel sheets. The bonds uniting carbon atoms within each sheet are many times stronger than the feeble tie that binds one atomic layer to its neighboring sheet above or below. For this reason, graphite has a perfect cleavage in one direction —somewhat akin to that of mica—with the result that it splits readily into thin flaky scales in about the same way that mica does.

MINERAL IDENTIFICATION

Of the nearly 2,000 minerals that have been named by now, only 11 are considered here, and these are among the more important of the rock-forming minerals. They are the building blocks of the rocks which themselves are the essential constituents of the lithosphere. Fortunately for us, all the rocks of the Earth are made up of varying combinations of surprisingly few minerals. Considering the relatively small number of elements that are truly abundant in the Earth's crust, it is scarcely surprising that most of the rock-forming minerals are compounds of silicon and oxygen, as the following list of minerals makes clear:

SOME IMPORTANT ROCK-FORMING MINERALS

NAME	COMPOSITION
Quartz	SiO_2
Feldspar	
Orthoclase	$KAlSi_3O_8$
Plagioclase	$NaAlSi_3O_8 - CaAl_2Si_2O_8$
Mica	
Muscovite	$KAl_3Si_3O_{10}(OH)_2$
Biotite	$K(Mg,Fe)_3AlSi_3O_{10}(OH)_2$
Ferromagnesian	
minerals	
Hornblende	$Ca_2Na(Mg,Fe)_4(Al,Fe,Ti)_3$ $Si_6O_{22}(O,OH)_2$
Pyroxene	$Ca(Mg,Fe,Al)(Si,Al)_2O_6$
Olivine	$(Fe,Mg)_2SiO_4$
Calcite	$CaCO_3$
Gypsum	$CaSO_4 \cdot 2H_2O$
Halite	$NaCl$

Properties of Rock-forming Minerals

QUARTZ.—This is the hardest of the common rock-forming minerals, with a hardness of 7 on the Mohs scale. Customarily it crystallizes in six-sided crystals (Fig. 2-1) which are terminated by a sharp-pointed pyramid at each end should the mineral have an opportunity to grow free from interference. Quartz that grew in cavities and geodes commonly has only one pyramid on the end of the crystal that extends into the opening. Crystals that grew into openings may sometimes reach dimensions of a foot or more, but in rocks such as granite, quartz crystals are much smaller, seldom over ¼ inch in diameter. Where they are fresh and unweathered they may sparkle like tiny fragments of glass. Quartz has a strong vitreous luster, and when pure is completely clear and colorless. In fact, the Greeks thought it was some kind of frozen water.

FELDSPAR.—This is the name for a group of minerals rather than a single mineral such as quartz. The feldspars are combinations of potassium (Fig. 2-2), or of sodium and calcium, with oxygen, aluminum, and silicon. The most abundant by far of the rock-forming minerals, they are the most important constituent of the lithosphere, probably making up at least 50 per cent of its substance and outnumbering quartz manyfold.

ORTHOCLASE.—This potassium-bearing feldspar (Fig. 2-2) forms the light gray or sometimes flesh-pink groundmass of such a rock as granite. Orthoclase, with a hardness of 6, is only slightly less hard than quartz. Perhaps its most distinctive property is a well-developed cleavage in two directions, with the cleavage planes intersecting at 90°. Although orthoclase, like quartz, has a pearly or a vitreous luster, it very often is less glassy in appearance in a rock, and in some cases even resembles unglazed porcelain or may look like the material inside the ceramic jacket of a spark plug.

PLAGIOCLASE.—This sodium- or calcium-bearing feldspar comprises a group of minerals constituting a so-called *isomorphous series,* which means that this group should be thought of as a solid solution with one end member being the sodium plagioclase, the other being the calcium-bearing form. The intermediate varieties, to which individual names have been given, comprise a continuous sequence.

Plagioclase has the same hardness as orthoclase, as well as a vitreous luster. Its color is most likely to be white or pale gray, although some varieties show a beautiful iridescence, or play of colors, much like those of a peacock's feathers. Some varieties, though, may be nearly as glass-clear as quartz. However, one means of distinction of plagioclase from quartz or orthoclase is the presence on some of the crystal or cleavage surfaces of a multitude of very closely spaced parallel straight lines, which are almost as fine as though they had been engraved there. The lines are made by the nearly right-angle intersection of close-interval, parallel internal planes with the surface of the crystal.

MICA.—This, too, is a group of closely related minerals that share the property of a sheet-like arrangement of their atoms, resulting in a good to excellent cleavage paralleling these internal planes of weakness. The two sorts of mica that we are concerned with here, muscovite and biotite, are the most important rock-forming varieties.

MUSCOVITE.—The common name for this mineral is white mica, and generally it is colorless to transparent, especially when it is peeled down to thin sheets. This is perhaps its unique property, and in centuries past mica was used in the tiny windows of the meager houses of medieval Europe before the widespread use of glass brought more light to their gloomy interiors. The name of the mineral comes from Muscovy-glass, derived from the ancient name for the Grand Duchy of Moscow or Muscovy. Muscovite is a soft, flaky mineral with a pearly or silky luster, and in a rock its tiny spangles shimmer when it catches the sunlight—the German name of *glimmer* for the mineral mica conveys an impression of this very property.

BIOTITE.—This variety commonly is called black mica, and, as its chemical formula indicates, it includes iron and magnesium in its composition, while muscovite does not. Commonly, biotite is colored dark brown or black, and thin sheets of it lack the transparency of muscovite. In rocks such as granite, it occurs as brilliant, jet-black flakes that shine like satin in the sun.

FERROMAGNESIAN MINERALS.—This group includes a great number of the darker minerals of rocks. The formulas of hornblende, pyroxene, and olivine, as well as biotite, show that these rock-forming minerals contain iron and magnesium. There are other ferromagnesian minerals in addition, but the first three are the principal rock-forming minerals within the group.

HORNBLENDE.—This name, too, applies to what is probably a complex isomorphous series of compounds of rather variable composition. The significant difference in composition between hornblende and its close relative, pyroxene, is shown in the listing of rock-forming minerals, where it can be seen that hornblende contains some hydrogen while pyroxene does not. Hornblende is a dark mineral, commonly dark green and black. When it is unweathered it may be brilliant jet black, and its strong vitreous luster shines as brightly as a lacquered surface. Hornblende crystals are long and narrow as a rule—such a form is called prismatic. The cleavage pattern of hornblende is one of its more distinctive properties. There are two principal directions and their planes parallel the long axis of the crystal, but intersect each other at oblique angles of 56° and 124° (Fig. 2-8). Hornblende in a typical occurrence, such as granite, shows up as brilliant black, lath-like crystals dispersed through the rock.

PYROXENE.—This dark ferromagnesian mineral has approximately the same general occurrence as hornblende. It is more common in the darker than the lighter colored rocks. The chemical content of pyroxene is much like that of hornblende; as the table shows, the chief difference is the absence of hydrogen in the pyroxene group. Pyroxene crystals generally are stubbier, in fact they often are nearly equidimensional. Their cleavage planes approximate a right angle in their intersection, since they are at 93° and 87°, respectively, as contrasted to the oblique cleavages of hornblende. Pyroxene crystals seen in cross section are nearly square (Fig. 2-8). The color is about the same as that of hornblende, very dark green or black, and the luster is vitreous. These properties necessarily are very generalized ones, because we are concerned with a rather diverse group of minerals having considerable variation in physical properties.

Hornblende and pyroxene are the more abundant of the darker rock-forming minerals. The principal distinctions between the two are: (1) hornblende crystals tend to be long and narrow while pyroxene crystals are short and stubby; (2) hornblende has oblique cleavages parallel to the long axis of the crystal, pyrox-

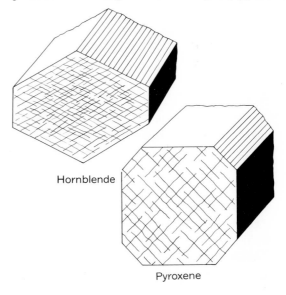

FIG. 2-8 *Illustration of the distinctive cleavage properties of hornblende and pyroxene.*

ene cleavage planes intersect each other at approximately right angles; (3) hornblende crystals seen in cross section approach a rhombic pattern, pyroxene crystals are more nearly square.

OLIVINE.—This is not an especially abundant ferromagnesian mineral, but it is a distinctive one. From its name we are likely to infer, correctly, that the color is green. Usually the mineral occurs as rounded, well-defined, granular, glassy crystals. When these are sufficiently large and free from blemishes they make the attractive, although fragile, gem stone called *peridot.* Olivine occurs most commonly in the dark, iron- and magnesium-rich igneous rocks, such as basalt. Olivine crystals in fresh basalt often look like tiny bits of dark green bottle glass, but when they weather they may alter to shades of brown and red. In some varieties of dark intrusive igneous rocks the percentage of olivine may be so great that the rock may consist almost wholly of a granular aggregation of this single mineral, as in the rock *dunite,* named for Dun Mountain in New Zealand.

CALCITE.—This widely occurring mineral, whose composition is calcium carbonate ($CaCO_3$), obviously would be expected to have a markedly different assemblage of physical properties from the minerals described above, all of which are compounds having silicon and oxygen as essential elements (Fig. 2-2; see also photo at beginning of chapter). Calcite is abundant enough in some circumstances to be the sole mineral in a rock. Examples of such a monomineralic rock are limestone and its recrystallized equivalent, marble. In these two rocks, both the mineral and the rock are a single compound, $CaCO_3$, and the rock is not an aggregate of minerals of diverse form and composition as is a rock such as granite.

Normally, calcite is a light-colored (white or pale yellow) or colorless mineral, although depending on the amount and nature of the impurities, the color may range across a spectrum including yellow, orange, brown, and black.

Calcite has a vitreous luster, and is a mineral that is easily scratched since its hardness is only 3. Calcite occurs in crystals which are difficult to categorize readily since they are found in such an extraordinary variety of forms. In general, they tend to be six-sided, and sometimes, like quartz, they are terminated by a long, narrow, many-faceted pyramid. A more diagnostic property is a nearly perfect cleavage in three directions (Fig. 2-2), and the intersections of these cleavage planes almost invariably produce a rhombohedral pattern. That is, when the mineral breaks into fragments, each of the faces is a rhombus, or approximately diamond-shaped figure (like the diamond suit in playing cards).

A final test which serves to discriminate between calcite and its close relative *dolomite,* $CaMg(CO_3)_2$, is the fact that calcite effervesces, or fizzes, very strongly in cold dilute hydrochloric acid, while dolomite reacts nowhere near so readily. Dolomite, like calcite, also occurs in large enough masses to constitute whole rock layers, which have the same name as the mineral of which they are made—dolomite. Aside from its inability to effervesce as readily, a further distinction from calcite is the fact that dolomite crystals are slightly harder (3.5), have higher specific gravity, and often have crystal faces showing slight curvature instead of being sharp, well-defined planes. The origin of the rock, dolomite, is still being debated; one possibility is that magnesium-bearing solutions may alter limestone through the replacement of some of the element calcium by magnesium.

Both calcite and dolomite are typical of sedimentary rocks, or of rocks recrystallized from them. Both minerals are distinguished from quartz by their lesser hardness, both have a vitreous luster, and both are markedly crystalline. Calcite is best discriminated from dolomite by its stronger effervescence in hydrochloric acid.

GYPSUM.—This compound, $CaSO_4 \cdot 2H_2O$, like calcite, is an example of a rock-forming mineral which is not a silicate. Gypsum is the name applied to a mineral as well as to rock layers consisting of this mineral alone. Gypsum is a very soft mineral with a hardness of 2. Commonly it is white or colorless, but, like calcite, if impurities are included it may show a wide color range. Large crystals are likely to have a nearly perfect micaceous cleavage in one direction, and less well-developed cleavages nearly at right angles to it. Thin sheets of gypsum, like muscovite, are colorless or white and are transparent to translucent. In medieval Italy gypsum sheets were once used in windows before glass became available. A massive and essentially structureless variety of gypsum with a soft, pearly luster is known as *alabaster,* and in the Classical Period, as well as in the Renaissance, was much favored for statuary. Alabaster has the advantage of uniform texture and softness, but for this very reason it is readily scarred or mutilated.

Satin spar is a familiar type of gypsum in the arid western states, where it commonly is found as a silky, fibrous mineral filling the narrow seams between layers of shale, with the fibers standing at right angles to the stratification. *Selenite* is a variety that is white or colorless and characteristically is found in broad flat sheets that separate along a cleavage plane only slightly less well-defined than that of muscovite.

Closely related to gypsum, and rather hard to distinguish from it, is *anhydrite,* $CaSO_4$. Chemically, the important difference is the absence of water of crystallization in anhydrite, while it is an integral part of the formula for gypsum. The chief practical distinction between the two minerals is the slightly greater hardness of anhydrite ($3-3\frac{1}{2}$).

Both gypsum and anhydrite are found in some parts of the world (West Texas is an illustration) in thick layers, or strata, fully comparable to beds of limestone, and are presumed to have crystallized from solution as the result of evaporation of what may once have been an arm of a shallow, nearly land-encircled sea. For this reason, these monomineralic rocks often are found closely associated with extensive bodies of rock salt, with which they share a common origin.

HALITE.—This mineral, which is the same substance as common salt, has been discussed earlier in this chapter. Its most diagnostic features are the most obvious—its solubility in water and its taste. Halite is a fourth example of a mineral that commonly makes a rock almost devoid of other minerals—called rock salt or simply salt. Because of the high solubility of halite, rocks containing it seldom are found at the Earth's surface except in quite arid regions. Among the more spectacular occurrences of rock salt are the salt domes found in many places in the world. These are discussed at length in Chapter VI.

Suggested References

Bragg, Sir William, 1954, Concerning the nature of things, Dover Publications, New York.

Berry, L. G., and Mason, B., 1959, Mineralogy, W. H. Freeman and Co., San Francisco, Calif.

Clark, F. W., 1924, The data of geochemistry, U.S. Geol. Survey, Bulletin 770.

English, G. L., and Jensen, D. E., 1958, Getting acquainted with minerals, McGraw-Hill Book Co., Inc., New York.

Fenton, C. L., and Fenton, M. A., 1951, Rocks and their stories, Doubleday and Co., New York.

Gamow, George, 1958, Matter, earth, and sky, Prentice-Hall, Inc., Englewood Cliffs, N. J.

Holden, Alan, and Singer, Phyllis, 1960, Crystals and crystal growing, Doubleday and Co., New York.

Hurlbut, C. S., Jr., 1956, Dana's manual of mineralogy, John Wiley and Sons, Inc., New York.

Krauskopf, K. B., and Beiser, Arthur, 1960, The physical universe, McGraw-Hill Book Co., Inc., New York.

Kuiper, G. P., and others, 1958, The solar system, Vol. II, The earth as a planet, Univ. Chicago Press, Chicago, Ill.

Mason, Brian, 1958, Principles of geochemistry, John Wiley and Sons, Inc., New York.

Pearl, R. M., 1955, How to know minerals and rocks, McGraw-Hill Book Co., Inc., New York.

Pough, F. H., 1953, Field guide to rocks and minerals, Houghton Mifflin, Boston, Mass.

Zim, H. S., and Shaffer, P. R., 1957, Rocks and minerals, Simon and Schuster, New York.

Eruption of Hekla, Iceland. (Photograph by Thorsteinn Josepsson.)

III

Igneous Rocks and Volcanism

Almost all the igneous rocks owe their existence to the cooling and crystallization of their minerals from a molten solution called magma. This process can take place on the surface of the Earth, in which case volcanic rocks are formed, or it can go on in the depths of the Earth, where plutonic rocks have their origin.

The origin of these magmatic fluids remains unknown after nearly two centuries of scientific observation and speculation. Where does the lava come from that is delivered to the surface of the Earth in such prodigious quantities as to cover tens of thousands of square miles to a depth of thousands of feet? As an illustration of the magnitude of molten material which may be involved, in 1887 one moderate eruption of Mauna Loa on the island of Hawaii produced something like 5,000,000 cubic yards (about 2,500,000 tons) of lava per hour (Stearns and Clark, 1930). Considering that the flow ran for approximately 150 hours, this gives us some idea of the tremendous effectiveness of these sources of naturally heated material, especially when it is realized that this immense quantity of very heavy basaltic lava was lifted a minimum height of 20,000 feet to the surface from its source within the Earth.

The first of many thorny questions about igneous activity is at what depth does magma originate? In earlier days the answer to this was simple because the belief was widely held that the whole interior was molten below a crust that was eggshell thin compared with the total diameter of the Earth. Obviously, then, volcanoes were simply weaker points in the crust where the incandescent fluid broke through.

From the study of earthquake waves, and from other physical evidence, we now know that much of the Earth's interior behaves as a layered solid of varying density and that the simpler and vastly more dramatic picture of a fiery, flaming furnace in the center is untrue. The data available to us indicate that the depth of the source for most volcanoes is shallow. Furthermore, the magmatic source for a volcano is very localized, compared to the total area of the Earth. This extreme localization of volcanoes will be made more apparent when we come to the discussion of volcanic activity. The map (Fig. 3-1) shows that, rather than being sprinkled at random over the Earth's surface, volcanoes are concentrated in well-defined bands, chiefly surrounding the Pacific Ocean, along the Mid-Atlantic Ridge, and through the Mediterranean Sea.

In comparison with the strongly concentrated distribution of these volcanic centers, a perplexing contrast is afforded by the fact that when erosion has cut deeply into the Earth's surface and stripped away the outer layers of its rocky veneer over a wide area, then thousands of square miles of granite—the most abundant of plutonic rocks—stand revealed. Most of this granite solidified deep within the heart of

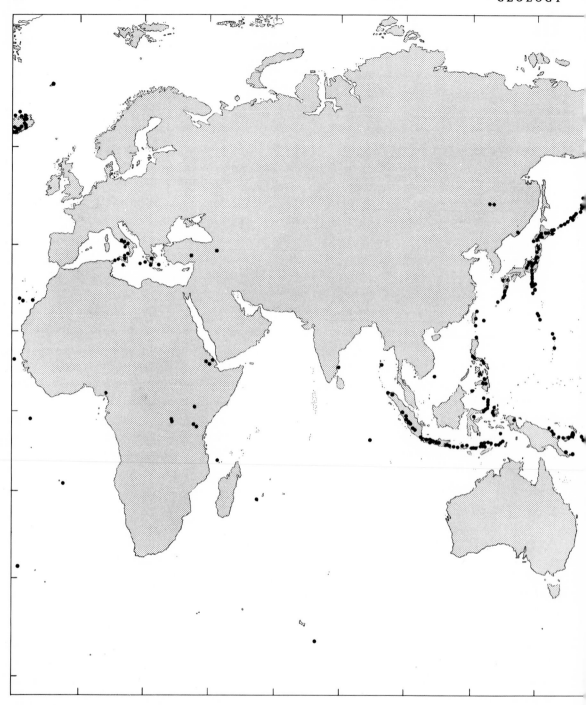

now long-vanished mountain ranges. What this means is simply that a high percentage of the rocks we now see exposed on the Earth's surface were once molten.

We shall return to this fundamental problem of magma in the Earth's crust near the end of this chapter. The important point to remember is that there are two major occurrences of igneous rocks; (1) on the surface of the Earth, and (2) within the crust itself. This distinction

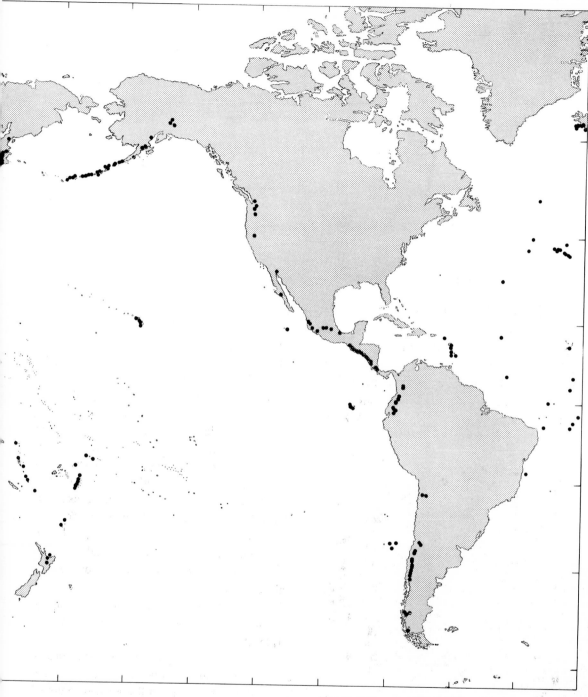

After W. Q. Kennedy and J. E. Richey, "Catalogue of the Active Volcanoes of the World," 1947. By permission of L'Association de Volcanologie, Edinburgh, Scotland.

FIG. 3-1 *Distribution of the active volcanoes of the world. Each black dot represents one or more presently or recently active volcanoes, of which there are more than 470.*

is of absolutely fundamental importance, because the mode of occurrence of an igneous rock—that is, whether the magma solidified above or below the surface of the ground—determines the rate of cooling, and the rate of cooling, in turn, is what establishes the texture of the rock.

Texture

Texture is one of the two leading properties used in classifying the igneous rocks (the other is the *mineral composition*). The word itself is familiar to most people as having something to do with cloth; in fact, it is derived from the Latin *textura,* a weaving. Today it means the arrangement and size of the threads in a woven cloth; for example, a burlap sack has a much coarser texture than a nylon stocking. When we apply the term to such a thing as an igneous rock, we mean the size of the crystals as well as their mutual relationships.

An igneous rock in which the minerals are visible to the unaided eye is said to have a medium- or coarse-grained texture depending on the size of the crystals. An igneous rock whose texture is crystalline, as revealed by the microscope, but most of whose crystals are too small to be seen by the eye alone, has a fine-

FIG. 3-2 *Obsidian, showing the characteristic conchoidal fracture. (Courtesy of Ward's Natural Science Establishment, Inc., Rochester, N. Y.)*

grained texture. Yet the mineral content may be nearly the same in the two rocks.

Why, then, the difference in the size of the crystals if the minerals are nearly alike? The answer lies in the way in which the magma solidified. If it cooled slowly and under relatively undisturbed conditions, then large crystals had a chance to grow around the various nuclei in the still fluid magma. They may grow to fair size, up to half an inch or more, in what is essentially a sort of crystal mush, with the last-forming minerals filling the interstices between the earlier forming minerals when the whole mass finally congeals. Should the magma cool rapidly, the same crystal growth will go on around floating nuclei as it did in the slow-cooling magma, but the whole process is halted when the magma solidifies before the minerals have a chance to grow to visible diameters. Then the rock, although crystalline, consists of a tightly knit fabric of minute crystals which are invisible to the unaided eye.

The answer to a large part of this problem of what factor controls the texture of igneous rocks is found in what is known as their *mode of occurrence;* in general terms, whether or not they solidified above the ground or below it. To phrase the statement another way, are they volcanic or plutonic rocks? Volcanic rocks cool with relative rapidity, and therefore for the most part have fine-grained textures; intrusive rocks cool more slowly, larger crystals grow as a result, and they are characterized by coarse-grained textures.

Two additional textures, important among the igneous rocks, are: (1) glassy, and (2) porphyritic.

A glassy texture is typified by the rock *obsidian,* which is also known as volcanic glass. Glass, although a solid, still possesses many of the attributes of a liquid. It is wholly noncrystalline, because it passed quickly from the liquid to the solid state without giving the ions in the original magma an opportunity to arrange themselves in ordered ranks as crystals. It is this liquid/solid state which gives obsidian many of its unusual properties. Because it is essentially textureless, it breaks or fractures in about the same way as a homogenous substance such as a black, solid chunk of roofing tar does when workmen chop open a barrel before melting the tar in the boiler. The sharp-edged, curving spall characteristic of shattered glass blocks, broken tar, and obsidian fragments makes such a distinctive pattern that it merits a name of its own, which is *conchoidal fracture,* meaning shell-like (Fig. 3-2). It is this pattern of breaking with a sharp edge that made obsidian such a deadly weapon, especially when it was flaked or chipped into the beautifully proportioned arrowheads, spear points, and knife blades used by many of the Indian peoples of the western United States and Mexico.

FIG. 3-3 *Obsidian artifacts. (Photograph by John Haddaway.)*

Porphyritic texture takes its name from the Greek word *porphyra,* which was the word used for the imperial purple—a highly prized dye extracted from an eastern Mediterranean shellfish. By extension the name was applied to a very specific kind of rock—a dark, uniformly textured igneous rock from Egypt that contains small white feldspar crystals embedded in the purplish groundmass. This is the rock that was

greatly favored in the Roman world for carving busts of emperors, as well as their sycophants and the lesser dignitaries of the court. The rock makes a striking purplish bust, especially when set off against an artfully draped white marble toga. Such a colorful petrographic arrangement could scarcely fail to make even such decadent figures as Nero and Caligula look regal.

Today, by a further extension of the original word, the term is applied to any igneous rock with a duality of texture; that is, crystals of two markedly different sizes are found in the same rock. Such a texture is interpreted to mean the magma underwent two generations of cooling, perhaps an earlier slow-cooling phase during which time the large crystals grew, followed by a later more rapid phase when the smaller crystals came out of solution. In such a rock the larger crystals are called *phenocrysts* (from a Greek root, *phainein,* to show, combined with crystal) and the background finely crystalline material in which they are embedded is called the *groundmass* (Fig. 3-4).

FIG. 3-4 *Igneous rock with porphyritic texture. The dark groundmass that encloses the large white crystals is much finer grained. (Courtesy of Ward's Natural Science Establishment, Inc.)*

Porphyritic texture is very characteristic of igneous rocks that solidified at shallow depths in such bodies as dikes and sills (described below). Such shallow intrusive igneous bodies are an example of a magma which may have been cooling slowly at great depths and was moved up into a shallower zone of the Earth's crust by the magma stream where it cooled more rapidly and in a sense froze around the still floating larger and earlier formed crystals.

Because the larger crystals in a porphyry form while the magma is still dominantly a fluid, they grow without interference and thus may often achieve a nearly perfect crystal form. The later crystallizing minerals come out of solution more rapidly, and since the growth of each one is interfered with by its neighbors, very few have the opportunity to develop the external form of a crystal, although their internal structure may show the complete atomic pattern for the particular mineral involved.

Mineral Composition

The other property, besides texture, used to classify the igneous rocks, is the mineral composition. Obviously, the kinds of minerals to be found in any igneous rock are dependent on the chemical composition of the magma from which the rock crystallized.

Igneous rocks resemble steel in the way in which they are formed. As everyone knows, steel is usually made in an open-hearth furnace, and the properties of any batch of steel are determined largely by the addition of such elements as tungsten, molybdenum, chromium, etc., to the original charge of pig iron and scrap. To put the case very simply, if the charge contains chromium and not nickel, then the production of a chromium-bearing steel rather than a nickel-bearing steel will be the result. Or if 18 per cent chromium and 8 per cent nickel are present, stainless steel will be made. So it is with the igneous rocks. If the magma is low in potassium, it is most unlikely, then, that a po-

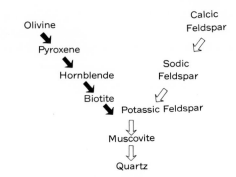

After N. L. Bowen, *Evolution of the Igneous Rocks*, Copyright © 1928 Princeton University Press. By permission.

FIG. 3-5 *The dual sequence of crystallization of minerals from magma.*

tassium-bearing feldspar such as orthoclase will crystallize. If the silica content of the magma is high, then quartz should be an abundant mineral, and if it is low, then the resulting rock very likely will be quartz-free.

Not all the minerals in a rock crystallize from a magma simultaneously; rather, the evidence available to us indicates their crystallization follows an orderly sequence which was worked out many years ago by the petrologist, N. L. Bowen. If conditions are favorable, minerals may crystallize from a magma in a dual sequence in the order shown in Fig. 3-5. The plagioclase feldspars crystallize in what is known as a continuous reaction series, which means that the early-formed crystals change continuously in their composition by reaction with the changing composition of the fluid magma still remaining. The other minerals, such as pyroxene, hornblende, and biotite, make a discontinuous series, so that an early-formed mineral reacts with the remaining fluid to form a completely new mineral with a quite different composition and crystal form, rather than an isomorphous series such as the plagioclases.

According to the Bowen reaction series, the first minerals to come out of solution in a magma are olivine and calcium-bearing plagioclase. Were the magma to crystallize at this stage, the resulting rock would be a *basalt* if it were volcanic, and a *gabbro* if it were plutonic.

Should, however, these early-forming minerals settle out, then the remaining magma will have lost much of its iron, magnesium, calcium, and some silicon. With a progressive decrease in these elements the magma will be correspondingly enriched in potassium, sodium, and silicon.

The next minerals to crystallize are the plagioclases of intermediate composition along with pyroxene and hornblende. Should the magma congeal at this point, it would yield rocks of intermediate composition, such as *andesite* if fine-grained and *diorite* if coarse-grained. Should these earlier crystallizing minerals be separated from the magmatic solution, the remaining minerals to crystallize will be sodium-rich followed by potassium-rich plagioclase and the two micas. Last of all to solidify is quartz, and then only if free silica is left over in solution after all the metallic ions are used up and none are left to enter into combination. Quartz is an interstitial mineral since it fills in the voids or spaces among the earlier-forming crystals. Typical rocks with a mineral composition of quartz, mica, orthoclase, and minor amounts of sodium-bearing plagioclase and hornblende are *granite* if plutonic and *rhyolite* if volcanic.

The validity of the so-called Bowen reaction series seems to be well established from experimental evidence and also through observation of the mutual arrangement of minerals in many naturally occurring rocks. It does explain how a magma of originally basaltic composition (one that on crystallizing yields olivine and calcium-bearing plagioclase) might go through a process of differentiation to yield a granitic magma from which quartz, biotite, and orthoclase crystallize.

Unfortunately, the origin of the massive bodies of granite that crop out so broadly in the heartlands of the world's continents is almost certain to be vastly more complex than this simple explanation. It is difficult to conceive of granitic intrusions as extensive as those in the core of many of the Earth's mountain ranges as having formed from a residual liquid represent-

ing not much more than 10 per cent of the original volume of a basaltic magma. We shall return to this problem of granite in the Earth's crust later on, but it is worth emphasizing here and reiterating later what a major puzzle in the occurrence of the igneous rocks is the curious reversal of roles in that the most common of all volcanic rocks is basalt, while the most widely occurring plutonic rock is granite, yet their respective mineral compositions are at nearly opposite ends of the spectrum.

CLASSIFICATION
OF THE IGNEOUS ROCKS

With a knowledge of the relationship existing between texture and occurrence, and the ability to recognize five or six of the more abundant rock-forming minerals, a workable field classification of the igneous rocks can be established by using the two properties of texture and mineral composition.

In the accompanying table (Fig. 3-6) which shows six of the more common igneous rocks, the fine-grained volcanic rocks, or *extrusive rocks* as they are sometimes known, are arranged along the upper row, and the plutonic,

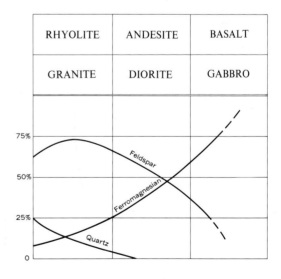

FIG. 3-6 *The mineral composition of igneous rocks.*

or *intrusive rocks,* are along the lower. The lighter colored and quartz-bearing rocks are to the left; the iron- and magnesium-rich, and consequently dark-colored, rocks are to the right.

Of the first two rocks listed, rhyolite is a volcanic and granite is a plutonic rock. The mineral composition curves below the table show that granite (the origin of the name is lost in antiquity, but it is believed by some to be derived from the Italian adjective, *granito;* grained) is a light-colored, coarse-grained rock whose chief constituents are quartz, feldspar (commonly orthoclase and some soda-bearing plagioclase), and some ferromagnesian minerals so named from their content of iron and magnesium (biotite and minor amounts of hornblende, as a rule). Since granite is a widely used rock for such things as tombstones, monuments, government and bank buildings (in fact, it has been used for stately edifices since the beginning of Western civilization), almost all of us readily recognize the characteristically speckled appearance of this most familiar of rocks, with its white to light gray background flecked with spangles of black mica or needles of hornblende, as well as its coarsely crystalline texture with some minerals (chiefly the feldspars) reaching dimensions up to perhaps one-half inch across (Fig. 3-7).

FIG. 3-7 *A rough surface of granite. The white grains are feldspar, the clear glassy ones are quartz, and the black grains are mica and hornblende. (Photograph by John Haddaway.)*

Rhyolite (named from the Greek, "lava stream" or "torrent" + stone), a volcanic rock with about the same chemical composition as granite, has a wholly different texture. Commonly the texture is porphyritic, with a groundmass so fine-grained that the individual minerals can be resolved only with a microscope. Embedded in the groundmass are small crystals of quartz, feldspar, occasional scales of biotite, and, rarely, ferromagnesian minerals. Quartz is an early-crystallizing mineral in rhyolite, which is the reverse of the state of affairs in granite. For this reason quartz crystals commonly appear completely formed and very often are doubly terminated, rather than having the mineral appear as it does in granite, as glassy blobs filling the spaces left between earlier-formed minerals. Rhyolite ordinarily is light colored, and may be white, light gray, pink, and even red where it has weathered—especially in the dry climate of the southwestern United States and northern Mexico. A textural feature that is quite characteristic of the groundmass of rhyolite is a streaked pattern in the rock known as *flow banding,* which is the result of differential concentration of material in layers or bands in the still sticky, viscous lava just before it solidified (Fig. 3-8).

Diorite (whose name comes from the Greek word, to distinguish) is a coarse-grained igneous rock whose mineral composition places it about midway between granite and gabbro. For this reason it, as well as a large number of kindred rocks, is spoken of as having an intermediate composition. This is a rock with sodium-bearing plagioclase feldspar as its chief constituent and lacking quartz and orthoclase. Hornblende is its leading dark mineral, and biotite commonly is an important constituent. Pyroxene is rare, as might be anticipated from its early crystallizing position in the Bowen reaction series, and is much more abundant in *gabbro,* the next plutonic rock in the classification.

Because of the lack of quartz and of orthoclase and the approximate equality of plagio-

clase and the darker minerals, diorite tends to be a drab gray rock. These rocks are not used as widely for building stones as true granites, because diorites are somewhat less abundant and possibly because their somber gray color is less pleasing.

Since diorites are igneous rocks with an intermediate composition, they are a rock class that embraces a wide range of related rock types. For example, some varieties of diorite do contain quartz, and these are known logically enough as *quartz diorite*. Other diorite-like plutonic rocks may contain orthoclase and plagioclase, with plagioclase dominant, and these two-feldspar rocks are *monzonites*. Should they also contain quartz, they are then *quartz monzonites*, and are difficult to distinguish from granite.

FIG. 3-8 *Flow banding caused by viscous flow in a magma that congealed as obsidian. Blocks at the base of a volcanic dome south of Mono Lake, Calif. (Photograph by John Haddaway.)*

Andesite (which is named for its occurrences in the Andean summit volcanoes of South America) is a gray to grayish-black, fine-grained volcanic rock. Commonly its groundmass is too dense for any individual minerals to be resolved without the use of a strong hand lens. Phenocrysts are common, and are likely to be either transparent or light gray crystals of plagioclase or are dark minerals such as hornblende or black scales of biotite. The term andesite is now used to cover such a wide range of volcanic rocks of intermediate composition that it has lost much of its precise meaning as a rock term. However, these rocks, in general, lack visible quartz, the chief feldspar is sodium-bearing plagioclase, and the dark minerals are principally biotite and hornblende. These lavas occur more abundantly on the Earth's surface than the rhyolitic rocks, but are less widespread than the basalts.

Gabbro (this is an old Italian name for many of the dark rocks—including serpentine—used in the Renaissance palaces and churches of Italy) consists typically of a coarse-grained inter-growth of crystals of pyroxene and calcium-bearing plagioclase. Many gabbros also contain olivine, and some include hornblende, too, although pyroxene dominates. Unlike the diorites, the ferromagnesian minerals are more abundant than the feldspars. There are exceptions, of course, and one variety of gabbro, *anortho-site,* consists almost entirely of a coarse-grained fabric of plagioclase crystals. Another variety of gabbro, much sought after as a decorative building stone for store fronts, banks, etc., contains large dark purplish plagioclase crystals that give a wonderfully impressive iridescent play of colors, much as peacock feathers do when they catch the sunlight.

Basalt (whose name is truly one of the most ancient in geology, since it apparently dates back to Egyptian or Ethiopic usage, and one of the first references to it by name is by Pliny) is by far the most abundant of all volcanic rocks. Some regions, such as the plateau bordering the Columbia River in the northwestern United States, the vicinity of Bombay in western India, and the part of South America where Brazil, Paraguay, and Argentina are close neighbors, were inundated by vast outpourings of basalt—some covering as much as 200,000 square miles. In addition, many of the truly oceanic islands, such as Samoa, Hawaii, and Tahiti, are basaltic volcanoes rising many thousands of feet above the sea floor. Deep-sea soundings also give us a clue to the broad expanses of basalt seemingly spread across the oceanic depths in the recent geologic past.

Basalt is a most commonplace-appearing rock for playing such a prominent role in volcanism. Ordinarily, when basalt is fresh or unweathered it is coal black or dark gray and the groundmass is too fine-grained for the minerals to be visible; but under the microscope they can be seen to be mostly pyroxene and plagioclase. If phenocrysts are present, they may be either of these minerals in addition to olivine. Some varieties of basalt crystallized in bodies thicker than thin lava flows and cooled slowly enough that the minerals in their groundmass are large enough to be visible. *Diabase* is such a rock, and its characteristic texture is a felted network of feldspar laths with the spaces between them occupied by later-crystallizing, irregularly shaped pyroxene crystals.

The distinction between andesite and basalt is largely artificial since the two types grade into one another. The separation of one from the other is based on (1) the character of the plagioclase, whether dominantly sodium-bearing (andesite) or calcium-bearing (basalt), and (2) whether or not the principal ferromagnesian mineral is hornblende (andesite) or pyroxene (basalt). These differences are determined by using a microscope and are not likely to be very meaningful in the field. A workable means of distinction in the field is to chip off a small flake of the rock. If when held up to the sun, the flake is opaque, the rock very likely is basalt; if translucent, andesite.

Basalt shows a much more interesting variability physically than it does mineralogically. Some basalt flows are as rough and jagged as so much furnace slag (Fig. 3-33). Other flows are smooth and ropy, with glazed surfaces that look as though they had once been a stream of tar that had been halted instantaneously (Fig. 3-34). Some basalts are dense, uniformly textured rocks with no visible minerals—others are frothy and cellular and are filled with innumer-

able small holes that were gas bubbles trapped in the still fluid basaltic lava (Fig. 3-9).

A rock structure typical of basaltic rocks—although by no means confined to them—is the development of geometrically regular columns (Fig. 3-10). Commonly these have five or six sides and are nested so closely together that when the columns are seen on end their pattern resembles that of hexagonal bathroom tiles (Fig. 3-11). This is the result of the contraction

FIG. 3-9 *Cellular or scoriaceous basalt.* (*Photograph by Hal Roth.*)

of the rock that starts when the lava has first solidified. Should crystallization take place radially outward from approximately equally spaced centers, then the most efficient pattern that can be developed between these individual cells is a hexagonal one, similar in most respects to the cellular hexagonal pattern in a beehive.

FIG. 3-10 *Columnar structure in basalt lava flow. The Devil's Postpile, Calif. (From the Cedric Wright Collection, courtesy of the Sierra Club.)*

Two familiar examples of columnar basalts are The Devil's Postpile in the Sierra Nevada of California and the Giant's Causeway of Northern Ireland.

OTHER TYPES OF IGNEOUS ROCKS

There are several other important kinds of igneous rocks that do not fit into a classification as rigid as the one just discussed.

Obsidian (whose name comes from the Latin word, *obsidianus,* after its describer, Obsius) is also called volcanic glass (Figs. 3-2, 3-8). Actually, it should be thought of as a supercooled liquid, since it is made from magma that passed from the liquid to the solid phase so rapidly that crystals did not have time enough to form. This means that the rock is textureless, and that its appearance and fracture pattern is much like a large mass of insulator or bottle glass that solidified out of control and had to be thrown out on the dump. Actually, a natural glass, such as obsidian, is not too unlike the artificial product, the chief difference being that the careful controls used in making artificial glass eliminate the impurities, while in obsidian they are all present in the magma. The result is that obsidian commonly is black, and it may be a very striking jet black.

Pumice (an ancient name, from a Greek word meaning worm-eaten, mentioned as long ago as 325 B.C. by Theophrastus) is a rather specialized kind of obsidian which has been so dilated by volcanic gas as to become a petrified glassy froth, much as though the foam on top of a beer stein were to be instantly converted to rock. Because it has been so frothed up by gases mixed in it before it solidified, pumice is one of the lightest of rocks and the more porous varieties float on water; if blown out of coastal or oceanic volcanoes it may drift for thousands of miles before becoming waterlogged and sinking to the bottom.

Both obsidian and pumice have chemical compositions that typically are akin to rhyolite —that is, they are rocks that carry relatively high percentages of silicon, potassium, and aluminum in their composition and are correspondingly low in iron, magnesium, and calcium. Although glassy phases do exist for rocks solidified from andesitic and basaltic magmas, they are of minor importance compared to the rhyolitic varieties.

Along with lava flows, volcanoes eject great quantities of solid or semi-solid material as part of their explosive activity. This material may range in size from particles as small as dust to blocks as large as houses. The products of such fragmental volcanic debris are called *pyroclastic rocks* (from the Greek; literally translated, the word means fire-broken).

Finer particles the size of dust or sand blown from volcanoes are called volcanic *ash,* and if the particles are the size of small pebbles they are sometimes spoken of as *cinders.* These are poor terms because neither volcanic ash nor cinders have anything to do with fire in the sense that they are not the residue left from the burning of something such as coal or wood. Actually, they are small fragments of volcanic rock with the same chemical composition as the lava that is in the crater or that is flowing down the

FIG. 3-11 *Upper surface of the Devil's Postpile, California, showing the ends or cross sections of the columns seen in Fig. 3-10. The grooves extending from left to right are glacial striae. The amount of weathering since the disappearance of the glacier is indicated by the loss of the striated surface. See Chapter XIII. (Photograph by Hal Roth.)*

FIG. 3-12 *Pumice blocks and lapilli. Mammoth Lakes District, Calif.*

flanks of the volcano, with the difference that they have been frothed up more by the entrapped gases. Fragments an inch or so in diameter are called *lapilli* (an Italian word for little stones) and fragments that are several inches across are best called volcanic blocks if they were solid at the time of their ejection (Fig. 3-12).

Blobs of lava are often blown out beyond a crater rim from the surface of the caldron within. At night they are a spectacular sight, especially if they are still brightly glowing. Their paths can be followed as they arc through the sky on about the same sort of trajectory as a mortar shell. On color photographs, their trails show as red lines in the air, and also as long streaks on the ground as they bounce and roll down the volcanic slopes. The surfaces of such lava blobs have a chance to cool in flight, and the whole blob itself may also solidify with a crust that looks much like a loaf of French bread. Such crusted-over lava blobs are called *bombs;* some are spindle shaped if they rotated in flight, while others may be nearly spherical.

Volcanic ash may blanket the countryside for many miles around a volcano like so much newly fallen snow, and, as at Paricutin in Mexico in its eruption of 1943, may accumulate to depths of more than 10 feet. A layered rock made of such compacted volcanic ash is *tuff* (Fig. 3-13), and over the centuries it has been a widely used building stone. Much of ancient Rome was built of tuff; it is the rubble masonry one sees today in the Colosseum and in the walls of the Forum since the marble facing was stripped away centuries ago. Tuff was extensively used on the volcanic islands of Greece, where many picturesque villages were excavated in part in it, and also at Naples and Pompeii, and a whole world away at Manila, to cite but a few examples. Tuff is readily excavated, it holds its shape well, and the surface hardens somewhat on exposure to the atmosphere.

Some falls of ash, such as the one that buried Pompeii, retain their heat for relatively long periods of time, and if hot enough the ash particles may fuse together to form a *welded tuff.* Many hundreds of square miles of the North Island of New Zealand in the Rotorua geyser district are covered with welded tuff. It is common throughout much of the western United States and in Alaska in the Valley of Ten Thousand Smokes, which is named for the fumaroles and hot springs produced as a result of the hot ash fall in an eruption in 1912. As a welded tuff consolidates and shrinks, it may develop geometrically arranged columns much like those in a basalt flow.

If pyroclastic material consists of blocks and other large angular fragments, these may be cemented together to form a layered rock, much

like tuff in its origin but consisting of visible, angular, sharp-edged blocks. Such a rock, composed of angular, indurated blocks, is a volcanic *breccia* (an Italian word meaning the "gravel or rubbish of broken walls"). Very often these breccias are formed on the slopes of volcanic cones, close to the source, or they may be made

FIG. 3-13 *Tuff, or consolidated volcanic ash, with lapilli and blocks of pumice. Deposits of* nuées ardentes, *the eruption of which preceded the collapse of Mount Mazama to form Crater Lake. The view is of The Pinnacles along Sand Creek, Crater Lake National Park. (Courtesy of Oregon State Highway Dept.)*

of fragmental material that accumulated in the volcanic throat and was cemented together by late-crystallizing magma to form a new rock once the volcanic fires were dead. Volcanic breccias are also characteristic of the early-congealing surfaces of lava flows whose interiors may still be fluid. Continued forward motion of this still molten mass may shatter the crust into a jumble of chaotically arranged blocks which, cemented together by lava injected into their interstices, will produce a flow breccia.

DEEP-SEATED INTRUSIVE BODIES

Plutonic rocks were an enigma to our ancestors because no one has ever seen such a rock as granite crystallize from a molten solution. Basalt, on the other hand, can be seen forming on the slopes and in the craters of active volcanoes, and thus to achieve at least a partial understanding of the nature of volcanic rocks is nowhere as difficult a problem. Nevertheless, one of the most acrimonious debates in the history of geology sprang up in the late eighteenth century over a curious belief held in Germany that not only basalt, but granite as well, was a chemical precipitate formed on the floor of a universal ocean. Fantastic as this concept might be, it had the virtue of forcing its opponents out into the mountains and over the face of the Earth to collect data to refute the belief in the aqueous origin of the igneous rocks and to demonstrate that they had indeed crystallized from molten solutions. Much of the evidence that was patiently gathered nearly two centuries ago is valid today, and when we consider the lines of argument advanced then and through the succeeding years, even now when we come to the central problem of the nature of igneous activity, we are still far from an answer.

Such rocks as granite, diorite, and gabbro are all coarse-grained igneous rocks consisting of interlocking mineral crystals. Presumably they owe this coarsely crystalline texture to slow cooling. However, as mentioned above, no one has ever actually seen this cooling take place, and that we know of these rocks at all is only because the rocky shell which once encased them has been stripped away, chiefly by erosion. The most widely exposed of these deep-seated rocks are granite and its closely related variants. Rocks like these may cover hundreds, or even thousands, of square miles in mountainous chains (Fig. 6-32), or in broad areas such as Labrador or northeastern Canada where the roots of long-vanished mountain ranges are laid bare by the removal of many thousands of feet of cover.

Such tremendous bodies of rock are called *batholiths* (a word introduced about 1895 and derived from the Greek words for depth + stone). In its original definition the term batholith was used for a large volume of intruded igneous rock, and in general usage today this means a body with a surface area of at least 40 square miles. A smaller, irregularly shaped body of coarse-grained igneous rock with a surface extent of less than 40 square miles is called a *stock,* and it very often may be a cupola on the surface of a more deeply buried batholith not as yet unroofed by erosion.

Much has been learned about the surface configuration of batholiths and stocks because erosion has cut down to different levels in them at different places and they have been uncovered in deep mining operations. By combining information from many of the accessible batholiths around the world, we know a great deal about their upper reaches and nothing whatever about their lower depths. No living geologist has ever seen the under side of a batholith, and the problems of how far down they extend, what the nature of their roots may be, from what depths they rise, and under what circumstances molten material originates within the Earth remain unsolved but fascinating problems to this day (Fig. 3-14).

Batholiths commonly are surrounded by a halo, or *aureole,* of what are known as contact-metamorphosed rocks. These have been recrys-

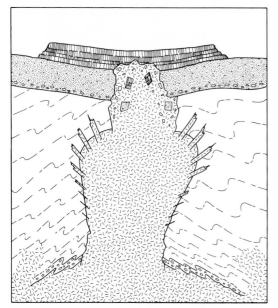

From E. S. Hills (after H. Cloos, Neues Jahrbuch für Mineralogie, Geologie und Paläontologie Beilage, Band 66, Abt. B, 1931), *Outline of Structural Geology*, 1953. By permission of Methuen & Co., Ltd. and E. Schweizerbart'sche Verlagsbuchhandlung.

FIG. 3-14 *Hypothetical vertical section through a batholith. The batholith of granite is the central mass in the diagram, with dikes extending outward into the surrounding folded and metamorphosed rocks. At the bottom in either corner the granite is shown without boundaries against the folded rocks, indicating that at a deep level the granite is reacting with the other rocks, or is being produced by melting of them, forming migmatite, or lit-par-lit structure.*

At the middle level the batholith is perhaps pushing aside the walls, and granite is forced into cracks.

At the top the batholith has penetrated sedimentary rocks (stippled) and lavas (ruled), blocks of which are shown sinking into the granitic magma.

tallized in place by the heat and chemical activity supplied from the granitic magma.

Unknown as the lower reaches of a batholith may be, one would think that few problems would beset us about the upper reaches of batholiths whose characteristics are better known. Unfortunately, the problem of their emplacement and mode of origin bristles with difficulties. In some instances, batholiths appear to have shouldered their way bodily into pre-existing rocks and their granite is uncontaminated and homogeneous right up to the knife-sharp boundary of the intrusion. In such cases the granite appears to have displaced the so-called country rocks into which it seemingly has made its way. The country rocks obviously are gone, but gone where? The granite has taken their place completely, and of the rocks that once occupied the space now usurped by the granite, no trace survives. Were they dissolved? Should this be true, some undigested traces of more stubborn minerals ought to have persisted in the granitic magma. Were blocks of the invaded rocks pried loose only to founder in the fluid magma and to sink to the bottom of the batholith? This last suggestion at least has the great virtue that it very handily disposes of the evidence. The fundamental dilemma here is the so-called "room problem" in the origin of batholiths, and it remains to this day as a knotty problem.

Other batholiths are surrounded with a wide marginal zone and the transition between the invading and the invaded rocks is much less abrupt. The contact between the unquestioned granite and its encasing shell may be blurred and a zone of *migmatite,* or mixed rocks—partially igneous and partially metamorphic—characterizes such a contact. These are rocks in which tongues of granite may extend far out into the adjacent host rocks, and bands of granitic material may follow selected layers for long distances into the metamorphic aureole. This is typical of the so-called *lit-par-lit,* or bed-by-bed, structure; which means that one layer of a rock may be granite, the next a metamorphic rock, the next granite, and so on. Or knots and clusters of orthoclase, or other minerals typical of granite, may appear in the metamorphic envelope some distance out from the main body of granitic rocks.

These phenomena, taken together, suggest that in some way the pre-granitic rocks were digested, or replaced by granite—in other words, they were converted in place from what they were originally into a brand-new rock, in this case granite. This process is called granitization by its advocates—a vocal lot—and they adhere to the belief that granitic rocks are formed in place through the alteration of large volumes of sedimentary rock by chemically potent solutions ascending from greater depths in the Earth's interior. An opposing view is that batholiths are the product of the invasion of molten material from the depths below into the upper levels of the Earth's crust and granite now occupies the place of the rocks into which it was intruded.

No one as yet has produced evidence establishing beyond a reasonable doubt what the origin of these immense bodies of granitic rock may be. Among some of the things that are known about them are the following: (1) they are found for the most part in the mountainous belts of the Earth—both geologically recent ones and ones of great antiquity; (2) although many batholiths may locally cut across the grain of their enclosing rocks, in the main these intrusive bodies are elongated paralleling the range of which they are a part; (3) all the available evidence indicates that the minerals in a granite crystallized from a melt and that they followed a systematic order of crystallization with the early-forming minerals developing geometrically regular crystal forms and the late-forming minerals filling in the interstices. In general, the minerals crystallize in the order given earlier in the Bowen reaction series—the ferromagnesian minerals and plagioclases first, and quartz last.

About all that can safely be hazarded at the moment in the controversy surrounding the origin of granitic batholiths is that, like many things in the real world, no single cause is adequate to explain the entire phenomenon. Both origins—(1) magmatic or invasion by fluids, and (2) granitization or transformation in place —probably occur, although very likely in different environments, or quite possibly in different places or at different depths in the same batholith.

INTRUSIONS
OF INTERMEDIATE DEPTH

These are much smaller intrusive bodies than their immense relatives, the mountain-inhabiting batholiths, and although along their length some are measurable in scores of miles, their breadth is more commonly measured in feet. These are called *hypabyssal rocks,* a word that means "of intermediate depth."

Hypabyssal rocks generally have textures intermediate between those of volcanic rocks and those of plutonic rocks. If they are part of bodies of moderate to large size they will have cooled sufficiently slowly that their minerals, although smaller than in batholithic rocks, will be visible to the unaided eye. If they are part of a small intrusion, whose walls were close together, the heat loss is comparatively rapid and crystal sizes are diminished accordingly, to the point where the texture of such rocks may be indistinguishable from their volcanic counterparts. In other words, the texture of hypabyssal rocks approaches those of volcanic rocks on the one hand and at the other extreme it may be about the same as those of plutonic rocks—depending very largely on the size of the intrusion and the composition of the magma. Incidentally, porphyritic textures are very typical of the group because there may have been a considerable amount of moving of magma from one environment to another in these shallow intrusive channels, with correspondingly different rates of crystallization before final solidification occurs (Fig. 3-4).

Dikes are a common variety of hypabyssal intrusive. They are tabular bodies, which means that of the three dimensions possessed by a solid body, two are very large compared to the third—in the case of dikes they have about the same geometry as that of a thin pad of notepaper. Another attribute of dikes is that they are *discordant*—that is, they cut across the layering, or stratification, or the grain of the rocks they invade (Fig. 3-15).

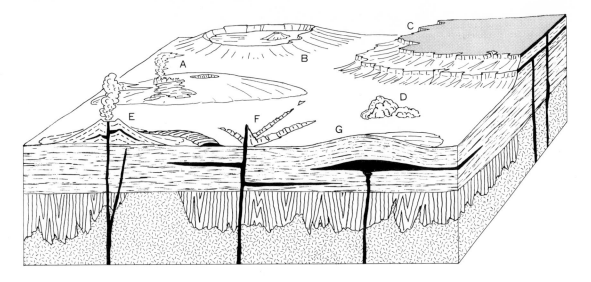

FIG. 3-15 *Occurrences of igneous rock. In the lower part of the diagram granite is shown intruded into metamorphic rock. Above this is a thickness of layered sedimentary rocks in horizontal position into which are intruded several types of igneous bodies shown in black. On the upper surface several volcanic features are shown. (A) A shield volcano with a summit caldera. A fissure eruption forming a lava flow is in progress at the left of the summit. (B) A large caldera with a minor younger volcano within it, surrounded by a "crater" lake. (C) A lava flow eroded so as to make a cliff in the landscape. The lava flow was fed by a dike that shows on the upper right hand side of the diagram. Beneath the lava flow is another similar lava flow also fed by a dike, which has been buried by sedimentary rock and the lava flow at the top. (D) A plug dome formed by the protrusion of a pasty mass of lava. (E) A stratovolcano, shown in section, with lava flows alternating with pyroclastic deposits. A lava flow is to the right of the cone. F. Three dikes radiate from a volcanic neck, exposed because the volcano formerly formed here has been eroded away. Below, two sills extend laterally from the feeder of the volcano. (G) Below the point G is a sill, fed from below by a dike or tube of magma. Directly above the feeder the sill is thickened and has lifted the surface into a dome. Such a lens-shaped body of igneous rock is called a laccolith.*

Dikes are seldom more than a few tens of feet thick, but some are hundreds of miles long. An exceptionally long one is the so-called Great Dike of Rhodesia in southeast Africa. It is more than 300 miles long but has an average width of only about 5 miles.

Dikes commonly occur in groups known as dike swarms (Fig. 3-16). Sometimes they may be aligned on roughly parallel courses, or they may radiate from centers, such as the host of basaltic dikes that lace the northern part of Great Britain, with some individual ribbon-like intrusions reaching lengths of 100 miles or so (Fig. 3-17). The focal point for such a radial set of dikes very likely will be the throat, or conduit, of a now extinct volcano, and subsequent erosion may reveal its connection with the dikes.

Depending on their resistance to erosion, relative to their host rocks, dikes may be distinctive features of the landscape. If they are more resistant they stand up somewhat as continuous walls, much like the two conspicuous ones radiating outward from Ship Rock, an eroded

FIG. 3-16 *Closely spaced and intersecting dikes exposed in a cliff. Kailua, Oahu, Hawaii. (Courtesy of G. A. Macdonald.)*

---

volcanic conduit in New Mexico (Fig. 3-18). Should they be weaker, they may be etched out, especially if they crop out in a sea cliff exposed to the full fury of the sea.

Columns also characterize dikes, but instead of standing vertically, they may lie horizontally if the dike itself is vertical, and then may look much like an immense stack of cordwood. Such columns grow at right angles away from a cooling surface—in a lava flow this will be upward from the ground and downward from the top of the flow, and commonly these inward-growing columns meet with a rather ragged matching up of the columnar sets along a line close to the center of the flow. In a vertical dike the columns grow inward horizontally from the vertical side walls which here are the cooling surfaces.

Hypabyssal rocks which have been injected into the Earth's crust as tabular, sheetlike bodies essentially parallel to the stratification of the enclosing rocks are called *sills* (Fig. 3-15). These are *concordant* intrusions, while dikes, with their cross-cutting relationships, are discordant. This does not mean that each sill follows only a

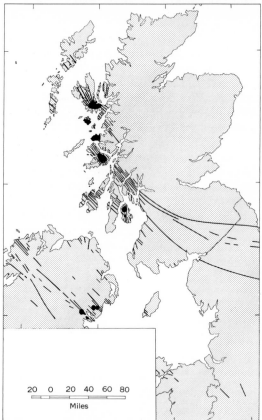

After J. E. Richey, H. H. Thomas, and others, "Scotland: The Tertiary Volcanic Districts," 1930. By permission of the Controller of Her Britannic Majesty's Stationery Office.

FIG. 3-17 *The dike swarms of Scotland and northern Ireland. The black areas are centers of igneous intrusion to which the dikes are related.*

single stratum, because it is not at all uncommon for them to cross up or down from one stratum to another and to follow it for perhaps hundreds or thousands of feet before making another cross-over.

Some sills run for great distances across the country and have lengths comparable to those attained by dikes. An excellent example is the Great Whin Sill in Northumberland in northeastern England. It looms as a dark, north-facing ledge dominating the surrounding country for much of its course, with the result that the Romans, with their experienced eye for the military potentialities of the terrain, seized upon this natural barrier as a foundation for Hadrian's Wall, which was built to keep the Picts from ravaging northern Britain.

Certainly the most familiar of all sills in the United States is the abrupt cliff of the Palisades that follows the Jersey shore of the Hudson and is clearly visible to the millions of inhabitants of Manhattan, let alone the multitudes of commuters who see it every working day. The Palisades sill is a large one, as these things go, and is over 1000 feet thick. It cooled slowly and without much internal disturbance, with the re-

FIG. 3-18 *Ship Rock, New Mexico, is a volcanic neck with radial dikes. The volcanic cone has been eroded away, leaving the filled throat of the volcano standing above the surrounding country. The dike in the foreground stands out as a thin wall. (Photograph by John S. Shelton.)*

sult that the magma within it had a chance to differentiate. That is, the heavier early-crystallizing minerals, such as olivine and pyroxene, sank to the lower levels of the large pancake-shaped magma chamber while the lighter plagioclase crystals were concentrated near the top.

A more renowned group of hypabyssal rocks, although perhaps not often considered in this light, are the dike and sill that played a decisive role in Pennsylvania during three hot summer days a century ago in July of 1863. One is the thick basaltic sill that underlies Cemetery Ridge and the other is the narrow but persistent dike that supports Seminary Ridge, both of which were the dominant elements of terrain at the Battle of Gettysburg. The Union Army held the former and the Confederate forces the latter. Both sides made the most of the so-called ironstone boulders which had weathered from basalt outcrops along the top of each ridge. Piled into fences these made excellent defensive positions against the round shot and Minié balls of that day. Cemetery Ridge, along which the Union brigades were deployed in full strength on the fateful third morning, makes such a continuous rampart, with a nearly unbroken forward slope up which Pickett's command had to charge, that the assault was virtually foredoomed to failure. This was doubly so when they were called upon to dislodge men sheltered behind a practically shot-proof basaltic barricade and supported, in addition, by one of the greatest concentrations of artillery assembled in the war.

Because contraction occurs in the solidifying magma of sills as well as in dikes and lava flows, columnar joints are characteristic of them, too; since most sills tend toward a horizontal position at the time of their origin, the columns in such an intrusion are likely to be vertical, having developed at right angles to the cooling surface.

Discriminating between buried lava flows and sills interbedded with sedimentary rocks is not one of the simpler field problems in geology.

Igneous rocks in both categories may have about the same texture, and both may have very well developed columnar joints. The most likely place to look for the evidence needed to decide between the two possibilities is at the contact between the sill, or buried lava flow, and the enclosing rocks.

In many sills there very commonly will be a chilled zone in the igneous rock at the margins where crystallization was the most rapid, and here the texture of the rock will be fine-grained, in some cases almost glassy. Additionally, there may be a baked zone in the invaded rocks immediately adjacent to their boundary with the sill. They will have been fired or hardened in much the same way that clay is fired in a kiln to make bricks or pottery. In a sill, fragments of the overlying host rock may be included in the igneous material. However, if the igneous body is an interbedded lava flow, then the baked contact will be lacking, at least on the upper surface of the flow. In addition to this, the strata overlying these volcanic rocks will have been deposited after the lava solidified, and more likely than not fragments of rock eroded from the flow will be found incorporated in the covering strata.

A third type of hypabyssal intrusive body is the channel or conduit that once served to connect a volcanic vent on the Earth's surface with the magma reservoir at depth. In an erosional sense, volcanoes are vulnerable features; much of their interior consists of loosely consolidated ash and pyroclastic material, their steep slopes lend themselves to gullying, and if they are high enough they may intercept more snow and rain than the surrounding countryside. The result of this augmented runoff working on such an exposed structure is that, geologically speaking, the interiors of many volcanoes are bared to view shortly after they lapse into dormancy.

Their internal skeleton of radial dikes and central conduit often proves to be made of sterner stuff, with the result that dikes stand up as partitions and the solidified magma of the conduit forms a central tower, known as a *volcanic neck*. A well-known example is the Ship Rock in New Mexico (Fig. 3-18).

More often than not, volcanic necks are found in clusters, rather than standing isolated. Prime examples in the United States are the volcanic buttes of the Navajo-Hopi country near the so-called Four Corners area. Here more than 100 volcanic centers interrupt the surface of the plateau.

Another group of volcanic necks that have achieved a measure of notoriety are the so-called pipes of *kimberlite*, a hypabyssal rock composed dominantly of ferromagnesian minerals, which are a source of the diamonds of the Republic of South Africa. The ancient volcanic conduits containing the diamonds are deeply weathered near the surface into what is called the "blue ground," a sticky clay from which the diamonds were separated by washing. The pipe-like columns of hypabyssal rock were mined in the Kimberley pit to a depth of 3,500 feet before the workings were abandoned—now they are idle and stand water-filled to within 600 feet of the surface. Since the pressures and temperatures necessary for diamonds to crystallize from solution are not fulfilled short of a depth several miles below the ground level, diamonds are one of the better geologic indicators which demonstrate that (1) volcanic magma can originate at considerable depths within the Earth's crust, and (2) because Kimberley diamonds are found at levels far above the depths where pressures necessary for their formation prevail, the magma of which they once were a part streamed upward in a pipelike conduit to reach the higher levels of the Earth's crust, even discounting the removal of some of the overburden by erosion.

VOLCANISM

Of all the geologic phenomena visible on the Earth's surface, none is more alien to the everyday American world than volcanism. Glaciers are logical constructions of such familiar substances as ice and snow, just as the erosional work of streams, the wind, and the sea are part of our daily experience. Volcanoes play a more exotic role, and also have the enchantment that distance lends, since none is active today within the contiguous United States. To see them within our country it is necessary to go to Alaska or Hawaii, and many of the world's more striking examples are in far-off lands, such as Kamchatka, Indonesia, or on the truly oceanic islands. Fortunately, from a scientific point of view, but not from that of the people whose lives are occasionally disrupted, some of the outstanding examples are in densely populated areas, such as the central Mediterranean and the main islands of Japan.

This brings up the interesting and significant point that volcanoes are not scattered randomly over the Earth, but many are concentrated within fairly well-defined zones or bands (Fig. 3-1). Perhaps the most renowned of these chains is the so-called ring of fire that girdles much of the Pacific Ocean. The map showing the distribution of active and only very recently dormant volcanoes demonstrates that they are spotted along most of the length of the eastern and western margins of the Pacific Ocean. They are also the reason for the existence of the mountains on the higher islands; Mauna Loa and Mauna Kea on the island of Hawaii are familiar examples.

The Mediterranean world has its share of volcanoes, too. Best known, perhaps, are Vesuvius near Naples and Etna on Sicily. Because of the long and literate span of history encompassed in this ancient world, these volcanoes have played a role in mythology and theology. "In the Middle Ages the Mediterranean volcanoes were appropriated by the theologians who regarded them as places of the eternal punishment of certain great sinners. Thus the Adrian emperor Theodosius was assigned to Vulcano itself; while Etna was regarded as the place of torment of unhappy Anne Boleyn, the innocent cause of Henry the Eighth's secession from the Faith" (Tyrrell, 1931).

Distribution

The map (Fig. 3-1) shows, when compared with a similar one for earthquakes (Fig. 9-5), the very close relationship in the distribution of these two disturbing elements of the Earth's crust. They do not coincide, but the resemblances are greater than the differences, and this leads most geologists to believe that some kind of relationship exists between the two. This is *not* to say that volcanoes cause earthquakes, or vice versa, but the forces operating within the crust to cause the one are also very likely producing the other as well. What, then, is the attribute both share?

Most earthquake and volcanic centers seem to be located in parts of the Earth where such things as actively growing mountain ranges are concentrated. This is especially true for the circum-Pacific belt of volcanoes, as well as those in the Mediterranean world. It is a little more difficult to demonstrate this relationship between volcanism and mountain-building, for some volcanic centers are situated in the more stable continental interiors.

The map showing volcano distribution also points up the fact that most of them are within sight of the sea (Fig. 3-20). In earlier days this led to the plausible explanation that eruptions were the result of downward-percolating sea water coming in contact with molten material in the Earth's crust, with the resulting steam explosion being responsible for the volcanic eruption. This seemed all the more reasonable in view of the fact that men recognized from early days that steam was the most important of all

FIG. 3-19 *Mount St. Helens, Washington, with Mount Rainier in the distance. These two typical strato-volcanoes are members of the chain of recent volcanoes of the Cascade Mountains that extend across Washington and Oregon and into California. All are typically composed of andesite. (Photograph by Ray Atkeson, Portland, Oregon.)*

FIG. 3-20 *A volcano erupts from the sea. Myo-jin Reef, about 170 miles south of Tokyo, Japan. (Official U. S. Navy photograph.)*

the volcanic gases. Unfortunately, as in the case of many other splendid hypotheses that have a brief vogue only to vanish into oblivion, this belief is not true. A number of volcanoes are far inland, many miles distant from the sea. Kilimanjaro, the peak of the celebrated snows, is a good example since it is close to 800 miles from the coast. Insofar as the truly oceanic islands are concerned, more convincing evidence is that the required physical and chemical con-ditions under which their magma originated prevail at depths far greater than could ever be reached by sea water percolating downward through interstices in the rocks.

A more significant control over the distribution of volcanoes is that the greatest number of

FIG. 3-21 *The tiny settlement on Tristan da Cunha was temporarily abandoned because of the threats posed by the eruptions of 1961. (British Admiralty Official photograph. British Crown Copyright reserved.)*

them are in places where fracturing appears to be active in the Earth's crust, and where there is strong evidence of a good deal of crustal unrest. Such fractures may provide the channels along which magma rises from great depths, ultimately to reach the surface. This explanation seems to work well for those volcanoes ranged in long lines or chains, such as those of the Aleutian Islands or Java. It is not as satis-

factory for those standing alone and well apart from the more typical volcanic lineaments. Volcanic centers on the Colorado Plateau in the southwestern United States are perhaps good examples of this latter type as they are characteristic of eruptive conduits which broke through to the surface by penetrating essentially flat-lying, undisturbed strata.

The total number of active volcanoes shown on the map (Fig. 3-1) should be 476. This number is based on information compiled in 1934 (Kennedy and Richey, 1947). A few minor volcanoes have appeared since then, chiefly off the coasts of Japan, Mexico, in the Azores and Tristan da Cunha (Fig. 3-21), but the general picture remains unchanged. According to Tyrrell (1931) there have been about 2,500 eruptions since the beginning of recorded history, and of these nearly 2,000 were in the Pacific Basin—an impressive demonstration of the dominant role this area plays in the volcanology of the Earth.

Types

Volcanoes show almost as much individuality as there are examples, and for this reason they are difficult to place in a rigid classification. In a general way, four major types of eruptions can be recognized, characterized as explosive, intermediate, quiet, and fissure. In the sections to follow, a famous historic eruption representative of each kind is described to illustrate each type; two explosive eruptions are listed because each had such distinctive characteristics as to merit consideration as a subtype.

EXPLOSIVE ERUPTIONS

Krakatoa

Three quarters of a century ago captains of sailing ships beating their way through the Sunda Straits which separate the great islands of Java and Sumatra in the East Indies knew the island of Krakatoa well. Its conical, green-clad slopes rose uninterruptedly about 2,600 feet to the summit of the central peak. The straits were important since they were on the shortest sea road for the tea clippers en route from China to England. These were dangerous, restricted waters, haunted by sea-roving Dyaks who could give the crew of a becalmed vessel a bad time. In this same seaway many years later the U.S.S. *Houston,* harried by pursuing Japanese in the early years of World War II, blew up and sank with the loss of almost all hands.

Though the island of Krakatoa had been spasmodically active since May, 1883, it seemed innocuous enough to the crew of the British ship *Charles Bal,* tacking under all plain sail through the hot tropical Sunday afternoon of August 26, 1883, until they arrived on one heading at a point about 10 miles south of the island. Minutes later the mountain exploded. Seldom in the long history of seafaring has the crew of any vessel been confronted by such a satanic outburst of energy. The entire mountain disappeared in clouds of black "smoke," and the air was charged with electricity—lightning flashed continuously over the volcano, as it very often does during eruptions, and the yards and rigging of the ship glowed with St. Elmo's fire. Immense quantities of heated ash fell on the deck or hissed through the surrounding darkness into the increasingly disturbed sea. As the vessel labored across broken seas through squalls of mud-laden rain, a thundering roar of explosions continued, much like a never-ending artillery barrage, accompanied by a ceaseless crackling sound which resembled the tearing of gigantic sheets of paper. This last effect was interpreted to be the rubbing together of large rocks hurled skyward by the explosions. After an interminable night, the dawn, dim as it must have been, came as deliverance, and with the coast of Java in view and a gale rising rapidly, the *Charles Bal* was able to set all sail and leave the smoking mountain far astern.

It is well she did, for paroxysms of volcanic fury continued to shake the mountain until the final culmination of four prodigious explosions came on Monday, August 27, at 5:30, 6:44, 10:02, and 10:52 a.m. The greatest of these, the third, was one of the most titanic explosions recorded in modern times—greater in intensity than some of our nuclear efforts. The sound was heard over tremendous distances: at Alice Springs in the heart of Australia, in Manila, in Ceylon, and on the remote island of Rodriguez in the southwest Indian Ocean, where it arrived four hours after the explosion had occurred, 3,000 miles away.

The explosion seriously agitated the Earth's atmosphere, and records of such a disturbance were picked up by barometers all over the world. They showed that a shock wave originating in the East Indies traveled at least seven times around the world—out to the antipodes of the volcano and back again—before it became too faint to register on the instruments of that time.

Visibly, a more impressive phenomenon was the huge cloud of pumice and volcanic debris that blew skyward. The steam-impelled cloud of volcanic ash is estimated to have risen to a height of 50 miles on August 27, and to have blanketed a surrounding area of 300,000 square miles. The ash poured down as a pasty mud on the streets and buildings of Batavia—now Djakarta—83 miles away. Pumice in great floating rafts blanketed much of the Indian Ocean, and captains' comments recorded in logbooks of ships suddenly enmeshed in far-reaching masses of pumice far offshore make interesting reading.

Volcanic ash hurled into the upper levels of the Earth's atmosphere was picked up by the jet stream—whose existence was not even suspected then—and carried with it as a dust cloud that encircled the Earth in the equatorial regions in thirteen days. Incidentally, the jet stream was virtually forgotten, only to be rediscovered in our age of high-altitude flight, jet travel, and radioactive fallout. The ash continued to spread across both hemispheres of the Earth and produced a succession of spectacular and greatly admired sunsets over most of the world—even in areas as remote from Java as England and the northeastern United States—for the two years that it took the finer dust particles to settle through the atmosphere.

The violent explosion of the morning of August 27 set in motion one of the more destructive sea waves ever to be recorded. It spread out in ever-widening circles from Krakatoa much as though a gigantic rock had been hurled into the sea. About half an hour after the eruption, the wave reached the shores of Java and Sumatra, and on these low-lying coasts the water surged inland with a crest whose maximum

height was about 120 feet. Since many of the people inhabiting such a densely populated tropical coast lived in houses built on piers extending out over the water, about 30,000 or 40,000 people lost their lives.

The sea wave, after leaving the Sunda Strait with diminishing height, raced on across the open ocean. It was registered long after it was too faint to see, as a train of pulses on recording tide gauges along the coasts of India and Africa and on the coasts of Europe and the western United States. For example, the tide gauges in San Francisco Bay showed a disturbance of about 6 inches by waves that traveled a distance of 10,343 miles at a speed of about 594 miles per hour, a value which seems high. In the Indian Ocean, the velocity of the wave appears to have varied between 200 and 400 miles per hour in the open ocean. This agrees with the better-timed earthquake wave that originated on the coast of Chile and destroyed the low-lying parts of Hilo, Hawaii, on May 23, 1960, 11 hours and 56 minutes later, having traveled 6,600 miles at an average speed of 442 miles per hour (Eaton, 1961).

After the explosions died down returning observers were startled to find that where the 2,600-foot mountain had stood was now a hole whose bottom was 900 to 1,000 feet below sea level, and that the sea now filled this large bowl-shaped depression. All that remained of the island were three tiny islets on the rim. All told, although the estimates vary, a little less than 5 cubic miles of material were hurled into the atmosphere. In popular accounts of the eruption the impression commonly is given that a volcanic mountain blew up and its fragments were strewn far and wide over the face of the Earth. Were this to be the case, we should expect most of the debris covering the little islands which are the surviving remnants of Krakatoa would be pieces of the wrecked volcano, and the oversize crater, or *caldera,* now filled with sea water would be the product of a simple explosion.

Unfortunately for this seemingly plausible explanation, few pieces of the original volcanic mountain are to be found, and instead of such fragments the ground is covered with deposits of pumice up to 200 feet thick. You may also recall in the description of the eruption the mention of the great rafts of floating pumice in the Indian Ocean which were a source of surprise to the mariners who encountered them drifting over much of the open sea. Pumice is original magmatic material, frothed up by gases contained in the magma, and has nothing to do with the internal composition of the vanished mountain. Thus, the abundance of pumice and the absence of pieces of the mountain lead logically to the belief that the volcanic cone foundered or collapsed on itself rather than having been blown to bits.

The explanation that appears to be correct was advanced by a Dutch volcanologist, van Bemmelen, in 1929, and refined by Howel Williams, of the University of California, in 1941. The accompanying diagram (Fig. 3-22), adapted from Williams, shows the sequence of eruptive events which very likely were responsible for the disappearance of a 2,600-foot mountain and the appearance of a 1,000-foot deep caldera in its place.

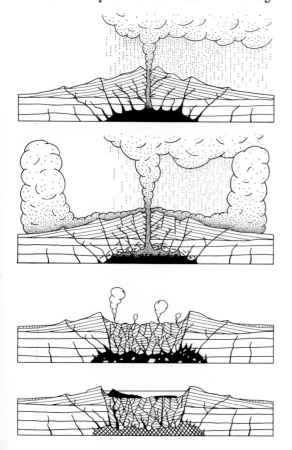

After H. Williams, *Geology of Crater Lake National Park, Oregon*, 1942. By permission of The Carnegie Institution of Washington.

FIG. 3-22 *Stages in the collapse of a volcanic mountain to form a caldera.*

Stage I.   The eruptive cycle commenced with fairly mild explosions of pumice. The magma chamber was filled and the magma stood high in the conduits. With an increase in the violence of the explosions, magma was drawn off more and more rapidly and the level dropped in the magma chamber.

Stage II.   The culminating explosions cleared out the volcanic conduits and rapidly lowered the magma level in the chamber. In this phase pumice was blown high above the cone, or glowing, pumice-laden clouds swept down the flanks.

Stage III.   With removal of support, the volcanic cone collapsed into the magma chamber below, leaving a wide, bowl-shaped caldera.

Stage IV.   After a period of quiescence new minor cones appeared on the crater floor. Some of these rise above sea level, such as Anak Krakatoa (child of Krakatoa) which appeared in 1927 and was growing as recently as 1960.

The story of the eruption and its explanation have been told at length here because of (1) the extraordinary violence of the event; (2) the interrelationship of the phenomena associated with it, such as the sea wave, the dust blanket in the atmosphere, the far-ranging sound wave, all supported by the remarkably complete way in which these unusual events were faithfully recorded; and (3) the logical fashion in which the explanation of the events of the historic eruption can be made to fit together.

FIG. 3-23 *Crater Lake, Oregon, looking south-west. The caldera is 6 miles in diameter, the lake is nearly 2000 feet deep, and the highest points on the rim are nearly 2000 feet above the lake. Wizard Island, a small cone that erupted on the caldera floor, is seen at the right of the lake. (Photograph by Ray Atkeson.)*

This last point is the most important because it illustrates one of the leading tenets of geology; the *principle of uniformitarianism*—which freely interpreted means that processes operating today very likely operated in past geologic times in about the same way. Thus, we can use the events of the present to interpret the origin and nature of rocks and structures in the Earth's crust that were formed in ages past.

With the knowledge we have of Krakatoa's eruption, we can attack the problem of the origin of Crater Lake in Oregon. Although Crater Lake stands at an altitude of 6,000 feet, rather than at sea level as Krakatoa does, their calderas have many similarities (Fig. 3-23).

The diameter of both craters is disproportionately large compared to the dimension of the mountain of which they are a part, and in each case most of the mountain has disappeared in the making of the caldera. It was seen to have disappeared in 1883 at Krakatoa, and its disappearance is inferred on the basis of compellingly strong evidence at Crater Lake. Arguments over the origin of Crater Lake have centered around the problem, not of the fact, of the disappearance of a volcanic mountain perhaps 12,000 feet high, to which the name Mount Mazama has been given, and containing as much as 17 cubic miles of material. Here the central issue is: was the mountain blown to bits, or was it destroyed as Krakatoa was by a combination of (1) explosion, (2) violent clearing out of the magma chamber, and (3) collapse of the unsupported volcanic edifice into the void suddenly created by the emptying of the magma chamber?

The most convincing evidence at Crater Lake, as at Krakatoa, is the fact that almost all of the immense quantity of debris surrounding the site of the vanished mountain is pumice, and since it fell on land, probably not more than 5,000 years ago, most of it has survived, and thus its volume can be estimated. According to Williams (1942):

> When the culminating eruptions were over, the summit of Mount Mazama had disappeared. In its place there was a caldera between 5 and 6 miles wide and 4000 feet deep. How was it formed? Certainly not by the explosive decapitation of the volcano. Of the 17 cubic miles of solid rock that vanished, only about a tenth can be found among the ejecta. The remainder of the ejecta came from the magma chamber. The volume of the pumice fall which preceded the pumice flows amounts to approximately 3.5 cubic miles. Only 4 per cent of this consists of old rock fragments. . . . Accordingly 11.75 cubic miles of ejecta were laid down during these short-lived eruptions. In part, it was the rapid evacuation of this material that withdrew support from beneath the summit of the volcano and thus led to profound engulfment. The collapse was probably as cataclysmic as that which produced the caldera of Krakatau in 1883.

Mount Pelée

In 1902, as today, Martinique in the French West Indies was one of the more picturesque links in the chain of islands reaching like green stepping stones across the Caribbean to join Cuba with the mainland of South America. Perhaps the most notable distinction of this small island is that it was the birthplace of Josephine, Empress of France, wife of Napoleon.

The island is quite mountainous, most of the interior is garlanded with a tropical forest, and the people then, as now, lived near the coast in villages, on plantations, and in the few large

towns, of which St. Pierre, with a population of 28,000, was the most important and had a history of continuous settlement extending back to 1635. There was a moderately good open roadstead and ships customarily moored in a line standing off the beach and were kept headed seaward. St. Pierre was then the leading commercial town of the island and had a fair number of French and Americans in residence. Most of the people were Carib Indians or descendants of Africans imported to work in the plantations, sugar centrals, and rum distilleries.

Mount Pelée, about 5 miles north of town, was known to be a volcano, but it had smoldered contentedly for several centuries in the mild climate of the trade winds. On April 23, 1902, it began to show signs of internal discontent, but these were little more than occasional rumblings, clouds of smoke, and spasmodic outbursts of ashes and cinders. This mildly petulant display rose to a more violent level of activity on May 4, when an outburst of hot mud, steam, and some lava broke through the crater wall, coursed down one of the radial stream canyons, buried a sugar central, and killed twenty-four persons.

By this time St. Pierre was thoroughly aroused and not even the presence of the governor and his retinue, together with the issuance of the usual tranquilizing proclamation, served to quiet the multitude. In fact, the city was kept in a continuous turmoil through the arrival of country people and villagers frightened into abandoning their homes.

The tumult and confusion were stilled forever, with appalling suddenness, early in the morning of May 8, 1902, at 7:45 a.m. According to the few eyewitnesses, the top of the mountain vanished in a blinding flash, and almost immediately thereafter a rapidly moving, fire-hot cloud advancing at prodigious speed engulfed the city, whose population, swollen with refugees, probably numbered more than 30,000. All perished within a few moments, save two, one of them in the eyes of society perhaps the least

FIG. 3-24 *St. Pierre, Martinique, after the eruption of Mount Pelée in 1902. (Photograph by Brown Bros., N. Y.)*

deserving since he was incarcerated in an underground dungeon on a charge of murder. All others of high and low degree—men, women, and children—died in a blazing instant in a cloud whose temperature was high enough to melt glass (650°-700°C.) but not quite hot enough to melt copper (1058°C.) (see Fig. 3-24).

About the only credible account of the eruption came from some of the survivors on ships in the roadstead. Eighteen vessels were in port at the time, and of these only the *Roddam,* with

more than half her crew dead, was able to up anchor and escape. The cable ship *Grappler,* directly in the path of the incandescent cloud, capsized and blew up. The purser of the *Roraima,* then approaching the harbor from the sea, left the most complete narrative of any observer. The *Roraima* was enveloped in the wall of flame that incinerated the town, was hurled over on her beam ends, the masts and stack were sheared off, her captain was blown overboard from the bridge and killed, and the ship herself burst into flames not only from the heat of the glowing cloud but, to add a bizarre touch to the holocaust, from the thousands of gallons of blazing rum that poured through the streets of St. Pierre and spread out over the waters of the harbor. Through heroic efforts the 25 injured survivors out of a crew of 68 were able to keep the *Roraima* afloat until they were taken off by the French cruiser *Suchet* in mid-afternoon.

Within the town itself only two human beings lived. All were dead except for Auguste Cyparis, the occupant of the dungeon, who languished there deserted, alone, and in a state of shock for four days until his rescuers, who had despaired of finding any living thing in St. Pierre, peered through the barred window of his dungeon when his cries attracted their attention. The other survivor, Léon Compère-Léandre, was one of those unusually tough, resilient men who occasionally survive in disasters when all about them die. Although he was covered with burns, and no conceivable circumstance favored his survival over others, he made his way on foot through the burning city of the dead and lived to tell his tale (Bullard, 1962).

Following the explosive eruption, the top of Mount Pelée was surmounted by a great spire which started to rise from the summit in August and continued to grow until the end of the year when it towered like an immense obelisk nearly 1,000 feet above its base. Gradually it disintegrated until by mid-1903 it had disappeared; but during its brief existence it loomed as an ephemeral memorial over the sepulcher at its feet. The lifting of this column of solidified lava by the gas pressures generated within the volcano is an eloquent testimonial to their power, since it is estimated to have weighed about three times as much as the Great Pyramid (Heilprin, 1904).

The escape of these entrapped high temperature gases is the chief reason for the appearance of the catastrophically violent clouds that overwhelmed St. Pierre. Since there is no satisfactory English name for them, the French term *nuée ardente,* which might inadequately be translated as glowing cloud, seems appropriate. These clouds move with great rapidity and have temperatures high enough to incinerate almost anything inflammable in their path. They are extremely dense clouds, heavily charged with pumice fragments and dust—so much so that in photographs of them taken following the titanic explosion of May 8, they resemble the solid, roiling sort of smoke cloud produced by burning oil tanks in refinery fires. Tremendous blocks of rock, some weighing many tons, were transported several miles. This was possible because of (1) the very high density of the gaseous cloud, (2) its extreme turbulence, and (3) the fact that incandescent blocks of pumice in the cloud were themselves discharging great quantities of gas. The effect of all this was to reduce surface friction and to allow these hot volcanic fragments, large and small, to be projected with tremendous velocities down the mountain slope.

The 1902 eruption of Mount Pelée was important geologically because it provided a stupendous example of a kind not too well understood before. No lava appeared in the early, violent phase of the eruption, as was possibly also true at Krakatoa, and the destruction of St. Pierre resulted from its position directly in the path of the gas-propelled cloud of incandescent volcanic fragments.

When the violently explosive phase ended, a viscous, stiff, blocky variety of lava was extruded into the summit crater, ending with the construction of a domelike protrusion of blocky lava, encrusted with lesser spires and pinnacles. By September 1903 the spire had attained a height of perhaps 1,000 feet and a diameter about twice as great. Estimates placed its volume at 100 million cubic meters.

Such volcanic domes are more common than many people think (Fig. 3-25). Lassen Peak in northern California is an excellent example: a domelike protrusion of blocky lava stands 2,500 feet above its crater rim, with a volume of approximately three-fifths of a cubic mile (Williams, 1932). The mountain was last active in 1914-17, when steam explosions, after blasting

FIG. 3-25 *Mono Craters, Calif., looking south-west into the Sierra Nevada. Mono Lake is in the foreground. At the lower right is Panum, a volcanic dome of obsidian protruded into a crater surrounded by a cone of pumice fragments. To the left of that is a larger dome of obsidian surrounded by a thick lava flow of obsidian bordered by a steep slope. Above and to the left of that is a two-pronged lava flow of obsidian that has almost buried the dome that was the source. Above that are three more domes and a large flow of obsidian. The chain of eruption centers continues to the base of the Sierra Nevada, forming a line of volcanoes nearly 10 miles long. (Photograph by John S. Shelton.)*

a vent on the northern slope, melted the snow cap. The resulting mud and ash flows not only devastated the forest at the base but swept 20-ton boulders for distances of 5 to 6 miles.

Among other examples of volcanic domes are the Mono Craters in east-central California (Fig. 3-25). Some of the volcanoes of the Valley of Ten Thousand Smokes in Alaska, as well as the Puys of the Auvergne region of France, are domes. Of the latter, the Puy de Dôme is perhaps the best known.

Recognition of the deposits dropped by such gas-charged, highly mobile, turbulently flowing incandescent clouds as *nuées ardentes* was uncertain before the demonstration of their nature at Mount Pelée. Commonly their stratification may be chaotic. Large blocks are mixed with finer particles; the uniformly layered appearance characteristic of pyroclastic deposits where the ash had an opportunity to settle more gradually through the atmosphere is lacking here. Such deposits of *nuées ardentes* encircle Crater Lake, for example, and there pumice flows swept down the Rogue River canyon for 35 miles (Fig. 3-13). Their velocities may have attained 100 miles per hour, and these glowing clouds were capable of carrying pumice blocks six feet in diameter a distance of at least 20 miles (Williams, 1942).

INTERMEDIATE ERUPTIONS

Vesuvius

Of all the world's volcanoes, none is more famous than Vesuvius, the only one active on the European mainland today (Fig. 3-26). Its renown probably results from its well-publicized eruption of A.D. 79 with the accompanying destruction of Pompeii, Herculaneum, and Stabiae. Although the mountain had been active in prehistoric times, no tradition existed among the Romans of its true nature except in a rather sketchy form. Strabo, for example, who visited the volcano about the beginning of the Christian Era, surmised its volcanic origin from what he interpreted as the burned and fused rocks near the summit. In fact, the 4,000-foot mountain we see today is superimposed in large part on the wreckage of the older, lower, pre-A.D. 79 crater, to which the name, Monte Somma, is given. Its inactive, vine-covered bowl, encircled by steep cliffs, briefly made a stronghold for the gladiator, Spartacus, and his fellow slaves in 73 B.C., when they defied the power of Rome until they were slain by the legionaries of Marcus Licinius Crassus in 71 B.C. In A.D. 63 the volcano showed some stirrings of life when a succession of earthquakes commenced and

caused some of the damage still to be seen around Pompeii. This, however, was but a prelude to the historic eruption of August 24, A.D. 79.

Fortunately, one of the most complete descriptions of the event has come down to us across the intervening years through two letters from the 17-year-old Younger Pliny to his friend Tacitus, the Roman historian. The letters were written primarily to describe the death of his uncle, Pliny the Elder, a leading philosopher of the day and also, rather surprisingly, an admiral of the Roman navy.

While Pliny the Younger was suddenly impressed with the necessity of studying his books, the Elder Pliny, soon to achieve the distinction

FIG. 3-26 *Mount Vesuvius during the eruption of 1944. The white-capped peak to the left of Vesuvius is the arcuate ridge known as Monte Somma, part of an older, prehistoric volcano. (Photograph by Brown Bros., N. Y.)*

of being the world's first volcanologist, and a Roman of the old school, marched forth to his death on the mountain. Parts of Pliny the Younger's letters are cited here because they are such good examples of straightforward reporting, quite unlike the exaggeratedly impossible version in Bulwer-Lytton's novel, *The Last Days of Pompeii,* in which most of the populace dies while watching a gladiatorial combat in the arena.

Parts of Pliny the Younger's letters follow:

Gaius Plinius sends to his friend Tacitus greeting.

You ask me to write you an account of my uncle's death, that posterity may possess an accurate version of the event in your history. . . .

He was at Misenum, and was in command of the fleet there. It was at one o'clock in the afternoon of the 24th of August that my mother called attention to a cloud of unusual proportion and size. . . . A cloud was rising from one of the hills which took the likeness of a stone-pine very nearly. It imitated the lofty trunk and the spreading branches. . . . It changed color, sometimes looking white, and sometimes when it carried up earth or ashes, dirty or streaked. The thing seemed of importance, and worthy of nearer investigation to the philosopher. He ordered a light boat to be got ready, and asked me to accompany him if I wished; but I answered that I would rather work over my books. . . .

Ashes began to fall around his ships, thicker and hotter as they approached land. Cinders and pumice, and also black fragments of rock cracked by heat, fell around them. The sea suddenly shoaled, and the shores were obstructed by masses from the mountain. . . .

My uncle, for whom the wind was most favorable, arrived, and did his best to remove their terrors. . . . To keep up their spirits by a show of unconcern, he had a bath; and afterwards dined with real, or what was perhaps as heroic, with assumed cheerfulness. But meanwhile there began to break out from Vesuvius, in many spots, high and wide-shooting flames, whose brilliancy was heightened by the darkness of approaching night. My uncle reassured them by asserting that these were burning farm-houses which had caught fire after being deserted by the peasants. Then he turned in to sleep. . . .

It was dawn elsewhere; but with them it was a blacker and denser night than they had ever seen, although torches and various lights made it less dreadful. They decided to take to the shore and see if the sea would allow them to embark; but it appeared as wild and appalling as ever. My uncle lay down on a rug. He asked twice for water and drank it. Then as a flame with a forerunning sulphurous vapor drove off the others, the servants roused him up. Leaning on two slaves, he rose to his feet, but immediately fell back, as I understand choked by the thick vapors. . . . When day came (I mean the third after the last he ever saw), they found his body perfect and uninjured, and covered just as he had been overtaken. . . (Shaler, 1896).

Pliny's letters clearly indicate that the destruction of Pompeii and Herculaneum resulted from the fall of hot ash, and in this shroud were buried the 2,000 of the 20,000 inhabitants who perished. Most of the dead were slaves, soldiers of the guard, or people who were too avaricious to leave their worldly goods. Most were suffocated by falling ash, by hot volcanic mud, or by volcanic gases, and the temperature of the ash was high enough that their bodies charred away. Centuries later when plaster of paris was poured into the cavities once occupied by their bodies, allowed to harden, and then excavated from the ash, their shapes as well as those of dogs and cats, loaves of bread, and all sorts of objects in similar cavities stood revealed. Hundreds of papyri were preserved in the library, along with murals on the walls of houses, and these give a most revealing insight into the interests and pursuits of these long-vanished Romans whose lives and preoccupations were so much like our own. The two cities of Pompeii and Herculaneum slept undisturbed for nearly 1700 years until the discovery of one of the outer walls in 1748 ushered in the period of modern archeology.

Vesuvius has continued its activity from A.D. 79 to the present; in A.D. 472 ashes drifted from its crater as far east as Constantinople. An especially violent eruption in 1631 is estimated to have killed 18,000 people, and came after a

FIG. 3-27 *The ruins of Pompeii, at the foot of Vesuvius, are now free of the volcanic ash that buried the city nearly 2000 years ago. (Photograph by Moody Institute of Science.)*

FIG. 3-28 *The dissected volcanic landscape of Oahu Island, Hawaii. Gently inclined layers of volcanic rock are exposed in the fluted cliff at the left. (Photograph by Ray Atkeson.)*

period of quiescence that lasted long enough for the volcano to be once again overgrown by vegetation. A large number of minor eruptions have been recorded, but major ones occurred in 1794, 1872, 1906, and in 1944 in the midst of the Italian campaign of World War II. Lava then overwhelmed the village of San Sebastiano, but the most destructive effect, as far as the allied military effort was concerned, came from the introduction of glass-sharp volcanic ash into the moving parts of airplane engines.

The first lava is said to have appeared at Vesuvius in A.D. 1036, and its appearance has been a standard accompaniment of most eruptions ever since. Because eruptions in the current phase of the volcano's life history commonly include both the upwelling of large quantities of lava and violently explosive activity that blasts great quantities of ash, cinders, bombs, and blocks skyward, the volcanic edifice that has built up during the past 1880 years is composed in part of solidified lava from flows and internally from dikes and conduits, and in large part from pyroclastic material blown out explosively. For this reason, such a volcanic mountain as Vesuvius is called a *composite cone, or strato-volcano* (Figs. 3-15, 3-19). Its flanks stand at an angle less than those of a cone consisting entirely of cinders, and are steeper than one built up of superimposed, highly fluidal lava flows, such as the Hawaiian volcanoes.

QUIET ERUPTIONS

Mauna Loa and Kilauea

The Hawaiian Islands, surely one of the most idyllic archipelagos in the world, owe their entire existence to volcanism. They are a chain of extinct, dormant, and active volcanoes built up from the depths of the sea and trending southeastward across the Pacific for 1,600 miles from Midway on the north to the largest island, Hawaii, on the south in an arc bowed slightly to the northeast. The eight larger islands are at the southeastern end, and the relative erosional age of their landscapes generally decreases southeastward. This means that Hawaii, the only island with active volcanoes, appeared above the sea more recently than Oahu, the island on which Honolulu stands. One way in which this conclusion is reached is from the more advanced state of stream erosion, valleys, cliffs, and canyons on Oahu as well as the deeper soil cover that has developed there.

There are five major volcanic centers on Hawaii, of which three are most important. Two of these are the immense volcanic mountains, Mauna Kea (13,784 feet) and Mauna Loa (13,679 feet) which rise out of the Pacific depths for at least an additional 15,000 feet,

making them mountains as high as Everest, but of enormously greater bulk since the circumference of Mauna Loa is about 200 miles at the base. Their slopes (Fig. 3-29) are extremely gentle by comparison with those of the Himalaya; seldom do they exceed 10°, and from a distance the volcanoes look like benign turtles of colossal size. With their near-circular outline and gently rounded profile they are sometimes called *shield volcanoes* because they much resemble the circular shields once mounted along the gunwales of sea-roving Viking ships.

Although some pyroclastic material is included in the mass of these huge volcanic piles, for the most part they consist of thousands of superimposed, relatively thin flows of basalt. Many of these at the time of their eruption were extremely fluid. The result is that the slopes of shield volcanoes are gentle because they are built up gradually by thousands of overlapping, tonguelike sheets of once-fluidal material, rather than being loose piles of heaped up volcanic fragments. The latter circumstance results in the building up of *cinder cones,* whose steep sides commonly stand with inclinations of 25° to 30°.

FIG. 3-29 *Hypothetical cross section through the island of Hawaii. The lower black masses show where magma is thought to originate. It is thought then to move upward to form the upper masses of magma which then erupt to the surface to build the volcanoes.*

After G. A. Macdonald, *Science,* Vol. 133, 1961. By permission.

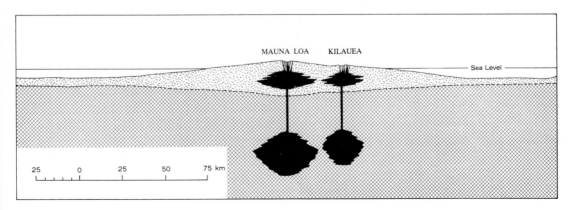

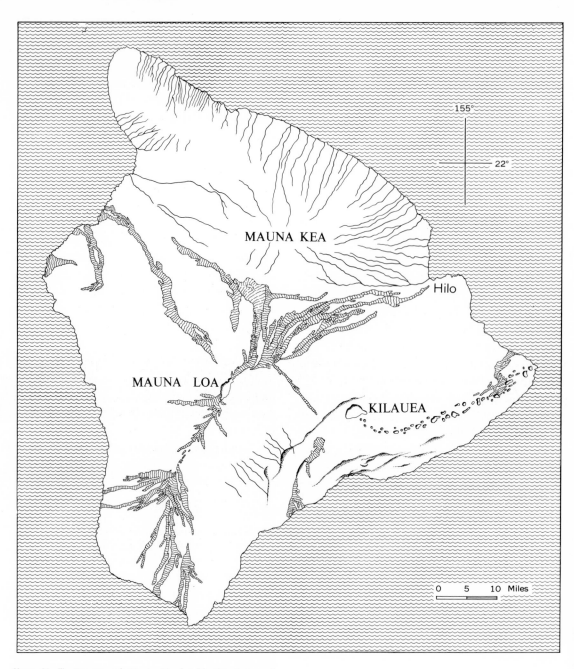

155°

22°

MAUNA KEA

Hilo

MAUNA LOA

KILAUEA

0   5   10 Miles

From H. T. Stearns and G. A. Macdonald, "Geology and Groundwater Resources of Hawaii," Bull. 9, 1946. By permission of U.S. Geological Survey.

FIG. 3-30 *Map of the island of Hawaii. The shaded areas are lava flows erupted since 1750.*

The fires of Mauna Kea are banked now, but Mauna Loa still maintains a high level of activity. The map (Fig. 3-30) shows that most of the historic lava flows have broken out on its flanks, rather than being the result of simple overflow from the summit caldera, known as Mokuaweoweo. In fact, activity in the caldera today is at a minimum, and the caldera itself has originated as the result of foundering through removal of support from below, rather than by (1) explosion, or (2) violently explosive emptying of the magma reservoir as at Krakatoa and Crater Lake.

Mokuaweoweo is no circular crater; the very steep walls, which are about 600 feet high, enclose a sink approximately 3.5 miles long by 2 miles wide. The long dimension trends northeast-southwest and this is on the same line as the so-called Great Rift Zone, out of which so many of the historic flows have issued (Fig. 3-30). The caldera itself has grown through the coalescence of several once independent pit craters on the summit of the mountain, and it is Williams's (1941) belief that this results from collapse brought about by the draining away of lava from the magma reservoir within the mountain through fissures on its flanks.

This belief is certainly supported by the pattern followed by typical eruptions. These may commence with some volcanic dust being blown from the summit crater and a column of steam standing over it by day as well as a glow of light that illuminates the clouds at night. Somewhat later, lava may break out on the flanks, and as the map shows (Fig. 3-30), almost always on the Great Rift Zone, either to the northeast or to the southwest of the summit.

Lava flows on Mauna Loa seldom issue from a single vent, but almost always break out from great cracks, or *fissures.* The first phase of such an outbreak may be the appearance of a line of *fire fountains,* or geyserlike columns of lava that may spurt as much as a thousand feet up into the air and line up as a nearly continuous curtain of fire along the fissure (Fig. 3-31). The basalt that streams from these fissures is at a high temperature, and consequently may be extremely fluid when it first pours out. It may flow down pre-existing stream courses with velocities approaching that of the rivers themselves; where there are irregularities, the lava plunges over these like a waterfall. When such a stream reaches the sea, a titanic conflict ensues between the forces of Neptune and of Vulcan, as it were. Immense clouds of steam boil upward, the sea seethes like a gigantic cauldron, and part of

FIG. 3-31 *Fire fountain at Kilauea, November 18, 1959. The lighter colored parts of the fountain are glowing fluid masses of basalt lava. The lava cools in the air and turns dark at the top of the fountain. (Photograph by G. A. Macdonald.)*

FIG. 3-32 *Basalt lava, pouring over the cliff to the right, reaches the sea. Hawaii, 1955.* (*Photograph by G. A. Macdonald.*)

the lava is quenched so abruptly that it froths up as a tawny, cellular sort of volcanic glass (Fig. 3-32).

Not all the Hawaiian basalts flow in torrential streams; blocky, ponderously advancing flows are common, too. These march forward much like a tank, or caterpillar tractor, when the surface crusts over and is carried ahead by the still molten interior. The advancing crust breaks up into blocks at the leading edge of the flow, and these cascade over the front to make a carpet or track over which the flow can advance. The top and bottom of such a flow will make a *volcanic breccia* when the whole flow has solidi-

fied, and the interior will be essentially uniformly textured homogeneous basalt.

Hawaii has given us two Polynesian terms to describe the surface character of lava flows, and these have now won such general acceptance that they are commonly used in the literature of geology. Basalt with a rough, blocky appearance, much like furnace slag, is called by the remarkably brief name of *aa* (Fig. 3-33), while the more fluidal varieties with smooth, satiny, or even glassy surfaces are given the more euphonious name of *pahoehoe* (Fig. 3-34).

Kilauea is like Mauna Loa in some respects and very different in others. For one thing it is at a much lower altitude, about 4,000 feet, and no longer is an independent mountain but is a partially buried satellite on the flank of the higher volcano. Perhaps within the next few millennia it will be inundated by flows from a flank eruption of Mauna Loa. Kilauea is the far better known of the two volcanoes since a paved road leads directly to its rim, and it has had a steady stream of visitors for more than a century.

The caldera of Kilauea is always a surprise to the first-time visitor, and for much the same reason as the Grand Canyon is. Both make such an extreme contrast with their nearly level surroundings. The elliptical caldera of Kilauea, whose dimensions are approximately 3 miles by 2 miles, is countersunk with almost vertical walls into the very gently sloping surface of the old volcano. The bottom of the caldera is nearly level and is made up of only very recently solidified lava which spread like a tarry stream over the entire floor. Activity today is confined to only part of the caldera—the volcanic throat or fire pit of Halemaumau, which bears a relationship to the larger caldera much like that of a drain pipe in the bottom of a wash basin. Basaltic lava rises and falls inside the fire pit. At times it spills over Halemaumau's rim onto the caldera floor; at other times it sinks down more than a thousand feet below the surface. Then the floor of the pit is filled with long talus aprons of basalt blocks that have broken away from the vertical walls.

Commonly, lava swirls and seethes within Halemaumau without violent explosive activity, but occasionally there are impressive departures from this pattern. Such a one was the 1924 eruption, in which the sequence of events was as follows: (1) in January the lava lake was especially active and the level rose to within about 100 feet of the rim, (2) in February it started to subside and by May had dropped to around 600 feet, (3) meanwhile the epicenters of a whole succession of minor earthquakes migrated steadily eastward along the line of the Puna Rift, accompanied by ground subsidence until almost certainly there was an eruption on the sea floor southeast of Hawaii, (4) immense quantities of lava blocks avalanched from the walls into the fire pit, (5) finally, these blocks and much of the debris that had accumulated on the floor of Halemaumau were hurled out in a series of violent explosions between May 11 and 27.

An interpretation of this sequence of events, which are a bit out of character for a quiet eruption, is that the lava column dropped because lava was being drained away through fissures from beneath Kilauea—whose entire level dropped, incidentally, by 13 or 14 feet—southeastward along the Puna Rift. This permitted

FIG. 3-33 *Flow of aa lava slowly advancing over a field. The flames and smoke are from burning vegetation. Hawaii, 1955. (Photograph by G. A. Macdonald.)*

ground water to move into the area vacated by the sinking column of lava. When a sufficiently high pressure was built up, and the lava column had subsided below sea level, the ground water was converted into steam under cover of the blocks of rock fallen into the fire pit. Then the pressure rose to a point high enough that these rocks were shattered and hurled out of the pit in what was a succession of steam explosions rather than ones produced by primary magmatic gases. To such a secondary eruption the name of *phreatic explosion* (derived from the Greek word for water well) is given, and they are very characteristic of minor eruptions the world over; in Iceland, New Zealand, Japan, and possibly the 1914-17 eruptions of Mount Lassen.

FISSURE ERUPTIONS

Several regions on the Earth's surface have been inundated by vast floods of lava that obviously could never have come from a single volcanic conduit or even from a chain of volcanoes. Prominent examples of these lava floods, which universally are basaltic rocks or closely related variants, are the Columbia lava plateau in the northwestern United States, with a surface extent of some 200,000 square miles and a volume of approximately 75,000 cubic miles, the Deccan lava sheet in western India inland from Bombay, and a broad area near the Parana River in South America (Fig. 3-35).

The Columbia lava plateau is the most thoroughly studied of the three. In places it is a mile thick, but the individual flows are much thinner, only a few being as much as 400 feet thick. Their composition is remarkably uniform, especially in view of the fact that such an enormous volume of basalt was not erupted all at once, but its outpouring stretches over a long span of geologic time. The surface of the

lava plateau covers a very broad area—extending from the Rocky Mountains on the east to the Cascades and Pacific border to the west. The basalt had no single route to the surface, but rose through hundreds, if not thousands, of fissures that today are to be seen as dikes where they are exposed in canyon walls. The country that was buried by the lava floods was one of moderate relief. Here again, the walls of canyons cut across the basalt plateau show that individual lava flows filled valleys, overtopped ridges and ultimately coalesced to form a nearly uniform plain which buried a wholly different sort of world beneath a frozen sea of stone.

The nearest counterpart ever reported of such a fissure eruption was a minor episode by comparison, impressive as it undoubtedly must have been. This was the eruption on June 8, 1783, of the Icelandic volcano, Skaptar Jökull. There, a stream of basalt poured out from a fissure about 15 miles long.

Iceland has one of the most dramatic landscapes on Earth, with over 100 volcanic centers, of which at least 20 are active, a score of glaciers, and the all-encircling sea. In few other regions is the elemental conflict of fire, ice, and ocean more stark. In the long and remarkable cultural history of the island, extending back to A.D. 874, there have been many of these encounters between outpourings of red-hot lava and streams of ice. The usual outcome is the melting of much of the ice, with the release of a sudden and devastating flood of water and mud.

This is exactly what happened in the disastrous eruption of 1783. With a fissure 15 miles long discharging basalt along its entire length, a broad tide of lava poured down the slope, filled the deep canyon of the Skapta to overflowing, and completely displaced a lake that lay in its path. The eruption continued for two years, and the two major lava torrents it produced had lengths of about 40 and 50 miles, respectively. Their average depth was 100 feet, but where canyons were filled to overflowing

FIG. 3-34 *Pahoehoe lava surface. Mauna Loa, Hawaii.* (*Photograph by Ansel Adams.*)

FIG. 3-35 *Flood basalt lava flows of the Thulean Plateau, Antrim, Ireland. The Thulean Plateau formerly extended across the north Atlantic from western Scotland and northern Ireland to Iceland and western Greenland. (Photograph by Aerofilms and Aero Pictorial, Ltd., London.)*

they were as much as 600 feet thick. Where the lava overtopped a stream valley and spread out across the plain it advanced along a front 12 to 15 miles wide. The flow is estimated to have covered 220 square miles and the volume discharged in the two-year period is thought to have been about 3 cubic miles, or a mass equal to that of Mont Blanc, the highest mountain in Europe (Coleman, 1946).

This was one of the greatest disasters in the turbulent history of the island. The lava, blocking and diverting rivers and melting snow and ice, liberated huge floods, thus destroying much of the island's limited agricultural land. Twenty villages were overwhelmed by the lava, and many others were swept away in the floods. About 10,000 people, or 20 per cent of the population, died; 80 per cent of the sheep (190,000), 75 per cent of the horses (28,000), and over 50 per cent of the cattle (11,500) perished.

Almost all the North Atlantic was obscured in the dust cloud, and this phenomenon greatly interested Benjamin Franklin, who wrote a brief description on the effect of the so-called dry fog in America (Griggs, 1922):

During several of the summer months of the year 1783, when the effects of the sun's rays to heat the earth in these northern regions should have been the greatest, there existed a constant fog over all of Europe, and great part of North America. This fog was of a permanent nature; it was dry, and the rays of the sun seemed to have little effect toward dissipating it, as they easily do a moist fog rising from the water. They were indeed rendered so faint in passing through it that, when collected in the focus of a burning-glass, they would scarcely kindle brown paper. Of course, their summer effect in heating the earth was exceedingly diminished.

Hence the surface was early frozen.

Hence the first snows remained on it unmelted, and received continual additions.

Hence perhaps the winter of 1783-4 was more severe than any that happened for many years.

In Europe the ash cloud had a most deleterious effect on the weather, too, so much so that it was called the year without a summer. Crops failed in Scotland, 600 miles away; fumes and ashes damaged crops in the Netherlands, and the ash cloud was reported from such widely scattered points as North Africa, Syria, eastern Russia, and Sweden. It rose to an altitude higher than the Alps, and the monks at the pass of St. Bernard correctly interpreted it as smoke and not haze. As might be expected, the event had a profound effect on people of the time, and among other things inspired the following passage of Cowper's (Krakatoa Committee, 1888):

"Fires from beneath, and meteors from above—
Portentous, unexampled, unexplained."
                              ("The Task," BOOK II)

Volcanism is one of the more dramatic of all geological phenomena, one that impinges directly on human affairs, that has been the source of comment and discussion from the days of Strabo and Pliny to ours, yet little is known of its true nature. We see but part of the picture, only the surface aspect. No living person can do more than speculate on the connection between volcanoes and the origin of plutonic rocks within the Earth. Reasoning tells us there probably is a relationship between the two, but of this we have no direct proof. Nor, for that matter, do we know the source of heat, the depth of burial of the volcanic hearths, or even more fundamentally, what the actual cause of volcanism may be. Many of these questions we shall take up again in Chapter IX, Earthquakes and the Earth's Interior. Through what we do know of volcanoes, active and extinct, and of the nature of their gaseous, liquid, and solid products, we have some basis for making a few controlled guesses about the origin of the atmosphere, the ocean, and what may very likely have been the composition of the original dry land surface of the Earth.

What, then, are some of the things actually known about volcanoes and the products of volcanism that can be summed up here and kept in mind as they bear on other fundamental problems of the Earth?

As we have seen, volcanoes are not randomly distributed over the surface of the Earth, but are found in the following environments: (1) along the margins of continents, especially the somewhat mountainous coasts bordering the Pacific; (2) within the ocean basins where the truly oceanic islands—such as Iceland and Hawaii—are dominantly volcanic; (3) in the regions bordering, but not actually within, mountain ranges in the continental interior (although this is a less familiar occurrence)—in this category are the volcanic provinces of central France and southern Italy; and (4) along large fracture zones or *rifts,* such as the remarkable system that extends through much of eastern Africa.

Geologically speaking, there are two major theaters where volcanoes are not found, and these are (1) the heart of mountain ranges whose rocks have been intensely compressed—such as the Alps and Himalayas—and (2) the broad expanses of deeply eroded, very ancient, and intensely deformed rocks which are spoken

of as *shields*—most of Labrador and northeastern Canada are typical of such a region.

Trying to find a common factor to explain
both the occurrence and non-occurrence of volcanism is perhaps beyond our capabilities today, but we have found that volcanoes appear
to shun areas of strongly compressed rocks and
to favor regions where some kind of fracture
system extends from the surface down to the
depths where magma can form. The importance
of this appears to be twofold: (1) fractures provide a channel by which magma can reach the
surface, and (2) their presence indicates that
under favorable circumstances there may be a
release of pressure at depth. This is important
because even at fairly moderate depths within
the Earth, the temperatures presumably are high
enough that rocks ordinarily would be expected
to melt, but the high pressures prevailing there
prevent this (for most substances, the higher the
pressure, the higher the temperature required
for melting to occur). With a release of pressure, melting takes place, and fracturing of the
rocks in the Earth's crust may be one of the
ways by which this release is achieved.

This raises the next question; what is the
depth from which the magma rises in a volcanic
eruption? Here, the evidence is mixed. Some
lavas appear to have had shallow sources. At
Tahiti, where the central conduit is bared
through deep erosion, the depth is perhaps a
mile (Williams, 1953); at Vesuvius the nature
of fragments brought up from subvolcanic basement led the German volcanologist Rittman to
the belief that magma probably rose about 4
miles. Diamonds in the pipes of Kimberley
probably crystallized at a depth of several miles
below the surface, judging from what we know
of the temperatures and pressures required to
make diamonds in the laboratory.

The tremendous outpourings of basalt in fissure eruptions very likely come from subcrustal
depths, in Hawaii perhaps 35 miles (Eaton and
Murata, 1960). The reasoning here is that
higher temperature is required to liquefy basalt

compared to other lavas, that enormous volumes are involved, which would appear to require more than a local source, and that these
plateau basalts are of remarkably uniform composition both in space and time.

Many additional problems await solution. In
an earlier day, when it was believed that the
Earth had solidified from a fiery, molten sphere
that on cooling developed a rocky shell, the
magma reservoirs within the crust could be interpreted as hot spots left behind when all else
had solidified. Today, through other lines of
evidence, we know that this is not so, but we
are still at a loss for an answer. Radioactivity
has been appealed to as a source of heat, but
serious objections intervene here, too. The lack
of radioactive constituents in the lavas with the
highest temperatures, the plateau basalts, mili-
tates against this, together with the lack of helium—a product of radioactive decay—among
the associated volcanic gases (Williams, 1953).

So the list grows. Even the mechanism by
which a column of lava and its entrapped gases
tunnels its way upward through the crust is unknown. In part it must involve fluxing, in part
wedging or shouldering aside, and in part stop-
ing or piecemeal engulfment; but what the
precedence of these relative roles is remains
speculative.

The even more fundamental problem of what
processes are responsible for the wide variety
of compositions of volcanic rocks still awaits
solution. Magmas of many compositions may be
erupted, even from the same vent or very closely
related conduits; an outstanding example is a
recently extinct volcano in Oregon which has
simultaneously erupted lavas as unlike as basalt
and obsidian.

Differentiation, the process described in the
discussion of the Bowen reaction series, almost
certainly plays a role, but this process moves
only one way. It is possible to have a basaltic
magma go through a series of reactions so that
a rhyolitic magma results, but it cannot go in
the opposite direction. This has led some geolo-

gists to the belief that all lavas of diverse compositions may have differentiated from an original magmatic source. The evidence is clear that many have, but we are by no means certain that this is a universal law.

In fact, the origin of magma itself is unknown, and finding an answer to that problem would put us well on our way toward finding a solution to the fundamental riddle of the origin of all igneous rocks.

Suggested References

Bowen, N. L., 1928, The evolution of igneous rocks, Princeton Univ. Press, Princeton, N. J.

Bullard, F. M., 1961, Volcanoes: in history, in theory, in eruption, Univ. of Texas Press, Austin, Texas.

Coleman, S. N., 1946, Volcanoes, New and old, John Day Co., New York.

Cotton, C. A., 1944, Volcanoes as landscape forms, Whitcombe and Tombs, Wellington, N. Z.

Daly, R. A., 1933, Igneous rocks and the depths of the earth, McGraw-Hill Book Co., Inc., New York.

Eaton, J. P., and Murata, K. J., 1960, How volcanoes grow, Science, v. 132, p. 925-938.

Eaton, J. P., Richter, D. H., and Ault, W. V., 1961, The tsunami of May 23, 1960, on the Island of Hawaii, Seismological Soc. of Amer., Bull., v. 51, p. 135-157.

Griggs, R. F., 1922, The Valley of Ten Thousand Smokes, Natl. Geographic Soc., Washington, D. C.

Kennedy, W. Q., and Richey, J. E., 1947, Catalogue of the active volcanoes of the world, Bull. Volcanologique, Supplement de Serie II, Tome VII.

Krakatoa Committee, 1888, The eruption of Krakatoa, The Royal Society, London.

LaCroix, A., 1904, La Montagne Pelée et ses éruptions, Masson et Cie., Paris.

Leet, L. D., 1948, Causes of catastrophe, McGraw-Hill Book Co., Inc., New York.

Maiuri, Amadeo, Bianchi, P. V., and Battaglia, L. E., 1961, Last moments of the Pompeians, Natl. Geographic, v. 120, p. 651-669.

Moore, Ruth, 1956, The earth we live on, A. Knopf, New York.

Poldervaart, Arie, and others, 1955, Crust of the earth, Geol. Soc. Amer., Special Paper 62, New York.

Read, H. H., 1957, The granite controversy, Interscience Publishers, Inc., New York.

Rittman, A., 1962, Volcanoes and their activity, John Wiley and Sons, New York.

Shaler, N. S., 1896, Aspects of the earth, Charles Scribner's Sons, New York.

Shand, S. J., 1927, The eruptive rocks, John Wiley and Sons, New York.

Stearns, H. T., and Clark, W. O., 1930, Geology and water resources of the Kau District, Hawaii, U. S. Geol. Surv., Water-Supply Paper 616.

Stearns, H. T., 1946, Geology of the Hawaiian Islands, Hawaii Div. of Hydrography, Bull. 8, Honolulu.

Tuttle, O. F., 1955, The origin of granite, Scientific American, April.

Tyrrell, G. W., 1931, Volcanoes, Henry Holt and Co., New York.

Umbgrove, J. H. F., 1950, Symphony of the earth, Martinus Nijhoff, The Hague, Netherlands.

Walton, Matt., 1960, Granite problems, Science, v. 131, p. 635-645.

Williams, Howel, 1932, The history and character of volcanic domes, Univ. Calif. Publ., Bull. Dept. Geol. Sci., v. 21, p. 51-146.

———, 1941, Calderas and their origin, Univ. Calif. Publ., Bull. Dept. Geol. Sci., v. 25, p. 239-346.

———, 1942, The geology of Crater Lake National Park, Oregon, Carnegie Inst. of Washington, Publ. 540.

———, 1951, Volcanoes, Scientific American, November.

———, 1953, Progress and problems in volcanology, Quart. Jour. Geol. Soc. London, v. 109, p. 311-332.

Wyler, R., and Ames, G., 1954, Restless earth, Abelard-Schuman, New York.

IV

Sedimentary Rocks

Widely spread over the surface of the Earth is a relatively thin blanket of sediment which has been consolidated into rock through slow-acting processes that are relatively simple to understand when compared with those responsible for the origin of igneous and metamorphic rocks. These sedimentary processes operate in environments on land or in the sea at temperatures and pressures much more like those familiar to us than the 2500°F. needed to keep basaltic magma molten. True, pressures on the floor of the ocean, the final repository of much of the waste of the land, rise to 6 tons to the square inch, but these pressures are still slight when compared with the crushing burdens prevailing in the crustal realm where processes operate to produce the metamorphic rocks.

Sedimentary rocks, for the most part, are secondary or derived rocks. One important category of them consists of layers made up of clay, sand, or gravel particles which are derived from the disintegration or decomposition of pre-existing rocks. Layered rocks made of such fragmental material are called clastic sedimentary rocks.

Another large and economically important group of sedimentary rocks is chemically precipitated in water such as evaporating lakes or shallow embayments of the sea. Perhaps the best known example of this category is rock salt. Closely akin to it in origin are such well-known substances as gypsum and borax—both of which are chemically derived.

Organic sediments are a third category, and an enormously important one. Coal, a vitally significant fossil fuel, is in this group, as are the so-called oil shales, a possible reserve for the future. Another familiar kind of organic sedimentary rock is limestone, and of its many forms several represent the slow accumulation over many centuries of the deposits made by lime-secreting plants and animals.

ENVIRONMENTS OF DEPOSITION

Sedimentary rocks can accumulate in a wide variety of environments on the Earth's surface —about as many as there are kinds of landscapes or different sorts of climates. Two major realms of sedimentation commonly are recognized, and these are (1) on land, or continental, and (2) in the sea, or marine. Like most classifications, there is much that is arbitrary about this one, and several occurrences might as well be placed in one category as in the other; for example, the silts and muds in the deltas of large rivers could be assigned readily to either province.

In the sea at least two of the factors controlling the distribution of sediment are (1) the

A monastery at Meteora, Greece, surmounts bluffs of stratified conglomerate of Tertiary age.

(Photograph by Jean B. Thorpe.)

distance from land and (2) the depth of water. To simplify the story, there are four leading zones where sediments accumulate that have sufficiently unlike characteristics to merit setting them up as separate units. These will be described in much greater detail in Chapter XIV, The Sea, but they are listed here very briefly to set the stage.

Seaward from the land, the first of these zones is the *shore zone,* and for all practical purposes this is where the surf breaks against the shore. On many coasts where the tidal range is large a very broad expanse of sea floor adjacent to the land may be laid bare at low water.

The *continental shelf* is a much broader zone and normally extends seaward to a depth in the general neighborhood of 100 fathoms. On some coasts this depth may be only a few miles offshore; on others, such as the coast of Siberia, it may be 200 miles or more. As a rule the continental shelf is the region where land-derived sediments are deposited after being winnowed and shifted about by waves and currents of the sea. This is the zone where most of the sediments were accumulated that we see exposed as marine sedimentary rocks on the Earth's surface.

The *continental slope* and the deep floor of the sea, or the *abyss,* are inaccessible by ordinary means of observation. It is now possible to take photographs of the ocean bottom with underwater cameras, and, by means of the bathyscaph, to visit this dark, silent realm, almost as remote in its way as the world of space.

Here, on the floor of the open sea, for the most part accumulate the finest sediments, the impalpable ooze composed of the remains of minutely ornamented, free-floating and swimming microscopic plants and animals, the extremely finely divided clays of inscrutable origin that carpet the abyssal plains, and the coating of dark, blue-green mud on the submarine slopes of the continents.

On the land many of us are aware of the large number and variety of possibilities available for the trapping of a multitude of different sorts of sediment and of their ultimate conversion into rocks. Among the many examples, the following are typical:

1. LAKES.—Some of these natural settling basins, such as the Great Lakes, the Caspian and the Aral seas, have such great size that in a sense they may be thought of as small oceans. All lakes, however, large or small, serve as local traps in which sediment transported to them by streams, moving ice, or the wind may accumulate.

2. FLOOD PLAINS AND DELTAS.—These depositional sites range all the way from plains bordering the Nile, the Yangtze, and the Mississippi down to narrow strips bordering small streams.

3. SAND DUNES.—These deposits testify to the effectiveness of the wind in those parts of the world where such factors occur together as an abundant supply of sand, little vegetation with which to stabilize it, and strong winds to move the sand about. Such combinations are likely to be encountered in deserts, along many of the world's coasts, and along the floodplains of large rivers, of which the Volga is an excellent example. Wind also sweeps lighter material than sand before it and this may pile up in vast windrows of dust, or silt size particles. Such a thick blanket of feebly consolidated dust is a dominating element of the tawny landscape of northern China near Peking.

4. GLACIAL DEPOSITS.—Deposits left by glaciers are a final category, and these will be discussed in much greater detail in Chapter XIII. Glaciers, which today are confined to higher mountains or to far distant Arctic and Antarctic shores, were once more widespread than they are today, and their deposits—usually more disordered than those laid down by streams or in the sea—blanket much of North America and northern Europe. A good example of a typical glacial deposit is boulder-clay, which is literally that—rocks the size of boulders set in a clayey matrix with very little sorting of particles according to size.

FEATURES OF SEDIMENTARY ROCKS

An outstanding physical attribute of sedimentary rocks is their original near-horizontality. Most of these rocks are made of particles, ranging from very large down to submicroscopic, that settled out through such a medium as air or water. In addition to this, the majority are layered (Fig. 4-1), and these layers, too, show a great range in their dimensions from laminae whose thickness is measurable in millimeters up to ones that are measured in hundreds of feet.

Such depositional layers in sedimentary rocks are called *strata;* an individual layer is a stratum. In everyday language such layers are commonly called beds if their dimensions are fairly large. If the layers are very thin (Fig. 4-2), they are better called *laminae* (from the Latin, *lamina,* for thin plate, leaf, or layer), and the term is used here in much the same sense that we speak of the laminations in plywood.

FIG. 4-1 *These colossal images of Rameses II 1301-1235* B.C.*), next to the Nile, are carved from horizontal sandstone layers that extend through the statues. (Photograph by Jean B. Thorpe.)*

FIG. 4-2 *Laminae in sandstone blocks.*

Color

Igneous rocks, unaltered by exposure to the atmosphere, typically are shades of gray or black, since these are the prevailing colors of their most abundant constituents, feldspar and the ferromagnesian minerals. Sedimentary rocks may be much more colorful. Some kinds are made up of large fragments of other pre-existing rocks, and if a wide variety of these is present, the resulting sedimentary rock will be correspondingly variegated.

In addition to the possibility of a variety of colors in a sedimentary rock resulting from the great range of colors in the rocks that comprise it, an important source of coloring matter may be the very fine interstitial material that fills the space between the individual grains. If this should contain hematite (iron oxide, Fe_2O_3), the resulting rock is likely to be colored red. This is the source of most of the red color in the walls of the Grand Canyon. Other forms of iron may stain a rock brown, or even shades of pink and yellow. Iron possibly may be responsible for much of the purple, green, or black colors of some sedimentary rocks, but what the true nature of some of the coloring matter may be is not known.

Many of the darker sedimentary rocks owe their color to the organic material they contain. Coal is an excellent illustration of this. Its composition is entirely organic and the very name is a synonym for black. With varying amounts of organic material, sedimentary rocks may have a color range from shades of light gray to black. In some cases, however, black muds owe their color to finely-divided iron sulphide dispersed through them rather than to carbonaceous matter.

The range in colors that sedimentary rocks may display is one of their more intriguing properties, and in dry countries where vegetation is lacking and the soil cover is sparse, the true color of these rocks stands revealed in striking fashion, as in Grand, Zion, and Bryce Canyons,

Monument Valley, Canyon de Chelly, and the Painted Desert. It is the brilliant coloring of their sedimentary rocks as much as any other attribute that makes these places so renowned.

Stratification

Besides its brilliant coloration, Grand Canyon is notable for the uniform stratification of the sedimentary rocks cropping out in the upper two thirds of the canyon walls. The long parallel bands in the photograph (Fig. 4-3) are strata, and they exemplify to a remarkable degree the physical properties that customarily are associated with this term.

This layering is due in part to differences in composition; for example, in the Grand Canyon (Fig. 4-3) the high cliff about halfway up the canyon wall is limestone, while the light-colored cliff just below the canyon rim is sandstone.

Among the many reasons for the rhythmic layering in sedimentary rocks is discontinuous deposition, with slight differences in coloration or grain size to mark the new laminae when deposition starts up after an interruption. An especially striking kind of rhythmic deposition is the annual layering characteristic of the very fine-grained laminae deposited on the bottom of cold-climate lakes that freeze over in the winter. These uniform layers are called *varves,* and the thicker, light-colored layers are generally interpreted as having been deposited during the summer when the lake is open and streams are free to sweep comparatively coarse sediment into the lake. The finer dark band is thought to represent fine-grained material, in large part organic, that settled out through the still water of the lake under the ice during winter.

Some sedimentary rocks deposited in the sea, especially some kinds of marine clay, show similarly repetitive laminae, too, and these are interpreted as annual layers, as are also the remarkably regular, paper-thin layers deposited on the floors of large nonfreezing lakes; perhaps the best known examples being the oil shales of

FIG. 4-3 *Horizontal strata in the walls of the Grand Canyon. The lower cliff is the Redwall limestone and the upper the Coconino sandstone. (Photograph by John S. Shelton.)*

the western United States, especially in the vicinity of Green River, Wyoming (Fig. 4-4).

Some sediments, ranging from coarse- to fine-grained, show a very different sort of stratification. In this category an individual layer, instead of having particles of the same, or even of different sizes distributed uniformly throughout, will have the larger particles concentrated at the bottom, the smaller at the top. Such a layer is said to have *graded bedding* and is believed to have been deposited by what is known as a *turbidity current*.

FIG. 4-4 *Very thinly laminated shale from near Green River, Wyoming, containing a fossil fish.*

Turbidity currents are dense, cloud-like streams that flow downslope, sometimes quite suddenly, when a mass of sediment is discharged into a relatively quiet body of water. An excellent example is the excessively muddy Colorado River where it flows into Lake Mead, which is backed up behind Hoover Dam on the boundary between Nevada and Arizona. The muddy river water seems to disappear as if by magic, and anyone who has seen the dark, blue-green water of Lake Mead cannot fail to be impressed by the contrast it makes with the turbid river. An explanation for the disappearance of the muddy water is that with its higher density it sinks below the surface of the lake and moves as an underflow along the bottom.

Such currents appear on occasion to move spasmodically over the sea floor from the upper part of the continental shelf down to the abyss at its base. Because sediment swept along in such a turbidity current settles out quickly, as compared to the grain-by-grain sifting down of material in an undisturbed lake or the sea, the larger particles drop out first and the smaller ones sink later. Incidentally, the *nuées ardentes* that caused such devastation when Mount Pelée erupted are good examples of turbidity currents which in that case were moving through air rather than water.

Special Features

Much can be inferred from the special features of sedimentary rocks about such things as the depth and temperature of the water in which the sand of a marine sandstone was deposited, or the distribution and probable amount of rainfall for the land climate prevailing at a time when a succession of continental strata were laid down. Most important of all, locked up in the sedimentary rocks is the record of past life on Earth—on land and in the sea—preserved in the form of fossils.

RIPPLE MARKS.—Nearly everyone has seen the characteristic corrugated surface made by a stream or tidal current flowing across a sandy bottom, or has seen photographs of virtually the same pattern produced by the wind blowing across a desert sand dune. Such ripples are likely to be asymmetrical with the gentle slope on the upstream, the steep slope on the downstream side. This pattern results from sand grains being rolled by the current of water or air, up the upcurrent side, and then sliding down the downcurrent slope which stands at an inclination known as the *angle of repose*. This term means the maximum slope at which sand grains will stand without sliding down this so-called *slip face* by gravity. Almost all such ripples form at right angles to the current that made them, and thus when they are converted into solid rock they can be used to establish the direction once taken by long-vanished currents in the atmosphere or under water. It was once thought the *current ripples* in water-laid sediments were an indication of shallow depth, but underwater photographs recently taken of the tops of submarine ridges show ripple patterns on the sea floor at a depth of 6,000 feet.

Another type of ripple has symmetrical sides, sharper crests, and more gently rounded troughs than current ripples do. These symmetrical corrugations are called *oscillation ripples,* and presumably they are the result of surface waves of a type known as waves of oscillation (Chapter XIV) stirring up the sandy bottom of a shallow water body.

MUD CRACKS.—When wet, clayey mud that is exposed to the air dries, it shrinks, and on shrinking, cracks, generally with the formation of a nearly uniform pattern of hexagons and pentagons—much resembling the tops of lava columns. In lava, the reason is contraction upon cooling; in wet muds, it is contraction resulting from dehydration. On continued drying, the mud layers on the tops of the polygons may curl up at the edges, so much so at times as to make complete rolls, much like a cardboard tube.

Mud cracks indicate that the sediment of which they were once a part was alternately wet and dry, and thus these cracks are very typical of mud-bottomed, shallow lakes that on occasion dry up. They are not so characteristic of muddy tidal flats because the time of exposure at low tide is too brief for much drying out.

FOSSILS.—No other property is so distinctively a characteristic of sedimentary rocks as fossils. These are the remains of once living things that on their death were buried in sand, silt, lime, or mud. Much of the organic matter that some of them originally contained gradually was replaced over the centuries by inorganic matter, until, to use petrified wood as an example, many of the woody fibers and cellulose have been replaced by silica. Representatives of just about everything that crawls, walks, swims, or flies among the animals, or that simply stands in place, such as the plants, have been preserved as fossils. This includes such improbable creatures as jellyfish, whose composition must be more than 95 per cent water, or such fragile things as the compound eyes of flies, as well as the delicate tracery of dragonfly wings. Such things are the exceptions, however, because the organisms most commonly preserved as fossils are those that already have durable elements in their make-up, such as shells, bones, and teeth. In fact, most fossils are the remains of shells or skeletons. In some instances the entire rock may consist of organic matter. A layer of coal is made up of plant fragments—chiefly spores—and some limestones may be composed of the remains of coral or of calcareous algae, or may be a felted mass of sea shells, in which case the rock is called a *coquina* (Fig. 4-5). In addition to the remains of organisms, footprints, tracks, trails, and burrows may be considered as fossils, too.

CROSS-BEDDING.—Earlier in this chapter the point was made that sedimentary rocks custom-

FIG. 4-5 *Coquina, from Saint Augustine, Florida. (Courtesy of Ward's Natural Science Establishment, Inc.)*

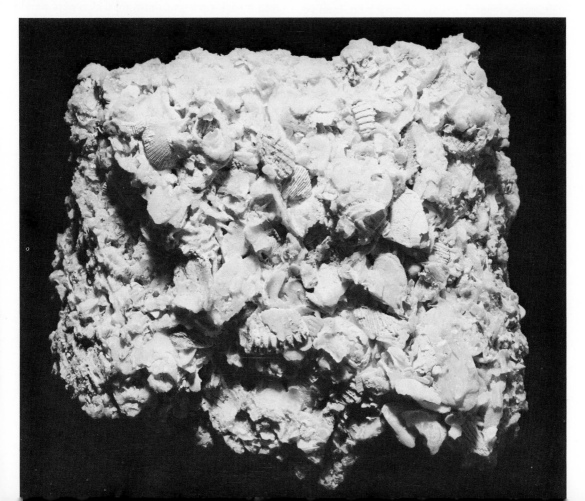

arily are deposited in essentially parallel layers known as strata. But as with most generalizations there are almost always bound to be exceptions, for there are several varieties of stratification in which the laminae are inclined at steep angles to the horizontal (Fig. 4-6).

One kind of cross-stratification forms in sand dunes. Each layer inside the dune at some time past was part of the surface, and since the dune's configuration was established largely through a balancing of wind transport upslope and gravity gliding downslope, most of these layers are sweeping curves which more typically than not are concave upwards. Since sand dunes are ephemeral land forms whose position and orientation change with the inconstant wind, it is not surprising that these sweeping, shingled layers may intersect one another in complex patterns such as are to be seen in the sandstone in the walls of Canyon de Chelly, Arizona, or in Zion National Park (Fig. 4-7).

Another kind of cross-bedding is made in deltas by streams carrying a fairly large load of moderately coarse debris, and then forced to deposit this sediment rapidly when their current is checked upon reaching a water body, such as a lake. Here, the sediment dropped by the

FIG. 4-6 *The body of the Sphinx is formed from nearly horizontal layers of rock, but the head and neck are carved from cross-stratified layers. The cross-strata are inclined toward the pyramid.* (*Photograph by A. E. L. Morris.*)

stream constructs a leading edge out into the lake, much as a highway fill is built out into a canyon by end-dumping from gravel trucks. The outer slope of such a delta, like the slip-face of a sand dune, also stands at the angle of repose. When these sediments are consolidated into rock, three distinctive layers may result. At the top and bottom of a deltaic deposit will be horizontal strata, which are known as *topset* and *bottomset* beds respectively, while the steeply inclined layers that once were the delta front as it advanced out into the lake are *foreset* beds.

CONVERSION TO ROCK

All that has been discussed thus far in this chapter fundamentally has to do with sediments and the process of sedimentation, and very little has been said about the way in which these are converted into solid rock. What process is it, for example, that converts loose sand, which at the beach can be idly sifted through the fingers, into a rock such as sandstone which may be almost as unyielding as granite?

Is it pressure? The answer to this is an emphatic, No. To apply enough pressure to force sand grains to adhere to one another would be to crush them into smaller and smaller particles. Pressure does play a role, however, in the process of *compaction,* which is the squeezing together of the particles in a sediment, with the result that the *porosity,* which is the fraction of the total volume that is pore space, is reduced. If, for instance, enough pressure is applied to fine-grained muds, such as clay or silt, most of the interstitial water is squeezed out, the sediment shrinks markedly, and if clay is a dominant constituent the particles tend to adhere to one another.

The closing up of the space between the particles through compaction is an important precursor for the most significant process involved in the conversion of sediments into sedimentary rock. This is *cementation.* Fundamentally it involves the deposition from solution of such a

FIG. 4-7 *Giant cross-strata at Checkerboard Mesa, Zion National Park, Utah. (Photograph by Ray Atkeson.)*

soluble substance as $CaCO_3$ and its building up as a layer of film on the surface of sand grains, silt particles, or clay flakes, as the case may be, until all the pore space separating them is filled. Such a limy cement is precipitated in much the same way, although at a lower temperature, as the scale that forms inside a kettle or a hot-water bottle.

Calcium carbonate ($CaCO_3$) is one of the more abundant of natural cements. It is among the more soluble of the common substances that may be dissolved in water in the ground and then be precipitated out of solution to fill the voids separating the mineral grains and ultimately to bind these grains together to make a solid rock. Obviously it will be most effective in regions where a large amount of lime is available, most typically from the solution of limestone. Another important natural cement is silica (SiO_2), which is also soluble, although less readily than $CaCO_3$. Iron oxide (Fe_2O_3), too, is a cementing agent, and, as mentioned earlier, wherever it is present the whole rock is correspondingly iron-stained or rust-colored.

TYPES OF SEDIMENTS
AND THEIR RELATED ROCKS

In the opening section of this chapter, the point was made that there are three major categories of sedimentary rocks: *clastic,* or fragmental; *chemical* precipitates; and *organic* deposits. Like many classifications of natural phenomena, these categories are more rigid than the actual state of affairs. There not only are gradational types from one category to the other, but there are also varieties that might just as logically be placed in one pigeonhole as the other, as well as a few that fit into none.

Clastic Sedimentary Rocks

The clastic rocks truly are secondary rocks since they consist of particles that are fragments of pre-existing rocks and these may range in size from blocks the size of boxcars down to colloids so fine as to remain in suspension almost indefinitely. Since these clastic rocks consist of fragments of other rocks, they are very likely to show a wide range of composition. So much so, in fact, that in setting up the classification of the clastic rocks the first property to be considered is the *size* of the particles that are cemented together to make a sedimentary rock, rather than the *material* of which they are made.

Take the word sand, for example. To most people sand has a double connotation: (1) it is a size term—all of us are conscious of the grittiness of sand in a bathing suit or between our teeth; and (2) for most of us it has a compositional meaning—the beach sand most of us think of ranges from white to a tawny yellow, and is likely to be thought of as consisting of quartz grains. In actuality many beach sands contain mostly feldspar grains as well as a liberal sprinkling of other sand-size rock particles and mineral grains. Sand can consist of almost any substance of sufficient durability. Along some of the rivers of the Atlantic states, sand bars are made of coal fragments. On some of the beaches of Hawaii the sands are coal black, too, but are composed of ground-up basalt. In the islands of the South Seas, the straw-colored sands of their fabled shores are made of fragmented coral heads, pieces of shells, and other organic debris.

The size terms that follow are in fairly common usage, though here they are arranged in a sequence and are defined in a more rigorous sense than is ordinarily employed. A major difficulty in trying to establish a hierarchy of sediment sizes is that there are no sharply defined, arbitrary boundaries between such things as sand and silt, for example, for these actually are part of an unbroken series.

A classification that has won wide acceptance is one that was originally proposed in 1922 by C. K. Wentworth and that has undergone some modification since. It has the advantages that almost all the terms used are everyday words, and that the size ranges are close to the ones in common usage, yet the actual dimensions are so arranged that they are in a geometric progression.

CLASSIFICATION OF CLASTIC SEDIMENTARY ROCKS

Sediment		Grain Size (in mm.)	Rock
GRAVEL	Boulder	256	
	Cobble	64	CONGLOMERATE
	Pebble	4	
	Granule		
		2	
SAND	Very coarse sand	1	
	Coarse sand	1/2	
	Medium sand	1/4	SANDSTONE
	Fine sand	1/8	
	Very fine sand		
		1/16	
MUD	Silt particle	1/256	SHALE or
	Clay		MUDSTONE

Almost all of the clastic sedimentary rocks are commonplace over much of Europe and the United States, and in centuries past they were widely used as building stones. The White House and the Capitol are both built of sandstone quarried a short distance down the Potomac from Washington, D. C. In the Victorian Era—especially the General Grant period—one of the favorite construction materials was the so-called brownstone—a drab red sandstone that regrettably will long outlast most of us. Many of Europe's celebrated landmarks are made of clastic sedimentary rocks—the castles at Heidelberg and Salzburg and most of the great ducal palaces of Florence are a few from among scores of famous examples. Sedimentary rocks were greatly preferred over granite by builders in those distant days because such stratified rocks split more readily along their bedding planes and also could be worked far more easily with the primitive hand tools of the time.

CONGLOMERATE.—These are cemented gravels, and the larger fragments may range in size from boulders with diameters of several feet down to particles the size of small peas (2 mm.). More commonly than not, the interstices or pore spaces between the larger boulders, cobbles, or gravel are filled with sand or mud and then the whole mass of sediment is cemented together to form a single rock (Fig. 4-8).

FIG. 4-8 *A piece of conglomerate.*

Breccia is a variety of conglomerate with angular rather than rounded fragments. The same word was used for pyroclastic volcanic rocks in Chapter III, Igneous Rocks and Volcanism. Here the same principle applies; if most of the large fragments in the rock are angular rather than rounded, the rock is a breccia—the adjective sedimentary or volcanic is usually added to indicate its origin.

SANDSTONE.—These sedimentary rocks consist of cemented sand grains and, as the table of sediment sizes shows, these are particles whose diameter ranges between 2 and 1/16 mm. Because this size occupies a middle ground of the classification, it is not surprising that gradations exist between sandstones and conglomerate on the one hand and shale on the other.

Sandstones very commonly include shale layers, or beds of sandstone may alternate quite regularly with beds of shale (Fig. 4-9) or with

FIG. 4-9 *Beds of hard sandstone alternate with beds of softer mudstone. Tyee formation, of Eocene age, Oregon. (Photograph by Parke Snavely.)*

lenses of conglomerate. Pure, well-sorted sandstone, as mentioned before, was often used as a building material before the advent of pre-stressed concrete or of light-weight aggregate. Quite a number of college campuses are adorned with pseudo-venerable examples of academic gothic—more often than not inhabited by the geology department—which were hewn out of sandstone blocks, and one in particular, at Stanford University, is a reincarnation in tawny sandstone of the Mission Era.

The cement is what determines the degree of induration, or hardness, of sandstones. In some the cement is weak, and individual grains separate readily from their neighbors; in others the cement may actually be tougher than the grains and when the rock breaks it breaks across them. When the cement is soluble it may dissolve readily and then the rock may seem to melt away, leaving a residue of sand grains behind.

Compositional differences affect the appearance of sandstone, too. Among the innumerable kinds of sandstone, two leading varieties are *arkose* and *graywacke*.

Arkoses are sandstones that are made up dominantly of quartz and feldspar grains, and therefore commonly are red or pink. As a rule, their grains are moderately angular, and their porosity may be high. Arkoses typically result from the erosion of granitic rocks, and for their formation they also require relatively rapid transportation and deposition without too much abrasion and rounding of the individual sand grains.

Graywackes were originally named for distinctive sandstones in the Harz Mountains of Germany. They are darker than arkoses, and although they commonly contain quartz and feldspar minerals, they have a much higher content of rock fragments—chiefly of the darker varieties of igneous and metamorphic rocks. These, too, are quite angular and unweathered, but unlike arkoses these sand-size particles are set in a clayey or silty matrix which at the time of deposition was essentially a muddy or clayey paste. Characteristically, these are dense, tough, well-indurated rocks whose colors are dark green, or gray, or black. Some graywackes appear to have been deposited in the sea, close in to a steep mountain range, and to have been in an environment where muddy water was carrying a large volume of sediment, including sand, which was moved but a short distance from its source and deposited so rapidly that little weathering and rock decay occurred.

This statement of the general characteristics of graywacke and its origin covers many of the points where a measure of agreement exists. The term is an unsatisfactory one, however, because a score of definitions now exist and almost as many interpretations of the origin of graywackes have been made as there are geologists engaged in studying these perplexing rocks.

SHALE.—This is a fine-grained rock whose original constituents were clay flakes and silt particles, and typically is now a laminated rock that splits readily into thin layers. Shale is an ancient term in our language; it comes from the Old English word *scealu,* meaning scale or shell. In geological terminology when we use a word as ancient as this it usually means we are dealing with a property so distinctive that it was recognized early enough to make its way into the rootstock of our native tongue.

Since these are rocks made of clay flakes and of individual mineral grains or rock particles less than 1/16 mm. in diameter, few of the constituents can be distinguished by the unaided eye. Under the microscope they can be re-
solved, and most shales are made of minute fragments of quartz, feldspar, and mica, and of rock fragments along with the ubiquitous clay flakes. Despite the small size of their individual grains, these are most important rocks since shales constitute very nearly half of the total of all sedimentary rocks.

Many shales are shades of dark gray or even black, especially if they contain organic matter. Other shales are dark red or green or particolored, depending on their iron content or upon the presence of other kinds of coloring matter.

Although *fissility,* or the ability to split along well-developed and closely spaced planes, is a leading property of shales, it is by no means characteristic of all of them. Some varieties whose composition and grain size appear to be comparable are not fissile at all, but break in massive chunks or small compact blocks. These are best given the descriptive name of *mudstone.*

Precipitated Sedimentary Rocks

In addition to the clastic rocks consisting of fragments and of mineral grains derived from pre-existing rocks, there is a second large clan of sedimentary rocks made of chemically precipitated materials. In the following pages these chemically formed rocks are discussed according to their composition as well as according to their mode of origin. This, unfortunately, makes for confusion since some varieties of rocks—specifically, the carbonates—may have similar compositions but unlike origins and thus of necessity the same term appears more than once in the classification.

EVAPORITES.—These are rocks that result primarily from the evaporation of water which contained dissolved solids. As the water becomes concentrated these ions separate out from solution until a crystalline residue is left.

Most familiar of all such rocks is *salt* ($NaCl$). Commonly it is formed when evaporation in an arm of the sea dominates over the inflow of water from outside. Judging from some of the renowned salt deposits of the world this must have been a process repeated many times over in order to have built up the great thicknesses that are found. The evaporation of an inland waterbody, such as Great Salt Lake, can also produce the same result, as anyone knows who has seen the nearby Bonneville Salt Flats—widely known for the ideal surface they provide for speed trials.

Layers of salt deposited in the geologic past are sometimes interbedded with other sedimentary rocks, and where these are near the surface, salt springs or "licks" may be found. From earliest times salt has been a highly prized commodity. Today we take it for granted, but in ancient times men gave their lives in battle to win control over salt deposits or to seize the trade routes over which it moved. Famous among these historic deposits were those of northern India—the locus of a flourishing trade before the time of Alexander—as well as those of Palmyra in Syria from whence salt moved by caravan to the Persian Gulf. The salt mines of Austria are deservedly famous, and in the Salzkammergut region around Salzburg they were in operation at least as early as 2000 B.C.

Gypsum ($CaSO_4 \cdot 2H_2O$) is closely related to salt in its origin. Like a great deal of the rock salt of the world, it, too, is a product of the evaporation of sea water. Gypsum is less soluble than salt and thus is precipitated earlier when sea water is evaporated. Along with it is also found an anhydrous (water-lacking) calcium sulphate ($CaSO_4$), *anhydrite*. Both gypsum and anhydrite come out of solution when about 80 per cent of the sea water has evaporated, and salt appears when 90 per cent has gone. Following the precipitation of salt, the very soluble halogens appear in such forms as NaBr (sodium bromide) and KCl (potash).

According to Pettijohn (1957) the evaporation of a 1,000-foot column of sea water would leave a residue of 9.4 feet of gypsum and anhy-

drite, 11.6 feet of salt, and 3 feet of potassium and magnesium-bearing salts. Considering the fact that gypsum and anhydrite make up strata many hundreds of feet thick in West Texas and New Mexico, an immense quantity of sea water must have been evaporated there in the geologic past. This is not meant to imply that an ocean thousands of feet deep was dried up leaving a thin layer of gypsum behind. This is an unreasonably difficult answer to the problem, nor does it take care of the question that immediately arises were simple evaporation to be the answer, and that is the absence of the extensive bodies of salt that should be associated with the gypsum beds.

An explanation advanced by P. B. King for the gypsum of West Texas is that water in a shallow, sun-warmed lagoon might reach the temperature and concentration where calcium sulphate would be precipitated, and this would be skimmed off, allowing the NaCl-rich residual water to flow back to sea before the stage would be reached where salt would come out of solution. Then more gypsum-carrying water could come in again and the process would be repeated. Were such a basin to be a subsiding one, an immense thickness of evaporites could accumulate without the water necessarily being deep. Studies by L. I. Briggs (1958) show that the saline deposits of Michigan may have been formed by a continuous inflow without the necessity of emptying and refilling if the proper balance were maintained between evaporation and influx of sea water.

There are many other kinds of evaporites, of minor significance in volume but of major consequence economically. Among these are *borax* ($Na_2B_4O_7 \cdot 10H_2O$), a compound of sodium-boron-oxygen and water, and *potash* (KCl), both of which are found in lakes or lake deposits of desert regions, such as the Mojave Desert in California.

CARBONATE ROCKS.—These are rocks that are chiefly compounds of calcium or magnesium with carbonate, generally in the form of calcite

($CaCO_3$) or dolomite ($CaMg(CO_3)_2$). These two rocks also have an organic origin as well, but the particular varieties described here appear to be primarily chemical deposits.

Travertine is a good example of a limy deposit that appears to have been deposited from spring waters saturated with calcium carbonate. It is of no great geologic significance, but plays a disproportionately large role in human affairs since it is so greatly favored as an architectural material. It is soft and readily worked, has an interesting array of colors—generally pale yellow or cream colored if pure, brown and darker yellow if it contains impurities—and often shows pronounced banding in wonderfully complex, curving patterns. *Tufa,* or *calcareous tufa* as it is sometimes called to distinguish it from volcanic tuff, also forms in springs and lime-saturated lakes, although to some degree its deposition seems to be fostered by the work of lime-secreting algae. Tufa and travertine when cut and polished make a building stone much favored for the lobbies of banks, building and loan associations, and the large railway terminals of a past era. Great quantities of tufa are imported from Italy and, as might be anticipated, much of monumental Rome is built of tufa, including Bernini's columns that nearly encircle the piazza in front of St. Peter's.

In dry countries, such as West Texas, the ground surface may be mantled with a crust-like cap of lime rock known as *caliche.* This was precipitated through the evaporation of ground water carrying $CaCO_3$ in solution which was drawn to the surface by capillarity.

No unequivocal evidence exists for the direct chemical precipitation of limestone from sea water, although a strong case can be made for the snow-like blanket of white, limy ooze on the sea floor of the Great Bahamas Bank. This appears to be a direct precipitate from the shallow, sun-heated, saturated sea water covering this shoal, and is a finely divided, mud-like deposit of microscopic crystals of aragonite, a chemically unstable form of calcium carbonate.

Another curious type of direct limy precipitate is the variety of limestone known as *oölite.* This is a limestone made of minute spherical grains of $CaCO_3$ the size of fish roe, from which it derives its name from the Greek word *oö* for egg + *lithos* for stone. Although the origin of this curious variety of limestone is debated, little doubt seems to remain that it results from the chemical precipitation in water of layers of $CaCO_3$ around a nucleus—perhaps in much the same way that layers of pearl shell are built up.

SILICEOUS ROCKS.—These are rocks made largely of chemically precipitated silica. A representative, although minor, type is *sinter.* This is a spongy or porous deposit of silica (SiO_2) that accumulates around hot springs or that builds up pedestals at the base of active geysers, such as those at Yellowstone.

A far more widely occurring siliceous rock is *chert,* a name serving as a blanket to cover a host of varieties of very dense, hard, nonclastic rocks made of microcrystalline silica. One familiar form is *flint,* which occurs in dark-colored siliceous nodules. These very often are found embedded in limestone. Since flint is uniformly textured, has a conchoidal fracture much like obsidian, and is easy to chip and at the same time retains a sharp edge, it proved to be the ideal strategic material for arrow- and spear-points in the Stone Ages of Europe and the east and central United States. In what was perhaps a braver day than ours, flints were essential for survival on the frontier, not only to strike sparks from steel for fire but also to fire the flintlock gun of the eighteenth and nineteenth centuries. Red varieties of the same rock commonly are called *jasper.*

Sometimes chert is found by itself in bedded deposits, thin-bedded as a rule and generally dark-colored. These chert beds are composed of very dense, closely fractured rocks that break up readily into small angular blocks (Fig. 4-10).

The origin of chert remains a vexatious problem. Much of the difficulty may be explained

Calif. State Div. of Mines Bull. 181, p. 397.

FIG. 4-10 *Bedded chert in the Franciscan For-mation, Marin County, Calif. The layers have been crumpled into nearly recumbent folds. (Photograph by Mary Hill.)*

on the same ground as the unlike interpretation of the elephant which was touched by the blind men in the fable, each one of whom held a different part. Unquestionably chert formed in more than one way and this may make for spirited arguments between people holding different views.

Among the preferred hypotheses are (1) that chert forms from direct chemical precipitation of SiO_2 on the sea floor, (2) that the silica is introduced after the rocks in which it is found were deposited and that this silica brought in by solutions has *replaced* parts of the original host rock. This is a process much like the one involving the replacement of woody fibers by silica in the making of petrified wood.

The source of the free silica from which the cherts are made is not clear. In part it may be supplied by springs on the sea floor, in part from magmatic sources such as submarine lava flows, or possibly from silica leached out of beds of volcanic ash, or from layers of organi-cally formed silica, such as strata containing shells of microscopic marine plants as the *dia-toms* or animals as the *radiolaria,* or finally from the weathering of silica-rich rocks.

Organic Sedimentary Rocks

These are rocks that are made of the remains of organisms, both animals and plants. *Coal* is an excellent illustration since it consists of partially decomposed remains of land plants. Much coal contains finer plant remains, such as spores, in spite of the popular view that it is a chaotic jumble of fallen trunks and tangled roots which were once set in a miasmic marsh peopled with monsters winging their way through a canopy of bizarre trees or slithering over the floor of the swamp.

With loss of hydrogen, coal moves along a progression from lignite (brown coal) to bituminous, to anthracite, and finally to graphite or pure carbon (these last two forms are regarded by many as metamorphic rocks).

The most abundant of the organic sedimentary rocks is limestone, and probably most examples of this particular rock are truly organic rather than being chemically precipitated. Some limestones have been built up by organisms as lime-secreting algae or the patient coral —builder of the great calcareous edifices of the tropic sea and whose greatest monument, the Great Barrier Reef, stretches for 1,200 miles along the coast of eastern Australia.

Beyond any reasonable doubt, some limestones are made of the tiny skeletons of such animals as coral, still preserved substantially in the positions of growth, or of $CaCO_3$ deposited directly by other lime-secreting organisms. Other limestones consist of fragmental calcareous debris and are comparable in many respects to sandstone, only the grains here are small pieces of fossil shells or fragments of coral rather than quartz or feldspar. Such clastic limestones, by their very nature, are likely to grade into limy shale on the one hand with increasing muddiness of the original sediment and into calcareous sandstone on the other if significant amounts of sand were present.

An interesting and perplexing accompaniment of many limestones is the very closely related rock, *dolomite,* which is an example of a monomineralic rock since it consists of the mineral dolomite, $CaMg(CO_3)_2$. Both limestone and dolomite look very much alike; the most practical field distinction between the two is that lime-stone will effervesce, or fizz, if cold hydrochloric acid (HC1) is dropped on it, while dolomite remains inert.

Limestone grades imperceptibly into dolomite when increasing amounts of magnesium enter into its composition. In some places dolomite occurs as widely spread layers or beds interbedded in a seemingly conformable way with ordinary limestone strata. In other occurrences, dolomitic masses cut across limestone layers or follow fracture patterns cutting the limestone in very much the same fashion that some hypabyssal igneous rocks do. For such dolomite masses, the belief is rather widely held that they are the result of partial replacement of calcite in the limestone by magnesia-bearing solutions. For the interbedded, rhythmically alternating layers of limestone and dolomite the evidence is less clear-cut. Some geologists believe that the dolomite layers were precipitated directly on the sea floor. Others take the view that the dolomite layers represent selectively replaced layers of limestone, and here there is an opportunity for further debate: (1) was the original limy material replaced by magnesia very shortly after deposition, or (2) did this chemical alteration occur long afterward when the limestone was completely lithified? To none of the queries can an absolute yes-no answer be given, but then geology would not be much of a challenge if there were no problems left to solve.

An interesting, although relatively minor, type of organically derived sedimentary rock is *diatomite.* Typically, this is a finely laminated, light-colored, sometimes brittle shale which includes myriad remains of diatoms. These are microscopically ornate, single-celled plants that proliferate by the uncounted millions in the surface waters of the colder seas of the world. This floating pasture of nearly invisible protoplasm is the chief food supply for the far-ranging Antarctic whales.

Unlike the plants with which most of us are familiar, these minute, free-floating, single-celled organisms are encased in tiny shells shaped

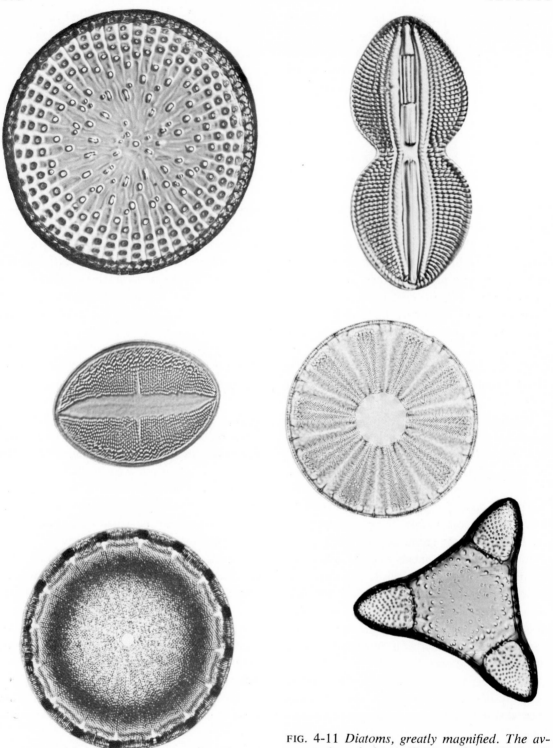

FIG. 4-11 *Diatoms, greatly magnified. The average size of these siliceous plant remains is about 50 microns—that is, about 2/1000 of an inch. (Photographs by G. Dallas Hanna, California Academy of Sciences.)*

much like an old-fashioned round pillbox and made of glass-like silica extracted from sea water (Fig. 4-11). When these plants die, their microscopic remains sift down through the water to accumulate on the sea floor. There they ultimately harden into shale with an above-average silica content. Such organically derived shales are typical of the central part of the California Coast Ranges and of some of the lands bordering the Mediterranean, where this type of deposit, to which we give the name of diatomite, is called tripoli.

Chalk is roughly comparable in its origin, in that it consists of organically formed calcite, and is a relatively pure deposit containing the remains of the minute, free-floating, single-celled animals, the *foraminifera,* whose tiny shells are made of calcium carbonate. Some chalk deposits, such as those near Dover, England, are 100 million years old, and the truly remarkable thing about them is how little alteration or recrystallization they have undergone in all this time.

Suggested References

Briggs, Louis Isaac, Jr., 1958, Evaporite facies, Journal Sedimentary Petrology, v. 28 No. 1.

Dunbar, C. O., and Rodgers, John, 1949, Principles of stratigraphy, John Wiley and Sons, New York.

Fenton, C. L., and Fenton, M. A., 1940, The rock book, Doubleday and Co., New York.

Grabau, A. W., 1924, Principles of stratigraphy, A. G. Seiler, New York.

Krumbein, W. C., and Sloss, L. L., 1951, Stratigraphy and sedimentation, W. H. Freeman and Co., San Francisco.

Pettijohn, F. J., 1959, Sedimentary rocks, Harper and Bros., New York.

Schrock, Robert, 1948, Sequence in layered rocks, McGraw-Hill Book Co., Inc., New York.

Twenhofel, W. H., 1926, Treatise on sedimentation, Williams and Wilkins Co., Baltimore.

Wayne, W. J., 1958, Let's look at some rocks, Geological Survey, Indiana Dept. of Conservation, Bloomington, Indiana.

Williams, Howel, Turner, F. J., and Gilbert, C. M., 1954, Petrography, W. H. Freeman and Co., San Francisco.

Intensely deformed metamorphosed sedimentary rocks at Convict Lake, Calif. Small contortions and dislocations of the bedding surfaces along faults are visible in the syncline in the center of the picture. (Photograph by John Haddaway.)

V

Metamorphic Rocks

A geologist studying igneous and sedimentary rocks has an advantage over one investigating the metamorphic rocks, in that some of the two other kinds form on the Earth's surface in environments where they can be observed.

A difficulty with understanding the origin of the metamorphic rocks is that no one has ever seen a metamorphic rock being formed, and for this reason much of our thinking about them is pure conjecture. This is not to say, however, that it is as fanciful as the speculations of science fiction; there are strongly limiting physical and chemical boundaries within which any theory of metamorphism must operate.

What, then, are some of the distinctive characteristics of these difficult rocks that serve to make them a group apart? In the first place they are derived rocks, as the name (taken from the Greek, meaning to change in form) indicates. In a more familiar usage, the same basic word is employed when we speak of the metamorphosis of a caterpillar into a butterfly.

Secondly, they are crystalline rocks, in roughly the same sense that the nonglassy igneous rocks are, but metamorphic rocks have not crystallized from a molten phase, such as lava. Most of them seem to have changed over from whatever they were originally to their new crystalline condition without becoming fluid, although many have been deformed plastically during recrystallization. Thus, they show many of the patterns, such as contorted parallel bands resembling the layers in marble cake, that are associated with flowage but not necessarily with liquidity.

Since recrystallization is the dominant element in the formation of the metamorphic rocks, accompanied in some cases by readjustment or rearrangement of many of the new minerals so that they occupy less volume, many hold the opinion that the process of metamorphism takes place within the crust—often at considerable depth—and that heat, pressure, and chemical activity operating through long periods of time are essential elements in the formation of metamorphic rocks, developing new minerals, crystal alignments, and structures that are in equilibrium with their new environment.

Let us illustrate with slate, one of the more familiar metamorphic rocks. It has been used for centuries as a roofing material, and, despite the advent of many synthetic substitutes, it remains the nearly ideal material for blackboards. Two properties are responsible for its desirable attributes: (1) good quality slates are dense and uniformly fine-textured rocks, and (2) they split, or cleave, along nearly perfect plane-parallel, closely spaced surfaces. This property is called *rock cleavage* to distinguish it from the *mineral cleavage* of such things as mica crystals.

The two attributes, mineral cleavage and rock cleavage, are related, however. Rock cleavage develops best when a large number of minerals with highly developed cleavage are so lined up that if one crystal fails under stress, the next gives way, then the next, and so on until through a kind of chain reaction the rock splits along a plane resulting from the cumulative effect of myriads of failures along the cleavage surfaces of parallel and aligned crystals.

It is in the near-perfect parallel alignment of mica flakes that slate differs from any of the rocks that we have studied heretofore. In shale the clay flakes and minute sedimentary particles are aligned, it is true, but not with the perfection found in slate.

Is there a significant difference between shale and slate in their chemical composition? The answer is no, with the exception, perhaps, that mica contains somewhat less water of crystallization than do the clay particles of shale. Clearly, then, something has happened to shale to convert it to slate. This has been a change involving a recrystallization of the minerals from clay to mica and a realignment of the individual mica flakes so that their cleavage planes are oriented parallel to one another instead of at random as in an igneous rock where they crystallized directly from solution.

Another important distinction between a shale and a slate is that the cleavage, which is indeed the hallmark of a slate, does not necessarily coincide with the original stratification. A close look at a slate sometimes will show sandy streaks, or flattened-out fossils, or some relic pattern inherited from the original fabric of the sedimentary rock, all cutting across the cleavage planes in the slate.

Geologists interpret all these lines of evidence to mean that an original rock, such as a fine-grained, laminated shale composed of clay particles, when subjected to high pressure was recrystallized to form a slate. In the process of recrystallization the clay flakes were altered to mica, and the new minerals were rearranged so that they were aligned parallel to one another and at right angles to the principal direction of the pressure which was applied to them.

This example of the conversion of shale to slate by recrystallization under directed pressure

and heat within the Earth's crust is an illustration of only one type of metamorphism. Unfortunately, the products of metamorphism do not lend themselves to such tidy systems of classification as do the igneous or sedimentary rocks. Reasons include the inaccessibility of the environment where these changes occur, their complex nature, and, most importantly, metamorphism generally involves at least three major elements—heat, pressure, and chemical activity. These may vary enormously; in some circumstances pressure clearly has been ascendant, in others chemical processes appear to have a leading role, yet in others the changes appear to be primarily the result of local heating.

The processes, their consequences, and the resultant types of some representative metamorphic rocks are listed in the table below so that their relationships relative to one another are made more apparent.

TYPE OF PROCESS	ROCK
a.) Heat dominant	
Contact metamorphism	*hornfels*
b.) Chemical-fluids dominant	
Hydrothermal metamorphism .	*serpentine*
c.) Directed-pressure dominant	
Dynamic metamorphism	*mylonite*
d.) Directed pressure and heat	
Regional metamorphism	
	slate
foliated	*schist*
	gneiss
	marble
nonfoliated	*quartzite*
e.) Uniform pressure and heat	
Plutonic metamorphism	*migmatite*

Contact Metamorphism

This variety of metamorphism is one in which heat played the leading role with chemical activity and pressure cast in secondary parts, the heat being supplied by an igneous body which has invaded the Earth's crust. The name is derived from the fact that this sort of metamorphism is most likely to be found in the shell, or halo, or *aureole* as it is called, in contact with and surrounding an igneous intrusion.

The simplest illustration of what is meant by contact metamorphism commonly will be found in the zone immediately adjacent to a dike or sill. If these hypabyssal igneous rocks have been injected into shale, for example, very commonly there will be a baked or hardened band a few inches or a few feet wide immediately next to the now-solidified igneous rock. The clay minerals in the original shale have been changed in much the same way that clay is fired in a kiln to make bricks or pottery.

Larger intrusions, such as batholiths and stocks, make their influence felt over a wider range. The wall rock next to the intrusion may be converted into a dense, hard, nonlayered rock called *hornfels*. Normally, these metamorphic rocks are not layered or banded, although they may be cut by such great numbers of closely spaced fractures that they separate readily into small angular fragments. Their mineral composition is highly variable, because they can be derived from such a host of original rock types—depending in part upon what kinds of rock were brought in contact with an intrusive body. Very often their texture is so fine-grained that new minerals formed through recrystallization are too small to be recognized by eye but have to be identified under the microscope.

Other changes induced by heating a rock may be brought about by reactions between minerals already present. An example would be the conversion of dolomite into an olivine-bearing marble:

$$2CaMg(CO_3)_2 + SiO_2 = 2CaCO_3 +$$
$$Mg_2SiO_4 + 2CO_2$$
$$\text{dolomite} + \text{silica} = \text{calcite} +$$
$$\text{olivine} + \text{carbon dioxide}$$

This means that a dolomitic rock with some quartz sand included in it when heated will have carbon dioxide liberated and driven off as a gas, leaving behind a rock composed of calcite and olivine crystals.

Hydrothermal Metamorphism

Not only is an immense quantity of heat liberated around an igneous intrusion, but great amounts of high-temperature gas and fluids also are freed. Very often these volatile elements of a magma travel for long distances through the enclosing host rocks. These fluids and gases are chemically potent and react readily with many of the minerals they encounter. This means that new material may be introduced into a rock as part of the processes of metamorphism, rather than simply a chemical rearrangement and recrystallization of the minerals already there. Or, conversely, material may be subtracted.

An example is the change of olivine to serpentine. Olivine is an unstable mineral chemically, and in rocks where it is abundant, as in dunite, the rock is altered readily from gabbro to serpentine when it is attacked by chemically active hot waters coming from an igneous intrusion. The fact that this type of metamorphism is one chiefly involving the addition of water is brought out by comparing an average formula of serpentine, $Mg_3Si_2O_5(OH)_4$, with olivine, $(Mg,Fe)_2SiO_4$, for here the principal change has been the loss of iron and the addition of the hydroxyl (OH) ion from water.

Since the hydrothermal metamorphism of dunite and related rocks which are high in iron and magnesium and low in silica is achieved largely through the addition of water, this means serpentine usually takes up a larger volume than the parent rock from which it is derived. As a result of this swelling, serpentine commonly is brecciated, and may be cut by a multitude of cracks and fractures. Sometimes these fractures will be filled in later with white veins of dolomite, and these make a bold and striking contrast to the prevailingly dark green of the serpentine. This unusual green rock, cut by white veins which in turn cross-cut one another in a most complex pattern, bears the picturesque name of *verde antique* and in a bygone age was greatly favored for the walls of florist shops, funeral parlors, and the lobbies of small-town hotels.

Serpentine itself is more likely to be a somber, dark green, or even black or red rock that will take a high polish. For this reason it is favored for bank lobbies, store fronts, and the foyers of buildings. It can be seen in the United States perhaps most strikingly in the imposing columns in the rotunda of the National Gallery of Art in Washington, D. C., as well as in the United Nations building in New York.

Dynamic Metamorphism

In localized parts of the Earth, crustal stresses may have built up to the point where rocks are sheared and crushed along large fracture planes which are known as faults. We shall see some of the effects of the operation of these forces when we discuss faulting (Chapter VI). Here we are concerned primarily with the small-scale changes brought about by the crushing and granulation of rocks at moderate depth under the application of severe local stress, but without the high temperatures that are characteristic of deeper burial.

The principal change in rocks subjected to the lateral stress developed along the slippage planes of large faults is the shearing, rolling out, and grinding up of mineral and rock fragments to ultimately produce metamorphic rocks with markedly parallel, lens-shaped, and banded patterns. This kind of metamorphism does not cause chemical changes to any pronounced degree—it is primarily responsible for a mechanical rearrangement, principally a realignment or even crushing of the more susceptible minerals.

Not all the minerals in rocks are equally resistant to such duress; they are much like people in this regard—some are stubborn and unyielding, others are pliant and readily molded. In a rock reshaped by dynamic or stress metamorphism, susceptible, flake-like minerals such as mica may be drawn out in parallel streaky bands or layers, while the more obdurate ones, such as feldspar, stand out as rounded or even lenticu-

lar, eye-like clots—in fact, they are called by the German word for eyes, *augen*.

A representative example of dynamic metamorphism is the rock *mylonite*. The name comes from the Greek word for mill, and these are rocks that in a figurative sense were caught in the geologic mill and ground until they were reduced to powder. The minerals in the original rock are crushed into minute fragments and may be completely pulverized. These are not loosely consolidated or friable rocks, however, but are completely recrystallized and may be as hard and durable as flint. They actually may be converted into glass-like, streaky material resembling obsidian.

A microscope usually is needed to determine the character of a mylonite, for it will appear as a hard dense rock with few, if any, visible minerals. It is only under magnification that they can be seen to consist of angular, minutely brecciated mineral fragments which are recrystallized to form a metamorphic rock.

Regional Metamorphism

This somewhat ambiguous term is used for metamorphic rocks that characteristically are exposed on the Earth's surface over broad areas, sometimes many thousands of square miles. Such wide expanses of crystalline rock—both igneous and metamorphic—were given the name of "shields" many years ago, and they were regarded as the foundation of the continents. Two well-known examples are the Canadian shield, the broad expanse of igneous and metamorphic rocks marginal to Hudson Bay and extending southward into Minnesota and Wisconsin and eastward across Labrador, and the Fenno-Scandian Peninsula, which includes most of Finland, Sweden, and Norway. In both of these shields, as well as in similar areas elsewhere, metamorphic rocks of great variety crop out, to the virtual exclusion of most other types. This is interpreted to mean that these rocks have been laid bare through erosion on a subcontinental scale and we know of them only through the stripping away of their original cover. Such rocks, with so wide a distribution, must have a more general cause than the heat generated by a single igneous intrusion, or the reactions produced by chemically activated water, or the grinding effect of movement along a fault plane.

Because of its widespread occurrence, this type of metamorphism is sometimes given the name of regional, but a more meaningful term is *dynamo-thermal,* which emphasizes that recrystallization is brought about by heat and directed pressure working in unison.

The outline near the beginning of this chapter lists two major categories of rocks in this class: nonfoliated and foliated. Foliated rocks—the word comes from the Latin, *foliatus,* meaning leaved—are those having well-developed rock cleavage in some varieties, and characterized by the parallel orientation of their tabular minerals and varying degrees of banding, or color layering.

FOLIATED ROCKS.—*Slate,* from the Old French word, *esclate,* or slat, demonstrates the nature of dynamo-thermal metamorphism. As already mentioned, slates are usually derived from finely laminated rocks such as shale, when the original clay particles were recrystallized to mica flakes under directed pressure and heat. Slates can be made from other fine-textured rocks, as volcanic tuffs, and very often these produce the more colorful varieties, such as red, green, and dark brown slates.

Schist, from the Greek word, *schistos,* cleft, or *schizein,* to split (we see the same word in schizophrenia, meaning a split personality, or in schism, meaning a division of opinion within a group), is probably the most widely occurring of metamorphic rocks. Slates grade into schists with increasing grain size. All schists include tabular, flaky, or even fibrous minerals in their composition, and the extent to which these are developed in parallel orientation determines to a considerable degree whether or not schistosity, the characteristically wavy or undulatory rock

cleavage, develops. Many schists split readily into tabular blocks. These are the familiar flagstones (Fig. 5-1) so widely used throughout Europe in courtyards and for castle walls, and in this country for fireplaces, patios, and barbecues. Some schist makes a good building stone because of this tabular habit; its edges are easily trimmed and it can then be used in much the same way as bricks.

Schists can be made from a wide variety of rocks by recrystallization under directed pressure and moderately high temperature. In the main, schists are rocks whose original grains and minerals were small, many of which on recrystallization were converted to plate-like minerals such as mica. Among the many rocks that are likely candidates for metamorphosis to schist

FIG. 5-1 *Foliated rocks (schist) used as roofing material in the Alps near Zermatt, Switzerland. The mountain in the background is the famous Matterhorn, which is composed of highly foliated regionally metamorphosed rocks.*

FIG. 5-2 *Folded calcareous schist derived from a thinly bedded clayey limestone.* (*Photograph by William Garnett.*)

---

are mudstone, muddy sandstone, basalt and other dark igneous rocks, and clayey limestone (Fig. 5-2).

Gneiss, an old Saxon miners' term for a rock which is rotted or decomposed (pronounced as though it were actually spelled nice), is a banded rock, usually with layers of light-colored minerals alternating with dark-colored bands (Fig. 5-3). This is a coarser-grained rock than the other two foliates described above. In fact, the size of the quartz and feldspar crystals it contains is about the same as in granite—the rock from which very often it is made. Gneiss can be derived from other coarse-grained igneous rocks, too, such as diorite and gabbro. Recrystallization of the rock has rearranged the minerals so that most of the light-colored ones are concentrated in one layer, while the dark ferromagnesian ones are grouped in another; these light- and dark-colored bands alternate rhythmically through the rock. These bands, unlike the cleavage planes of slate, do not make uniformly parallel planes that continue for long distances, but more commonly are strongly distorted. They probably were deformed plastically—that is, although the rock was still in the solid phase it was able to flow, in about the same way that butter or sheet lead can be made to do without becoming liquid at all.

Gneisses do not have the highly developed rock cleavage of slate or schist. In spite of the roughly uniform spacing of their bands, they break in about the same unpredictable fashion as a piece of granite does when struck a hammer blow.

NONFOLIATED ROCKS.—These are rocks that were shaped by the same processes as those responsible for the foliated rocks, but they are not banded nor do they have well-developed rock cleavage. Two leading examples are *marble,* which consists of the mineral calcite whose composition is $CaCO_3$, and *quartzite,* which has quartz as its leading constituent.

Marble is the coarsely crystalline equivalent of limestone, and thus in the majority of cases very likely had an organic origin. In limestone, the organic material very often is still visible as shells or structures built by lime-secreting plants, such as algae, or animals, such as coral. In marble, these traces of past life very largely are erased. Marble is a good example of a metamorphic rock which has undergone a physical transformation without necessarily having undergone any drastic change in chemical composition.

Under sufficiently high temperatures and pressures the lime of the original rock was recrystallized—in many cases by accretion—around earlier formed seed crystals of calcite. If this process continues long a coarse-grained rock of nearly equidimensional crystals of calcite results,

FIG. 5-3 *Biotite gneiss from Uxbridge, Mass.* (*Courtesy of Ward's Natural Science Establishment, Inc.*)

and these will be visible to us in a rock which has a rather sugary texture.

Pure marble is snow white, and one of the most highly prized varieties from ancient times down to our day comes from the quarries of Carrara on the west coast of Italy. This is a remarkably uniformly-textured rock which is ideal for sculpture because of its freedom from impurities, as well as the fact that its hardness is no more than 3 since it consists of the single mineral, calcite. Granite, by contrast, is nearly as hard as steel.

All marble is not pure white and this is immediately clear to anyone who has observed it in banks, building façades, lobbies, public lavatories, and old-fashioned table tops and dressers. In general, the black and gray areas in marble probably are colored by carbonaceous matter, brown and red zones are made by iron oxide, and green reflects the presence of various iron- or magnesium-bearing silicate minerals.

Marble is the result of the metamorphism of limestone, and since many of these limy rocks once contained muddy or sandy layers, the silica present in such beds will be recrystallized, too. A fairly typical reaction under sufficiently high temperature is the following:

$$CaCO_3 + SiO_2 = CaSiO_3 + CO_2$$
lime + quartz = wollastonite + carbon dioxide

Wollastonite is a colorless, bladed mineral, commonly arranged in fan-shaped radiating needles that penetrate the host rock, marble. It is representative of a wide variety of related minerals that develop with increasing clay and sand content in impure limestone to yield the so-called *calc-silicate rocks* when they are metamorphosed. Commonly these rocks have higher specific gravity than marble, and of course become harder with increased silicification.

Quartzite is metamorphosed quartzose sandstone, and in it the pore spaces once separating the individual grains are filled with newly formed quartz. In some rocks, the so-called sedimentary quartzites, this quartz has been added to the al-ready existing sand grains. The ghost-like boundary separating the original quartz grain from the silica added to it may be barely discernible. The silica cement which fills in the pore spaces of the original sandstone may prove to be stronger than the sand grains themselves, and when the rock is struck a hammer blow it breaks through the grains, rather than around them.

Quartzites are nearly always light colored; light pinks or reds are very characteristic. Many are white or light gray, and with increasing amounts of impurities their colors darken until some may be black. Very often quartzites are interbedded with marble, calc-silicate rocks, and other rocks derived from sedimentary sources. Relic sedimentary structures, such as cross-bedding, are sometimes preserved and these are emphasized by slight color differences which superficially may resemble the banding in a gneiss.

Plutonic Metamorphism

This is the type of metamorphism believed to occur deep within the crust under conditions of very high pressure and elevated temperature. The pressure is more likely to be hydrostatic than directed as was the case in the making of the foliated rocks. By hydrostatic pressure we mean the pressure, for example, that bears down on a submarine deep in the sea. This sort of pressure, transmitted through liquids, is equal in all directions, not greater in one nor less in another as is true of directed pressure. Such a pressure—equal in all directions—is sometimes called the confining pressure, in order to eliminate the idea that it is necessarily restricted to objects immersed in a fluid.

The great pressures in these deeper realms of the crust are responsible for the formation of more compact, or denser, varieties of minerals. Minerals crystallizing in this metamorphic zone are likely to be stubbier or more equidimensional than elongate.

A striking characteristic of plutonic metamorphic rocks is their intimate association with intrusive igneous rocks. Often these two types of rocks will alternate with one another in a single outcrop; for example, there may be a layer of granitic material, then of schist, then of granite, then of schist, and so on.

An extreme example of plutonic metamorphism is the rock *migmatite,* taken from the Greek word *migma,* a mixture, and this, indeed, is what the rock looks like. In part, these rocks have the banded or layered appearance of gneiss, and yet in other parts of the outcrop, the constituent minerals will have the nonoriented, random, scattered pattern so typical of granite.

With the problem of the origin of migmatites we have traveled full circle, and once again are confronted with the vexing question raised in Chapter III on the origin of granite. In a migmatite in which igneous material interfingers with metamorphic in such an intimate fashion, how was the granite formed? Was the granite injected as a magmatic fluid into a pre-existing rock, such as gneiss; or was the gneiss transformed into granite by a replacement process? Strong support for the latter theory is given when the shadowy parallel alignment of minerals, say in a bordering schist, can be traced across an igneous contact and out into the granitic body itself. This is especially likely to be the case where the igneous body is a concordant one and the contact conforms to structural patterns within the body of metamorphic rocks.

Contrariwise, if a granitic body has sharp, clear contacts cutting abruptly across the grain of the enclosing wall rocks, and if in addition the granite holds unmodified angular inclusions or *xenoliths* (a Greek word meaning stranger stones) within it, then very likely the granite had a truly magmatic origin and shouldered its way into the metamorphic shell encasing it.

To summarize, then, there are at least three very plausible ways in which granite may originate (there may be others, too, but these three are the most likely): (1) it may be truly magmatic and have invaded the upper levels of the Earth's crust as an igneous intrusion; (2) it may result from the melting or fusion of pre-existing rocks through the application of enough heat to melt them; and (3) it may be the result of recrystallization of some other wholly different kind of rock by the movement of ionic solutions through it and its conversion into granite by the essentially metamorphic process of *granitization.* To this metamorphic process the Greek-derived name of *metasomatism,* or change in body, is given, and in this application the word means the transformation of one rock into another with a different chemical composition.

Thus, rocks may progress through an evolutionary cycle of their own. They may be created in Vulcan's forge, speaking metaphorically, by crystallizing from a molten solution, magma. Exposed at the Earth's surface through long stretches of geologic time, their constituent minerals when weathered out are redeposited as sedimentary rocks. Should these later be buried deeply enough, they may be recrystallized as metamorphic rocks, such as hornfels, slate, schist, marble, or any one of a wide variety of types. Then if circumstances are favorable, they may be remelted, or they may be recrystallized through granitization to be reborn again, indistinguishable in every respect from their original igneous incarnation.

Suggested References

Barth, T. F. W., 1962, Theoretical petrology, John Wiley and Sons, New York.

Harker, Alfred, 1939, Metamorphism, Methuen and Co., London.

Mason, Brian, 1958, Principles of geochemistry, John Wiley and Sons, New York.

Ramberg, Hans, 1952, The origin of metamorphic and metasomatic rocks, Univ. Chicago Press, Chicago.

————, 1960, Metamorphism, in Encyclopedia Britannica, v. 15, p. 321-326.

Turner, F. J., and Verhoogen, J., 1951, Igneous and metamorphic petrology, McGraw-Hill Book Co., Inc., New York.

Tyrrell, G. W., 1929, The principles of petrology, E. P. Dutton and Co., New York.

Williams, H., Turner, F. J., and Gilbert, C. M., 1954, Petrography, W. H. Freeman and Co., San Francisco.

Deformed sedimentary strata. Murdafil, Iran.

(Photograph by Aerofilms and Aero Pictorial, Ltd., London.)

VI

Structural Geology

Earthquakes may forcibly remind us from time to time that the solid Earth is considerably less than solid; in fact, during one of them it may seem to have as much stability as a bowl of jello. Earthquakes are a tangible indication that stresses can build up in the Earth's crust to the point where rocks fracture suddenly, resulting in a shock which sets off vibrations that travel in all directions. It is these vibrations that topple buildings and that we call earthquake waves.

Other indications that the rocks of the Earth's surface are not stable have been known for a long time. For example, fossils of animals which once lived in the sea are now found far inland entombed in rocks of mountains thousands of feet above sea level. Fossil shells preserved in the rocks of the Tuscan hills were to the Renaissance genius, Leonardo da Vinci (1452-1519), sufficient evidence that the Appenines had once been covered by the sea. The same arguments were also advanced by Nicolaus Steno (1638-87) in Florence, who made the additional observation that horizontally stratified rocks not only could be lifted far above the level at which they were deposited, but also could be tilted as well, as much as 90°. Probably the most impressive example of this interchange of land and sea comes from the world's loftiest mountain, Everest, for high on its flanks are found water-laid rocks containing fossils of organisms that lived in the sea during the Eocene Epoch (about 60 million years ago).

The realization that forces working in the Earth's crust can bring about such drastic changes was a long time dawning. In ancient times, such things as deep canyons were thought to be the result of great convulsions. When men first speculated on the origin of sedimentary rocks, many people were quite willing to believe that layers of sandstone and conglomerate which are now standing vertically were deposited that way. Benedict de Saussure (1740-99)—one of the first alpinists, whose statue in Chamonix honors his first ascent of Mont Blanc (15,771 feet)—was one of the first men to make intelligent observations on the nature of the rocks exposed in such a lofty mountain range as the Alps. Even he required a long time to convince himself of the original horizontality of sediments. Before his time, mountains were much dreaded places, the abode of bandits, and travel over the high passes was difficult beyond anything most of us can conceive, even with the possibility of succor by the keg-bearing Saint Bernards. Until the rise of alpinism, mountains were shunned by educated people, unless they marched across them on an armed tour of their neighbor's territory. This avoidance of mountainous terrain greatly retarded the growth of geology, because if there is any realm where the science flourishes it is in the mountains. Here the greatest variety of rocks is displayed, and here the forces of erosion, such as glaciers and torrential streams, are vastly more effective than on populated plains.

RECENT DEFORMATION
OF THE EARTH'S CRUST

Much more than casual visits to the mountains are needed, though, to arrive at an understanding of the nature of the forces operating within the Earth which deform its rocks. This awareness in a popular sense owes its beginnings very largely to the work of Sir Charles Lyell (1797-1875), who wrote the first modern book concerned with the principles of geology.

Because Lyell was able to visit many lands, he acquired a world outlook conspicuously lacking among many of his Victorian contemporaries. To reach an understanding of the rates at which deformation proceeds there are few more favorable spots he could have visited than the shores of the Mediterranean. Buildings have been constructed along the shores of this nearly tideless sea for millennia, and because the more durable were made of stone, they have withstood the ravages of time and weather in this relatively dry climate remarkably well. Those built close to the shore serve as unusually sensitive recorders of changes in the level of the sea.

An example Lyell made much of is the three surviving columns of the Temple of Jupiter Serapis, not far from Naples (Fig. 6-1). The three columns have a line encircling them about 23 feet above sea level. Below this line each of the columns is riddled with holes throughout a band about 9 feet wide. These holes were bored by shallow-water shellfish. The uppermost line on each column represents a former stand of sea level, and the holes drilled by the sea-inhabiting mollusks further support the belief that the temple was once partially submerged.

The historical record bears out this conclusion. Apparently the temple was built around the second century B.C., and, although it was constructed on land, it must have started to subside shortly thereafter because a new floor was built on a fill of about 18 inches covering the original mosaic floor and false bases were built around the columns. At an unknown later date a fall of volcanic ash buried the court of the temple to a depth of about 12 feet and continued subsidence of the land allowed the sea to invade the entire structure. The 9-foot band on each of the columns where they are pierced by borings of marine organisms represents the depth of water between sea level and what was then the mud- and ash-covered floor of the Mediterranean.

When the land started to rise is not known. In medieval times the sea extended inland to the bluff behind the temple. Certainly the rise was well under way by A.D. 1503, for in that year, according to Lyell, Ferdinand and Isabella of Spain granted to the University of Puzzuoli "a portion of the land, 'where the sea is drying up' (che va seccando el mare)." Also, according to Lyell, the main rise of the land occurred at the time of the historically destructive eruption of Monte Nuovo in A.D. 1538. Then "the sea abandoned a considerable part of the shore, so that fish were taken by the inhabitants; and, among other things, Falconi mentions that he saw two springs *in the newly discovered ruins*" (Lyell).

This example, based on observations he made in 1828, demonstrated to Lyell that much of the deformation of the Earth goes on relatively slowly, and is a far cry from the catastrophic explanations appealed to by most of his contemporaries to account for the more striking elements of the landscape. His book, *The Principles of Geology* (1830), is the first genuine textbook of geology, and it exerted a profound influence on the Victorian world of letters. Tennyson, with many other literary lights of the period, was excited by Lyell's discoveries, as these emotion-charged passages indicate:

> There rolls the deep where grew the tree
>   O earth, what changes hast thou seen!
>   There where the long street roars hath been
> The stillness of the central sea.
>
> The hills are shadows, and they flow
>   From form to form, and nothing stands;
>   They melt like mist, the solid lands,
> Like clouds they shape themselves and go.
> IN MEMORIAM, 1850.

From Charles Lyell, *Principles of Geology*, 1830. By permission of John Murray (Publishers) Ltd.

FIG. 6-1 *Temple of Jupiter Serapis, near Naples, showing the zone of marine clam borings made in the columns during submergence.*

Scientifically, Lyell's idea of gradual, rather than catastrophic, change had a far-reaching effect in other fields than geology and greatly influenced the thinking of Charles Darwin, much of whose scientific training had been in geology before he was assigned as a naturalist to H.M.S. *Beagle* on its world-encompassing voyage.

Another example of slow change of level of the Earth's crust in historic time, also taken from the Mediterranean, is the Blue Grotto on the Isle of Capri. No mention of such a sea-flooded cave was made by the Romans, and since they were inveterate recorders of everything, it would be extraordinary indeed if such a remarkable phenomenon as the grotto, with its haunting blue light, were overlooked, especially since Capri was for years the favorite haunt of the Emperor Tiberius and his strange companions. Tiberius knew the site of the present Blue Grotto well and apparently it was one of his favorite resorts. In order to bring some light to the interior of the cave, which was then above the sea, he had a window cut in the limestone cliff. It is through this window that small boats enter the cave today. In other words, the island has sunk until the sea enters what was a window cut in Roman times, far above the floor from which sunlight is reflected through the now submerged door. All the rays, except blue, are filtered out to produce the ethereal lighting within the grotto. Here, then, is an example of land that sank in historic time, but did not rise again as did its counterpart at the Temple of Jupiter Serapis across the Bay of Naples.

These are relatively minor changes, however, compared to the subsidence now affecting nearly the entire economy of the Netherlands. Everyone knows that the coast of Holland is protected by dikes and that much of the country, including the cities of Rotterdam and Amsterdam, is below sea level. Few realize how unremitting and laborious a struggle must be waged to hold back the sea, because the coastal part of Holland is sinking at the rate of about 21 centimeters (8 inches) per century (Umbgrove, 1950). This makes the achievement of the Dutch all the more remarkable, as shown by the accompanying map (Fig. 6-2), also taken from Umbgrove, which outlines the area of the Netherlands won from the sea since A.D. 1200.

We might well ask here, how do we know that the land is actually sinking at any one place—might not the same effect be produced by a rise in sea level? The answer is yes—in part. Records of the tidal range are kept at most of the world's seaports, and these records indicate that beginning around 1890 sea level in all the oceans of the world started rising and that today the rate of rise is about 12 cm. (4¾ inches) per cen-

tury. This is the result of the general warming up of the Earth's climate in the past half-century, and the corresponding recession of the Greenland and Antarctic ice caps, as well as most of the world's glaciers, whose melt-waters have helped swell the volume of the sea. Such a universal shift in the level of the sea as this—whether up or down—is called a *eustatic change,* and on any coast where the effects of submergence are apparent, one has to determine whether or not this is the result of a local sinking of the land, or is the consequence of a eustatic rise of sea level.

The Dutch, then, are confronted by a double threat—the gradual sinking of the land on which they have built their nation, and the inexorable rising of the sea that beats against their shore.

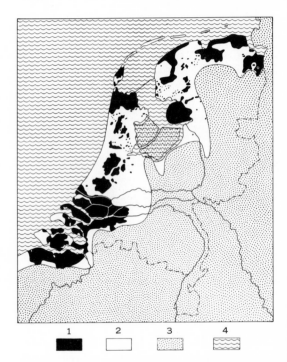

After J. H. F. Umbgrove, *Symphony of the Earth,* 1950. By permission of Martinus Nijhoff, The Hague, Netherlands.

FIG. 6-2 *Map of the Netherlands, showing reclaimed land. 1, land reclaimed since 1200; 2, land which would be flooded if not protected by artificial means; 3, land above sea-level; 4, the sea; combination of 3 and 4, land in process of being reclaimed.*

The motto of the ruling house, *Je Maintendrai* —I will maintain—are no idle words.

What do we actually know about the rates at which the Earth's crust is being deformed? The answer is not a great deal, because accurate surveying records go back only about two centuries, and in many cases the best surveyed areas are among the more stable parts of the Earth. Fortunately, precise surveys dating back around thirty years have been made in the Los Angeles region, a notably unstable area in more ways than one. According to Gilluly (1949), data obtained as the result of repeated leveling by the U. S. Coast and Geodetic Survey show that the region northeast of Long Beach rose in a broad arch about 7 inches in the period between 1931 and 1933, the year of the Long Beach earthquake. The Coast Survey also ran precise levels in 1906, 1924, and 1944 across Cajon Pass between Victorville and San Fernando in southern California. These measurements show that the entire pass where it crosses the San Gabriel-San Bernardino Mountains rose as a gentle arch during these thirty-eight years by nearly 8 inches—or at the rate of 20 inches per century.

As Gilluly points out, though these rates may appear modest indeed, with sufficient time—and time is a quantity not lacking in geology—such a rate yields an uplift of 400 feet in 25,000 years for the San Gabriel-San Bernardino Mountains. Mount Everest, at a comparable rate, could have reached its present height in around 2 million years, which is not unreasonable for what is known of the probable length of time required for the uplift of the Himalayas.

These examples of Earth movement have all been in a vertical sense, either the land sinking or rising, or, in the case of the Temple of Jupiter Serapis, doing both. It may come as a surprise that horizontal shifts have been recorded, too. Sometimes as along the San Andreas fault in California, described below, a slippage of one segment of the crust past another may be very dramatic. In 1906 roads, fences, etc., were off-

set along this fault by as much as 21 feet almost instantaneously. In addition to these abrupt displacements, repeated surveys show a gradual creep of points on one side of the fault past corresponding ones moving in an opposite direction on the other side without any discernible break on the surface of the ground.

Such slow adjustments are difficult to detect because it is necessary to assume that a base line some distance away from the affected area has not moved at all, and then the shift of other points relative to it may be determined by repeated triangulation. Figure 6-3 shows the relative movement of triangulation stations in the vicinity of San Francisco, California, in the period from 1882 to 1946 (Whitten, 1948) based on the assumption that the line from Mt. Diablo to triangulation station Mocho has remained fixed. The stations west of the San Andreas fault consistently have drifted northwestward, while stations east of the fault have moved about much more erratically.

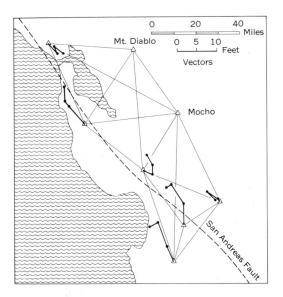

After C. A. Whitten, *Trans. Amer. Geophys. Union*, vol. 29, 1948. By permission.

FIG. 6-3 *Relative movement of triangulation stations in vicinity of San Francisco, based on the assumption that line from Mt. Diablo to Mocho has remained fixed.*

EVIDENCE IN THE LANDSCAPE
OF PREHISTORIC DEFORMATION

A person approaching the Palos Verdes Hills, the bold headland that partially shields the harbor of San Pedro in southern California, is impressed by the promontory's seaward slope which rises out of the sea like a cyclopean stairway. Wave-cut benches separated from one another by steep cliffs rise in thirteen steps to 1,300 feet above the sea. They are evidence that this part of the California coast has been elevated vertically nearly one quarter of a mile so

recently geologically that fossil sea shells preserved on the flat benches are identical with ones living today in the nearby ocean (Fig. 6-4).

Another, even more impressive, set of uplifted wave-cut platforms are those marginal to the coast of Peru. Some of them are 10-15 miles wide and are littered with marine shells, as fresh

FIG. 6-4 *Elevated marine terraces, Palos Verdes Hills, Calif. Terrace levels mark former marine planation surfaces cut when the land here stood lower with respect to the sea.* (*Photograph by John S. Shelton.*)

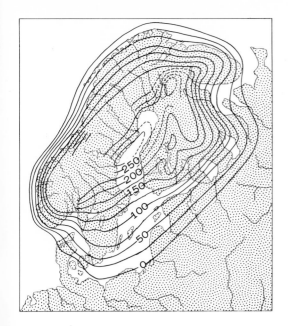 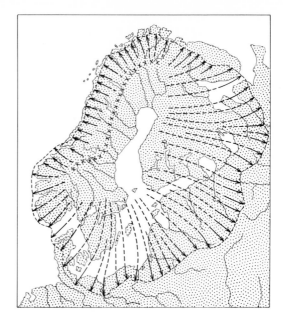

After R. A. Daly, *The Changing World of the Ice Age,* 1934. By permission of Yale University Press, Macmillan and Co., Ltd. and the Geological Survey of Finland.

FIG. 6-5 *Post-glacial uplift of Scandinavia. The map on the right shows distribution of the last glacial ice cap that covered the region. Arrows indicate flow directions, and the line of crosses shows the approximate position of axis of ice cap. The map on the left shows the amount of post-glacial uplift (in meters).*

---

appearing as though they had lived in the sea only yesterday.

The recent uplift of the interior of the Scandinavian Peninsula by about 900 feet is a well-known example of geologically recent deformation. Since the rate of uplift today is about 4 feet per century near the northern end of the Gulf of Bothnia, this means that many hundreds of square miles of land have been added to Finland in modern times. The lines on the map (Fig. 6-5) connect points of equal uplift, and indicate that the amount decreases outward from the Angarmanland region of Sweden. Since this is roughly the same general area as the maximum ice accumulation for the recently vanished glaciers of northern Europe, most geologists are convinced that the nearly thousand-foot rise of the land is a rebound of the Earth's crust result-

ing from the removal of the load imposed on it by the melting of a layer of ice approximately a mile thick. If so, the rise of Scandinavia did not precede the arrival of the ancestors of the Vikings by too many centuries.

THE RECORD IN THE ROCKS
OF ANCIENT DEFORMATION

Back in Chapter IV we learned that sedimentary rocks, as a rule, are deposited in horizontal layers known as strata (Fig. 6-6). Where these layers are strongly tilted, or even vertical, they have been deformed (Fig. 6-7). It is with this record of ancient deformation that the geologist is much concerned. By studying the *attitude* of the rocks—which in this context means their geometric orientation—he can tell a great deal about the past deformational history of a particular part of the Earth's crust. From a practical point of view a study of the geometry of the rocks, or *structural geology,* as it is known, is of utmost importance because, by projecting the attitude of the rocks as they are exposed at the surface of the Earth, the geologist is often able to predict the depth to ore-bodies, coal seams, or oil sands.

FIG. 6-6 *Effects of erosion of horizontal sedimentary strata in an arid region. The outcropping edges of more resistant strata simulate contour lines. (Photograph by William Garnett.)*

FIG. 6-7 *Steeply tilted strata adjacent to a fault, Dinosaur National Monument, Utah. (Photograph by Philip Hyde.)*

If the sedimentary rocks in our example originally were deposited horizontally, then their inclination was 0°. If forces operating within the Earth tilt them up until they are vertical, they have an inclination, or *dip* as it is called, of 90°. Thus, the dip is an *angle* measured between the surface of a layer of rock and a horizontal plane, such as the surface of the sea, or, as in the illustration, a level part of the Earth's surface (Fig. 6-8).

If we are considering a series of inclined rocks whose tilted bedding planes intersect the surface of the Earth, and we isolate a single stratum, or layer, this intersection makes a *line*. One of the properties of a line is that it has direction. For example, it may trend, or *strike* to use the geologic term, across country along a north-south line, or perhaps east-west, or more than likely at some intermediate direction (Figs. 6-8, 6-9). Directions on the Earth's surface are almost always given in terms of the compass, but of compass types there is a great variety. In sailing-ship days, when making a course good was difficult, compasses were divided into an

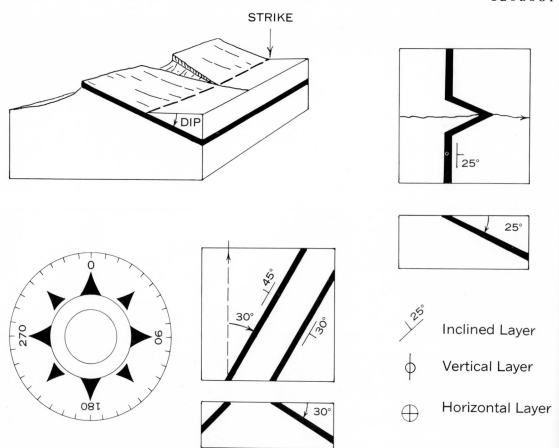

FIG. 6-8 *Sketches showing the relations between strike and dip, the 360-degree compass, and commonly used geologic map symbols.*

array of points, such as north-northeast, southeast by south, etc. Since there are 32 points in such a system, this makes an individual point 11°15′ from the next, which is a bit generalized.

About World War I, with the advent of faster, power-driven ships, the 360° compass came into general use at sea, and since it is now standard on ships large and small, as well as power boats and aircraft, and is the one used by all military services, we shall use it here. On such a compass, North is 0°, East is 90°, South is 180°, and West is 270°.

Obviously, any line can trend in two directions; for example, 270° or 90°. For convenience's sake, and to avoid confusion with the

amount of the dip, as we shall see in a moment, the three-digit number is customarily used for the strike. Thus, we say that a layer of rock strikes across country at 265°, rather than using its opposite bearing of 85°.

To summarize: The strike of a layer of rock may be defined as the direction (actually an angle measured from the north) taken by the line determined by the intersection of a horizontal and an inclined plane. In realistic terms the inclined plane is the surface of a dipping layer of rock, fault, or dike, etc.; the horizontal plane is an imaginary one determined by a level bubble in a surveying instrument.

The dip now can be defined more rigorously as the angle between a horizontal and an inclined plane, which is measured at right angles to the strike. The reason for this last qualifying clause is that this is the maximum possible angle that can be measured, and in no case, of course, can the angle exceed 90°. Furthermore, measuring the dip at right angles to the strike means that the dip has a direction, too. Usually, though, it is sufficiently accurate to express this direction in such general terms as northeast, southwest, etc.

To illustrate, if a stratum strikes 270°, it may dip north, or south, or vertically. To select a more complex case: if a layer strikes 185° it may dip northwest, southeast, or vertically. Let us suppose that the dip is 35° southeast. Then this would be written in a geologist's notes as 185°–35° SE. This final notation makes clear the reason for the explanation that has gone be-

fore, but to summarize—the thing to remember is that the three-digit number is for the direction of the strike; the two-digit number is for the angle of the dip, and the written direction is for the direction of the dip, as there are two possibilities.

In the field a geologist represents these attitudes of rocks on his map or aerial photograph by means of symbols. The more commonly used of these are shown in Fig. 6-8.

FOLDS

If layered rocks are compressed by forces active within the Earth's crust they may be deformed into wave-like structures. The ones resembling wave crests are called *anticlines*—from the Greek, to be inclined against itself (Figs. 6-10, 6-11), and the ones resembling wave

FIG. 6-9 *A strike ridge, or hogback, formed in dipping strata near Shiprock, New Mexico. (Photograph by John S. Shelton.)*

troughs are *synclines*—from the Greek, to lean together.

FIG. 6-10 *Types of folds.* A-D, *types of anti-clines and synclines.* A, *open;* B, *asymmetrical;* C, *overturned;* D, *recumbent.*

The sides of such folds are called *limbs* or *flanks.* A line along the highest part of each bed as it bends over the crest of such a fold as an anticline is the *axis.* It would correspond to the ridge line of a house roof, for example, just as the axis of a syncline corresponds to the keel of a ship. Another factor to remember is that not

always is the structure of the underlying rocks reflected directly in landforms on the surface. That is, anticlines do not necessarily make hills or mountains, nor synclines valleys.

Few anticlines or synclines show such regularity as those in Fig. 6-11. Much more frequently one limb will be steeper than the other, and such a fold is said to be *asymmetrical.* In this case the rocks in the two limbs dip in different directions by different amounts (Fig. 6-10B). With severe compression the folds may be *overturned,* in which case the two limbs dip in the same direction, but the strata in the lower limb are canted sometimes to the point where

FIG. 6-11 *Anticlinal and synclinal folds of the "Grande Chartreuse," north of Grenoble, French Alps. (Photograph by Swissair-Photo, A G, Zurich.)*

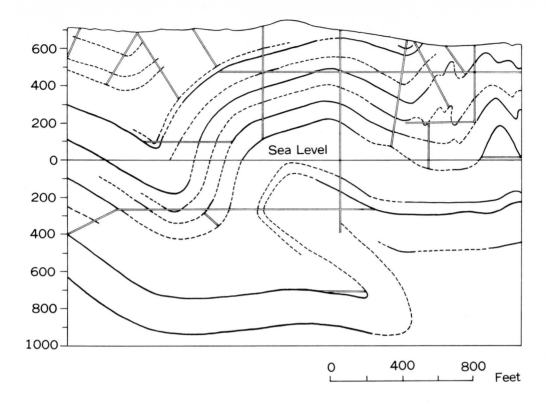

After N. H. Darton, 1940. By permission of U.S. Geological Survey.

FIG. 6-12 *Disharmonic folds. The cross section of the anthracite coal basin in northern Pennsylvania shows the lack of relation between subsurface structures and those near the surface of the ground.*

they are upside down. In an extreme case, the whole fold may be forced over on its side so that its axial plane (plane passed through the axes of all the individual layers) is horizontal, or very nearly so (Fig. 6-10D). Such a structure is called a *recumbent* fold (see Fig. 4-10) and some of them reach enormous size in the Alps.

Deep mines and oil wells demonstrate that very often the geometry of a fold deep underground may be very different from what it is at the surface. Such structures are called *disharmonic folds* (Fig. 6-12), and they are probably more typical than not of folding. Trying to second-guess what a fold at the surface will do at depth is the sort of gamble that makes the work of a geologist, especially a petroleum geologist, such an intellectually stimulating challenge.

Anticlines and synclines do not continue forever over the face of the Earth like corrugations on a tin roof. In many cases such folds seem to disappear underground if they are followed for any length along the axis. If this occurs, they are said to *plunge,* as shown in Figs. 6-13, 6-14.

Careful study of the diagram, supported by the evidence of the photograph of an actual plunging anticline, should bring out the following relationships more clearly than many paragraphs would.

1) Anticlines plunge in the direction that their sides converge (come together).
2) Synclines plunge in the direction that their sides diverge (spread apart).
3) In the diagram, stratum A is older than stratum B. Thus in anticlines it can be seen that the rocks become progressively older toward the axis; in a syncline they are younger.
4) The dip measured on the axis also gives a measure of the amount the fold plunges (Fig. 6-14). Note also that the strike of the beds where they cross the axis is at right angles to the axis in both the anticline and syncline.

Domes and basins are two other types of folds deserving of mention. In geological usage,

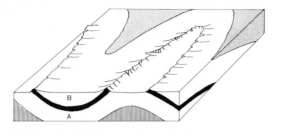

FIG. 6-13 *Plunging folds, in which the axis is not horizontal, but* plunges (*in this case toward the back of diagram*). *The strike of the ridge formed on the black stratum turns abruptly where the stratum crosses the trace of the axial plane.*

a dome is an anticline whose limbs dip outward in all directions (Fig. 6-15). Some domes may be nearly circular in plan, but commonly they are elongate and on a geologic map the various strata appear as long ellipsoidal rings. A basin is the counterpart of a dome in that it, too, is an enclosed fold, but the limbs dip inwardly toward the axis rather than outwardly as in a dome.

FIG. 6-14 *Looking eastward along an anticlinal fold that plunges westward, toward us. The strike of the beds changes from east-west on the flanks of the fold to north-south (at right angles to the axis) at the plunging end of the fold. Near Vernal, Utah. (Photograph by John S. Shelton.)*

FIG. 6-15 *Little Maverick Dome, northwest of Riverton, Wyoming. The strike of the beds changes abruptly at the plunging ends of the structure. (Photograph by John S. Shelton.)*

SALT DOMES

These bizarre geologic structures, though rare, have a disproportionately great economic significance. Typically, they rise underground as tall, thin, cylindrical columns of salt, perhaps a mile or so in diameter and as much as 15,000 to 20,000 feet high through the enclosing sedimentary material which they have pierced (Fig. 6-16). They have their most noteworthy de-velopment in North America along the coast of the Gulf of Mexico, where at least 150 are known. Salt domes are also important in Russia, bordering the Caspian Sea, where about the same number may exist. For more than a century such intrusions have been a source of salt in northern Germany, and they also occur in the Carpathians of Romania. Possibly the most interesting are those of Iran, because there the salt has forced its way to the surface where it flows out in glacier-like masses from the centers of eroded anticlines. Because of the dry climate the salt is not dissolved.

No salt domes reach the surface in the United States, so they are a striking example of a geologic structure known only through the partial evidence obtainable from deep oil wells and shallow salt and sulphur mines. At Avery Island, near New Orleans, in one of the better known salt domes of the Gulf Coast, the salt rises to within about 16 feet of the surface, and has been drilled to a depth of about 14,000 feet without reaching the base. Incidentally, knowledge of the occurrence of the oil trapped around the flanks of a salt dome was first discovered in a most unexpected way when an oil well being drilled in 1901 by Captain A. F. Lucas at Spindletop, Texas, blew in completely out of control and flooded the surrounding countryside with oil in one of the great wildcat discoveries of all time.

Many of the Gulf Coast salt domes are crowned with an irregular covering of limestone, anhydrite, gypsum, and occasionally sulphur, termed the *cap rock*. As might be anticipated from this rather unusual assemblage, their origin is controversial. Some geologists reason that this may be insoluble material left behind when salt near the top of the rising column of the salt dome was dissolved away. Others argue that the mass of material in the cap rock was carried upward, perhaps from the immediately overlying beds, by the salt on its rise toward the surface.

There seems to be little doubt that salt domes have risen from the depths below like giant fingers thrust upward into the crust. For one thing, they cut across strata in very nearly the same way that hypabyssal igneous intrusions do. Also, the marginal strata abutting against the salt have been dragged upward as though the salt were punched through them.

What made such a plastic substance as salt accomplish the seemingly impossible feat of shouldering its way upward through as much as three miles of solid rock? No one knows, but a preferred theory is that the salt rises because it is very much less dense than the enclosing rocks. A widely held opinion is that if an underlying, essentially horizontal layer of salt is warped slightly, then an incipient channel is opened up, and with the pronounced differences in density working in favor of the salt, pressure forces it upwards like toothpaste. Yet it retains enough strength within itself to push its way through rocks such as shale, sandstone, and limestone.

JOINTS

Nearly all the rocks visible on the Earth's surface are cut by cracks or fractures. They are so commonplace that few people grant them more than the most casual notice. If noticed at all, they probably are regarded as something that has always been and that requires no explanation.

Actually, the nature of such cracks, or *joints,* does require an explanation. The spacing between individual cracks may be less than an inch, or it may be scores of feet. Large intervals between cracks are rare, however. Joints very often are spaced rather uniformly, and the spacing interval may be quite constant for a given rock type. In general, the interval is less in fine-grained rocks, more in coarse-grained ones. Hornfels, shale, and mudstone, as well as ig-

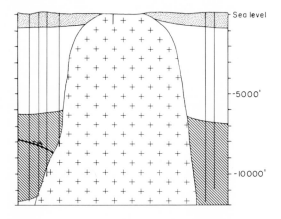

After P. B. King, *The Evolution of North America,* Copyright © 1959 Princeton University Press. By permission.

FIG. 6-16 *A cross section of the Avery Island salt dome, in south-central Louisiana. The vertical lines indicate drill holes. Salt (crosses) is shown piercing Cenozoic sedimentary rocks.*

neous rocks, such as basalt and obsidian, are likely to be closely jointed. Granite, gneiss, and thick-bedded sandstone, such as the sandstone that makes the sheer cliffs in Zion National Park, may be widely jointed (Fig. 6-17). In some areas joints *are* the landscape (Fig. 6-18). This is especially true at Arches National Monument in Utah, and the regularly spaced joints intersecting at nearly right angles look from the air like the ruin of an ancient city. This is a striking feature on the air route from Los Angeles to Denver, especially at Zion Park.

Joints typically occur in *sets,* and in many cases these intersect each other in three directions approximately at right angles to one another (Fig. 6-19). Should these fractures be uniformly spaced, a rock outcrop may resemble

FIG. 6-17 *Widely spaced joints mark out the chimney-like pinnacles of thick-bedded sandstone in Monument Valley, Arizona. (Photograph by William Aplin.)*

masonry, and such a pattern is responsible for the name mural (wall-like) jointing. In fact, the word joint is said to have been used long ago by British coal miners because such rhythmically fractured rocks resembled the way in which bricks are joined in a wall.

In some rocks there may be one set that dominates over the others, and if the spacing is close and the pattern uniform, it may superficially resemble stratification. Such well-developed jointing is called *sheeting,* and is very characteristic of granitic rocks.

FIG. 6-18 *Closely spaced joints in sandstone are exposed in the core of an anticlinal ridge northwest of Moab, Utah. (Photograph by John S. Shelton.)*

Another type of jointing found in granite is the curved shells most strikingly displayed on the great vault of Half Dome which towers above Yosemite Valley. The distance between the individual layers in these rock shells is much

more than 10 feet; far more than could ever have been produced by weathering. Their regularity requires an explanation.

A widely held belief is that many joints, including these convex, slab-layered joints, are the result of release of pressure. The granite in what is now Half Dome crystallized at a great depth within the Earth, under very high confining pressure. Now that the granite is exposed at the surface, through the stripping away by erosion

FIG. 6-19 *Sets of joints split the granitic rocks on the east face of Mt. McAdie, Sierra Nevada, Calif. (Photograph by Tom Ross.)*

of the cover of metamorphic rocks, these shell-like fractures have developed as the result of rebound. That the direction the rocks would spring is upward is logical since the atmospheric pressure is so much easier to overcome than the confining effect of the granite of the Earth's crust (Fig. 13-14).

Obviously, not all joints can be explained by such a single cause. Some are the result of shearing or of tension developed in rocks undergoing deformation in the Earth's crust. Others, and these are among the more perfectly formed, result from contraction on drying or cooling on crystallization. The columns that are typical of basalt flows and sills such as the Devil's Postpile (Fig. 3-11) and the Giant's Causeway (Chapter III) are outstanding examples of this type of joint.

FAULTS

Joints are fractures in rocks along which very little movement has occurred. Faults, on the other hand, are fractures along which significant displacement has taken place. In some cases this is very slight, in others it may amount to several hundred miles—in which case it is virtually impossible to match the rocks on one side of the break in the Earth's crust with their counterparts on the other. For lesser faults this frequently is possible, and thus we are provided with a means of telling what the relative displacement along the fault may have been (Fig. 6-20). Actual movement along a fracture plane

FIG. 6-20 *Small faults displace the rock layers near Zuma Beach, Calif. (Photograph by William Aplin.)*

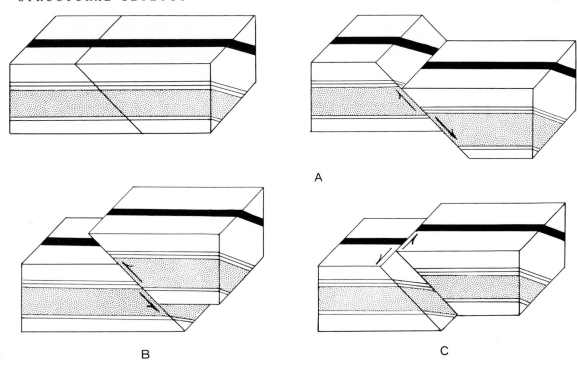

A

B

C

FIG. 6-21 *Types of faults. Block diagrams of stratified rocks displaced by:* A, *normal fault;* B, *reverse fault;* C, *strike-slip fault.*

is demonstrated not only by the discontinuity in the rocks on either side, but also by the presence of frictional grooves or scratches, called *slickensides,* on the fault surface. Sometimes, too, the rocks immediately adjacent to the fault are pulverized or ground to bits, forming a clayey material called *gouge.*

For centuries such breaks in the rocks have been a challenge to the miner, and oftentimes the source of despair. It is most disconcerting to be following a coal seam or vein of ore underground and then to have it sheared off completely, leaving one staring bleakly at a face of barren rock. The very name, fault, suggests a degree of rationalization, and to the miner of long ago it was perhaps looked upon as not a very helpful gesture on the part of Pluto, god of the lower world.

Since faults are fractures, they are surfaces that sometimes may approximate a plane. The rocks on one side of the fault have slid past those on the other, it is true, but our first concern before becoming involved with more complex matters is with the fact that since we are

dealing with an inclined plane it, too, has a dip and strike, just as the plane surfaces of stratified rocks have.

Suppose we consider the fault in Fig. 6-21A. It has a dip of 45° and the black layer of rock above the fault appears to have been dropped down, as shown by the arrows, with respect to the same layer of rock below the fault plane. The terms above and below do not have an especially precise meaning, and in their place the old mining terms, *hanging wall* and *foot wall,* are more appropriate. The word 'wall' has not always been limited to the sides of a room; as an ancient mining term it meant the coating or crust of a lode or vein, or by extension, the side of a mine next to the vein (1728). Thus, if we imagine that the fault has been followed underground by an inclined shaft, then the lower side is underfoot (hence foot wall) while the upper side hangs overhead (hence hanging wall).

Now, if we employ these words as part of the definition, then the fault in Fig. 6-21A can be defined as one in which the hanging wall has apparently moved down with respect to the foot wall. Such a fault is called a *normal fault*.

The opposite sort of occurrence (Fig. 6-21B) in which the hanging wall apparently moved up with respect to the foot wall, rather than being called an abnormal fault, as one might think, is actually known as a *reverse fault*. This term is used rather generally by geologists for faults with this type of displacement when the dip is 45° or more. When the dip is low, and the movement large, then faults of this general character commonly are called *thrust faults*. They are discussed in more detail near the end of this section.

In all this discussion you will note that the relative movement described thus far for normal and reverse faults has been up or down the dip of the fault plane. The term that is used to account for the actual relative displacement of once adjacent points, *measured on the plane of the fault,* is the *slip*. Fig. 6-22 illustrates the three kinds of slip to remember. *Strike slip* (C) is a measure of the displacement parallel to the strike; *dip slip* (A) is movement on the fault plane parallel to the dip. The actual movement in this particular fault is along the line B, and this is called the *oblique slip*. In this example the actual *amount* of this displacement is called the *net slip*.

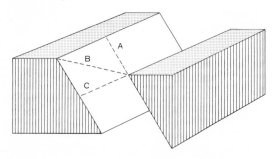

FIG. 6-22 *Types of slip on fault plane. The block is cut by an inclined fault showing:* A, *dip slip;* B, *oblique slip;* C, *strike slip movements on fault plane.*

Strike-slip faults are a specialized category, but one of great importance. These are faults in which the displacement is primarily *horizontal,* although in many cases the dip of the fault plane is essentially *vertical*. This sounds confusing, but the relationship involved here is no more complicated to grasp than the thought of sliding two bricks past one another on the surface of a flat table. The bricks move horizontally, but the crack separating them along their edges is vertical. Some strike-slip faults are very large fractures and have displacements measuring scores of miles. Two well-known ones are the Great Glen fault of Scotland (Fig. 6-34) and the San Andreas fault of California (Fig. 6-32), both described below.

Normal Faults

The diagrams in Fig. 6-21A and B are unrealistic in overlooking the fact that if rocks below the ground are displaced to the extent shown, there should be a visible offset of the ground surfaces as well. Should such an offset be present it is called a *fault scarp* (Fig. 6-23), and it may appear as a low, linear cliff cutting indiscriminately across all the terrain features that it encounters. Quite a number of these low, fault-induced cliffs have appeared suddenly in widely scattered parts of the world where earthquakes are especially prevalent. In the United States an impressive one is in Alaska, where, after the Yakutat Bay earthquake of 1899, a fault scarp about 50 feet high was produced. Such historically recent scarps are especially characteristic of Japan, New Zealand, and India, and in the contiguous United States in California and Nevada. Among these, one of the more interesting and accessible is at the base of the Alabama Hills, an outlier of the Mt. Whitney sector of the Sierra Nevada. This scarp, in places as much as 20 feet high, resulted from the Lone Pine earthquake of 1872 in which 29 people were killed. Fittingly enough, their mass grave is close to the upper edge of the scarp.

FIG. 6-23 *A fault scarp in alluvium, produced during the Hebgen Lake earthquake, Montana. (Courtesy of Montana Highway Dept.)*

The tremendous eastern wall of the Sierra Nevada in the Mt. Whitney sector very often is cited as an example of a fault scarp (Fig. 6-24). Although it is true that faults have blocked out the front of the range, the escarpment is not actually an uplifted fault plane. Steep as the mountain front appears when viewed full face, when looked at from the side the average inclination of most of the ridges can be seen to be about 25°, while the faults within the range have average dips of 60° or 70°. This simply means that the face of the range is a fault-controlled erosional landform and that its slope is in balance for the type of weathering, climate, vegetative cover, and kind of rock, rather than being an elevated part of the fault plane itself.

The altitude and unusual configuration of the Sierra Nevada is, however, a result of differential uplift—a consequence of faulting. In a typical mountain range the drainage divide customarily is in the central part of the mountains. The Sierra Nevada, on the other hand, is strongly asymmetrical, with the divide very close to the eastern edge (Fig. 6-25). The slope down to the eastern base is bold and precipitous (Fig. 6-24); to the west towards the San Joaquin Valley it is continuous and gentle—in places the average declivity is closer to 3° than 30°. In fact, it is slight enough that much of the pioneer route of the Central Pacific Railroad followed the crest of one of these west-sloping ridges and was feasible even for the wood-burning, diamond-stacked engines of a century ago. Without burdening the discussion with the details of the internal structure of the range, in its central part (the Mt. Whitney sector) it is basically a west-

FIG. 6-24 *The eastern scarp of the Sierra Nevada, Calif., showing the accordant summit of the range and the steep eastern face. Mt. Whitney is in the left background. (Photograph by Roland von Huene.)*

tilted block of the Earth's crust elevated along faults which form its eastern margin.

Mountains such as the Sierra Nevada commonly are called fault-block mountains by geologists. The western desert area of the United States abounds with them, and they are espe-cially conspicuous elements of the landscape in Nevada and western Utah between the Sierra Nevada and the Wasatch. Actually, they have their purest form in the stark desert—almost lunar in its desolation—of southeastern Oregon. Here, marginal faults have elevated or depressed nearly flat-lying basalt flows as single units, so the blocklike configuration of the range is far more apparent than it is in the desert ranges of the southwest where the internal structures of the mountains are more complex.

Not only may crustal blocks be tilted upward along faults on one margin in a fashion similar

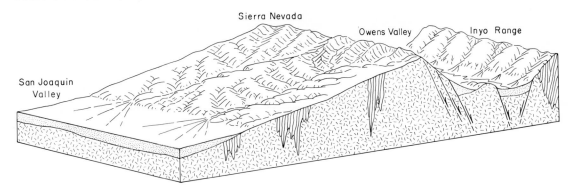

FIG. 6-25 *The structural and physiographic relations of the Sierra Nevada and adjacent regions, shown diagrammatically.*

to the Sierra Nevada, but they may be elevated as a block between faults on both margins. Such a fault-bounded plateau is called a *horst* (Fig. 6-26), although the original German word means a variety of things, such as a clump of trees, or a thicket, or in this case, a ridge.

If such elongate crustal blocks can be elevated, then conversely others can be depressed. Such downfaulted wedges bounded by fault scarps are called *graben* (Figs. 6-26, 6-27) after the German word for trough, or trench. A renowned example is the Rhine Graben which is followed by the Rhine River from Basel to Mainz. Here the valley is linear and trenchlike with walls that are fault scarps marginal to highlands—the Schwarzwald to the east in Germany and the Vosges to the west in France (Fig. 6-28).

This same cross section (northwest of the Vosges) shows a distinctive structure similar to that of the Paris Basin. Paris is in the center of a pile of saucerlike ridges which are arranged in eight concentric arcs easterly from the city. The ridges have long gentle slopes to the west and abrupt ones to the east. Throughout the strife-wracked history of Europe these have always been one of the great natural defenses of France. An invader from the east has had to fight his way up the steeper slopes while under observation from the defenders who had the advantage of the long gentler slopes for their supply lines.

Unfortunately for France, the saucer rims decline in height northward until they disappear

beneath the muddy Flanders plain. This, therefore, has been the preferred invasion route, which was, for example, followed by the German Imperial Army in 1914 in its sweep through Belgium toward Paris. In World War II essentially the same tactic was employed, this time successfully, following the evacuation of Dunkerque.

An impressive set of graben is the nearly continuous line of fault-bordered troughs that extend the length of Africa and part of the Middle East, from Mozambique to the Dead Sea. These great down-dropped segments of the Earth's crust are far too large to be referred to as "trenches," and for this reason the frequently used term, *rift valley,* is appropriate.

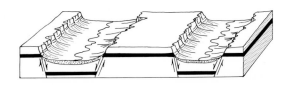

FIG. 6-26 *The block diagram illustrates the structural and physiographic relations of a horst (center) and adjacent graben (valleys).*

FIG. 6-27 *Wildrose Graben, along the west side of the Panamint Range, Calif., is a fault trough in soft Cenozoic alluvial-fan sediments. Numerous small fault scarps cross the dissected surface* *at the right end of the graben, and other scarps are visible on the far side of the graben, near the base of the alluvial cone. (Photograph by John S. Shelton.)*

FIG. 6-28 *A cross section illustrating the graben nature and the complex geologic structure of the Rhine Valley and adjacent areas.*

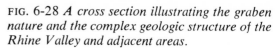

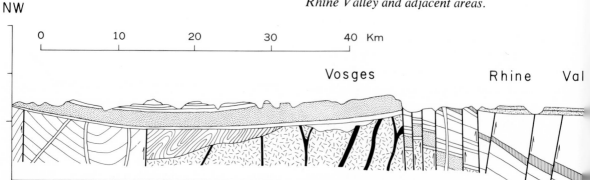

One of the better known rift valleys is the one that holds Lake Tanganyika, whose length is 420 miles and whose width ranges from 20 to 40 miles. The water surface is 2,530 feet above sea level, but the bottom is 1,660 feet below. Lake Albert Nyanza, possibly the most impressive, is set in a trough whose eastern wall is 1,000 to 1,500 feet high and whose mountainous western slope rises to 8,000 feet.

According to some geologists, the Red Sea and its eastern affiliate, the Gulf of Aden, as well as its northern continuation, the Gulf of Aqaba, are structurally part of the same rift valley system. Certainly, the troughlike valley between Israel and Jordan through which the River Jordan flows and which holds the Sea of Galilee as well as the Dead Sea (whose surface is 1,292 feet below sea level and whose depth is 1,308 feet) appears to have had a kindred origin.

What is the nature of these long, straight-sided valleys, some of which hold deep, narrow lakes, and some of which—especially those of Central Africa—are the sites of volcanoes, a rarity indeed deep in a continental interior? Here, there are two schools of thought, and a definitive answer to the problem has yet to be reached. One belief is that they are simply large graben with the bounding scarps between the rift valley floor and the bordering, plateaulike veldt following the strike of what are essentially

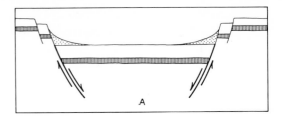

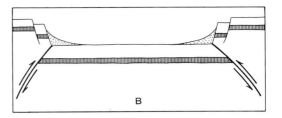

From B. Willis and R. Willis, *Geologic Structures,* Copyright © 1929 by McGraw-Hill Book Co., Inc. By permission.

FIG. 6-29 *Sketches illustrating two opposing views of the structural origin of African rift valleys. A, graben interpretation; B, valley held down by overriding of marginal blocks on thrust faults.*

inward-dipping normal faults—a structure like that of the Rhine Valley, except on a vastly larger scale (Fig. 6-29A).

The opposing point of view, held by a number of British geologists familiar with the area, is that the rift valleys in reality are wedges held down by what essentially are outward dipping, reverse faults which have permitted the plateau-like rims of the rift valley to ride up over the wedged-down floor of the valley (Fig. 6-29B).

Redrawn from "Geologische Übersichtskarte von Südwest-deutschland," Württemberg Staat. Landesamt, 1938. By permission.

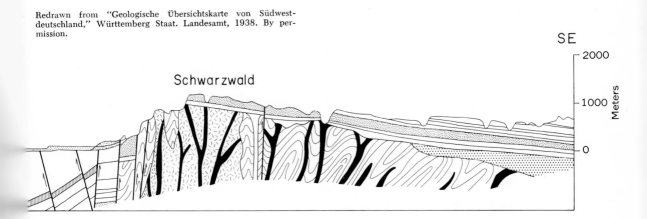

Adherents of the first view point out in its support (1) the lack of any compressional features—such as thrust faults or folds in the vicinity; (2) the straight, rather than sinuous, margins of the rift valleys; (3) the presence of volcanoes—since these conspicuously avoid regions of intense compression; and (4) the fact that there are no known examples of normal faults at the surface, such as those in Fig. 6-29B, which give way to reverse faults at depth. Mechanically it seems unlikely that they could (Fuller and Waters, 1929).

The most significant evidence advanced by the partisans of the pushing down and the holding down of the rift valleys by overriding marginal blocks is the fact that measurements of gravity made in the rift valleys show them to be underlain by material of significantly lower density than the rocks beneath the bordering highlands. This is interpreted to mean that a block of lighter surface material was forced down into the denser subcrustal layer and is pinned down by the overriding marginal plates (Fig. 6-29B). Actually, this evidence can be argued either way. Either the line of argument advanced above can be followed, or the opposite tack might be taken as follows. If these great depressions actually are large graben, then it is expectable that lighter material will have been downfaulted into denser levels of the Earth's crust, and much of the material that floors these trenches will be unconsolidated, relatively porous sediments derived from erosion of the marginal fault scarps. Thus, the origin of the African rift valleys remains in the realm of uncertainty, and is a problem to be solved in some future day.

Strike-slip Faults

It took the events of the early morning of April 18, 1906, to convince many American geologists of a half-century ago of the reality of strike-slip faults of large magnitude. On that day the California earth in the vicinity of San Francisco shifted almost instantaneously along the San Andreas fault, with the western side sliding northward as much as 20 feet past the eastern, to the dismay of landowners, county road departments, and a number of luckless individuals whose houses and barns were sheared in half.

Since that time, the San Andreas fault, and others like it, have been studied in increasing detail, and such faults have been recognized in parts of the world as distant from one another as California, Canada, Scotland, Switzerland, the Philippines, Japan, and New Zealand. With such a wide range of occurrences in so many lands, it is not surprising that a widely varied terminology has been applied to them. British geologists are likely to call such fractures *transcurrent faults* or *wrench faults*. In America the proposal has been made that they be known as *lateral faults* (Hill, 1947); thus we can speak of left-lateral faults for those in which the side opposite a person when he faces the fault has apparently been displaced to the left, and right-lateral if the movement has apparently been to the right.

Displacement along a strike-slip fault is not always the easiest thing to demonstrate, as the examples in Fig. 6-21 show. Ordinarily, in order to establish whether or not movement has been strike-slip or dip-slip, it is necessary to have layered rocks with strongly differing dips cut by the fault. In Fig. 6-21C, which shows dipping strata cut by a fault, and then, following the faulting, the entire region reduced by erosion to a level plain, the solution is indeterminate. Rather than having the apparent offset in the strata produced by strike-slip—as appears to be the case—it may result from uplift of the fault block to the right of the fault, as in Fig. 6-21B. With continued lowering of the scarp by erosion the outcrop of the dipping bed, shown in solid black, will be shifted progressively in the direction of the dip.

In Fig. 6-30, which is of a plunging anticline cut by two faults and then eroded to a level

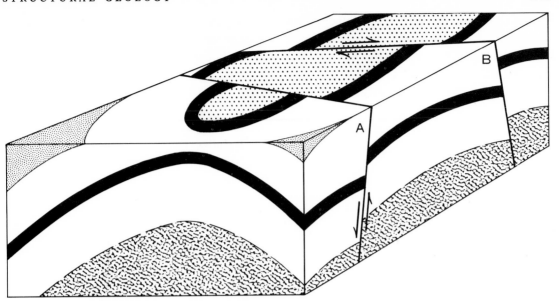

plain, fault A is a normal fault which illustrates the effect of dip-slip and fault B is a strike-slip fault. Along fault B the oppositely dipping strata apparently are shifted in the same direction; along fault A they are apparently shifted in opposite directions, and note especially on the uplifted block that they are seemingly shifted in the direction of the dip—in accordance with the rule stated in the paragraph above.

Incidentally, you can also see in the *cross section* along the side of the diagram that the *apparent* movement of fault B is that of a reverse fault—namely dip-slip—although the *actual* movement as demonstrated by the outcrop pattern was strike-slip. It is for this reason that the term *apparent* has been used throughout this discussion. In many cases it is not possible to determine geologically from a single outcrop what the actual direction and nature of the movement may have been.

With respect to the relative movement along a fault, all that we know is how one side of the fault seems to have moved with respect to the other. It is a rare occasion when we can say that the hanging wall moved and the foot wall remained passive, or vice versa. Perhaps both sides moved, and in the case of strike-slip faults

FIG. 6-30 *Comparison of dip-slip and strike-slip faults. In the block diagram, a plunging anticline is cut by:* A, *a dip-slip normal fault in which oppositely dipping strata are shifted (on the surface) in the direction of their dip;* B, *a strike-slip fault in which oppositely dipping strata are shifted (on the surface) in the same direction. Note that in the cross section, the beds next to fault* B *are shifted in the same manner as in a reverse fault.*

they almost certainly did. It is for this reason that arrows pointing in opposite directions commonly are indicated on faults shown in cross section.

From many of the brief statements that have been made thus far, it should be apparent that the San Andreas is one of the world's more renowned examples of a strike-slip fault (Fig. 6-31). The map (Fig. 6-32) showing a number of California's leading faults demonstrates its great length, roughly 600 miles from where it cuts the coast north of San Francisco until its several branches disappear beneath the waters of the Gulf of California. The map also shows that it is not a single fracture but is a complex system of faults.

Theoretically, it would seem reasonable that a fault system as great as this in one dimension

—length—should be equally large in others, such as depth and amount of movement. The depth, obviously, is beyond our ability to measure, but one would think that the distance that rocks are offset would be an easy thing to determine. Actually, it is very difficult. Part of the problem arises from the fact that the strike of the rocks cut by the San Andreas is nearly the same as that of the fault itself, so that clear-cut, sharply defined intersections are lacking. Also, the more ancient displacements along the fault are concealed beneath more recent deposits, which, in a sense, have covered over old scars. A tentative recent estimate (Hill and Dibblee, 1953) would place the amount of movement on the San Andreas fault complex as 120 miles in the last 60 million years and possibly 350 miles since 120 million years ago—roughly the age of the oldest rocks marginal to the fault.

FIG. 6-31 *The trace of the San Andreas fault across the Carrizo Plain, Calif., is marked by disrupted drainage lines and offset stream courses. (Photograph by John S. Shelton.)*

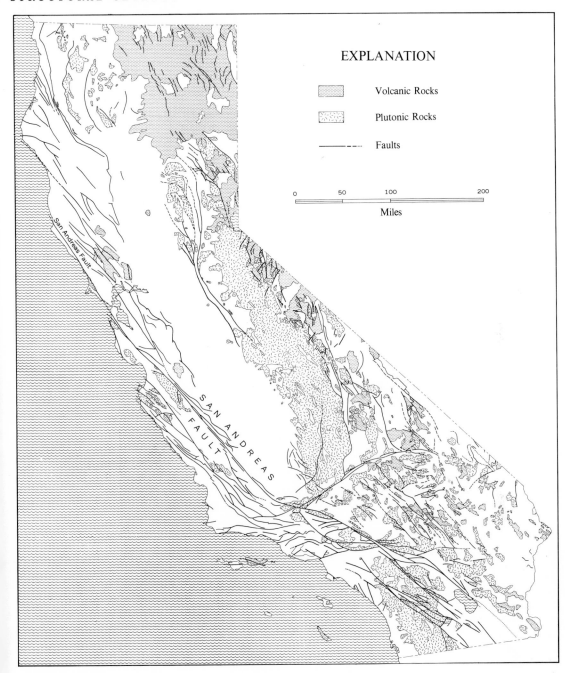

EXPLANATION

Volcanic Rocks

Plutonic Rocks

– – – – Faults

0   50   100   200

Miles

San Andreas Fault

SAN ANDREAS FAULT

After "Tectonic Map of the United States," U.S. Geological Survey and Amer. Assoc. of Petroleum Geologists, 1961. By permission.

FIG. 6-32 *A generalized geologic map of California shows the extent of the San Andreas and other faults and the distribution of plutonic and volcanic igneous rocks.*

A well-documented example of a strike-slip fault is the Great Glen fault in Scotland. Almost everyone who has ever looked at a map of Scotland is likely to wonder about the nearly continuous vale that extends across the middle all the way from the North Sea to the Atlantic Ocean. (This valley is also the site of Loch Ness, home of the legendary sea serpent, Fig. 6-33.) Fortunately, the rocks and structures on either side of the Great Glen fault can be matched up with some confidence (Fig. 6-34), and according to Kennedy (1946) they indicate a strike-slip movement of about 65 miles, with the northern part of the Scottish Highlands being displaced relatively southwestward.

FIG. 6-33 *Loch Ness, in the Northwest Highlands of Scotland, is a lake in the basin along the trace of the Great Glen fault. (Photograph by Aerofilms and Aero Pictorial, Ltd., London.)*

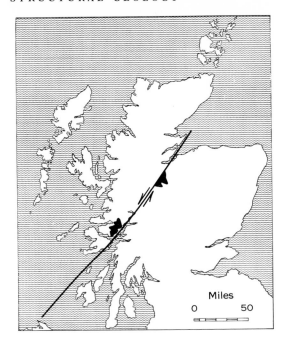

After W. Q. Kennedy, "The Great Glen Fault," 1946, *Quarterly Journal of the Geological Society of London*. By permission.

FIG. 6-34 *Left-lateral offset on the Great Glen fault, Scotland, as determined by the separation of two granite bodies (black) interpreted to have been once contiguous.*

Thrust Faults

Geologists struggling to interpret the perplexing relationships of the Northwest Highlands of Scotland early in the nineteenth century—around the time of the War of 1812—were puzzled to find sandstone, shale, and limestone interbedded in what appeared to be a normal sequence with gneiss and schist. Even such a notable person as Lyell accepted this as a conformable succession of seemingly related rocks. Fortunately for Lyell's reputation, no one in that day was really too certain of the true nature of metamorphic rocks.

However, with continued field work throughout the nineteenth century, the complacent state of mind brought about by this misconception was increasingly disturbed by (1) the awareness that metamorphic rocks *are not* normally interbedded with sedimentary rocks, (2) the fact that some of the contacts separating different rock units were not normal depositional surfaces but were faults and showed the effects of movement by such evidence as crushed zones, slickensides, and mylonite, and (3) rocks containing fossils of earlier geologic periods were found resting on rocks holding fossils known to have lived in later geologic time.

In a region as renowned for disputation as Scotland, it is no wonder that the "Highland Controversy" is one of the more celebrated intellectual conflicts in the history of geology. By 1861, the view gained acceptance that perhaps these aberrant geological relationships were the result of the gliding of great sheets of rock over one another in a fashion similar to what had been found in 1849 to be part of the internal structure of the Alps. As a result of nearly a century of effort, the existence of large-scale almost horizontal displacement of many miles' extent was demonstrated to the satisfaction of most. Here in the Scottish Highlands the presence of at least three rock slices was established, and these were shown to have moved from the southeast toward the northwest carrying schistose rocks over younger unmetamorphosed sedimentary rocks.

Such faults are called *thrust faults,* and in typical examples their dips are low, ordinarily less than 10°, and the displacement may be very large, 10 or 15 miles are not uncommon, and some may amount to 30 or 40 miles.

In the United States, the pioneer work in establishing the existence of thrust faults was done around 1900, in large part through the efforts of Bailey Willis, for many years professor of geology at Stanford University. An example he used to prove the existence of such a structure in this country is familiar to thousands since it is in large part responsible for the landscape of Glacier National Park. Willis showed that the eastern wall of the Rocky Mountains consists of very ancient sedimentary rocks, more

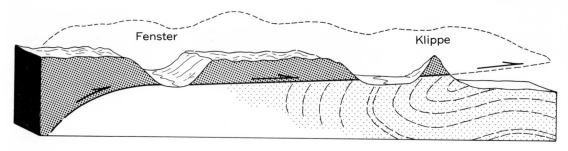

FIG. 6-35 *A cross-sectional diagram showing a low-angle thrust fault, above which old rocks (heavy dots) have moved from left to right. An outlier (klippe) and an inlier (fenster) have been produced by erosion of the thrust sheet. This diagram illustrates conditions prevailing along the Lewis Overthrust, Glacier National Park, Montana.*

than 500 million years old, but that these rest on rocks whose age ranges from 60 to 130 million years. The differences in these unlike strata are further accentuated by the fact that the older sedimentary rocks above the thrust fault are much more resistant to erosion and form the castellated ridges and steep cliffs, scored by deep canyons, that make the park landscape so justly renowned. The rocks below the thrust are less resistant and are responsible for the gently rolling, undulating landscape of the high plains of Montana to the east.

One of the remarkable features of the great thrust fault of Glacier Park—to which the especially appropriate name of *Lewis Overthrust* was given to commemorate the pioneer exploratory efforts of Meriwether Lewis in 1803-06— is the outlying peak, Chief Mountain. This mountain is a remnant of the hanging wall of the fault, isolated by erosion, and thus in a sense is a "mountain without roots." Such an erosionally isolated fragment of a thrust sheet is called a *klippe* (from the German word for cliff; pl. *klippen*). Conversely, erosion may succeed in cutting through the overthrust plate of such a fault and exposing the rocks beneath (Fig. 6-35). The place where we are granted such a revealing insight into the realm below the thrust

plane is called quite fittingly a *fenster,* which is the German word for window.

Many thrust faults are not regular geometric planes, but have complexly curved surfaces; in places the dip may be 10° or less, in others it may steepen to 45° or so (see, for instance, Fig. 7-9). Some are formed this way, while others have been folded or bent after formation by a continuation of mountain building. Regardless of whether or not they have been folded, they appear to have very gentle dips near the leading edge of what may once have resembled a tongue-like lobe, and steeper dips in the root zone to the rear.

The final demonstration of the existence of thrust faults has occurred within the lifetime of geologists still living, and the working out of the complex pattern on such mountains as the Alps, the Scottish Highlands, the Appalachians, and the Rockies stands as one of the hard-won triumphs of geology.

Having established the geometry of these great overriding rock plates, which have produced such large-scale displacement, somewhat like the telescoping of an old-fashioned collapsible drinking cup, geologists are now ready to attack the central problem of determining the mechanism responsible for their existence. Were they shoved from behind? Are they the result of gravitational gliding of great masses of rock down gentle slopes? Neither of these possibilities can be advocated with certainty. Recent investigations, however, have shown that if the pore spaces within the rocks are filled with water under abnormally high pressure, so that a buoyant effect results, less force is required to overcome friction and set such a mass in motion than formerly had been believed (Hubbert and Rubey, 1959).

UNCONFORMITIES

The view from either the north or south rim of the Grand Canyon is one of the celebrated geologic spectacles of the world. Here is visible at least a mile-thick pile of sedimentary rocks, such as limestone, sandstone, shale, and conglomerate, deposited in layers one upon the other and resting at their base upon a platform of metamorphic rocks.

The story of these rocks is not, however, an unbroken record comparable, for example, to the tree rings in a giant Sequoia log in a park museum with such dates as 1066 and 1492 carefully marked on it. There are stupendous gaps in the geologic record—whole chapters are missing out of the book—and in geologic terms these commonly represent periods of erosion rather than of deposition.

The surface that separates two rock units and represents such a time of nondeposition or of erosion may be knife-edged in its sharpness. It is called an *unconformity,* and may very well be all there is to show for a hiatus of several hundred million years. There are a number of varieties of unconformity, depending on the relationship of the rocks above and below the erosion surface, but the two most important are: (1) where the rocks on either side are parallel

---

FIG. 6-36 *The Keystone thrust, in the Spring Mountains west of Las Vegas, separates dark-colored Cambrian limestone above from light-colored Jurassic sandstone below. (Photograph by John S. Shelton.)*

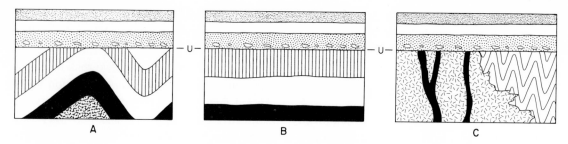

A   B   C

FIG. 6-37 *Varieties of unconformities (marked by U). A and C, angular unconformity; B, parallel unconformity.*

to one another (*parallel unconformity*, Fig. 6-37B), or where (2) they make an angle with one another (*angular unconformity*, Figs. 6-37A, 6-38, 6-39, 6-40). A variant of this second type occurs where the younger rocks above the unconformity rest on the eroded surface of crystalline, nonstratified rocks such as igneous or metamorphic rocks (Fig. 6-37C).

Returning to the Grand Canyon, the cross section, Fig. 6-38, shows the principal rock units exposed in its walls. There are three great divisions, and these are: (1) the basement com-

plex of various kinds of metamorphic rocks which are cut by small intrusions and dikes, chiefly of diorite; (2) the Grand Canyon series of tilted sedimentary rocks; and (3) the Plateau series of flat-lying sedimentary rocks. Notice that the Grand Canyon series is separated from the rocks above and below by profound angular unconformities, indicated by the letters A and B. The gap in the ages shown for the various rock layers within the Plateau series shows that there are two major parallel unconformities within this pile of strata, and these lost intervals are shown by the letters C and D. To illustrate: the lowermost layers of the Plateau series were deposited 440-520 million years ago, and are separated by a period of nondeposition of 120

FIG. 6-38 *A geologic cross section of the Grand Canyon of the Colorado, showing the structure and general stratigraphic succession: (1) basement complex; (2) Grand Canyon series (tilted); (3) Plateau series (horizontal). A and B, angular unconformities; C and D, parallel unconformities.*

After P. B. King, *The Evolution of North America*, Copyright © 1959 Princeton University Press. By permission.

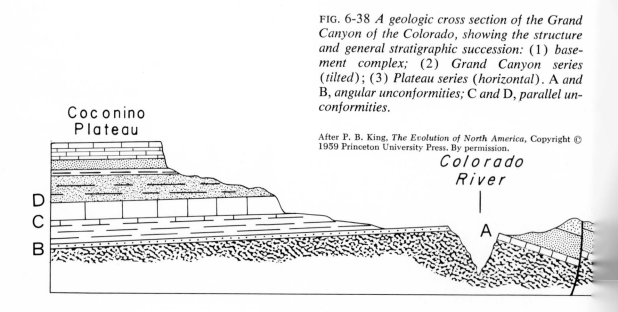

FIG. 6-39 *The angular unconformity separating tilted strata belonging to the Precambrian Grand Canyon System from horizontal Paleozoic rocks is exposed on the north wall of the Grand Canyon. (Photograph by John S. Shelton.)*

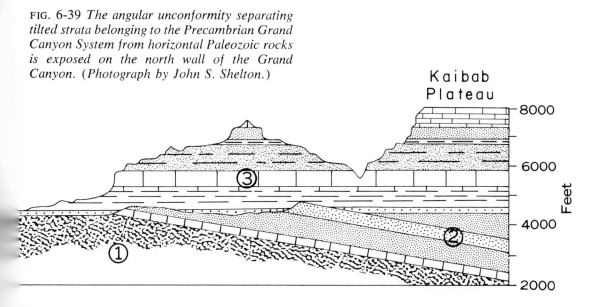

million years from the layers above unconformity C because these strata above the unconformity were deposited only 235-320 million years ago. The upper of the two parallel unconformities (D) represents roughly 145 million years of nondeposition, yet shows up as an insignificantly thin line in the canyon walls—little more than the change in lithology from limestone to shale, with the strata above and below the unconformity essentially parallel to one another.

The Grand Canyon also provides a superb illustration of the kind of reasoning followed by a geologist in unraveling the past story of a region from the kind of rocks, the inferred nature of the environment of their origin, and their structural pattern. The Grand Canyon is also an outstanding place to demonstrate how a single segment of the Earth's crust alternately may be elevated and depressed.

FIG. 6-40 *Folded Cenozoic strata in the Barstow syncline, near Barstow, Calif., are overlain unconformably by younger stream deposits, in horizontal layers. (Photograph by John S. Shelton.)*

To emphasize this last point, the major events in its geologic history may be recapitulated briefly:

1) *Deposition* of the sedimentary rocks which today make up the schists of the Inner Gorge.
2) *Metamorphism* of these sedimentary rocks, accompanied by the *intrusion* of small diorite bodies.
3) Profound *erosion* and reduction of the entire region to a nearly level lowland.
4) *Deposition* of the sediments of the Grand Canyon series, chiefly on the floor of the sea that spread inland over the nearly level surface of erosion produced in Step 3.
5) *Deformation* of these rocks, chiefly by large normal faults with the resulting production of fault block mountains.
6) *Erosion* of these faulted mountains until they, too, were reduced to a nearly flat surface. This is unconformity B.
7) *Deposition* of 1,200 feet of sandstone, shale, and limestone in the sea that spread inland across the erosion surface of Step 6.
8) *Uplift* and *erosion* with the removal of an indeterminate thickness of sedimentary rocks and the cutting of the erosion surface shown in unconformity C.

9) *Deposition* of about 600 feet of limestone on the sea floor. This rock, incidentally, makes the most conspicuous cliff within the canyon.

10) Slight *uplift* and *erosion* with almost no accompanying deformation, since the strata above and below this surface, unconformity D, are virtually parallel.

11) *Subsidence* and *deposition* of about 2,000 feet of limestone, sandstone, and shale, in part on land and in part in the sea.

12) Here the local record that can be read in the rocks ends. The limestone that makes the rim on which the various park hotels and campgrounds stand is at least 185 million years old. Obviously, a great deal has happened in the chapters that are missing here, but from the record that can be pieced together elsewhere in nearby regions, there was deposition throughout much of the remainder of geologic time, then uplift and the stripping off of several thousands of feet of rocks, followed by volcanic activity (represented by the neighboring San Francisco Mountains), and finally downcutting by the Colorado River to excavate its present course across the Kaibab and Coconino Plateaus. These have been uplifted vertically for more than a mile with almost no internal disturbance of the underlying strata.

Notice that the canyon, as shown in the cross section, Fig. 6-38, is at least thirteen times as broad as it is deep, and that strata in the Plateau series exposed in the South Rim can be matched up with their counterparts in the North Rim with no visible offset. These are strong arguments that the canyon is the product of normal stream erosion, and that it is *not* a colossal downfaulted graben of some unusual form.

Suggested References

Billings, Marland, 1954, Structural geology, Prentice-Hall, Inc., Englewood Cliffs, N. J.

Blackwelder, Eliot, 1928, The recognition of fault scarps, Jour. Geol., v. 36, p. 289-311.

Bucher, W. H., 1933, The deformation of the earth's crust, Princeton Univ. Press, Princeton, N. J.

Compton, R. R., 1962, Manual of field geology, John Wiley and Sons, Inc., New York.

Crowell, J. C., 1962, Displacement along the San Andreas fault, California, Geol. Soc. Amer., Special Paper No. 71.

De Sitter, L. Y., 1956, Structural geology, McGraw-Hill Book Co., Inc., New York.

Eardley, A. J., 1951, Structural geology of North America, Harper and Bros., New York.

Field, R. M., 1933, The principles of historical geology from the regional point of view, Princeton Univ. Press, Princeton, N. J.

Fuller, R. E., and Waters, A. C., 1929, The nature of the horst and graben structures of southern Oregon, Jour. Geol., v. 37, p. 204-238.

Gilluly, James, 1949, Distribution of mountain building in geologic time, Geol. Soc. Amer., Bull., v. 60, p. 561-590.

Goguel, Jean, 1962, Tectonics, W. H. Freeman and Co., San Francisco.

Hill, M. L., 1947, Classification of faults, Amer. Assoc. Petrol. Geol., Bull., v. 31, p. 1669-1673.

Hill, M. L., and Dibblee, T. W., Jr., 1953, San Andreas, Garlock, and Big Pine faults, California, Geol. Soc. Amer., Bull., v. 64, p. 443-458.

Hills, E. S., 1940, Outlines of structural geology, Nordeman Publ. Co., New York.

Hubbert, King, and Rubey, W. W., 1959, Mechanics of fluid-filled porous solids and its application to overthrust faulting, Geol. Soc. Amer., Bull., v. 70, p. 115-166.

Kennedy, W. Q., 1946, The Great Glen fault, Quart. Jour. Geol. Soc. London, v. CII, p. 41-76.

King, P. B., 1937, Geology of the Marathon Region, Texas, U. S. Geol. Survey, Prof. Paper 187.

———, 1959, The evolution of North America, Princeton Univ. Press, Princeton, N. J.

Lahee, F. H., 1961, Field geology, McGraw-Hill Book Co., Inc., New York.

Lawson, A. C., and others, 1908, The California earthquake of April 18, 1906, Carnegie Inst. of Washington, 3 vols. and atlas.

Murray, G. E., 1961, Geology of the Atlantic and Gulf coastal province of North America, Harper and Bros., New York.

Reid, H. F., 1913, Report of the committee on the nomenclature of faults, Geol. Soc. Amer., Bull., v. 24, p. 163-186.

Ross, C. P., and Rezak, Richard, 1959, The rocks and fossils of Glacier National Park; the story of their origin and history, U. S. Geol. Survey, Prof. Paper 294-K.

Whitten, C. A., 1948, Horizontal earth movement, vicinity of San Francisco, Amer. Geophys. Union, Trans., v. 29, p. 318-323.

Willis, Bailey, 1930, Living Africa, a geologist's wanderings through the rift valleys, Whittlesey House, McGraw-Hill Book Co., Inc., New York.

———, 1936, East African plateaus and rift valleys, Carnegie Inst. of Washington, Publ. No. 470.

Petroleum geologists in Alaska make a preliminary study, using a helicopter for transportation in a rugged mountainous area. (Courtesy of Humble Oil and Refining Company.)

VII

Petroleum Geology

No single application of geology has a greater impact on our lives today than the world-wide search for oil. Without this far-flung activity, geology very likely would occupy a modest corner in the academic world and the few practitioners of its rites would be viewed with amused tolerance by their colleagues. Of the estimated 20,000 or so geologists now active in the United States, the work of perhaps 15,000 is related to the exploratory efforts of the oil industry. This represents a truly remarkable growth; at the beginning of the century only a handful of men were engaged in such an undertaking.

Before talking about the occurrence of petroleum in the ground, we might take a retrospective glance over the past century and consider briefly what a remarkable effect the utilization of oil has had on our whole pattern of living. The first well purposely drilled for oil in the United States was completed just over 100 years ago in the northwestern corner of Pennsylvania at a depth of 69½ feet on a hot, sultry August afternoon of 1859 by a forty-year-old railroad conductor, "Colonel" E. L. Drake, who in his wildest fancies scarcely could have imagined himself in the role of the Columbus of this newly discovered industrial empire.

Although Drake, like many a man before and after him, was hailed as the "discoverer" of a technical innovation, the well drilled for oil, his achievement did not result from an inspirational flash, but was based on the forgotten work of scores of his predecessors. In this case it was the labor of the salt-well drillers in what was later to become West Virginia that cleared the way. Chief among these technological pioneers were the Ruffner brothers, David and Joseph, who beginning in 1806 gradually evolved a system of using a spring pole, a bit at the end of linked poles, and casing of twine-wrapped wood to prevent the collapse of the well walls. This was an enormous step forward from the primitive hand-dug, wooden-cribbed wells of their time. Nor does it detract in the least from their achievement to know that Chinese salt drillers in Szechwan Province by A.D. 347 had reached 800 feet and by A.D. 1132 wells were regularly sunk to 3,000 feet using bamboo rods and essentially the same spring-pole method.

In connection with the search for salt, large quantities of oil and gas were discovered in pre-Civil War days throughout Virginia, Pennsylvania, and Ohio (Price, 1947). These discoveries, however, should be regarded as precursors rather than the main event. They made people aware of the presence of oil, but without a market this black, messy substance must have been an unmitigated nuisance as a scummy coating on such streams as Oil Creek and the Allegheny and Kanawha Rivers.

Few human endeavors, grown to such titanic dimensions as the oil industry, have had a more fraudulent origin. The first real economic use of petroleum, or "rock-oil," was as a patent medicine. In fact, it was the colorful advertise-ments of Samuel M. Kier, an old-time medicine man, that caught the fancy of the first investors. One of Kier's ads resembled a $400 bill drawn on the "Bank of the Allegheny River." Close inspection showed that the 400 stood not for dollars, but for feet, which was the imagined depth the rock-oil came from. In 1850 Kier built and operated a one-gallon still, America's first refinery, and peddled his remarkable "car-bon oil" panacea, by which "The Lame, through its instrumentality were made to walk—the Blind, to see." In the course of time a bottle of this miraculous nostrum made its way to New Ha-ven, Connecticut, where a group of enterprising individuals (1) organized the Seneca Oil Com-pany, (2) engaged the services of Professor Silliman of Yale University to analyze this sin-gular fluid, and (3) sent "Colonel" E. L. Drake on an expedition to Pennsylvania to drill a well to obtain the necessary ingredients for this cure-all—one of the factors leading to his selection was the fact that as a former railroad conductor he could ride on a free pass.

Silliman's analytical work proved to be an inspired undertaking. By what was essentially fractional distillation, he separated out of this black, sticky, odoriferous liquid such potentially profit-making substances as kerosene, paraffin, natural gas, and a clear, fast-burning fluid for which he could imagine no conceivable use, which later came to be known as gasoline.

Kerosene and paraffin struck a death blow to what was one of America's more picturesque and at the same time profitable industries—whal-ing out of New Bedford, Nantucket, and other New England seaports. Most people have some awareness of that primitive, harsh, courageous way of life through reading *Moby Dick,* but few have any conception of how important an indus-try it was in pre-Civil War days. In New Eng-land, in 1846, the peak year of activity, the whaling fleet numbered 736 vessels, and their crews, as well as the men engaged on shore, totaled about 70,000. It was a $70,000,000

business, and in the peak year of production, 1854, the catch amounted to 12,000,000 bar-rels of whale oil (Heizer in Pemberton, 1940). Such unrestrained activity brought about the near extinction of the world-ranging sperm whale at just about the same rate that his plains-inhabiting contemporary, the buffalo, was being exterminated.

Before the Civil War whale oil had no effec-tive competition for producing a soft and re-markably mellow light—as well as being a source of soap and a moderately effective lubricant. Today, with petroleum as a commonplace lubri-cant, few of us appreciate what a taxing prob-lem faced our ancestors with their dependence upon vegetable and animal oils. These inade-quate greases broke down under high tempera-ture, turned rancid, had no predictable operat-ing characteristics, and at some critical moment invariably failed, leaving burned bearings, fro-zen journals, and a whole succession of mechan-ical ills and blazing tempers in their train.

With the realization that oil could be recov-ered by drilling, and that it had real monetary value, a rush that defies description began in the hilly, wooded country of northwestern Pennsyl-vania along the banks and tributaries of the Allegheny River, centering in the region about Titusville.

Photographs of the oil-producing area of western Pennsylvania immediately following the Civil War show a devastated landscape, de-nuded of trees, which were replaced on hill-slopes by a forest of spidery, close-packed wooden derricks. Oil was stored in wooden-stave barrels. Sweating horses—as many as 6,000 teams were used—toiled over alternately muddy or dusty roads hauling them to the refineries. The pandemonium, smell, mess, uncontrolled waste, and unbridled greed surpassed anything conceivable to us today.

Transportation was the great bottleneck. When railroads reached Oil City and Titusville, oil was at first hauled in ordinary barrels on flat cars, then in 1865 in wooden-staved upright tanks like oversized wash tubs, and finally in 1869 in horizontal iron tanks modeled on the boilers of the day but clearly the progenitors of the modern tank car. A tremendous struggle ensued, with the railroads battling for this remunerative freight. Their friends were rewarded with profitable rebates; their enemies were punished with impossibly high charges. Actually, it was through gaining control of railroad transportation that Rockefeller and his associates stood accused of the monopolistic practices that ultimately led to the dissolution of the Standard Oil Trust in 1911.

By 1875, the Bradford field in Pennsylvania had been discovered and soon reached the impressive dimensions of 7,000 wells and a daily production of 100,000 barrels. This single field was the chief reason that Pennsylvania was the leading oil-producing state until as late as 1895. In order to battle the Rockefeller control of rail

transport, the Tide Water Pipe Company, Ltd., built the first lengthy pipe line, 110 miles long over the 2,500-foot high Appalachians from Bradford to Williamsport, Pennsylvania, and ultimately on to Bayonne, New Jersey. Its 6-inch diameter and closely spaced steam-operated pumping stations are a far cry from such titans as the trans-Arabian pipeline, with a diameter of 30 inches, but it represented a wholly new departure in transportation and was the beginning of the arterial system 200,000 miles long that criss-crosses the United States today.

FIG. 7-1 *Modern portable drilling rig on the California coast near Ventura. The well is curved or slanted beneath the ground surface, so that the bottom of the well is more than a mile away under the ocean floor. (Courtesy of Standard Oil Company of California.)*

GEOLOGIC
OCCURRENCE OF PETROLEUM

Every conceivable method was used by the oil pioneers, except science, in their search for oil in the hills and dales of Pennsylvania. According to Price (1947), "It was a popular saying among early-day oil men that 'geology never filled a tank' and one prominent producer remarked that if he wanted to make sure of a dry hole he would employ a geologist to make the location."

In spite of such slurs, the geologists of that distant time were not disheartened, and although ignored, they persisted in their theorizing. Oddly, because most of us look on it as a largely United States enterprise, the first explicit statement of the close relationship between the occurrence of oil and the structure of the enclosing rocks came from Canada. This was the

result of the studies of Sir William Logan in 1844 in the Gaspé Peninsula and of T. Sterry Hunt in 1861. Both men were impressed by the fact that tar seeps were associated with anticlinal folds. Professor E. B. Andrews of Ohio made the same observation, also in 1861, and in addition he drew a geologic map and cross section of an oil field, but he suffered the universal fate of the too-early pioneer—oblivion.

This key relationship of anticlines and oil was rediscovered in the United States by I. C. White of West Virginia and Edward Orton of Ohio. Dr. White staked his reputation in 1889 on the drilling of the Mannington field in West Virginia, at least 25 miles from the nearest producing well. His theory was abundantly vindicated, but he had to battle for at least eight years more to convince the skeptics, both professional geologists and practical oil-seekers, that geology had some relevance to the occurrence of this fugitive substance.

One of the first geologists actually hired by an oil company to look for oil was W. W. Orcutt, a Stanford classmate of Herbert Hoover, and he was employed by the Union Oil Company of California in 1899. By 1900, grudging

---

FIG. 7-2 *The vessel* Atlas, *shown at San Francisco, Calif., in the year 1907, carried packaged petroleum products to other Pacific ports. (Courtesy of Standard Oil Company of California.)*

approval had generally been won throughout the industry, and with increasing success came increasing acceptance until, today, the percentage of wildcat wells located with geological advice has risen to 83 per cent. That not all of them are crowned with success, however, is brought out in the graph (Fig. 7-3).

A question that may very well be asked here is just what has the geologist learned about oil in the sixty years he has been seeking it, during which time his employers have grown to become America's second largest industry. The answer is, a great deal, but there is still much more to be learned—possibly more than all the knowledge acquired up to now.

FIG. 7-4 *Modern tankers carry petroleum in enormous quantities over the seven seas. (Courtesy of Standard Oil Company of California.)*

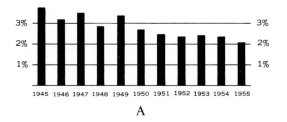

A

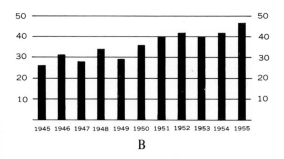

B

After J. B. Carsey and M. S. Roberts, Bull. Amer. Assoc. Petrol. Geol., vol. 46, 1962. By permission.

FIG. 7-3 *Chart A shows, for the 17 principal oil-producing states, the percentage of all the exploratory wells that discovered an oil field with more than one million barrels in reserve. If the figure one million barrels seems large, remember that the consumption of petroleum in the United States is more than seven million barrels per day. Chart B shows, for the same 17 states, the number of exploratory wells drilled for each well that discovered a new oil field with more than one million barrels in reserve.*

SOURCE BEDS

Oil clearly is related to sedimentary rocks, and its accumulation appears to be part of the normal sedimentary process, rather than some freakish event. Most oil seemingly has accumulated in sedimentary rocks deposited on the sea floor, and these apparently were laid down in shallow to moderate depths, rather than in the abyss. Although an organic versus an inorganic origin for petroleum was once vigorously debated, the fires of this controversy are quenched, and there seems to be little doubt that most petroleum started out as an organic accumulation within sediments on the sea floor.

Beyond this simple statement there is little agreement and much uncertainty. One of the essential requirements is a large and continuing supply of marine life—close to the surface of the sea. Then there should be rapid accumulation of their dead remains on the sea floor, followed by burial that is quick enough so that decay is inhibited and the natural distillation of the organic litter can commence. An additional factor that seems helpful is the accumulation of organic debris in a nearly enclosed basin where circulation of water is at a minimum and oxidation is retarded. Examples of such basins today are the Persian Gulf, the Red and Black Seas, and the bottoms of some of the Norwegian fjords.

Nearly all sedimentary rocks, with the exception of some unusual types, such as red beds, contain significant amounts of organic matter. Oddly enough, the amount present seemingly bears little or no relationship to the color. Formerly it was believed that black or dark-colored rocks are the only ones rich in oil, but this need not be true. At most the organic content of typical marine sediments is low, seldom does it exceed 5 or 10 per cent. How this organic matter is converted into the liquid hydrocarbon, petroleum, is still unknown, but the evidence is strong that burial is required, and perhaps not too great a lapse of time, although some geologists are convinced that at least a million years are necessary.

RESERVOIR ROCKS

More than source sediments are required to make a successful oil field, because as a rule their organic content is too slight and, since many of them are shales, their permeability is too low to permit oil to flow freely and relatively rapidly—an essential requirement for a producing oil well. What is needed next is a reservoir rock. Nearly 60 per cent of the world's petroleum reserves are in sandstone, the remaining 40 per cent are in limestone, dolomite, etc., and perhaps 1 per cent are contained in other rocks which are sufficiently fractured to permit oil to accumulate. This means that some time after its formation in source rocks, oil has migrated slowly to be concentrated in more permeable strata, such as sandstone and limestone.

Oil might well escape from its reservoir unless there is some sort of lid, and this is the *cap rock*. This may be nothing more elaborate than a stratum of fine-grained shale overlying the more permeable reservoir rock. All it need be is a layer of such low permeability that it acts as a diaphragm, preventing the upward escape of oil.

STRUCTURAL TRAPS

Anticlines

The third requirement is some sort of *trap*. This usually means some kind of geological structure that (1) retards the free migration of oil and (2) concentrates the oil in a limited space. The most common of such traps is the anticline, and as pointed out earlier, this is the structural control that was deduced in 1885 by I. C. White. The basic factors needed to make such a trap operate are shown by the cross section of the Kettleman Hills, California (Fig. 7-5). The reservoir rock which crops out in Reef Ridge picks up water at the surface of the ground, and as this water travels through the permeable reservoir rock it does two things: (1) builds up an increasing hydrostatic pressure with depth, and (2) carries the oil along with it.

When the natural gas-oil-water mixture reaches the anticlinal crest, the three constituents have an opportunity to separate from one another on the basis of their density differences. Most of the natural gas rises to the crest of the fold, and since oil is lighter than water it rises to the next higher level in the structure. Actually, these three constituents do not separate quite so tidily; a considerable amount of water may be mixed with the oil as an emulsion, just as a good deal of gas will be dissolved in the oil. This gas is of the greatest importance in the productive life of an oil field. Gas pressure can be utilized to drive oil to the surface in the early life of a well drilled near the top of a structure. Eventually, the pressure declines, and the well is no longer free flowing, but has to be pumped. As the oil in the main part of the anticlinal structure is withdrawn, water at the edge of the

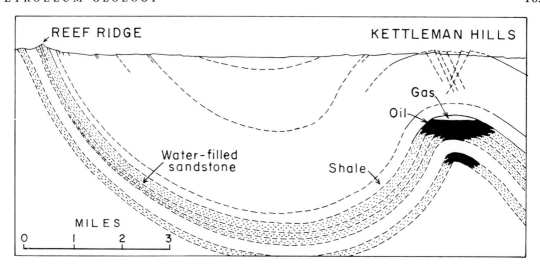

From J. Galloway, "Kettleman Hills Oil Fields," 1943. By permission of California State Division of Mines.

FIG. 7-5 *Cross section from Reef Ridge on the west to the Kettleman Hills on the east showing the distribution of gas, oil, and water in porous sandstone. The oil is held in the anticlinal trap by the overlying cap rock of shale.*

FIG. 7-6 *The Long Beach, Calif., oil field in 1941. The trap is an anticline and the hill (Signal Hill) reflects the underlying structure. This prolific field, discovered in 1921, had produced by the end of 1961 more than 819 million barrels of oil from its 1,235 productive acres, an average of nearly 700,000 barrels per acre. (Photograph by Spence Air Photos.)*

FIG. 7-7 *The famous Lakeview No. 1 gusher, Kern County, Calif. The figures in the foreground are reflected in a pool of oil. (Courtesy of Union Oil Company of California.)*

hundreds of feet into the air to tower above the floor of the San Joaquin Valley. The whole derrick collapsed into the crater that had been blasted out of the ground. The flow in the first twenty-four hours was estimated at 125,000 barrels and for months afterwards was around 50,000 barrels per day. No available storage capacity could hope to hold the tide—at least 600 men, with scores of them hauled out of bars and hobo jungles all over California, were sent to dig ditches and build reservoirs to stem the flood. By building earth dams across the nearby creeks, a series of immense oil lakes was created which impounded at least 9,000,000 barrels of oil before the gusher subsided after 18 months of uncontrolled flow (Taylor and Welty, 1950). The economic effect of such an inundation was to flood the limited market of that day and to drive the price of oil down to 30 cents a barrel.

The world is not likely to see such a spectacle again. Today, with half a century of experience and a whole arsenal of technology, gushers are virtually extinct. We can only lament the passing of a more colorful age.

Salt Domes

Another gusher that made history blew in on January 10, 1901, when Captain A. F. Lucas, whose determination was only equaled by his ignorance of geology, drilled a well on an unobtrusive little hill at Spindletop, near Beaumont, Texas. It blew in as an uncontrolled gas-propelled fury in the same way as Lakeview did nearly a decade later, and as a consequence the Texas Gulf Coast was swept up in a speculative frenzy that was the equal of the Pennsylvania scramble of a generation before. Without knowing how on earth it had happened, the dazed captain had discovered a second major type of structural trap—the *salt dome*. Oil can be trapped against the impervious salt, especially where strata are bent up around its margin, as at Avery Island, Louisiana (Fig. 6-16).

fold and at the oil-water interface moves into the space once occupied by the oil and then this part of the field is through.

Few more spectacular examples could be cited of the efficacy of expanding gas in driving oil to the surface than the Lakeview gusher in California (Fig. 7-7). This potential one-well oil field was taken over by the Union Oil Company after the four original drillers gave up at a depth of 1,800 feet following a succession of setbacks, financial, and technical. When Union took over the drilling, no one could possibly have forecast what was to come. On March 14, 1910, Lakeview No. 1 blew in totally out of control with a column of oil and gas that rose

Scores of similar structures are found along the coastal margin of Texas and Louisiana, as well as off-shore in the Gulf of Mexico. Their discovery has required the expenditure of millions of dollars and the utilization of the full resources of geology and geophysics, since a surface indication of these inscrutable structures is a rarity.

Stratigraphic Traps

The East Texas field, the largest single oil field in the Western Hemisphere and one of the most prolific in this country's history, with a total production of around 3,000,000,000 barrels, could scarcely have selected a worse time for its debut. In 1931, the nadir of the depression, it loosed a flood of oil upon an unwilling market, resulting in a drop in price to 10 cents a barrel.

This sea of oil is concentrated, not along an anticlinal axis, but in a stellar example of a third type of accumulation—the so-called *stratigraphic trap*. The oil is trapped under an unconformity where the gently dipping reservoir rock wedges out beneath the overlying impervious layer; actually, the field is at the intersection of two unconformity planes.

Organic Reefs

An unusual type of trap because of the exotic imagery it provides is a buried, or fossil, *organic reef*, such as a former coral reef. These are analogous in their form to that of living reefs, which are described in Chapter XIV, except, of course, for their burial under later sediments. Perhaps the best known of such structural traps are the oil fields of Canada, near Leduc, Alberta, and those in north central Texas.

The nature of such a structure is shown in cross section in Fig. 7-8, which is that of the so-called Golden Lane of Mexico. The main thing to notice is that sediments, which once were muds, terminate abruptly against limestone, which once was the main body of the reef. Limestone, if cavernous, holds oil, and once this narrow, buried limestone ridge near Tampico, nearly 50 miles long but mostly less than a mile wide, held more than a billion barrels. The all-time wonder well of oil history, Potrero del Llano No. 4, came in as a gusher

FIG. 7-8 *Cross section of the Golden Lane, Mexico. (Courtesy of Petroleos Mexicanos.)*

After D. W. Rockwell and A. G. Rojas, Bull. Amer. Assoc. Petrol. Geol., vol. 37, 1953. By permission.

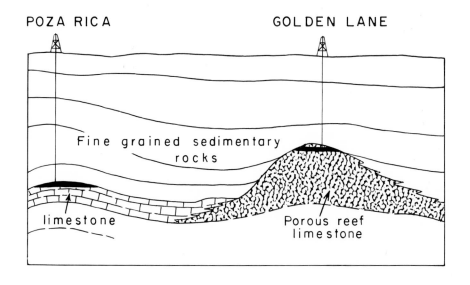

POZA RICA   GOLDEN LANE

Fine grained sedimentary rocks

limestone   Porous reef limestone

with a daily production of 260,000 barrels, and a total output of around 60 million barrels, until one awful night when it failed completely and went to salt water.

There is a wide variety of other structural traps, which make interesting challenges for the geologist but quantitatively are not very impor-

tant. Among these are accumulations of petroleum along faults. These may act as an impervious membrane against which oil collects when its flow is halted along a reservoir bed (Fig. 7-9). The relative economic importance of a variety of structural traps described in this chapter are shown in Fig. 7-10.

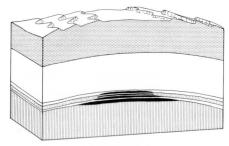

ANTICLINE

FIG. 7-9 *Cross section of the Ventura Basin, Calif., showing accumulations of oil (in solid black) at the right, below Santa Paula Peak, trapped beneath the San Cayetano Fault. Movement along the fault totals about three miles, so that the rocks exposed on Santa Paula Peak are much older than the lowest rocks shown in the syncline at the center of the section. At the left, oil is shown in the anticline of South Mountain, and oil also occurs nearby trapped beneath the Oak Ridge Fault. Movement of more than three miles has also taken place along this fault. Rocks once continuous with strata in the lowest left hand part of the syncline beneath the fault have been raised to the highest part of South Mountain.*

From T. L. Bailey and R. Jahns, "Geology of the Transverse Range Province, Southern California," 1954. By permission of California State Division of Mines.

FIG. 7-10 *Types of oil traps shown in their order of economic importance. Anticlines and salt domes account for about 58 per cent of the oil fields and 80 per cent of the world's total oil production. Faults, organic reefs, stratigraphic combination and other traps are far less important.*

Compiled from publications of the Standard Oil Company of California and Standard Oil Company of New Jersey. By permission.

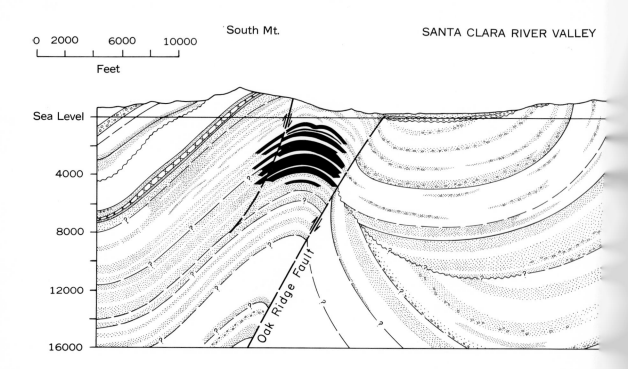

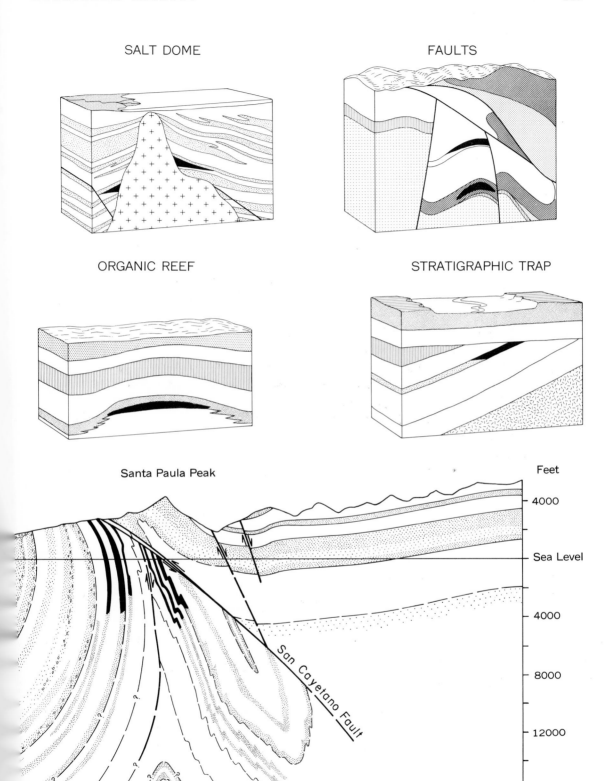

SALT DOME

FAULTS

ORGANIC REEF

STRATIGRAPHIC TRAP

Santa Paula Peak

Feet

4000

Sea Level

4000

8000

San Cayetano Fault

12000

16000

THE MODERN ERA

Although the first half of this oil century was turbulent, it pales by comparison with the revolutionary events that rocked it in the past fifty years—among these are two wars that literally involved all mankind and that were separated from each other by a major depression. As though these were not enough, the exponentially rapid growth of population which coincided with the world-wide spread of the internal combustion engine created a tremendous demand. The automobile began to appear in quantity in 1903, although at first still a curiosity. The truck, tank, airplane, and submarine were to play decisive roles in the 1914-18 war, only eleven years later.

Most of the world powers, consciously or unconsciously preparing for war in this critical decade, sought sources of oil that could be depended upon. The great need, as they saw it then, was for fuel for naval vessels. This was an impressive need and readily grasped by anyone who has ever seen the diabolical scene unveiled in the fire room of a coal-burning ship as compared with the orderly concentration of power in its oil-burning counterpart. A coal-burning ship could keep at sea for only short periods of time, great numbers of men were required to stoke this sooty fuel, great volumes of space had to be surrendered for its storage, and coaling in an out-of-the-way port was indescribably laborious and dangerously time-consuming during a war.

Although many admirals of that day were violently opposed to such an innovation in the Royal Navy—they had scarcely recovered from the shock of a generation before of having to give up their beloved sails and wooden decks —they encountered two dynamic advocates of the conversion to oil in the persons of Lord Fisher, the First Sea Lord, and his chief supporter, Winston Churchill, then First Lord of the Admiralty. Since there are no significant oil deposits in Britain, England turned to the Middle East in its search for an overseas source.

In America the forces in our economy that were unleashed following World War I and which reached their zenith in 1929 had a profound effect upon the oil industry. During this decade many of the American oil companies whose brand names are familiar today came into being, and it was also the great discovery period for new fields and new oil provinces in the United States.

In the beginning, as in Pennsylvania, oil fields were found (1) by sheer accident, (2) by drilling near oil seeps, or (3) by a few tentative applications of geology. From 1900 to roughly the mid-'twenties a strenuous search for anticlines ensued, and these were located largely by measuring dips and strikes, by following the course of strata across country, and by preparing geologic maps showing the distribution and attitude of rocks. A powerful adjunct, then and now, was the use of paleontology, or the study of fossils. Through their careful identification and comparison with other fossils whose geologic age was established, the age of their host rocks could be determined. Thus, in places where the structure was complicated, the relative order of the strata could be disentangled. Microscopic animals and plants are the more important of these extinct organisms because their tiny remains can be recovered in rock cores taken during the drilling of the well (Fig. 7-11).

By the mid-'twenties, when surface geology was approaching the point of diminishing returns in many areas, geophysics—or the branch of science concerned with the physical properties of the Earth—came up with two tremendously effective tools that enabled geologists to interpret the structure of the rocks down to depths of many thousands of feet, and often in areas where there were no surface outcrops at all. The first of these methods involved the measuring of local differences in gravity, at first with a torsion balance and more recently with a gravity meter. Gravity differences are measurable over such structures as the salt domes of the Gulf Coast—the density of salt is less than that of the surrounding rock, with the result that a gravity meter set up over a buried salt dome yields a lower reading than it does over the surrounding rock. Such an area is said to have a *negative gravity anomaly*.

Seismic surveying is a more dramatic geophysical method, and has been employed successfully since 1924. Basically it consists of creating an artificial earthquake by setting off a dynamite blast at the bottom of a shallow drilled well (Fig. 7-12) and then picking up on recording instruments the elastic waves reflected back to the surface of the ground from the various rock layers within the Earth's outer shell. From the resulting records a reasonably accurate in-

terpretation of the underlying structure can be made.

The ultimate test remains the drill. Only by actually drilling a well can we establish whether or not there is oil in the earth. That this has become an increasingly expensive and uncertain business is shown by the accompanying graphs (Figs. 7-4 and 7-13). The first shows that 48 dry holes had to be drilled for each profitable oil discovery in 1955. The second shows how the postwar surge of exploratory history appears to have reached a peak in 1956, and also dramatizes how great a gamble the oil industry faces in attempting to develop reserves for the future.

FIG. 7-11 *Shells of microscopic protozoans, the Foraminifera, are extracted from cores of sedimentary rock. (Courtesy of Standard Oil Company of California.)*

FIG. 7-12 *Water and mud spout from a "shot hole" as an explosive charge is set off to create an artificial earthquake in seismic exploration for oil. (Photograph by Anthony E. L. Morris.)*

WHAT OF THE FUTURE?

Since the beginning of the first act, the oil industry has had its Greek chorus on one side predicting financial chaos, exhaustion of reserves, and the probability of running out of oil; while on the other side of the stage an equally vociferous chorus has kept up a continuous clamor about our ever-expanding reserves and discoveries that are sure to meet our every need and requirement, *ad infinitum.* Which is one to believe?

Probably, like many things in life, the truth lies somewhere between these extremes. An analysis of the whole fossil fuel problem made by M. King Hubbert of the Shell Oil Company (1956) gives a very fair projection of what the

FIG. 7-13 *An estimate of the future oil prospects of the United States. Each rectangle represents 25 billion barrels of oil. The black area, cumulative production to 1956, amounts to 53 billion barrels. The stippled area, proved reserves, amounts to 30 billion barrels. The lower dashed curve is drawn so that the area under it, added to the cumulative production and the proved reserves, amounts to 150 billion barrels, an estimated ultimate production or total amount of oil available. The upper dashed curve is similar, but for an estimated ultimate production of 200 billion barrels.*

After M. K. Hubbert, 1956. By permission of Shell Development Co. and American Petroleum Institute.

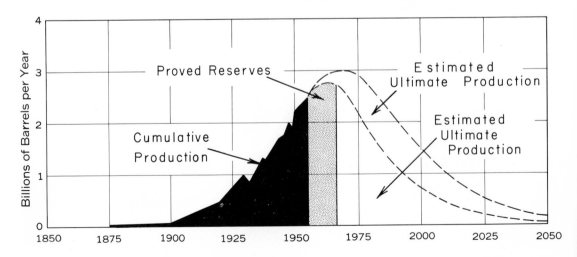

future is likely to hold. Hubbert points out that of the 53 billion barrels of oil produced in the United States between 1859 and 1955, the first half required eighty years—from 1859 to 1939 to be produced, while the last half has been taken out of the ground in the past sixteen years. This means that a withdrawal rate as steep as the one shown by the curve in Fig. 7-13, is not likely to last forever. Before 1859, as Hubbert indicates, our production of oil for all practical purposes was zero, and again at some future date it will become zero. Somewhere between these limits there will be a day when production reaches a peak. Ideally, such a curve would look like that of Fig. 7-13. Rarely is such perfection of form attained in the real world, but an approximation of its form is expectable. In other words, if the rate of exploitation is extremely rapid for a finite resource, such as oil, then the rate of decline very likely will be steep also. This is especially likely to be true if our demand continues to rise with an increasing population and ever-increasing use of internal combustion engines.

A good estimate for the total ultimate production of the United States is between 150 and 200 billion barrels. Should this be so, then the arrival of the high point cannot be long delayed if oil continues to be withdrawn at anything like its present rate. If the 150 billion figure is used, then the peak of the curve should almost be here; if the 200 billion total should prove valid, it also will not be long delayed and very likely should arrive about 1970 (Fig. 7-13).

Another point to consider is that the graph (Fig. 7-13) is drawn so that each rectangle equals 25 billion barrels. Under the curve there are six rectangles, and since the total production to date is about 50 billion barrels, then four rectangles are left. "Also," as Hubbert says, "since the production rate is still increasing, the ultimate production peak must be greater than the present rate of production and must occur some time in the future. At the same time, it is impossible to delay the peak

for more than a few years and still allow time for the unavoidable prolonged period of decline due to the slowing rates of extraction from depleting reservoirs."

This is *not* to say that all the oil wells will suddenly run dry in 1965 or 1970; it *does* mean that if our present or anticipated demand is to be satisfied we shall have to look beyond our shores. This, of course, the American oil companies have long been doing. Fortunately for us the threatened oil shortages in the early 1920's, in addition to the spectacular eruption of Mexican oil along the banks of the Tuxpan River, served as a stimulus to send American geologists venturing over the world.

OIL OVERSEAS

The map of the world (Fig. 7-14) showing where the leading oil producing areas are located indicates the existence of two major centers. One is the region bordering the Gulf of Mexico-Caribbean Sea, the other is around the Persian Gulf. Scores of lesser areas, such as California, Canada, the Caucasus, and the Far East obscure this generalization, but large as these others are individually they are substantially less than the two giants. What the future will hold, no man living today can say; but with the results of more than half a century of field work to draw upon, geologists are gaining some insight into the structure and distribution of rocks in the Earth's crust. They know, too, that the search for large accumulations of oil is limited to areas underlain by marine sedimentary rocks which additionally must have been deposited in rather specialized environments and must also meet the additional requirements outlined earlier that are needed to make a successful oil field.

The consensus reached by most geologists is that the general pattern of distribution is not likely to change in the next decade or so. The

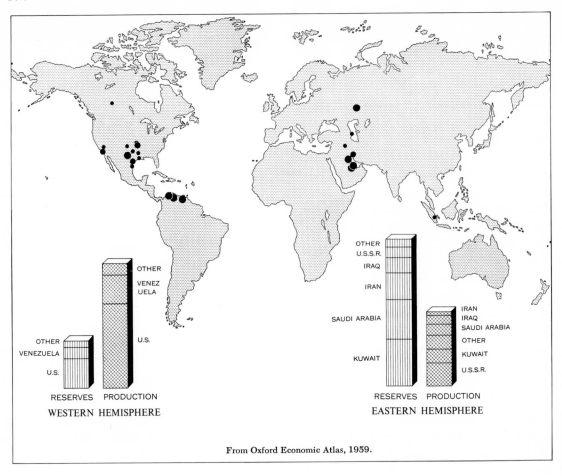

From Oxford Economic Atlas, 1959.

FIG. 7-14 *Principal world oil occurrences.*

map (Fig. 7-15) of the international flow of petroleum shows how this pattern is developing, and may also give us a glimpse of future trends. In 1946 the United States was a net exporter of oil; today we import more than we send abroad. Although the 1959 map still shows an external flow, this is less than the amount reaching our shores, which now (1962) is more than 1,000,000 barrels per day.

The Caribbean sends most of its oil to us, where a decade ago it went to Europe. Most of the Caribbean oil comes from Venezuela, which is now the second-largest producing country in the world, with an output of about 3,000,000 barrels a day; other sizable contributors are

Colombia, about 125,000 barrels per day, and Trinidad, with slightly less than 100,000.

THE MIDDLE EAST

Here in these hot and burning lands bordering the Persian Gulf is concentrated the largest single reservoir of energy yet known on the Earth's surface. The occurrence of oil has been recorded here since the dim beginnings of history. Noah's Ark was caulked with bitumen. This is the "hot, and fiery earth" of ancient Babylon as described by Plutarch. Tar seeps are common throughout the Middle East and asphalt has been used for caulking boats and as a construction material from Nebuchadnezzar's day to this. Gas, escaping from such seeps, when ignited burned for years, and quite understandably this may have laid the foundations for fire worship in ancient Persia.

Persia once included Baku, which lies on the Caspian Sea at the east end of the Caucasus Mountains, and this prolific area of gas and oil springs was visited by Marco Polo in A.D. 1271 (Forbes, 1958), who said:

On the confines (of Armenia) towards Zorziana (Georgia) there is a fountain from which oil springs in abundance, insomuch that a hundred shiploads might be taken from it at one time. This oil is not good to use with food, but 't is good to burn, and also to anoint camels that have the mange. People come from vast distances to fetch it, for in all the countries round about they have no other oil.

FIG. 7-15 *The chart shows the world's flow of oil by tankers in the year 1959. The relative amounts of oil transported are indicated by the thickness of the arrows. At that time the United States exported 80 thousand barrels per day and imported 1,350 thousand barrels per day, of which almost two-thirds came from Venezuela.*

From Aramco Handbook, 1960. By permission of Arab. Amer. Oil Co.

Two centuries later another Venetian, Giosafo Barbaro, passed the same way, and his account is an interesting display of truly permissive spelling. The camels seem not to have improved in 200 years of anointing either:

Vpon this syde of the sea there is an other citie called Bachu, whereof the sea of Bachu taketh name, neere vnto which citie there is a montaigne that casteth foorthe black oyle, stynkeng hooryblye, which they, nevertheless, vse for furnissheng of their lytes and for anoynteng of their camells twice a yere. For if they were not anoynted they wolde become skabbie.

A prize as important as this was not to be overlooked, and Russia moved in to seize Baku from Persia at the time of Czarist expansion into the trans-Caucasus, or what is now the Georgian SSR. The oil fields bordering the Caucasus are still among the leading producers of the Soviet Union. It was to capture them that Hitler sent the Wehrmacht on its way to defeat at Stalingrad (now Volgograd) in World War II.

After centuries of neglect, the possibility of the Middle East as a source of oil began to occur to the western world around the beginning

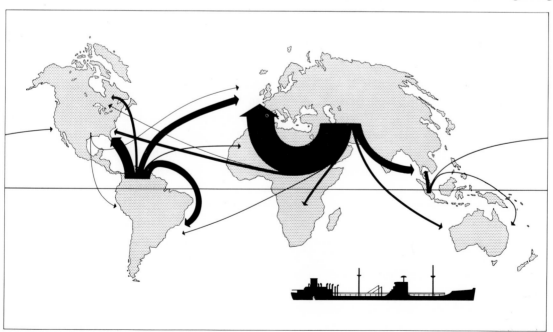

of the century. From then on a drama more fascinating than anything out of the Arabian Nights has unfolded, involving intrigue, conflicts of national interest, anti-colonial uprisings, maneuver and countermaneuver, and punctuated with revolt and assassination. Because of the importance of this energy pool to the economy of the western world, a brief résumé of some of the significant highlights of this story is outlined here.

Before World War I there were only two major powers to be reckoned with in the Middle East: the Ottoman Empire under the Sultan at Constantinople and Persia under the Shah at Teheran.

Iran

The Shah gave an exclusive concession for developing the country's oil resources in 1901 to William Knox D'Arcy, an adventurer of the Elizabethan mold. After the usual staggering defeats and difficulties, oil was discovered in 1908 at what was to become the great Masjid-i-Sulaiman (Mosque of Solomon) oil field. By this time D'Arcy had disappeared and the Anglo-Persian Oil Company was created in 1909 with the old Burmah Oil Company as a leading participant and the British Admiralty as a silent partner. By 1914 the British government had the controlling (51%) interest. Winston Churchill and Lord Fisher were the leading architects of this enterprise, and by this maneuver the Royal Navy was guaranteed a plentiful supply of fuel oil.

In the postwar era the name of Persia was changed to Iran, and Anglo-Persian obligingly became the Anglo-Iranian Oil Company. The fires of nationalism continued to mount, however, and finally in 1951 under Premier Mossadeq, Anglo-Iranian was confiscated. After a chaotic period during which Iranian production practically ceased, and the world's largest refinery at Abadan languished, a new agreement was reached in 1954 and a many-headed entity,

a consortium, was created to operate the oil fields. National interests were represented as follows: United States, 40%; Great Britain, 40%; British-Dutch, 14%; French, 6%.

The geology of Iran is complex, and folds and faults abound. In such an arid land the rock structure stands out boldly, and many of the anticlines in which the oil fields are located are impressive landforms. Among the more amazing geological features of Iran are the salt domes which, unlike those of the Gulf Coast of the United States, break through to the ground surface. In such a dry climate, some of these "salt glaciers" form the highest points of the landscape—4,000 to 5,000 feet—and stand well above their encircling limestone escarpments.

Iraq

Before World War I the Sultan of Turkey was being vigorously courted by both the British and Germans. Part of German foreign policy was to build a railroad from the Bosporus—the Ottoman-Anatolian—to the head of the Persian Gulf to circumvent British control of Suez. As part of this general scheme, the Turkish Petroleum Company was organized in 1912, largely as the creation of an Armenian entrepreneur, C. S. Gulbenkian. Immediately, a great squabble ensued between all the parties competing for pieces of the tottering Ottoman Empire. The disputants met in the Foreign Office in London in 1914, and after a considerable amount of infighting came up with a participation plan consisting of Deutsche Bank (Germany) 25%, and British interests, 50%. Shortly thereafter an even more acrimonious dispute broke out among the partners, and when the smoke cleared away in 1918, the Germans were out and the French and British were in.

At that time, the principal oil fields of the Middle East, aside from Persia, were in Mesopotamia. When the new country of Iraq was created as part of the postwar establishment of spheres of influence, the rights of the old Turkish Petroleum Company went with the new country. Who was to exercise these rights, though? A thorny question, indeed, and one which was resolved by dividing up the pie directly between England and France, with France receiving the original German 25%. Calouste Gulbenkian set up an immediate outcry, and shortly thereafter the United States put in a plea for some tangible recognition of the role it played in the 1914-1918 war. By 1928 the long negotiations were terminated with the creation of the Iraq Petroleum Company, Ltd., in which the various slices were distributed: United States, 23.75%; Great Britain, 23.75%; British-Dutch, 23.75%; French, 23.75%, and C. S. Gulbenkian, 5%. Incidentally, Gulbenkian's share, in addition to other fortunate ventures, served to make him for many years the world's wealthiest individual.

A curious aside in this corporate confederacy was the so-called self-denial clause, or "red-line agreement." This was based on a line drawn on a map at the San Remo Conference around the limits of the former Ottoman Empire. Within the limits set by this line each of the participants agreed not to carry on negotiations or exploration of its own—a sort of all for one and one for all arrangement.

The fields of Iraq are comparatively simple anticlines and organic reefs, and their production runs around 700,000 barrels a day. Few countries have been beset with more difficulties or problems, and what the future holds is inscrutable. A large share of Iraq's production moves to the Mediterranean by pipeline, a politically vulnerable route. The original pipeline across Israel has been closed for years, and during 1956 the pumping stations in Syria were blown up.

Kuwait

This tiny sheikdom at the head of the Persian Gulf, with dimensions of only 50 by 80 miles, seems like a blanket of sand floating on a lake of oil, the Burgan oil field. It is worth reflecting that the proved reserves of this one field, 40 billion barrels, are greater than *all* the proved reserves of *all* the United States, 30 billion barrels.

Kuwait was a pawn of power politics in World War I. It seceded from the Ottoman Empire shortly before the war, and perhaps was too far from Constantinople for the Sultan to do much about this lack of fealty. Kuwait was part of the Anatolian railroad project, and was to be a German-operated seaport at the head of the Persian Gulf.

Many years later the effect of this secession was to place Kuwait outside the limits of the red-line agreement. As a consequence, the partners within Iraq Petroleum Company did not have to practice self-denial here. As a result of an ardent courtship, the Sultan of Kuwait signed up with *both* the leading suitors—in this case Gulf Oil Company (United States) and Anglo-Iranian (now British Petroleum Company, Ltd.) —as equal partners in Kuwait Oil Company.

The oil fields of Kuwait are very broad anticlines with gently dipping strata on their flanks. The production curve from Kuwait's three oil fields has risen from practically zero in 1945 to 1,400,000 barrels a day in 1958. The result has been to launch this minute sheikdom, which was little more than an impoverished sand dune through the centuries, into one of the most elaborate self-betterment programs of all time.

Saudi Arabia

Over much of its surface this is the true Arabia Deserta, the most barren land on Earth (Fig. 12-14). It is also the site of the Holy Cities of the Islamic world, and every year thousands of the faithful make the pilgrimage to Mecca.

During the years of Turkish rule this far-off, desolate land received scant notice, although it, too, played a part in German expansionist schemes. Germans were responsible for the construction of the Hejaz railroad down the west side of the Arabian Peninsula, built in an attempt to gain control of the pilgrim traffic to Mecca. The destruction of this railroad in World War I makes some of the more stirring episodes in the books, plays, and movies of and about Lawrence of Arabia.

Beginning in 1902, ibn Sa'ud, the dedicated enemy of the reigning Hashemite clan, led a series of forays against them. Although the Hashemites were supported by the British, ibn Sa'ud succeeded in bringing almost all of Arabia under his control, especially after the capture of the capital, Riyadh, and of Mecca. The Kingdom of Saudi Arabia was established in about its present form in 1932.

In this same year, the Sheik of Bahrein, on an island in the Persian Gulf off the Arabian coast, signed a concession with the Standard Oil Company of California. A well was drilled shortly afterward and oil was discovered to the great surprise of many geologists active in that part of the world. The oil-bearing formations here are wholly different from those in Iran,

directly across the Persian Gulf. For this reason, geologists working in Iran had looked with disfavor on Arabia as a possible oil source—an expensive point of view to maintain as later events were to prove.

Although Bahrein was an important discovery, it was not an immense one. It did have the significant effect of opening the eyes of California Standard's geologists to possibilities that might lie ahead on the Arabian mainland. An agreement was reached with ibn Sa'ud in 1933, after he rejected an offer made by Iraq Petroleum Company, and suddenly a moderate sized California oil company found itself carrying on an exploratory campaign half a world away in some of the world's most desolate terrain, a region culturally remote from ours, unchanged since the time of the Crusades.

A major oil field was discovered in 1938 at Damman near the coast after five years of toil and frustration. In succession thereafter the great fields of Arabia were brought in. Chief among these is Ghawar, surely the *Moby Dick* of the oil business, which was found in 1948. The productive portion of this immense structure has an area of 875 square miles and a length of at least 140 miles.

Such an endeavor as operating the oil fields of Arabia proved to be beyond the resources of a single company, with the result that the Texas Company acquired a half-interest in 1936, and in 1944 the present name of Arabian American Oil Company was adopted. In 1948 both the Standard Oil Company (New Jersey) and the Socony Mobil Oil Company became participants. This required some adroit maneuvering since both these corporations were part of the Iraq Petroleum Company. They were bound, therefore, by the red-line agreement since Saudi Arabia had once been part of the Ottoman Empire. A heated dispute arose, which was finally resolved by the dissolution of the agreement. Aramco, now the second largest producer in the Middle East, is exceeded only by Kuwait Oil Company, and in this world of complex corpo-

FIG. 7-16 *Saudi Arab drilling crew at work in Arabia. (Courtesy of Aramco.)*

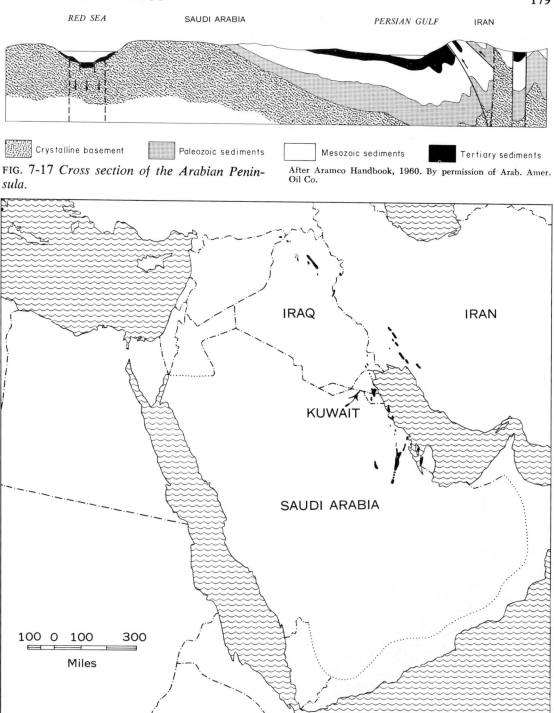

RED SEA   SAUDI ARABIA   PERSIAN GULF   IRAN

[Legend:] Crystalline basement   Paleozoic sediments   Mesozoic sediments   Tertiary sediments

FIG. 7-17 *Cross section of the Arabian Peninsula.*

After Aramco Handbook, 1960. By permission of Arab. Amer. Oil Co.

IRAQ   IRAN

KUWAIT

SAUDI ARABIA

100 0 100   300
Miles

FIG. 7-18 *The oil fields around the Persian Gulf, shown in black.*

After Aramco Handbook, 1960. By permission of Arab. Amer. Oil Co.

rate and national entanglements is unique as being one of the few wholly American ventures. Its ownership is now divided as follows: Standard of California, 30%; Texaco, 30%; Standard Oil Company (N.J.), 30%; Socony Mobil Oil Company, 10%.

The cross section (Fig. 7-17) shows that the Arabian Peninsula is essentially a very broad platform of igneous and metamorphic rocks covered with a veneer of sediments that dip eastward toward the Persian Gulf. In this sedimentary blanket the broad anticlines are found that hold this dark flood of oil. Some of the uniquely noteworthy features of these Middle Eastern fields are: the region has been explored geologically mostly in only the past twenty-five years; during this time a total of thirty fields has been discovered, including the largest sandstone and the largest limestone field in the world (Fig. 7-18). The proved reserves of the Middle East are at least three times greater than those of the United States, and possibly even more. A

FIG. 7-19 *Exploration for oil has moved off the land and out to sea. The picture shows a movable drilling barge at work in the Gulf of Mexico. A helicopter, on the landing platform at the left, transports the drilling crew back and forth. A permanent type of drilling platform is shown in the upper right section of the picture. (Courtesy of Humble Oil and Refining Company.)*

conservative estimate would be 34 billion barrels for North America and 126 billion barrels for the Middle East. More exuberant, but very plausible, estimates for the Middle East are as high as 230 billion barrels.

The discovery rate in the Middle East has been running at an average of 10 billion barrels a year, which means an addition of oil to the world's supply at the rate of 27 million barrels a day.

Here the story pauses, but the search for sources of energy will continue during our lifetime, and the demands for new sources and new applications are almost certain to mount. Perhaps this discussion has strayed a bit from what might be viewed as the orthodox concern of geology, but there is no other aspect of the science today that is so closely identified with our pattern of living, or even our survival. Exploration provides the lifeblood of the industry, and in the final analysis, exploration is the application of the principles of geology to the problem of finding oil in the Earth.

Suggested References

There is no dearth of reading matter on this topic, from the political and financial columns of the daily paper and many leading magazines to the most abstruse treatises on reservoir mechanics. Scores of books and pamphlets covering the many phases of the oil industry appear almost daily, and these require careful discrimination in their reading. Special pleading flourishes, and reading must be done with understanding if the truth is to be found, or even if reality is to be distinguished from excessive optimism or pessimism.

Most of the leading oil companies issue publications, such as annual reports and employee and stockholder magazines, many of which contain articles of general interest as well as of specific concern to their own organization. Among these, some of the outstanding ones are: *The Lamp*, Standard Oil Company (New Jersey); *Aramco World*, Arabian American Oil Company; *El Farol* (in Spanish), Creole Oil Company; *The Humble*

Way, Humble Oil and Refining Company; *The Bulletin*, Standard Oil Company of California; *The Texaco Star*, Texaco; and *The Pipeliner*, El Paso Natural Gas Company.

Ayres, Eugene, and Scarlott, C. A., 1952, Energy sources—The wealth of the world, McGraw-Hill Book Co., Inc., New York.

Ayres, Eugene, 1956, The age of fossil fuels, in Man's role in changing the face of the earth, Univ. of Chicago Press, Chicago, Ill.

Ball, Max, 1940, This fascinating oil business, Bobbs-Merrill Co., Indianapolis, Ind.

Christie, J. J., and others, 1959, Centennial issue, Amer. Petroleum Inst., Quarterly.

Fanning, L. M., 1936, The rise of American oil, Harper and Bros., New York.

————, 1950, Our oil resources, McGraw-Hill Book Co., Inc., New York.

Forbes, R. J., 1958, Studies in early petroleum history, E. J. Brill, Leiden, Netherlands.

Hubbert, M. K., 1956, Nuclear energy and fossil fuels, Drilling and Production Practices, Amer. Petrol. Inst.

Knebel, G. M., and Rodrigues-Eraso, Guillermo, 1956, Habitat of oil, Amer. Assoc. Petrol. Geol., Bull., v. 40, p. 547-561.

Knowles, Ruth S., 1959, The greatest gamblers, McGraw-Hill Book Co., Inc., New York.

Lebkircher, Roy, Rentz, George, Steineke, Max, and others, 1960, Aramco handbook, Arabian Amer. Oil Co., New York.

Levorsen, A. I., 1954, Geology of petroleum, W. H. Freeman and Co., San Francisco.

Longhurst, Henry, 1959, Adventure in oil, Sidgwick and Jackson, London (story of British Petroleum Co.).

Murphy, C. V. J., 1956, Oil east of Suez, Fortune, v. LIV, p. 131-138, p. 255-256.

Pemberton, J. R., 1940, Economics of the oil and gas industry in California, Calif. Div. of Mines, Bull. 118, p. 3-14.

Pratt, W. E., 1942, Oil in the earth, Univ. of Kansas Press, Lawrence, Kans.

Pratt, W. E., and Good, Dorothy, 1950, World geography of petroleum, Amer. Geog. Soc., Spec. Publ., Princeton Univ. Press, Princeton, N. J.

Price, P. H., 1947, Evolution of geologic thought in prospecting for oil and natural gas, Amer. Assoc. Petrol. Geol., Bull., v. 31, p. 673-697.

Taylor, F. J., and Welty, E. M., 1950, Black bonanza, McGraw-Hill Book Co., Inc., New York (story of Union Oil Co. of California).

Weeks, L. G., and others, 1958, Habitat of oil, Amer. Assoc. Petrol. Geol., Tulsa, Okla.

Lettuce field, Salinas Valley, California. (Photograph by Ansel Adams.)

VIII

Ground Water

"In Xanadu did Kubla Khan
A stately pleasure-dome decree
Where Alph, the sacred river, ran
Through caverns measureless to man
Down to a sunless sea."

Coleridge's verse quoted above reflects a re-markable image of most people's picture of the nature of water within the Earth. Many of us are prone to speak glibly of underground rivers flowing for miles beneath the parched surface of some of the world's most absolute deserts, and to many of us springs are nearly as mys-terious as they were to men of long ago.

Springs played a leading role in Greek and Roman mythology. An example is the spring of Arethusa, named for the water nymph, which appeared in the harbor of Syracuse when she was abducted by the river god Alpheus. This gave rise to the legend that the waters of the river Alpheus flowed all the way under the Med-iterranean from Greece to Sicily finally to reap-pear in the sea at Syracuse.

Comparable beliefs were held in earlier days. They were certainly picturesque and more col-orful than the prosaic opinions we now hold. Generally there were two leading schools of thought. One held that springs drew their water from the sea—how the salt was eliminated and how the water was elevated to the great heights it reached in mountain springs remained un-answered questions. The other belief was that springs and streams had their origin within sub-terranean caverns, large enough perhaps to have atmospheres of their own from which water condensed as a sort of rain within the Earth to feed them. Aristotle (384-322 B.C.) was con-tent with the idea that such water must have come from within the Earth since obviously rainfall was inadequate:

The air surrounding the earth is turned into water by the cold of the heavens and falls as rain," so "the air which penetrates and passes into the crust of the earth also becomes transformed into water owing to the cold which it encounters there. The water coming out of the earth unites with the rain water to produce rivers. The rainfall alone is quite insufficient to supply the rivers of the world with water. The ocean into which the rivers run does not overflow because, while some of the water is evaporated, the rest of it changes back into the air or into one of the other elements (Tolman, 1937).

Seneca (3 B.C.–A.D. 65) gave the seeming death blow to any concept so preposterous as one that water in the ground had anything to do with rain:

Rainfall cannot possibly be the source of springs because it penetrates only a few feet into the Earth whereas springs are fed from deep down. . . . As a diligent digger among my vines I can affirm my observation that no rain is ever so heavy as to wet the ground to a depth of more than ten feet (Tolman, 1937).

It was the middle of the seventeenth century before the key to the problem, that there was a relationship between rainfall and the discharge of springs, was demonstrated by two Frenchmen, Pierre Perrault (1608-80) and Edme Mariotte (1620-84). The approximate relationship of evaporation from the sea to the amount of rainfall and runoff was worked out by the astronomer Halley—known to us for his comet. According to Meinzer (1934):

Perrault made measurements of the rainfall during three years, and he roughly estimated the area of the drainage basin of the Seine River above a point in Burgundy and of the run-off from this same basin. Thus he computed that the quantity of water that fell on the basin as rain or snow was about six times the quantity discharged by the river. Crude as was his work, he nevertheless demonstrated the fallacy of the age-old assumption of the inadequacy of the rainfall to account for the discharge of springs and streams. Perrault also exposed water and other liquids to evaporation and made observations on the relative amount of water thus lost. He also made investigations of capillarity, established the approximate limits of capillarity in sand, and showed that water absorbed by capillarity cannot form accumulations of free water at higher levels.

Mariotte computed the discharge of the Seine at Paris by measuring its width, depth, and velocity at approximately its mean stage, making the velocity measurements by the float method. He essentially verified Perrault's results. In his publications, which appeared after his death in 1684, he defended vigorously the infiltration theory and created much of the modern thought on the subject . . . he maintained that the water derived from rain and snow penetrates into the pores of the earth and accumulates in wells; that this water percolates downward till it reaches impermeable rock and thence percolates laterally; and that it is sufficient in quantity to supply the springs. He demonstrated that the rain water penetrates into the earth, and used for this purpose the cellar of the Paris Observatory, the percolation through the cover of which compared with the amount of rainfall. He also showed that the flow of springs increases in rainy weather and diminishes in time of drought, and explained that the more constant springs are supplied from the larger underground reservoirs.

Although little was known by our ancestors of the reasons for water being in the ground, there was a considerable use made of it in ancient times. The well was the center of village life for centuries and still is over much of the world. Indeed, the office drinking fountain is no substitute for it as a communication center. Not only was the well the focal point of village life, but it was an absolute essential to the survival of a walled city or castle. It would be a foolhardy baron who would attempt to hold off a siege without an intramural source of water.

The demand for water created by large concentrations of people in urban centers has resulted in a more extensive development of underground sources of water supply than most people realize. Almost everyone knows of the heroic measures the Romans took to conduct water to their cities by building imposing, valley-spanning aqueducts. Oddly enough, the Romans knew little of the nature of water in the ground. They placed their chief dependence on springs and streams, with the result that they went prodigious distances to the Apennines for water when they had a perfectly adequate supply almost directly underfoot had they dug for it.

Others did, and their underground pursuit of water led to the construction of some of the more remarkable burrow-like excavations known. The chief example are the *kanats* of ancient Persia, now Iran. The kanats center largely around Teheran, and for the most part are dug in the gravels of the great apron of alluvial fans at the base of the Elburz Mountains. The kanats are long, mole-like burrows that serve as collecting galleries in the porous gravels of the fan. Some are 15 miles long, and individual tunnels may be as much as 500 feet deep. In the old days they were truly multi-purpose structures because they served as a source of drinking water and as a means of sewage disposal. In general a kanat follows a water-bearing layer of sand or gravel within the fan, and every few hundred yards is connected with the surface by a shaft sunk during construction.

A remarkable water-collecting tunnel of antiquity was built in Egypt around 500 B.C. This tunnel in the Nubian sandstone gathers water which has probably been introduced into the rock as seepage from the Nile. All told, the tunnel system has a length of a hundred miles or so (Tolman, 1937), although no one can say with certainty because it is almost entirely caved in. Enough water still escapes from the tunnel entrance that it was once thought to be a spring. Actually, the construction of this extraordinary enterprise was recognized as being of such importance that the temple of Ammon was dedicated in its honor and the Egyptians were reconciled to acknowledging the Persian, Darius I, as their Pharaoh.

Not only did men of long ago drive tunnels to intercept water in the ground, but they drilled wells to surprising depths. An outstanding achievement among dug wells was one at Orvieto, in Italy, which was sunk to a depth of 200 feet in 1540. It had two spiral staircases inside the walls, one above the other, with one being used by descending, the other by climbing, water-bearing donkeys.

Drilled wells, once the spring-pole method came into use, went to great depths, as much as 5,000 feet in China, for example (Chapter VII). Deep wells drilled at Artois in France in the twelfth century and Modena in the Po Valley of Italy flowed water at the surface. These excited great interest since they were the first true artesian wells of medieval times.

ORIGIN OF GROUND WATER

Nearly all the water in the ground comes from precipitation that has soaked into the Earth. Additionally, some water is included with marine sediments when they are deposited, and some (called *juvenile*) reaches the upper levels of the crust when it is carried there by igneous intrusions, volcanoes, hot springs, etc. In practical terms, these two are minor parts of the total budget of usable water in the ground.

Many things happen to water that falls as rain or snow. Much of it evaporates and goes directly back into the atmosphere. Some of it is picked up by plants and returned to the air by their process of transpiration, which is about the same for them as sweating is for us. Then, as we know from ordinary observation, a good deal of the rainfall runs off over the surface of the ground in rills and streams. Finally, some part of it sinks underground and becomes the ground water responsible for springs, and caves, and wells.

No one actually knows how water is divided among these various destinations proportionately, but Leopold and Langbein (1960) estimate it as being somewhat like the following.

Over the United States an *average* of about 30 inches of rain falls per year. Of this amount, approximately 21 inches are returned directly to the atmosphere by evaporation and transpiration. Only 9 inches runs off in streams directly to the sea, and of the total runoff nearly 40 per cent escapes by the Mississippi River—an impressive fraction of the continental supply.

Where does ground water come from, then, if the budget balances as closely as $21 + 9$ inches accounted for out of the 30 inches that fall? The answer is that although the amount of water entering the ground by infiltration is slight—perhaps as little as 0.10 inch per year in some places, more in others—with the passage of many millennia great quantities of water slowly accumulate in the ground. It is this vast reservoir built up gradually in the thousands of years since the end of the ice age that we draw on today—unfortunately in some areas more rapidly than it is replenished.

OCCURRENCE OF GROUND WATER

Probably the most familiar aspect of ground water is to see it standing—very often green, scummy, and unappetizing—in a shallow well. If we simply bail the water out with a bucket or a hand pump, very little happens to its level. If we install an electric pump and run it wide open for a while, the water level drops. If this process is continued actively for a long time in a number of wells, the water level continues to drop. This has happened in scores of irrigation districts, especially in the arid and semi-arid West, where, in a sense, farmers are mining their water supply more rapidly than it is being replenished.

To return, however, to the undisturbed water level in the well. If we were to determine its altitude and then to compare it with the level at which water stands in nearby wells, then in many regions we should quickly discover that the water surface is nearly level. This surface at which water stands in wells is called the *water table*. All the voids, or openings, in rocks below its surface are filled with water, or are *saturated*. Above the water table the pore spaces in the ground may be any combination from completely dry to partially full, and these openings are said to be in the *zone of aeration*.

Actually, the water table very rarely is dead level. Instead it is more likely to be a blurred replica of the ground surface (Fig. 8-1), rising under hills and sinking under valleys. It intersects the surface at lakes (Fig. 8-2) and streams, and also at springs. Sometimes a stream has water added to it from the water

table, especially if the stream is at a lower level (Fig. 8-1). Then it is called an *effluent stream*. If the stream is above the water table, and thus adds its contribution to the supply of water in the ground, it is an *influent stream* (Fig. 8-1).

The diagram (Fig. 8-1) shows that there are three elements in the occurrence of water in the uppermost layers of the Earth. These are (1) the belt of soil moisture, (2) the intermediate belt with its variable amounts of water or air filling the voids between sand grains, and (3) the water table and the saturated ground below it.

The belt of soil moisture is the portion of the profile with which we are likely to be familiar. This is the ground layer that becomes wet after a rain or a lawn watering. Sometimes this layer may become completely saturated and be converted into a quagmire of mud and water; at other times it may be bone dry and dusty from the top of the ground down.

Commonly there is a lower margin to this surface belt of soil moisture. It may be only a few inches down or it may be several feet. When we dig downward the ground generally becomes drier, until perhaps most of the soil moisture seemingly may have disappeared—as Seneca believed it did. Typically, though, in this intermediate belt the water has percolated

FIG. 8-1 *Occurrence and flow of ground water.*

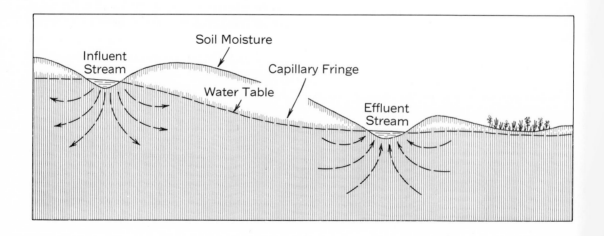

FIG. 8-2 *A small volcanic explosion pit on Paoha Island in Mono Lake, Calif. The level of water in the explosion pit is controlled not by the drainage area of the pit, but by the level of the ground-water table which in turn is con-* *trolled by the surface elevation of Mono Lake itself. Note the matching sets of ancient beach lines on the shores of Mono Lake and in the explosion pit resulting from changes in hydrologic conditions. (Photograph by Hal Roth.)*

slowly downward through soil openings until it reaches the water table. How well or how rapidly it percolates is dependent largely upon the porosity and permeability of the ground. What these two terms mean will be described in a few paragraphs ahead.

Extending a short distance upward from the water table is the *capillary fringe*. This is a band of thread-like extensions of water which has migrated upwards in the minute passageways between the individual soil grains. This movement is achieved in about the same way that kerosene climbs in the wick of a kerosene-burning lamp, or water in the confines of a narrow glass tube in a chemical laboratory.

Figure 8-1 shows average conditions over much of the world. However, in such places as swamplands and marshy ground, the water table is either at or very close to the surface and the intermediate zone is lacking. Elsewhere, as in desert lands, the water table may be scores, or even hundreds, of feet underground. Contrary to what many people think, the zone of high water content under the water table does not continue downward indefinitely into the earth. In other words, drilling a well to great depths will not necessarily increase the flow of water. With increasing depth the pore spaces in the rocks close up, and with this decrease in size the water-bearing capacity diminishes until the rocks may be completely dry. In deep mines the upper level may be flooded and require constant pumping to keep them operational while the lower levels are dry and water has to be brought down for use in drilling.

Porosity

This property is of the greatest importance in controlling the movement of water in the ground. We are familiar with the general meaning of the word when we think of a porous substance as one that contains many holes.

Actually, porosity is the ratio of solid material to open spaces, or voids, in a rock or soil. If half the available space were to be in openings, the material would have a porosity of 50%; if only one quarter, then 25%, and so on.

Many factors determine the porosity of a rock, and chief among them is the arrangement of the constituent particles in such material, for example, as sand. Should the sand grains be arranged as in Fig. 8-3A, the porosity is around 47%; if they are packed more densely, as in Fig. 8-3B, the porosity drops to approximately 26%.

An important point is that the *size* of the spherical grains in this illustration remains the same in both cases; it is the arrangement that is different. It does not matter at all if the grains are the size of BB's or basketballs. Porosity is a wholly relative matter. In fact, relatively fine-grained materials, such as silt, may

---

FIG. 8-3 *Porosity* (A), *spherical grains packed in such a way that intergrain voids make up approximately 47 per cent of the volume;* (B), *spherical grains packed in such a way that intergrain voids make up approximately 26 per cent of the volume.*

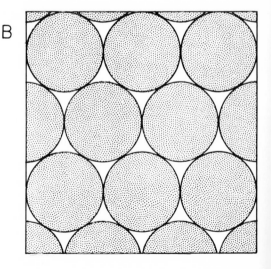

have higher porosities than such seemingly open material as gravel. Part of the reason for this is the pore spaces between the individual gravel particles may be occupied by sand, or even finer fragments, and this sharply reduces the size of the pores. The porosity is also drastically decreased if any natural cement is introduced into the interstices. In other words, the porosity of sandstone will be less than that of sand.

Among the higher porosities are those of newly deposited muds, such as those of the Mississippi Delta. These may actually reach the incredible value of 80-90%—which means they are *dilated*. This is to say that they contain so much water, as a quicksand does, that the individual particles scarcely touch one another. This situation is the exception, and more normal porosities are less than 15-20%. In tough, dense, homogeneous rocks, such as obsidian, basalt, or granite, the porosity may be as low as a few hundredths of a per cent.

spaces in a rock are not joined together, then water will not flow, no matter how large they may be.

Aquifers

Not all rocks are equally permeable, nor do they all have equal water-holding capacities. A layer such as a permeable, highly porous sandstone not only may be able to hold much more water than its enclosing rocks but also may provide a route along which ground water moves with relative freedom. Such a favorable layer that readily yields water to a well is called an *aquifer*. One that is too impermeable or tight to accept water is called appropriately an *aquifuge*.

There are many different kinds of aquifers, but two of the common types are shown in Fig. 8-4. The first, or *unconfined aquifer,* is the simpler. This may involve little more than a relatively permeable layer of sand under perhaps a cover of clay or loam. The water table,

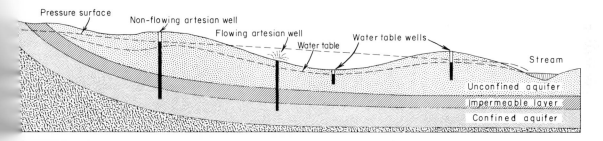

FIG. 8-4 *Aquifers and water wells.*

Permeability

This property of a rock is a measure of its capability of having a liquid transmitted through it. Therefore, the actual size of the openings in a rock is of vastly greater importance than the percentage that is open space. For example, a silt or clay may have a higher porosity than a gravel, but the permeability is less. Along with the size of the openings—large ones obviously being more permeable than small—is the matter of connections between the openings. If the pore

as we have already seen, is very likely to be a subdued replica of the ground surface, and for this reason the water level in any two wells may not stand at quite the same altitude. Furthermore, the two wells shown on the diagram are non-flowing and thus will have to be pumped.

Figure 8-4 also shows a *confined aquifer*. Here a layer of permeable sandstone is enclosed between layers of impermeable shale. Typically, a sandstone aquifer may crop out in a band paralleling a mountain front and then dip below the adjacent plain. This is the relationship east of the Rocky Mountains and under the Great Plains portion of the Dakotas and Colorado. The aquifer there is the Dakota sandstone, and since the first wells were drilled into it in the 1880's it has yielded a prodigious quantity of water. Wells when they were first drilled flowed at the surface of the ground over much of the area underlain by this productive, water-bearing layer. With the loss of pressure through the years, many of the wells are now on the pump.

Artesian Wells

Wells that flow at the surface of the ground, such as the early ones drilled to the Dakota sandstone, were called *artesian wells* from the Roman province of Artesium, now Artois in southern France. For almost everyone the term artesian means a well that flows freely. In practice, though, the term has a more restricted use, and is now applied to a well in which the water is under pressure because a confined aquifer has been penetrated. Whether or not the water reaches the top of the ground depends on the relationship of the *pressure surface* and the shape of the terrain (Fig. 8-4). In a flowing artesian well the pressure surface is above the ground and in a nonflowing well it is below the ground level.

The pressure surface is the level to which water rises in a confined or unconfined aquifer. Theoretically, in a confined system it could be equal to the highest point on the aquifer which is shown on the diagram projected as a level line from the water table out into the air (Fig. 8-4). The pressure surface does not coincide with this line because of the frictional loss of energy of the water as it moves through the aquifer.

Should a large number of wells tap an artesian reservoir, the pressure drops and the flow will ultimately diminish. Such was the case with the Dakota sandstone and the other aquifers associated with it. Where forty to seventy years ago water poured out of the ground under high enough pressure in some places to operate waterwheels, now, after the drilling of around 10,000 wells, the pressure has dropped to the point where many have to be pumped, and in flowing wells the yield is only a few gallons per minute.

Pumping Wells

Those who have lived on a ranch dependent on a well for irrigation water are fully conscious of the fact that when the well is pumped the water level in it drops. A short time after pumping ceases, the water rises, although not always to the level it may have had before should the drawdown be exceptionally severe and continued.

How much of an effect does a single well have on the water table of an entire district? Does the water level in all the adjacent wells rise or fall in concert? The answers to these questions have been established through observation in many localities over many years. If the well is pumped heavily, and water is taken out of the ground faster than it can be replenished, then the water table is pulled down in the form of an inverted cone centering on the well, and this is known as a *cone of depression*. Obviously the water level in nearby wells will be affected more drastically than in more distant ones. Studies show that the effect of an individual well may be felt by others over distances of as much as a quarter of a mile away.

Hard pumping by many wells serves to make the rims of individual cones overlap until the water level of an entire basin may be lowered. A striking example in the United States is the southern part of the San Joaquin Valley in California. This central valley of the state has long depended on pumped water for its agricultural survival. Something like 40,000 wells lift around 7,000,000 acre feet (an acre foot is 326,000 gallons) a year out of its underground reserves, which is approximately 25 per cent of all the ground-water yield of the United States (Thomas, 1951). This quantity of pumped water is 1,500,000 more acre feet than are supplied by infiltration from streams of the nearby Sierra Nevada, from rainfall, and from other sources such as leakage from irrigation ditches. The result has been a lowering of the water table throughout the years; in some places as much as 250 feet since 1905. Close to the western margin of the Sierra Nevada and about the mid-point of the valley, the water level in wells in one district dropped from 55 feet in 1921 to about 150 feet today. No wonder, then, that California is engaged in one of the most prodigious efforts in the history of mankind to transfer water from the northern, more generously endowed parts of the state to the parched southern counties.

GEOLOGIC ROLE OF GROUND WATER

Water in the ground does work of geologic significance comparable in many ways to the more visible achievements of rivers, glaciers, lakes, and the sea on the Earth's surface. Among its more significant accomplishments is providing the means by which the various natural cements are introduced into the pore spaces of unconsolidated sediments. Among these cements are calcite ($CaCO_3$), silica (SiO_2), and iron oxide (Fe_2O_3). These are reasonably soluble substances, and they may be dissolved from rock or soil layers by water when it starts its journey underground. Later, when the saturation is sufficiently high, and temperature and pressure relationships are right, these substances may come out of solution. Gradually, as they are deposited on the surface of individual grains, much like scale is deposited on the inside of a kettle or hot-water heater, pore spaces become drastically reduced until finally they may become sealed off almost completely, with an accompanying fall-off in permeability.

Ground Water in Soluble Rocks

Ground water plays a unique role where rocks are readily soluble in water. Among these are limestone, marble, gypsum, salt, and other evaporite deposits. The dissolving of these rocks and thus the slow wasting away of their substance underground, may be compared to erosion by surface streams, just as the process of cementation described in the preceding paragraph in a sense is equivalent to deposition.

Limestone Caverns

The most widely known effect of the solution of rocks by ground water is the formation of caves, such as the Carlsbad Caverns, Mammoth Cave, and the ones decorated by Stone Age Man in Europe. In addition to these examples, there are scores of others in many parts of the world. Their dark, silent recesses have intrigued explorers since the beginning of time, and even today there are few states without active speleological groups within their borders.

The origin of limestone caves has long been debated, and is far from being settled. The crux of the debate is whether or not the solution responsible for the removal of thousands upon thousands of cubic yards in some of the larger caverns occurred above or below the water table. The problems here are: (1) in those parts of caverns today that are above the water table the leading process appears to be deposition rather than solution. At least this is the process responsible for making stalactites and stalagmites. The alternative (2) that solution occurred below the water table encounters diffi-

FIG. 8-5 *Lehman Caves, Nevada.* (*Photograph by Hal Roth.*)

culties because the water very often is already saturated with lime; it cannot pick up any more and thus solution stops. To get around this dilemma a continuing supply of circulating water is called for, and this also has to have a low content of lime in solution—a difficult feat to achieve in a region dominantly underlain by limestone.

A further complicating factor is that many caverns include deposits of clay, silt, and even gravel. This leads some geologists to conclude that many such caves were eroded, at least in part, by subterranean streams. Such rivers are fairly common in limestone terranes; there are quite a number in Indiana and Kentucky.

A theory that appears to be applicable to the

Carlsbad Cavern is that caves were formed by solution at a time when the water table stood higher than it does now. As a result of canyon cutting by nearby streams the water table was lowered and passageways made by solution along joints and bedding planes were then opened to the air. Following this it was possible for such distinctive features of the cave world as stalactites, stalagmites, columns, and ribbons and sheets of travertine to grow.

Few geologic phenomena arouse more curiosity than the strange, in fact, eerie patterns made by dripping water in the timeless darkness of caverns underground. Most familiar of these to visitors to the great number of national, state, and privately controlled caves are the iciclelike pendants of travertine hanging down from the cave roof (Fig. 8-5). These are *stalactites,* and they normally form where dripping water seeps from the rocks above the cave. When this water reaches the air some of the CO_2 contained in solution escapes, thus increasing the saturation of the water to the point where $CaCO_3$ is deposited. Also, if some of the water evaporates, a residue of lime is deposited. Since the drop of water that hangs suspended momentarily from the cave roof is likely always to be about the same size, the tiny ring of travertine left by it will nearly always have the same diameter. Gradually, these successive rings pile up to form an icicle-like pendant, customarily with a narrow tube extending for its length. Seldom, though, is such perfection actually achieved or long maintained. The tube may become plugged, the amount of water may vary, or new holes may break out along the sides rather than at the tip. All these vagaries lead to the great variation in form that stalactites show.

Stalagmites are deposits built upward from the cave floor, and characteristically they grow below a stalactite. When a drop of water falls from the tip of a stalactite it may lose some of its CO_2 content on landing; or its water may become concentrated through evaporation, with the result that more lime is deposited. Thus a counterpart accumulation of lime gradually builds up from the floor of the cave to oppose the stalactite growing downward from the roof. Stalagmites, unlike stalactites, do not have a central tube, and since they are built up by the water that spatters over their surface they usually are thicker and have more diversified shapes.

With two such structures growing toward one another, if the initial distance separating them is not too great, and if an adequate rate of growth can be maintained, stalactites and stalagmites eventually meet and fuse. The resulting column of travertine is called a *pillar.*

Other cave deposits may take on a wide variety of shapes, and these fluted, or columnar, or sheet-like masses are the ones that guides or operators of caves use in achieving imposing feats of indirect lighting effects.

Karsts

The landscape that may develop in a region underlain by limestone differs in a multitude of ways from one charactertistic of less soluble rocks. A striking and well known region of this type is the *karst,* the portion of Yugoslavia bordering the Adriatic, the Dalmatian Coast. This is one of the picturesque coasts of the world, with the sea penetrating far inland in long, fjord-like inlets. These are separated by barren, whitish limestone ridges and islands which contrast vividly with the wine-dark waters of the sea—to use the 2,700-year-old imagery of Homer.

This is one of the historic coasts of Europe. The once-forested slopes of the now barren hills of what was then known as Illyricum provided timbers for the galleys of Rome, and later for the wide-ranging vessels of the Venetian Maritime Republic. Today this is a harsh, stony land, and it is difficult to visualize the widespread forest that once mantled its slope before destruction by overcutting and overgrazing.

This region has one of the heavier rainfalls of Europe, yet it is strikingly devoid of surface streams. Limestone is so permeable that rainwater sinks rapidly into the ground, especially if joints and other fractures abound. Streams flow for short distances, disappear underground, and then reappear several miles away as a river emerging full-born from a giant spring.

Such a limestone terrane as this is pocked with large numbers of closed depressions, some

large, some small. Commonly such depressions are floored with clay, and this thin accumulation of reddish soil (characteristically called *terra rossa* in the Mediterranean world) is likely to be all that is available for agriculture. In Yugoslavia the larger depressions may be several kilometers across—large enough at any rate to shelter a village and its surrounding patchwork of fields. The origin of these large depressions is uncertain. While they are partly due to removal of material by solution, part of their origin also appears to be the result of the folding and faulting of the underlying limestone.

Smaller closed depressions in Yugoslavia are almost certainly caused by solution. Some of

FIG. 8-6 *Karst topography south of Bedford, Indiana. (Photograph by John S. Shelton.)*

FIG. 8-7 *Sink holes in Kaibab limestone and the channel of Chevelon Creek, seventeen miles southeast of Winslow, Arizona.* (*Photograph by John S. Shelton.*)

them extend downward into the earth by near-vertical shafts which commonly lead into deep caverns. In America, such solution pits are called *sink holes,* and they may be open to the air, or they may be closed and floored with clay, or they may hold small lakes. These lakes are an impressive sight from the air, especially when sunlight glances from their surfaces. Unlike lakes in other kinds of ground, the water surface stands at different levels because the lake is floored with virtually impervious clay. Should this clay seal be broken, then the lake will drain away through solution channels into the underlying limestone.

Sometimes sink holes serve as natural wells. Their steep sides extend downward for scores or even hundreds of feet, until they intercept the water table which stands as a pool of water, somber and green, at the bottom. Renowned of such occurrences are the *cenotes* of Yucatan.

The Yucatan Peninsula is a nearly level lime-stone plain, devoid of surface streams because the rainwater sinks almost immediately into the ground. When the peninsula was the site of the Mayan Empire the dense agglomerations of people at such cities as Chichen-Itza were dependent upon so slender a supply of water as the dank fluid at the bottom of a limestone sink. No wonder that, to preserve this tenuous link with survival, a maiden burdened down with bangles and ornaments was ceremoniously hurled into the cenote each year in order to assure a continued supply.

GEYSERS AND HOT SPRINGS

By far the most spectacular manifestation of ground water is its appearance at the surface in the form of geysers and hot springs. Certainly they are the leading attraction of Yellowstone National Park, and it is a rare household that does not include a member who has seen Old Faithful run through its repertoire. Yellowstone is not the only geyser area in the world; in fact, the extensive one of Iceland gives its name to this sort of aqueous outburst, since all are named for a large Icelandic spring, *geysir*. Another large and touristically attractive geyser region is the Rotorua region of North Island in New Zealand. This is currently being developed as a source of thermal power.

Although the actual process that goes on in an erupting geyser is something of a mystery, enough is known of the physical laws operating so that a plausible explanation can be offered. Incidentally, its general elements are much the same as the one advanced by the German chemist, Bunsen, whose burner is known—sometimes by direct personal contact—to every student of chemistry.

FIG. 8-8 *Old Faithful geyser, Yellowstone National Park, Wyoming.* (*Photograph by Ansel Adams.*)

A generally held view is that ground water percolating downward in a geyser area comes in contact at depth with a source of heat. This may be cooling volcanic rocks, or steam, or other gases given off by magma. Even though the water at the bottom of a tube may be heated to 212°F. it does not boil because the boiling point is raised with an increase in pressure. We are more familiar with the opposite effect—the lowering of the boiling temperature in the thin air of high mountain tops to the point where potatoes, for example, do not cook through.

Thus in a column of water standing in a tube-like opening in the ground the temperature at the bottom of the column may rise above the boiling point at normal atmospheric pressure. However, nothing is likely to happen until all the water is heated to the top of the column, perhaps to the point where it begins to surge, or spill over the rim. Should enough drain off, then the pressure throughout the column is reduced, with the result that superheated water near the bottom flashes over into steam. This is enough to propel the whole column of water upward, and since a similar pressure reduction and near-instantaneous conversion to steam occurs throughout its length, a mixture of hot water and steam is hurled skyward—in Old Faithful for something like 150 feet. It is on the details of how the subterranean geyser reservoir is filled after being blown clear, and on how some geysers achieve their remarkable periodicity that much of the debate centers.

The castellated rims, platforms, and parti-colored deposits surrounding the geysers and hot springs of Yellowstone are especially interesting features for the park visitor. In general, there are two kinds of hot water deposits. Those deposited directly from mineral-rich geyser water often are composed of silica—supplied in part from the underlying volcanic rock—and these deposits are called *siliceous sinter*. They are likely to be grayish colored and to consist of amorphous silica, very much like opal. Limy deposits, made by calcareous algae that can survive in the temperatures of hot springs and pools, are called *travertine* (Fig. 8-9).

Hot springs are more widely distributed over the face of the Earth than geysers. There are over one thousand in the United States, and most of them are located in the montane parts of the Far West. Fundamentally, hot springs are a consequence of bringing ground water into contact with a source of heat in the Earth's crust. Typically, this source may be volcanic rocks

that have not yet lost all their initial heat. Or it may be juvenile water, freed by igneous bodies at depth, which has cooled to something less than the boiling temperature by the time it has reached the surface.

Ground water may also make its way by means of an aquifer down to a level where the temperature of the water is raised by the temperature increase of around 1°F. for every 60 to 100 feet of depth. If this heated water can be returned to the surface quickly, without too great a reduction in temperature, a hot spring results. A very common way by which this may

FIG. 8-9 *Jupiter Terrace, Yellowstone National Park, Wyoming. (Photograph by Ansel Adams.)*

be achieved is along a fault plane. The fault plane itself, and the crushed and sheared rocks associated with it, act as an impermeable membrane along which water rises to the surface. Several hot springs aligned along a single trend, taken with other evidence, are a clue throughout much of the mountainous West to the presence of a large and deeply penetrating fault.

Suggested References

Allen, E. T., and Day, A. L., 1935, Hot springs of the Yellowstone National Park, Carnegie Inst. of Washington, Publ. No. 466.

Barth, T. F. W., 1950, Volcanic geology; Hot springs and geysers of Iceland, Carnegie Inst. of Washington, Publ. No. 587.

Bretz, J. H., 1949, Carlsbad Caverns and other caves of the Guadalupe Block, New Mexico, Jour. Geol., v. 5, p. 447-463.

————, 1956, Caves of Missouri, Missouri Geol. Surv. and Water Resources Div., Rolla, Mo.

Davis, W. M., 1930, Origins of limestone caverns, Geol. Soc. Amer., Bull., v. 41, p. 475-628.

Krynine, P. D., 1960, On the antiquity of "sedimentation" and hydrology, Geol. Soc. Amer., Bull., v. 71, p. 1721-1726.

Kuenen, Ph. H., 1955, Realms of water, John Wiley and Sons, Inc., New York.

Leopold, L. B., and Langbein, W. B., 1960, A primer on water, U. S. Geol. Survey, Washington, D. C.

Meinzer, O. E., 1939, Ground water in the United States; a summary, U. S. Geol. Survey, Water-Supply Paper 836-D.

————, and others, 1942, Physics of the earth, Vol. IX, Hydrology, McGraw-Hill Book Co., Inc., New York.

Sayre, A. N., 1950, Ground water, Scientific American, November.

Stefferud, Alfred, and others, 1955, Water; Yearbook of Agriculture, U. S. Dept. of Agriculture, Washington, D. C.

Thomas, H. E., 1951, The conservation of ground water, McGraw-Hill Book Co., Inc., New York.

Tolman, C. F., 1937, Ground water, McGraw-Hill Book Co., Inc., New York.

Earthquake damage in San Francisco, California, April 18, 1906.
(Courtesy of the California Historical Society.)

IX

Earthquakes and the Earth's Interior

THE SAN FRANCISCO EARTHQUAKE

Early in the morning of April 18, 1906, the schooner *John A. Campbell* was running on a southeast course before a fresh NNW breeze, with Point Reyes in northern California due east 145 miles. With no warning the vessel shuddered suddenly with almost the same sensation as if she had run aground. The startled crew could scarcely believe their senses because the chart showed a depth of 2,400 fathoms at their position.

Although the crew had no way of knowing it, they were only a few among the many whose daily routine was disturbed, or even ended forever, by the events set in motion at 5:12 a.m. throughout a region covering about 375,000 square miles surrounding San Francisco. This disaster of more than a half-century ago is still a most instructive example today because it devastated an essentially modern city. The population of the United States is becoming increasingly urbanized, and many of the problems faced by our predecessors in San Francisco are exactly the same ones that might confront Civil Defense agencies today, with the additional burden of immense traffic jams, unimaginable a generation ago.

San Francisco in 1906 in some ways resembled the city of today, but in others it was very different. As today, its rows of closely crowded houses swarmed over the many hills. The cobblestoned streets along the waterfront were clangorous from the iron-tired wheels of horse-drawn drays. The pungent atmosphere of the waterfront was compounded in large part of the aromatic by-products of this multitude of horse-powered vehicles, as well as the fragrance of roasting coffee and the beery blast that emanated from the dark, block-long sawdust-floored saloons. The San Francisco waterfront was an infinitely more picturesque sight then than now, with the delicate tracery of the upper yards and rigging of the wind-driven Cape Horners rising above the pier sheds, and the waters of the bay whitened by the paddle wheels of ferries and Sacramento River boats.

Much of this colorful world, including the "Barbary Coast," was obliterated in a series of violent shocks in the early morning hours when most people were asleep. Had the earthquake struck later when people were up and about, the casualty roll would have been far greater. How many people died will never be known, but it may have been as great as 700 (Richter, 1958). Many transient residents in such structures as sailors' boarding houses simply vanished, and since even the sketchy pre-1906 records disappeared in flames, many of the former permanent inhabitants could not be traced. In several of the investigations made after the event, almost all the destruction was attributed to the fire. It was indeed the leading destroyer, but earthquake damage was not negligible, perhaps averaging as much as 25 per cent.

Newer buildings in the San Francisco of 1906

looked much like those in the older downtown sections of American cities today. By 1906 riveted steel frames were coming into wide use for taller structures. Exterior walls were more commonly faced with masonry than they are today, and reinforced brick was widely used for smaller commercial buildings. Windows were narrower than we are used to now, ceilings were higher, and since this was a time when the Victorian influence prevailed, most buildings were crusted with ornamentation and gingerbread—real earthquake hazards. San Francisco was unusual in one regard, and that to its sorrow, in that it was one of the larger wooden cities of the world. Typically, the residential section consisted of block-long rows of multistoried houses or apart-

ments crowded next to one another on 25-foot lots.

A significant lesson emphasized by the San Francisco earthquake was the importance of the kind of ground in determining the extent and nature of damage to buildings. Those founded on solid rock showed slight damage when compared with virtually identical structures built on waterlogged or unconsolidated ground. This environmental control was especially impressive in downtown San Francisco where an area about 20 blocks square is built on ground reclaimed from the sea by filling in this part of San Francisco Bay after the Gold Rush of 1849. Here on this sludgy foundation, made up of sunken ships, water-soaked refuse, bottles and bodies, all buried under poorly consolidated mud and silt, the most severe damage was concentrated.

Fires broke out at many points almost immediately following the strongest shocks, which oc-

FIG. 9-1 *Damage in the city of San Jose resulting from the San Francisco earthquake. (Courtesy of the California Historical Society.)*

FIG. 9-2 *Damage in the city of San Jose resulting from the San Francisco earthquake. (Courtesy of the California Historical Society.)*

FIG. 9-3 *Sacramento Street in San Francisco, April, 1906, following the great earthquake. Notice how the brick fronts of the buildings spilled across the street. The people are watching one of the great fires resulting from the earthquake. (Photograph by Arnold Genthe, courtesy of California Palace of the Legion of Honor.)*

FIG. 9-4 *The San Andreas fault in the Carrizo Plain, Calif. The stream in the left center of the picture turns and flows along the fault toward the observer. In the center foreground it turns to the right. Such streams are said to be "offset" and may result in part from movements along the fault. This part of the fault did not move in 1906. (Photograph by William Garnett.)*

curred within three minutes. The fires started from a variety of causes: overturned stoves, ruptured gas lines, and short-circuits from the primitive wiring systems of the time. At first there was little awareness that these fires were the true enemy. People either gawked at them or attacked them on a piecemeal basis—and not too successfully, because the alarming discovery was made almost at once that there was no water for the fire hoses. For one thing, most of the pressure lines below the streets were ruptured at innumerable points. Of even more fundamental importance, the main reservoirs of the city were Crystal Springs Lake and San Andreas Lake, which gives its name to the San Andreas fault which runs beneath the two lakes for their full length. Since it was slippage along this fault that caused the earthquake, a less favorable location for a city's water supply scarcely could be imagined. Fortunately, the dams held so that a flood was not added to the other afflictions of that unhappy day; the failures were in the pipe lines.

Fires started near the waterfront and swept inland across the broken city. Should you ever visit San Francisco, try to visualize the swath, eighteen blocks deep, swept by fire from the Embarcadero at the waterfront inland to Van Ness Avenue, the first wide street where a fire line could be held. Elsewhere vain attempts were made to check the advancing flames by dynamiting whole rows of buildings in their path, to keep the fire from leaping from roof to roof in the same fashion that a crown fire does in the forest.

From technologic and scientific points of view the San Francisco earthquake provided a big forward step. The California State Earthquake Commission, appointed by the governor but supported financially by the Carnegie Institution, conducted an exhaustive investigation. Hundreds of people were interviewed and evidence was collected from every damaged area, as well as records from virtually every seismograph station in the world.

Sudden slippage along a fault was the primary cause for this earthquake, and this was demonstrated beyond any reasonable doubt. Not only was faulting established as the mechanism, it was shown unequivocally that the displacement was strike-slip. Before 1906 the importance of this type of fault movement was only dimly appreciated. But here for all to see was a nearly continuous trail of furrowed ground, fractured barns, and various other mishaps strewn across the northern California countryside, with all the evidence showing that the western side of the San Andreas fault moved horizontally northward with respect to the eastern side which moved southward. The fault has a length of perhaps 600 miles on land, and in 1906 around 250 miles were in motion—from Point Arena north of San Francisco to San Juan Bautista to the southeast.

The maximum offset of 21 feet was near Tomales Bay; elsewhere in the neighborhood of San Francisco it held rather consistently at around 15 feet. This meant that once the dust subsided along the active part of the fault, roads, fences, lines of trees, and buildings intersected by the fault line were sliced through as neatly as though by a saber and everything west of the fault no longer matched up with anything east of it.

CAUSES AND DISTRIBUTION OF EARTHQUAKES

It is apparent that a strong causal relationship exists between faults and earthquakes. Where there are no active faults there are no large earthquakes, with the exception of minor ones caused by volcanic eruptions, nuclear explosions, and possibly the collapse of caverns underground. Thus it is not surprising that the majority of the world's earthquakes occur where there are growing, active mountain ranges, rather than in the stable, relatively inert parts of the Earth's crust. A comparison of the map indicating the centers of major earthquakes

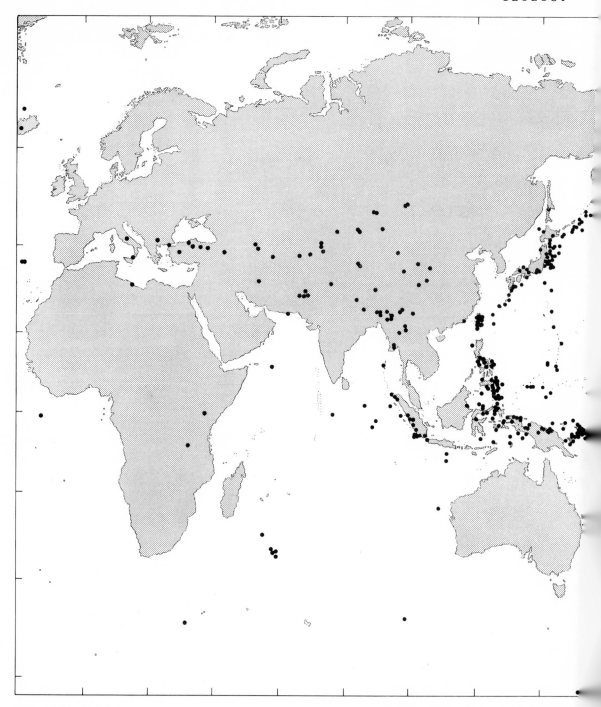

(Fig. 9-5) with the one showing the location of the world's active volcanoes (Fig. 3-1) demonstrates some of the similarities in their distribution. This is *not* to say that volcanoes cause earthquakes, but that in general they are both found where the Earth's crust is being deformed, with some exceptions, as pointed out in Chapter III. This means that earthquakes,

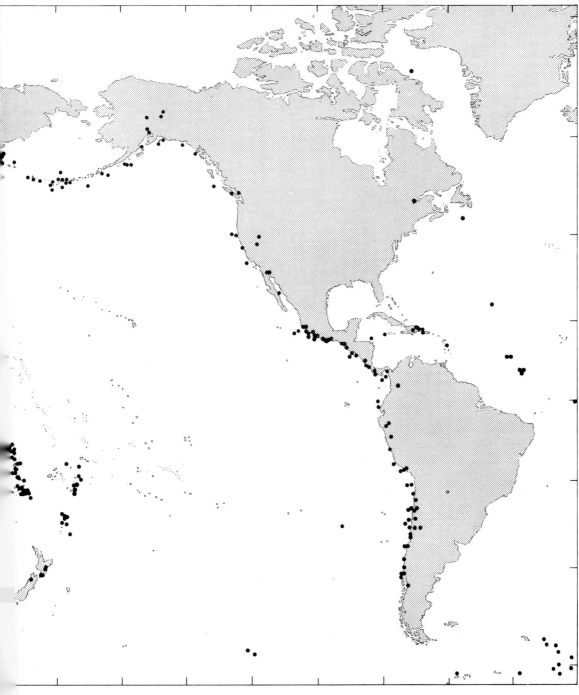

like volcanoes, have a notable concentration around the borders of the Pacific Ocean and westerly from its rim along the line of the Himalayas and the mountains of the Middle

After B. Gutenberg and C. F. Richter, *Seismicity of the Earth and Associated Phenomena,* Copyright © 1949 Princeton University Press. By permission.

FIG. 9-5 *The distribution of major earthquakes.*

East through to the Mediterranean. Japan among the industrialized nations is almost certainly the uncontested champion with regard to earthquake frequency and intensity. Not far behind, however, are the islands of Indonesia, as well as New Zealand, the Philippines, and the west coasts of North and South America.

Some regions, such as the great shield areas of North America and Europe, are virtually free of devastating earthquakes. The north European plain is a good example of a relatively earthquake-free area, and here the most telling evidence of their absence in past centuries is the heaven-aspiring steeple of the Gothic cathedral. It would be difficult to devise a worse structure for an earthquake country.

SOME OTHER ILLUSTRATIONS

Lisbon, 1755

Southern Europe, however, has not been free of earthquakes, and one of the more renowned of all historic ones is the stupendous disaster that struck the ancient city of Lisbon on the banks of the Tagus River in Portugal on All Saints' Day, November 1, 1755. There were three major shocks at 9:40 a.m., 10:00 a.m., and at noon. Many of the people who were at Mass perished in the collapse of the multitude of medieval churches whose spires had been so notable a feature of Lisbon's skyline.

With buildings made of loosely bonded masonry, huddled along narrow, irregular streets, no wonder most of them collapsed in one thunderous crash, perhaps not greatly different from the succinct description given by Voltaire in *Candide* (Kendrick, 1956):

When they had recovered a little, they walked towards Lisbon, hoping to get something to eat after their ordeal, as Candide still had some money left; but they had scarcely entered the city when suddenly the earth shook violently under their feet. The sea rose boiling in the harbour and broke up all the craft anchored there; the city burst into flames, and ashes covered the streets and squares; the houses came crashing down, roofs piling up on foundations, and even the foundations were smashed to pieces. Thirty thousand inhabitants of both sexes and all ages were crushed to death under the ruins.

A startling phenomenon to the unhappy survivors at Lisbon, as well as to observers at other places along the Portuguese coast was the sudden appearance of a great sea wave or, as we now call it, a *tsunami,* after its Japanese name. Such a wave is *not* a tidal wave, since it has nothing whatever to do with the tide.

In Lisbon, a wave with a height of about 20 feet set in motion by a submarine shock off the coast of Portugal swept up the Tagus River. Ships and boats were smashed together and sank, and much of the wave's fury was concentrated on a newly constructed marble pier, the *Cais de Pedra,* whose level surface was black with people fleeing from the burning city. Their drowning gave rise to the legend that the pier and all the people on it had been engulfed in a great fissure that opened and closed over them so that they were never seen again. In fact, Lyell believed on the basis of a visit to Lisbon that such a burial occurred (Davison, 1936). As Reid (1914) points out, this simply is not true. The quay probably broke up under the earthquake shock and the attack of sea waves, and "the story of the engulfing of the Lisbon quay must be ascribed to the love of the marvelous and the mysterious, which has not yet entirely disappeared from the accounts of earthquakes."

The distance to which effects of the Lisbon earthquake were felt throughout Europe was one of the remarkable features of this shock. It was strong throughout the Spanish peninsula and well into France and caused severe damage in Morocco (although this may have been a separate shock). A striking phenomenon was the disturbance created in bodies of water, such as castle moats, estuaries, canals, and lakes. In many of these water bodies at places as far distant as southwest Finland, southern Scandinavia, much of England, Germany, Switzerland, and nothern Italy, stationary waves, or *seiches,* were set up even though the earth shock itself was not felt. Seiches are waves that characteristically have rhythmical movement from side to side of a lake and usually show a marked fluctuation of water level. In a typical earthquake-induced seiche the water sloshes, much like the familiar wave in a bathtub, and in one variety of seiche it may be alternately high and low at opposite ends of a lake.

The seiches set in motion by the Lisbon earthquake excited a great deal of interest in the southern part of England where they were widely observed. It must have been an impressive sight to see a castle moat suddenly agitated and the water lunge to and fro on a completely windless day and with no perceptible ground motion. In a closed basin, such as the Portsmouth drydock, a seiche caused H.M.S. *Gosport,* 40 guns, to surge back and forth more than 3 feet, at the same time plunging like a bucking horse, even though well secured by hawsers to the dock (Reid, 1914).

The Lisbon earthquake was an intellectual watershed in European thinking. It led Rousseau to point out in his *tout est bien* philosophy that earthquakes were all for the best; it was the evils of civilization that were bad. If we were not cooped up in cities, earthquakes would not kill us. Voltaire struck a devastating blow of ridicule at such unthinking optimism. As we have seen, Candide and his insufferable companion, Dr. Pangloss, were caught in the Lisbon earthquake. For Dr. Pangloss this proved to be a time to test his belief that every horror encountered was a necessary event in the pre-established harmony of the universe.

Spiritually, the Lisbon earthquake was a challenge to the theologians of the time. Why did one of the most devout and justly renowned cities of the world suffer such a fate at the hands of a loving God—so that the innocent should perish in such multitudes along with the guilty? According to Kendrick (1956) in his excellent study, *The Lisbon Earthquake,* which is concerned primarily with the related themes of eighteenth-century earthquake theology and the end of optimism, a widely held belief with regard to the earthquake was:

> The reason why God had overthrown Lisbon was not only because He intended to shock the whole of Christendom into a state of penitent obedience to Him by the staggering destruction of such a celebrated and wealthy city, one that was perhaps, thanks to its maritime trade, the best-known city in Europe; but also because Portugal was a kingdom under the special and principal care of Heaven, so that according to the rules of the divine discipline, the Portuguese for their own good and as a result of the heavenly priority that was their due, were singled out for the honour of being the first to be punished and those who were punished most severely.

Politically, the Lisbon earthquake was a prophetic event because it provided the setting for the playing out of the role of a modern dictatorship; the dictator in this case being the Marquez de Pombal. Although he was ultimately to seize all the trappings of power, to reduce the king to ineffectiveness, to expel the Jesuits, and execute his opponents, during the disaster Pombal unquestionably preserved order where chaos would have prevailed and never faltered in his determination to rebuild a greater Lisbon. The modernization of the city, the cutting of boulevards and the restoration of its ancient glories—if not its liberties—were essentially Pombal's doing. In the tradition of most dictatorships the contributions of others were written out of the official history, and to Pombal were attributed almost superhuman virtues and accomplishments.

The Lisbon earthquake, in addition to being a theological and literary milestone, marked a great forward step scientifically. Pombal required every parish priest to fill out a questionnaire comparable in most respects to a similar one sent out today by the U. S. Coast and Geodetic Survey—the governmental agency responsible for the study of earthquakes. Pombal's questionnaire included such questions as the time of the shock, its direction, the extent of damage, the number of casualties, and so on. These records, preserved in the Portuguese archives, must give a fascinating insight into the life and thought of the times.

The outcome of Pombal's questionnaire and the carefully documented history of the event prepared by several Portuguese writers was to give a more coherent picture of the nature of such a cataclysm than had ever been available before. This, coupled with the observation of seiches and other events throughout Europe, established the belief that earthquakes were natural rather than supernatural phenomena, and thus were amenable to observation and to explanation by a rational theory.

New Madrid, Missouri, 1811-1812

America's most severe earthquake took place only eight years following the Louisiana Purchase. This was at the time of the War of 1812, when the region was still barely opened to settlement, and life on the Mississippi was harsh.

The New Madrid earthquake started at about 2:00 a.m. the morning of December 16, 1811, and was felt over an area of around 1,000,000 square miles—from the Canadian border to the Gulf of Mexico and from the Rocky Mountains to the Atlantic Ocean. It originated in the central part of the Mississippi Valley, very near Cairo, Illinois, where the Mississippi and Ohio rivers unite. A more unlikely spot would be hard to select—in a vast lowland plain, remote from any actively growing mountain range. By far the largest number of historic earthquakes in the United States have been concentrated in the mountainous parts of the Far West.

Although there were tremors for a year after, the main earthquake effects resulted from three major shocks, beginning very early in the morning of December 16 and continuing into December 18, and again on January 23 and February 7, 1812. Were shocks of a similar

FIG. 9-6 *Horizontal offset of an orange grove in the Imperial Valley, Calif., caused during the earthquake of May, 1940. Evidence of movement outside the grove has been obscured by later human activity. (Photograph by John S. Shelton.)*

FIG. 9-7 *Slippage of a section of highway into Hebgen Lake, Montana, after the earthquake of August, 1959.* (*Courtesy of Montana Highway Dept.*)

magnitude to occur today, most of the cities of the central Mississippi Valley would be flattened, and newspapers, newsmagazines, newsreels, and TV programs would carry photographs of little else.

According to Fuller (1914) whose investigation a century later resulted in a detailed picture of the extent to which the landscape of the Mississippi Valley was altered by this cataclysm:

The ground rose and fell as earth waves, like the long, low swell of the sea, passed across its surface, tilting the trees until their branches interlocked and opening the soil in deep cracks as the surface was bent. Landslides swept down the steeper bluffs and hillsides; considerable areas were uplifted, and still larger areas sunk and became covered with water emerging from below through fissures or little "craterlets" or accumulating from the obstruction of the surface drainage. On the Mississippi great waves were created, which overwhelmed many boats and washed others high upon the shore, the return current breaking off thousands of trees and carrying them out into the river, sand bars and points of islands gave way, and whole islands disappeared.

Fortunately, the history of this earthquake was better documented than might be thought since there were a number of very capable observers in the region at the time, including the renowned naturalist, Audubon. The region was visited by Sir Charles Lyell at the time of his American tour in 1846, and he left a wealth of observations made when the evidence was still fresh.

There were three truly noteworthy geologic effects of the earthquake: (1) the appearance of low cliffs cutting across country, very possibly fault scarps—some of these produced waterfalls around 6 feet high where they intersected the Mississippi River; (2) the elevation of long, low, archlike ridges or domes—on these, former swamp areas were uplifted perhaps 10 or 20 feet, and one of the ridges had a length of 15 miles; (3) the sudden appearance of the so-called sunken ground, which was a broadly depressed part of the Mississippi flood plain extending along the river for 150 miles and also the site of two very large lakes—St. Francis and Reelfoot. The latter, now a bird sanctuary, is an imposing sight; the gray trunks of cypress trees drowned more than a century ago stand in the somber waters which in places are as much as 20 feet deep.

The New Madrid earthquake is interesting because of its extraordinary magnitude and its far-reaching effect in altering the landscape. Why it should occur in such an unlikely spot as the middle of the Mississippi Valley remains an unanswered question. Very possibly it is the result of deep-seated faulting in the bedrock concealed beneath the sediments deposited by the Mississippi River. The effect of this displacement transmitted into these water-logged sediments is expressed in the form of minor faults, sand boils, sand-filled fissures and cracks, uprooted forests, landslides, sunken areas, and elevated domes.

Owens Valley, California, 1872

Travelers driving north from Los Angeles to the High Sierra scarcely notice the obscure monument that stands withdrawn from the road a short distance north of Lone Pine, a town at the southern end of Owens Valley in California. The bronze plaque on the monument tells us that here in a common grave lie 22 people who had an unexpected rendezvous with death at 2:30 on the morning of March 26, 1872. By a grim appropriateness they are buried at the crest of a low bluff that stands 15 or 20 feet above the highway—a bluff that is a measure of the displacement along the fault responsible for the earthquake.

The 1872 earthquake appears to have been the most violent of modern times in the western United States. When the dust settled in the streets of Lone Pine, 52 out of 59 of its adobe houses were flattened, and of the 250 or 300 inhabitants 29 were dead and 60 were seriously injured. The shock was felt as far south as San Diego and north to Sacramento. It was strong enough in Yosemite Valley to shake down some of the rock pinnacles, an event graphically described by John Muir.

The first of the two occurrences that greatly impressed the Owens Valley pioneers were the avalanches and tremendous showers of boulders that cascaded down the steep Sierran slopes, with the result that dust hung heavy in the valley for days after the shock. The second was the appearance of sharply defined cracks, many bordered by low cliffs, some as much as 20 feet high, that could be traced along the base of the Alabama Hills—an outlier of the Sierra Nevada —and for 70 miles north and south along the floor of the Owens Valley from Lone Pine. Incidentally, almost every reader of this book has seen the Alabama Hills, at least vicariously in the movies or on TV, since they have been a favorite locale for several decades for filming westerns.

Geologically, this was an unusual earthquake for the large-scale visible faulting that accompanied it. This faulting was also unique in that not only did up-and-down displacement occur, with the production of fault scarps, but horizontal movement occurred as well, with roads and lines of trees offset as much as 15 feet in much the same way they were at San Francisco in 1906 (Bateman, 1962).

Three of the earthquakes that have been described—San Francisco, New Madrid, and Lone Pine—share a common attribute. In all three there was visible surface evidence of faulting, and thus the causal relationship between faults and earthquakes could be demonstrated. The point to be remembered here is that movement on faults *causes* earthquakes, and that the displacement on faults is *not* the *result* of earthquakes. The point is worth emphasizing because the Owens Valley pioneers after their harrowing experience believed just the opposite, and there are a large number of people today who share the same conviction.

Yokohama and Tokyo, 1923

This catalog of catastrophes could be continued through many more pages, but little would be gained beyond a surfeit of examples, all tending to read the same.

Most of the impressive earthquakes have occurred in the regions of the greatest frequency. They are familiar visitors in Japan and among them have been some of the more destructive in history. In addition to those experienced in Japan, some of the most violent on record have been those that afflicted the foothill regions of the Himalayas, in northern India, Assam, and Nepal. The landslides, stream blockages, and other disruptions of the terrain accompanying these shocks are on so vast a scale, in keeping with this prodigious landscape, as to make all others seem insignificant.

The important earthquakes from our point of view are not those in remote, exotic regions that affect only the landscape, but those involving people and affecting their daily affairs. These are the ones that seem most important to us because we can achieve some feeling of identification. Statistically, Rousseau is more right than wrong; if we didn't live in cities, earthquakes wouldn't kill us.

One of the great disasters in modern times was the earthquake and fire that leveled Yokohama and Tokyo on September 1, 1923. No worse time of day could be selected than the moment this earthquake struck, at 11:58 a.m. Almost everyone was up and about, and thousands of little charcoal braziers were ablaze all over both cities. All but the most modern structures, or the most solidly built ancient ones, came crashing down. Steel-framed buildings survived quite well, and the Imperial Hotel, which Frank Lloyd Wright designed to float, as it were, on a concrete pad, rode out the seismic storm virtually unscathed.

With such widespread collapse, fire was an inevitable accompaniment, and also the great destroyer. At least 250 fires started in Tokyo, and since there was no possibility of fighting them they swept through the shattered city ultimately burning nearly 40,000 houses and about 70 per cent of the urban area. The situation was even worse in Yokohama; there nearly 100 per cent of the city was burned (Leet, 1948).

About 100,000 people died, and of this total the greatest number, 38,000, were burned or suffocated in one of Tokyo's parks on the banks of the Sumida River, where they had huddled for protection.

Seismologists agree that the shock originated in Sagami Bay, the large funnel-shaped entrance to Tokyo Bay. Several lines of faulting were found on land after the earthquake, some with vertical displacements of as much as 6 feet. Most remarkably, careful triangulation after the event showed that the entire Tokyo-Yokohama area was shifted horizontally toward the southeast, with the greatest displacement, amounting to 15 feet, on the peninsula across the bay from Tokyo (Richter, 1958).

The most controversial aftermath of the earthquake was the remarkable changes of level of the floor of Sagami Bay. These were so great that the Japanese Navy undertook an elaborate resurvey involving the use of four vessels and the taking of 83,000 soundings. When these were compared with soundings taken in 1912, increases in depth averaging 300 to 600 feet, with a maximum of about 1,300 feet, appeared

FIG. 9-8 *Fresh fault scarp formed along the mountain east of Hebgen Lake, Montana, during the earthquake of August, 1959. (Courtesy of Montana Highway Dept.)*

to have occurred (Richter, 1958). These are far too great to be surveying errors, especially when the accuracy with which Japanese governmental surveys are conducted is considered. They are too large to be accounted for by faulting, since nothing comparable to such changes in altitude occurred on land. It is most improbable that the presence or absence of a blanket of water should have anything to do with the amount of movement on such a break in the Earth's crust. In short, a fault with a 6-foot displacement on land is not likely to increase to 300 feet as abruptly as called for here. Large-scale landsliding or submarine slumping was given by some geologists as a

cause, but this hypothesis is faced with the difficulty that the greatest apparent sinking is in a closed basin where slumped debris would be expected to accumulate, rather than to disappear. Possibly this lowering of the basin floor may be the result of sudden compaction of these water-logged sediments. Whatever actually did occur under the waters of Sagami Bay is unknown, but the zone of apparent maximum subsidence coincides with the instrumentally determined location of the earthquake's origin. These sea floor changes doubtless had a good deal to do with setting in motion a 30-foot high tsunami that destroyed the Yokohama waterfront.

EARTHQUAKE DAMAGE

From our point of view the most important lesson to be learned from these historic earthquakes is their effect on structures of all kinds, because it is the collapse of buildings that chiefly places lives in jeopardy.

First of the several factors determining the amount of damage is the *distance from the epicenter*. Close to an epicenter the damage may be severe; with distance it diminishes. Obviously this means that the earthquake hazard is greater in California and Japan than it is, for example, in South Dakota and Great Britain.

Second of the factors is the *nature of the ground*. San Francisco, 1906, and Long Beach, 1933, both in California, are stellar examples of the importance of this control. In these earthquakes buildings of essentially equivalent construction were most severely damaged if they stood on filled, unconsolidated, or water-soaked ground and least if they were founded on solid rock or on dry, well-consolidated soil. Selection of an actual building site is a factor over which we can exercise some choice. It is surprising how little thought seems to be given to this factor in regions of high earthquake hazard.

The third element, and the one over which we have the most direct control, is the *type of construction* used in the buildings we inhabit. Perhaps the most important single principle to keep in mind is to so construct a building that it vibrates as a single unit. It helps, too, if it is not too rigid. Fortunately, most wooden-framed houses fit these requirements, especially if the mud sills are bolted to a concrete foundation and the studs are strengthened by angle-bracing at the corners. Another important requirement is that reinforcing rods be run the length of brick

FIG. 9-9 *Closeup of escarpment showing vertical movement of as much as 30 feet. Hebgen Lake, Montana. (Courtesy of Montana Highway Dept.)*

chimneys and be tied to a concrete slab at the chimney base. Among the more memorable sights after the Long Beach earthquake were the hundreds of brick chimneys snapped off short at the roof line.

In larger structures, such as two-story professional buildings, small hotels, and rooming houses, the most startling failure is the collapse of exterior walls. This characteristic feature of the small-town, post-earthquake California scene is always an unnerving experience for the luckless inhabitants of hotel rooms, suddenly exposed to the public gaze when the outside walls of a building fall away.

Among the more vulnerable structures very commonly are those with roofs extending over a comparatively broad span, such as those of supermarkets, bowling alleys, and auditoriums. Here, if the roof is arched, it exerts an outward thrust against the bearing walls and these may be hammered down, as it were, until they collapse completely.

School buildings were exceptionally vulnerable in the Long Beach earthquake of 1933, in part through faulty construction and in part through flaws in the typical design in vogue at the time. Wide spans were used for classroom floors in multistory buildings and at the same time outer walls were weakened through the extensive use of large windows.

The Arvin-Tehachapi, California, earthquake of July 1952 was particularly instructive because it was investigated in great detail seismologically, and instrumentally located epicenters were related directly to field evidence of faulting on the ground (Oakeshott and others, 1954). The buildings damaged were typical of the small American community, and here the results showed the same general principles that operate in large-scale catastrophes. Damage to brick and adobe structures was much more severe over thick deposits of unconsolidated sediment than it was to buildings founded on solid rock or a thin veneer of sediment.

There were, however, some unique forms of damage in this earthquake that make it stand apart from others. For one thing, the San Joaquin Valley is an agricultural area in an arid climate and is dependent upon ground water and irrigation for survival. Most of this water is lifted to the surface by deep well electric pumps. Transformers are needed for almost all of these, and commonly are placed on narrow wooden platforms supported high above the ground by poles at either end. All told, 846 transformers were damaged; some severely, others scarcely at all. Many toppled over on their platforms, while others fell to the ground. The resulting unavailability of irrigation water caused by this multiple power failure was one of more serious single losses caused by the earthquake.

Another of the more spectacular effects was the destruction of tunnels and damage to about 11 miles of track where the Southern Pacific Railroad crosses the Tehachapi Mountains as well as the White Wolf fault, whose displacement was the cause of the shocks. Four tunnels were badly shattered and the linings of four more were cracked (Oakeshott, 1955). Tracks were thrown into S-curves, rammed into tunnel walls, and left suspended in air where fills dropped away. Service was restored in twenty-six days after one of the greatest short-term earth-moving jobs in construction history, through the utilization of more than 1,000 men, 175 pieces of heavy equipment, and the expenditure of over $2,500,000. Reconstruction involved the complete removal of two tunnels, partial removal of another, and extensive repairs to a fourth.

THE DEVELOPMENT OF SEISMOLOGY

Earthquakes, simply because they are dramatic natural events, have invited speculation as to their origin even from the earliest times. Since they are especially prevalent in the Mediterranean, the Greek philosophers concocted many theories to explain them. These sound to us today like mythology, and not half as interesting as the adventures of the far-wandering Odysseus at that. Aristotle, who lived in the fourth century B.C., and whose interpretation of natural phenomena once had the force of dogma, believed that earthquakes resulted from the escape of air trapped within the Earth.

The Lisbon earthquake prompted the first serious effort to study earthquakes scientifically. By 1760, as a result of the evidence from seiches and from swinging chandeliers all over Europe, John Michell, an English physicist, surmised that earthquakes produced wave motion in the rocky crust of the Earth. A hundred years ago, in 1859, the seismological pioneer, Robert Mallet, who had been thinking about earthquakes in theoretical terms, had an opportunity to study the results of a true one when he visited Italy and saw the damage done to the hill towns of the Apennines east of Naples by a destructive earthquake in 1858. Although he believed incorrectly that earthquakes were explosive in origin and were related to volcanic activity, he laid the foundations of observational seismology. By studying the direction of the fall of buildings and monuments, the nature of cracks in the ground, and other lines of evidence, he worked out a rough method for determining the location of the earthquake source. He was also among the first to try an experimental approach in earthquake study by setting off explosions and measuring the travel time of the resulting waves. He also made the beginnings of an earthquake catalog and achieved a fair understanding of the geographic distribution of earthquakes.

The founder of modern seismology—a word that comes from the Greek, *seismos,* for earthquake—was an English mining engineer, John Milne. He went to Japan in 1875 as one of the dedicated group of men who were responsible for bringing the technology and educational systems of the West to the Japanese people under the Meiji restoration. By 1880, he had had sufficient stimulus from a nearly continuous exposure to earthquakes to emerge as the first full-fledged seismologist, interested, active, and effective in every facet of that many-sided science. Through his efforts the seismograph became a precise instrument, and Milne-Shaw horizontal pendulum seismographs were installed at approximately 50 co-operating stations by 1892. From that modest beginning seismology has advanced until today (Richter, 1958) there are probably between 500 and 600 stations in operation, with 97 in the United States and 76 reported for the Soviet Union. An international summary of the world's earthquakes is issued by the Bureau Central Internationale Seísmologique in Strasbourg—a program supported by UNESCO. Seismology, since it is concerned with the Earth as a whole rather than some political subdivision of its surface, is a truly bright star in the firmament of international scientific co-operation.

THE SEISMOGRAPH

A seismograph is the instrument used to record the vibrations set in motion by an earthquake. The perfection of this instrument is the result of an immense amount of inspired and patient work over the many years since the first one was contrived by L. Palmieri in Italy in 1855. The problem that had to be solved was how to isolate an object on the Earth's surface so that when everything surrounding it was set in motion by earthquake waves it remained stationary, or as nearly stationary as it could be kept. Then the motion of the Earth's crust relative to the immobile mass could be measured.

The most successful device for meeting this difficult requirement is the pendulum. Its inertia tends to hold it at rest in space while the ground beneath and the support holding it up are in motion. Then, if some method can be worked out so that a stylus, or pen point, can be attached to the inert mass, it will inscribe a record showing the amount of motion of the ground relative to the mass standing still in space. This is roughly comparable to the illusion we experience when we are sitting in a stationary passenger train and suddenly a freight train starts to move on the adjacent track. For a moment we think that we are moving and that it is the other train that is standing still.

The first primitive seismographs traced their record in smoothed loose sand or on a piece of smoked paper, and could give little information on direction or even the characteristics of the vibration they recorded. Milne made a vast improvement over the limitations of such crude instruments when he mounted the pendulum in a horizontal position. It was then possible to determine the characteristics of earthquake waves traveling in a given direction. A completely equipped seismological station in the early part of this century customarily would have had three instruments: two horizontal pendulums, one mounted on an east-west axis, one mounted on a north-south axis, both to record horizontal ground movement, and the third pendulum suspended on a sensitive spring to measure the vertical component of motion.

Actually, it is virtually impossible to completely isolate a pendulum from its environment; inevitably it picks up a certain amount of motion. This is likely to become troublesome when the natural period of swing of the pendulum approaches the period of vibration for the ground motion. Another problem is to stop the pendulum from swinging, once it has been set in motion and the earthquake waves have ceased. This is done by damping the pendulum by providing some kind of drag. Sometimes this is achieved by using a small vane—which acts much like the flaps on an airplane wing—or by trailing the pendulum through a bath of oil, or in more modern seismographs by placing the copper vane between the poles of a magnet. The eddy currents set in motion when the vane moves have a damping effect that is quite independent of atmospheric influences, such as humidity, temperature, and pressure.

A further vexatious problem is that the amplitude of waves recorded directly by a seismograph is likely to be too small to enable us to

study them profitably. This means magnification is necessary, and if this is to be achieved mechanically, then operating problems arise which seriously affect the accuracy of the result.

The desired magnification can be achieved photographically by using light rays rather than springs or levers and by recording the results on photographic paper rather than by dragging a stylus or pen over the surface of a sheet of paper. The torsion seismograph (Fig. 9-10) is such an instrument. Basically, it consists of an 8- or 9-inch tungsten wire with a pencil-thin weight mounted on it and suspended between the poles of a magnet. A tiny mirror is mounted on the weight, which in effect is the pendulum. The mirror reflects light from a source back through a set of prisms and lenses onto the surface of a rotating drum on which is mounted a sheet of light-sensitive paper. On this paper the light will appear as a minute, but very sharply defined, square spot. If no shocks are recorded, the spot leaves a perfectly straight line behind it on the rotating sheet of paper, which shows up when it is developed. A typical instrument of this sort for recording rapid vibrations may have a pendulum with a free period of 0.8 seconds and a magnification of 2,800 times—which is the ratio of light-spot displacement to ground displacement (Benioff, 1955). For waves from slower, more distant shocks, a pendulum with a free period of 8 seconds and a magnification of 800 would be representative.

Instruments of far greater subtlety and accuracy than the ones described above are in existence today. Many of them were created through the efforts of Dr. Hugo Benioff and his associates at the Seismological Laboratory of the California Institute of Technology. In one of these the movement of the pendulum generates power electromagnetically, and this may be used to drive recording galvanometers with differing periods and magnification. This instrument bears the imposing name of a variable reluctance electromagnetic seismometer.

With seismographs of such complexity and

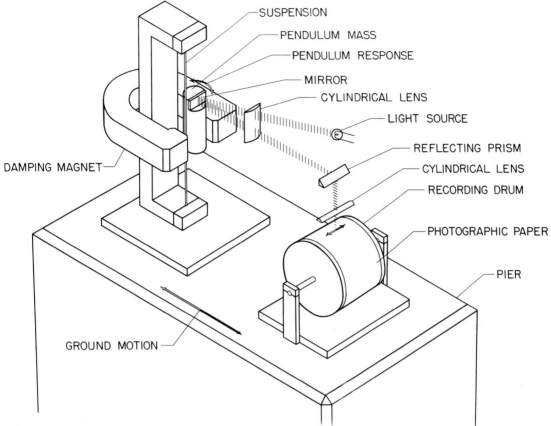

- SUSPENSION
- PENDULUM MASS
- PENDULUM RESPONSE
- MIRROR
- CYLINDRICAL LENS
- LIGHT SOURCE
- REFLECTING PRISM
- CYLINDRICAL LENS
- RECORDING DRUM
- PHOTOGRAPHIC PAPER
- PIER
- DAMPING MAGNET
- GROUND MOTION

From B. Gutenberg, "Earthquakes in Kern County," 1955. By permission of California State Division of Mines.

FIG. 9-10 *Schematic diagram of a torsion seismograph.*

precision as those now available we have come a long way since the chandeliers in the churches of Europe were set swinging on All Saints' Day more than 200 years ago by the Lisbon earthquake. The pulsating record that a seismograph traces on a moving roll of paper not only tells us much about the earthquake itself, but reveals more of the nature of the Earth's interior than any other device known.

WHAT THE RECORD TELLS

To the uninitiated, the squiggles on a seismograph record seem wholly without meaning and have no more significance than a random series of not very well executed doodles. They are wave trains left by a variety of different kinds of waves transmitted through, as well as over, the surface of the Earth. Those that follow paths that lie within the Earth are *body* waves, while those that follow paths in the outer crust of the earth are *surface* or *long* waves.

The long, or *L,* waves are the ones we feel during an earthquake and they are the ones that cause destruction. The *L* waves travel at slower velocities than the body waves, which are too faint to be perceived by anything but sensitive instruments, such as seismographs, tidal gauges, well recorders, gas-line pressure gauges, etc. The *L* waves are the ones that write the largest squiggles on a seismogram (Fig. 9-11), but their effect diminishes rapidly with distance.

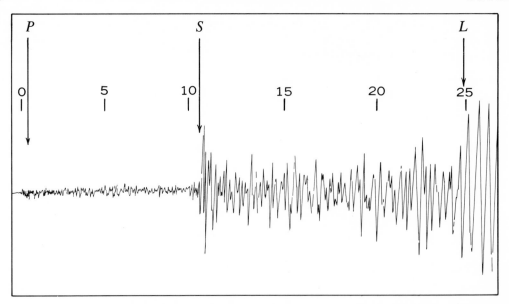

FIG. 9-11 *A typical seismogram. The horizontal scale represents the number of minutes after the arrival of the first P wave. S waves began arriving at time S, and L waves at time L.*

The *L* waves are limited to the *crust,* whose average thickness appears to be in the neighborhood of 10 miles. The crust is thicker under continents—possibly 20 to 25 miles—and is perhaps thickest under mountain ranges where it may be as much as 50 miles. Under oceans the crust may thin down to as little as 5 miles. The boundary between crust and mantle bears the difficult name of the *Mohorovičić discontinuity,* after the Croatian seismologist who noticed in 1909 that there was a marked change in the character of body waves at this level. Above this discontinuity, geologic controls (such as rocks of widely differing densities and structures) dominate, and the pattern with respect to the interpretation of earthquake waves is complex. Below the discontinuity, uniformity is more frequently the rule. Such things as *P* waves traveling close to the top of the mantle can be counted on to have a velocity of around 5 miles per second in all parts of the Earth.

To greatly simplify a very complex story, there are two major classes of body waves, and these are (1) *primary* and (2) *secondary* waves. Primary waves are also known as *longitudinal* or *compressional* waves. Since they are customarily abbreviated as *P* waves, perhaps the easiest way to remember them is as *push* waves. This not only is a good mnemonic device but also the word, push, gives a clue as to their behavior, as we shall see in a moment. Secondary waves also may be called *transverse* or *shear* waves;

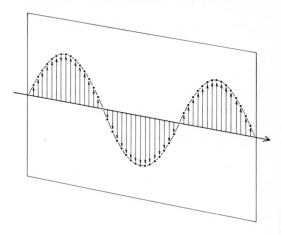

FIG. 9-12 *The movement of particles in S waves. The particles move up and down while the wave moves horizontally.*

they are abbreviated as *S* waves, and one way to keep them in mind is to call them *shake* waves.

Primary waves are akin to sound waves, and thus produce alternate compression and rarefaction in the medium through which they travel —much like the waves that spread out through the air in all directions from a tuning fork. Each particle moves to and fro in the same direction that the wave is traveling. This is a behavior pattern somewhat like the slam-bang pulse that travels the length of a long freight train when the engine takes up the slack, especially if it were possible for all the couplings to be elastic.

In secondary waves, the particles in the rock through which the wave is traveling vibrate at right angles, or transversely, to the direction of propagation. The waves that travel down a stretched clothesline, or a garden hose, or a throw rug when one end is shaken vigorously are familiar examples. This sort of wave is called a shear wave because the particles within a rock *shear,* or glide, past one another much like the individual cards in a deck of cards can be made to slide past one another. Incidentally, a few terms involving wave motion can be introduced here, and these should be kept in mind because they are equally applicable when we come to describing waves of the sea. The distance between two similar wave phases, such as two crests or two troughs, is the wave length. The half-height, or the distance above or below the mid-point, is the *amplitude*. The time interval between the passage of two successive similar phases past a given point is the *period*. The direction and the speed at which waves travel is their *velocity*. The velocity of *P* waves is very nearly twice that of *S* waves, and in general the velocity of both increases with depth in the Earth. For example, at a depth of 25 miles *P* waves travel at 5 miles per second and *S* waves at 2.7. At a depth of 1,800 miles the velocity of *P* waves has increased to 8.5 miles per second and the velocity of *S* waves has increased to 4.6 miles per second.

This immediately raises the question: why this seemingly strange behavior of body waves within the Earth? Why should the velocity of *P* and *S* waves increase with increased depth in the Earth? Laboratory experiments under conditions of temperature and pressure at the surface of the Earth made to determine the speeds of such waves in solids show that the velocity of these body waves increases with the rigidity and decreases with the density of the medium through which they are moving. Both rigidity and density increase with pressure, and if anything is certain about the interior of the Earth, it is that pressure increases toward the center, finally to reach values incomprehensible to us on the surface.

The important thing here is that the effect of the increasing pressure on the rigidity of materials within the Earth is greater than the increase in density with regard to body waves, and therefore their velocity increases in general down to a depth of 1,800 miles. Below this depth there is a sharp decrease in velocity, and we shall return to the explanation offered for this strange behavior farther on in this discussion.

The unequal speed at which *P* and *S* waves travel provides us with an effective means of determining the distance between a seismograph station and the starting point of an earthquake, or its focus.

The problem here is much like a horse race. Both the *P* and *S* waves start out together, a great deal like two horses at the instant the barrier is raised. The *P* waves are a sure thing, however, since they always run about twice as fast as the *S* waves. The longer the distance the two waves travel, the wider the gap separating them becomes. The diagram (Fig. 9-11) shows the pattern of an idealized and greatly simplified seismogram, and on it the pulses announcing the arrival of first the *P* and then the *S* waves can be accurately timed. Then the seismologist can turn to his travel-time curves, of which Fig. 9-13 is a simplified illustration. We can see from it that if the difference in arrival time of the *P*

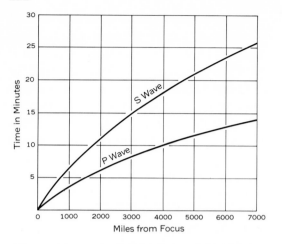

From J. H. Zumberge (after Bullen, *Seismology*, 1954), *Elements of Geology*, 1958. By permission of John Wiley & Sons, Inc. and Methuen & Co., Ltd.

FIG. 9-13 *Travel-time curves for P and S waves. The time lag between first arrivals of the P and S waves is used as a measure of the distance to the epicenter.*

and *S* waves is about 5 minutes, then the epicenter is about 2,000 miles away; if the difference is 10 minutes then it is about 5,500 miles away.

This reading of the seismograph record tells us only the distance; it gives no clue as to the direction of the source. All we can do is draw a circle on a map with the location of the seismograph station as the center and the radius of the circle equal to the distance between the seismograph station and the *epicenter* or geographic location of the earthquake source. If we use the example shown in Fig. 9-14, and consider first of all the record received at Pasadena, then all we know is that the epicenter is somewhere on the circumference of the circle drawn with Pasadena at the center. When Pasadena exchanges its records with Berkeley, then two locations are possible, because two circles can intersect at two points. When the third station, in this case Reno, is heard from then the epicenter can be located with considerable accuracy because three nonconcentric circles intersect only at a single point.

In practice, the actual determination is usually more complex because, for one thing, many earthquakes do not originate at a point but may commence simultaneously along a fault line. The San Francisco earthquake of 1906 is a representative example since it originated along a 270-mile failure of the San Andreas fault.

The actual point where the earthquake originates is called the *focus*. Its projection, or geographic location, on the surface of the ground is the *epicenter*. *P* and *S* waves traveling on the shortest route are the ones recorded by the seismograph, and when their arrival times are converted to distance, this will prove equal to the shortest distance between the seismograph (S) and focus (F). Should the earthquake prove to be the variety known as a *deep-focus earthquake*, then a circle with a radius of SF drawn on a map will overshoot the epicenter, and it

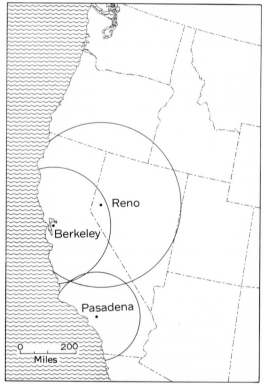

FIG. 9-14 *Determination of epicenter of earthquake by knowing its distance from the seismographs. The three independently determined circles intersect at a common point.*

will prove impossible to get the three circles to intersect at a point. In other words, the method we have been describing works well for shallow-focus earthquakes, but different travel-time tables must be used for those that originate at great depths below the crust.

The existence of deep-focus earthquakes was first discussed in 1922 by H. H. Turner and after debate and discussion during the following decade their reality was widely accepted. Part of the evidence for their existence is that they write a different sort of seismogram from shallow-focus earthquakes. For one thing, the *L* waves are lacking, or are likely to be ambiguous. More critically, though, the *P* waves that pass through the Earth arrive sooner than they would have had the focus been nearer the surface. They should because they have the advantage of a considerable head start.

To the initial surprise of many geologists, deep-focus earthquakes were demonstrated to have originated at depths as great as 400 miles. This is taken as an indication that at depths as great as this, rocks rupture in about the same way they do at shallower depths to produce a surface shock. According to Richter (1958, p. 305):

All this evidence indicates that deep-focus earthquakes originate in a process involving shear and elastic rebound and of the same general nature as that causing shallow shocks. The problem of plastic flow at great depth must then be faced; the apparent contradiction is resolved by appealing to a time parameter. Slowly accumulating strains will be relieved by flow before they can arrive at fracture, but rapidly accumulating strains may progress until fracture is reached. The behavior may be compared with that of a block of wax, which flows gradually under pressure or even under its own weight but fractures sharply if struck with a hammer.

A map of the distribution of deep-focus earthquakes would show that the locations of their epicenters correspond to some extent with those of surface quakes and yet differ in some significant respect. The coincidence is closest perhaps

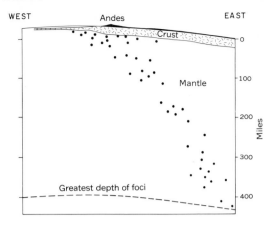

After Jacobs, *Physics and Geology*, Copyright © 1959 McGraw-Hill Book Co., Inc. By permission.

FIG. 9-15 *The position of earthquake foci under western South America.*

on the western side of the Pacific; on the eastern side the most noteworthy thing is their absence under the North American continent. There is also a significant concentration of deep-focus earthquakes far below the Himalayas and under the Andes—much farther inland in South America than the shallow-focus earthquakes clustered along the Pacific coast. Much the same distribution characterizes the epicenters of deep-focus earthquakes below the island arcs of the western Pacific. The same pattern characterizes the Andean deep-focus earthquakes, with the deepest which are also the farthest inland starting from foci far below the Bolivian plateau.

This curious linear distribution of deep earthquake foci along the surface of what appears to be a dipping plane has suggested to some geologists that these may represent points of failure where strains have built up along fractures akin to thrust faults inclined inland away from the Pacific basin.

SEISMIC WAVES
AND THE DEPTHS OF THE EARTH

As was mentioned before, seismology is an international science, and quite early in its history a number of perplexing patterns became apparent in the reception, or lack of it, of body waves transmitted through the Earth. When seismological observatories in different parts of the world compared records, a puzzling pattern emerged with regard to the disappearance of *S* waves. Both *P* and *S* waves are recorded by seismograph stations within a distance of about 103° of arc or 6,800 miles from the epicenter. Beyond this point both the *P* and *S* waves fade away and there is a wide band, approximately 3,200 miles across, the so-called *shadow zone,* in which no body waves are received. Then at a distance of 143°, or 10,000 miles (6,800 + 3,200) from the epicenter the *P* wave is recorded, usually with quite a strong signal, but *S* waves appear no more.

Another curious behavior pattern of the *P* waves that follow a path through the center of the Earth is their apparent delay en route. Were they to travel with the same velocity they have at a depth of 1,800 miles, they should go completely through the Earth in about 16 minutes, whereas actually it takes them 20 minutes to make the trip. Obviously something has happened in the deep interior to cancel out the *S* waves and to retard the *P* waves by approximately 4 minutes.

An explanation for this anomalous behavior was given in 1913 in Europe by Beno Gutenberg, who for many years was director of the Seismological Laboratory at the California Institute of Technology. His widely accepted theory is that this wave behavior can be explained by the presence of a profound discontinuity within the Earth at a depth of approximately 1,800 miles. The part of the Earth above this discontinuity is called the *mantle;* the inner 2,100 or 2,200 miles of the Earth is the *core* (Fig. 9-16).

Seismic observations made over the past half-century have established with reasonable certainty that the velocity of *P* waves drops abruptly at the Gutenberg discontinuity from about 8.5 miles per second to around 5 miles per second, or back to very nearly the same velocity they

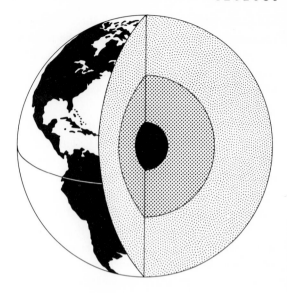

FIG. 9-16 *The Earth's interior, showing the relative size of the mantle (light stippling), outer core (dark stippling), and inner core (black). The crust is approximately the thickness of the line on the outer surface of the Earth.*

had at the base of the crust close to the surface (Fig. 9-17). The graph also shows the disappearance of the *S* waves at a depth of 1,800 miles as well as the fall-off and then gradual increase of velocity of *P* waves within the mantle.

What is the explanation for this behavior of the two waves? All we can do is make a number of surmises about the physical state of the core based on what we know of the behavior of matter at the Earth's surface. We do know that *S* waves at the Earth's surface are *not* transmitted through liquids. They are shear, or distortional, waves, and since fluids do not have distortional elasticity the inference drawn from this is that under the temperatures and pressures prevailing there, the core has more of the physical attributes of a liquid than it does a solid.

The fact that *P* waves cross the core does not help us settle this specific problem of the physical state of the Earth's central zone because they are comparable to sound waves and thus can be transmitted through either solids or liquids. The abrupt reduction in velocity at the

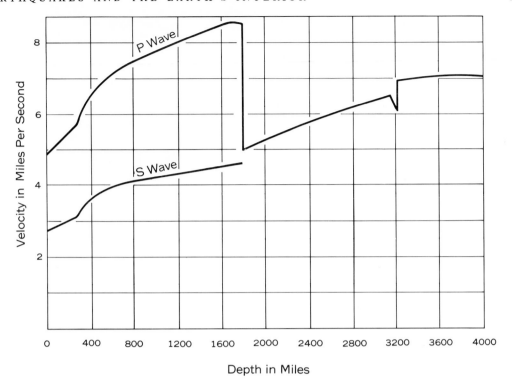

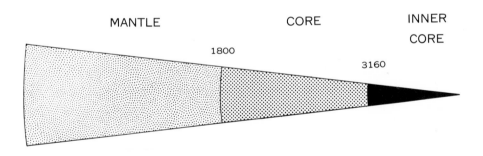

boundary between the mantle and the core is a puzzler, because not only does the velocity diminish almost by half, but it picks up again and increases slowly toward the center of the Earth (Fig. 9-16), until it reaches about 7 miles per second.

Reasoning by analogy from what we know of the compressional or longitudinal waves in the surface layers of the Earth, their velocity is affected by (1) the density and (2) the rigidity of the medium through which they are traveling. The more rigid and incompressible the rock, the

From J. H. Zumberge (after P. Byerly, *Seismology*, 1942), *Elements of Geology*, 1958. By permission of John Wiley & Sons, Inc. and Prentice-Hall, Inc.

FIG. 9-17 *Discontinuities in the Earth's interior as inferred from changes in the velocity of P and S waves.*

higher the velocity. On the other hand, increasing density brings about a decrease in velocity.

The big drop in velocity of *P* waves at the Gutenberg discontinuity can be interpreted to mean that this boundary marks a change in the physical state of material in the Earth's interior at a depth of 1,800 miles. This is a change involving a marked loss in rigidity and at the same time an increase in density.

This supposition fits well with the blanking out of S waves mentioned in the paragraph preceding—that the Gutenberg discontinuity is the boundary surface separating a solid mantle above from a liquid core below. In a seismological sense a substance is a solid if it has both incompressibility and rigidity. It is a liquid if its rigidity is insignificant compared to its incompressibility, rather than whether or not we can drink or wash in it. Water, incidentally, has negligible rigidity, or resistance to shear, but it is a relatively incompressible substance.

This is not to say that the deep interior of the Earth is like water on the surface, or even like lava, because among other things its rigidity, after the initial drop-off at the upper margin of the core, picks up again until it reaches a value of perhaps as much as two to four times that of steel. This is interpreted by many seismologists to mean that there may be a smaller inner core, perhaps 1,600 miles in diameter, that is solid, thus giving the Earth a structure consisting of a solid mantle, liquid outer core, and possibly a small, dense solid inner core.

That the core itself is denser than the mantle is demonstrated by the peculiar behavior of the P and S waves where they fade out and disappear in the shadow zone. Waves between the epicenter and a point 6,800 miles away travel on direct, but slightly curved, paths until they emerge at the surface (Fig. 9-18). On the other hand, waves that penetrate the interface at the top of the core have their paths bent or deflected. This is called *refraction,* and is familiar to all of us in the way that light waves are bent on passing from air into water. The same thing happens, too, when light waves are bent on passing from air into a glass lens. The light rays converge toward the center as their speed is slowed down in the denser medium. This is the principle that is used with such telling effect

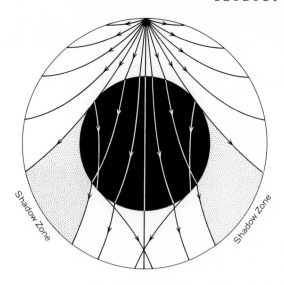

FIG. 9-18 *Earthquake wave paths in the Earth's interior. The shadow zone is caused by refraction of P waves at the boundary of the core.*

in a magnifying glass when all the light rays falling on its surface are concentrated into a spot which is intense enough to start a fire. The cross section of the Earth (Fig. 9-18) shows how the paths of P waves are deflected toward the center of the Earth when they enter the denser material of the core and then away from it when they leave the core on the opposite side and start out into the lighter material of the mantle. The diagram shows how this bending, or refraction, of the P waves—especially of the ones that just penetrate the discontinuity at the top of the core—is responsible for the shadow zone on the far side of the Earth. Either increased density or decreased rigidity can account for this effect. The important thing is that anything that decreases the velocity can achieve this result.

Much of our picture of the true nature of the Earth's interior is veiled. We do know that pressure increases with depth until, if our assumptions are correct, it may reach the enormous figure of 20,000,000 pounds to the square inch.

We believe, too, that with this rise of pressure there is a corresponding increase in density. In Chapter I we learned that the Earth has a density, or more properly a specific gravity, 5.519 times greater than an equal volume of water. This high value for the Earth's over-all density poses an interesting problem because the average for rocks visible at the surface is about 2.7. To arrive at an average figure of nearly twice as much as that, somewhere within the Earth there must be a concentration of heavier material. Logically, this would be in the inner core, and density expectedly would increase from the surface of the Earth to the center. In a general way it very likely does, but a debate is still being conducted over how materials of different composition and density are distributed within the Earth.

There is no practical way yet known for us to reach the center of the Earth, or even to obtain a sample of it. All our knowledge comes from indirect evidence, such as the cryptic squiggles written by the waves from far-distant earthquakes on a seismograph drum. Here the evidence we have discussed in the preceding paragraphs makes it seem clear that a great increase in density occurs at the interface between the mantle and the core—perhaps from 4.7–5.7 to as much as 9.4–11.5 (Bullen, 1957).

We have no direct knowledge of what the density may be in the inner core, but according to Bullen, an Australian geophysicist (Fig. 9-19), it may rise to as much as 14.5 to 18 times as much as an equal amount of water. Bullen's diagram also shows that this is not an increase at a constant rate from the surface to the center of the Earth, but indicates graphically the large increase in density at the top of the core.

What is the core made of that it should be so heavy? The answer is simple; no one knows. Once again we can only surmise from what we know of the rocky outer shell and from the tenuous Ariadne's thread provided for us by earthquake waves as they penetrate the interior. The best, although far from unanimous, opinion appears to be that the same chemical compounds that make up the rocks on the Earth's surface are also present in the interior, but in more compact, high-pressure modifications. The core very likely consists of a denser phase of material made up of iron plus silicon and other constituents of the lithosphere, rather than a metallic inner zone.

From the limited information obtainable from studies of deep wells and mines we know that temperatures in the uppermost layers of the Earth increase with depth. We do not, however, have much of a base from which to extrapolate because the deepest mines go down to only 9,800 feet and oil wells have been drilled to slightly more than 25,000 feet. In these probes which seem so deep to us, but still at the very most are only 1:1,000 part of the distance to the center, the temperature increases with increasing depth. The amount of this increase varies from place to place, and is greater in the vicinity of hot springs and geysers than in less thermally stimulated regions. A rough average for the outermost skin of the Earth accessible to us would be about 1°F. for every 60 feet. If this rate of increase is projected all the way to the

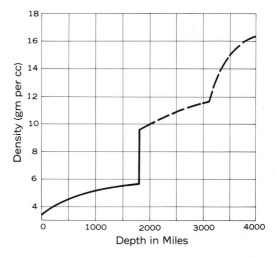

After K. E. Bullen, *An Introduction to the Theory of Seismology*, 1953. By permission of Cambridge University Press.

FIG 9-19 *Densities at various depths in the Earth.*

center of the Earth, remarkably high figures result, perhaps as much as 100,000°C.

Very likely it has been such straight-line projections as this which have led to the picturesque interpretation that the Earth has a flaming, molten core enclosed by a shallow envelope through which volcanoes have forced their way to pour out their fiery streams.

A second concept that has probably influenced our thinking about the internal temperatures of the Earth is the belief that if the Earth solidified from a once-molten sphere, then high internal temperatures may be a residue, as it were, of this cosmic event.

With the recognition of the importance of radioactivity in the rock-forming minerals, a new source of heat within the Earth could be proposed. Careful study through the years has shown that most of the radioactivity is concentrated in such elements as thorium, radium, and potassium. Since these are relatively more abundant in the minerals of granite than they are in those of basalt, it seems reasonable to expect that temperatures will be higher in the first rock and lower in the second. A great variety of evidence, much of which is internally consistent, demonstrates with reasonable certainty that rocks of granitic composition are limited to the Earth's crust and that those that are related to basalt dominate at greater depth. Therefore, much of the heat supply available within the Earth is concentrated within its higher levels rather than in the depths below as the molten core hypothesis calls for.

With this revision in our thinking, there unfortunately is almost no certainty as to what the actual temperatures in the inner recesses of the Earth may be. The consensus today appears to be that temperature does not increase directly with depth, but that the greatest *rate* of increase is near the surface, and of course the highest actual temperature is near the center, possibly something like the pattern shown in Fig. 9-20. What this temperature will be is sheer speculation, but in all acceptable theories today the

amount is thought to be not over 10,000°C. and, according to J. Verhoogen (1956) of the University of California, it is probably not less than 2,000°C. Possibly 3,000°C. or 4,000°C. may be closer to the answer.

Confining pressures within the Earth are high enough that probably nowhere are there large volumes of molten rock. Solid rocks must expand to melt, and pressures in the deeper parts of the Earth are too great to allow this expansion. Very likely melting through a drop in pressure occurs only locally where a sudden release of stress occurs, as in regions of active stress or crustal activity. Perhaps this explains the largely coincident patterns of the distribution of volcanoes, earthquake centers, and recently elevated mountain ranges.

From what has gone before, we learn that earthquakes result from the failure of rocks in the Earth's crust when stresses have built up to the point that rupture occurs. Most often such a rupture takes place along a plane of weakness, such as a fault, and of these, the San Andreas fault in California is one of the world's preeminent examples.

Such failure sets in motion a variety of waves; surface or long waves which are responsible for the destruction of cities and buildings, and body waves, such as longitudinal (or compressional) waves and transverse (or shear) waves that move through the Earth.

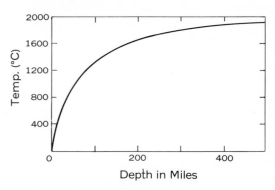

After B. F. Howell, Jr., *Introduction to Geophysics,* Copyright © 1959 McGraw-Hill Book Co., Inc. By permission.

FIG. 9-20 *Internal temperature of the Earth.*

Patient unraveling of the tangled skein of the records written by seismographs at observatories all over the world show that the composition of the Earth's interior below the crust is remarkably uniform. The Earth appears to be arranged in concentric shells, with the greatest discontinuity occurring 1,800 miles below the surface. Above this profound change, the mantle is solid, shear waves are transmitted through it, and it yields elastically to sudden stresses, although it may deform plastically under long-continued deformation. Below the interface the core appears to behave toward shear waves as fluids do and its material is of greater density than that of the overlying mantle.

Much more is to be learned about the Earth's interior than is known today. The gulf of our ignorance is both deep and wide. In many ways the realm beneath our feet is as mysterious as interstellar space. It is true that we have come a long way down the road of understanding, but the goal of full knowledge still is far distant. It is a strange commentary, though, that the pendulum, seemingly the simplest of all instruments —even with all the subtleties of the modern seismograph added to it—should be the means by which we have gained the insight we possess.

Suggested References

Anderson, D. L., 1962, The plastic layer of the earth's mantle, Scientific American, v. 207, p. 52-59.

Bascom, Willard, 1961, A hole in the bottom of the sea; the story of the Mohole project, Doubleday and Co., Inc., Garden City, New York.

Bateman, P. C., 1961, Willard D. Johnson and the strike-slip component of fault movement in the Owens Valley, California, earthquake of 1872, Seismological Soc. of Amer., Bull., v. 51, p. 483-493.

Bates, D. R., and others, 1957, The earth and its atmosphere, Basic Books, Inc., New York.

Bronson, Wm., 1959, The earth shook, the sky burned, Doubleday and Co., Inc., Garden City, New York.

Bullen, K. E., 1954, Seismology, Methuen and Co., London.

Byerly, Perry, 1954, Seismology, Prentice-Hall, Inc., Englewood Cliffs, N. J.

Davison, Charles, 1936, Great earthquakes, Thomas Murby and Co., London.

Eiby, G. A., 1957, Earthquakes, Frederick Muller, Ltd., London.

Freeman, J. F., 1932, Earthquake damage and earthquake insurance, McGraw-Hill Book Co., Inc., New York.

Fuller, M. L., 1914, The New Madrid earthquake, U. S. Geol. Survey, Bulletin 494.

Gutenberg, B., and Richter, C. F., 1949, Seismicity of the earth, Princeton Univ. Press, Princeton, N. J.

Howell, B. F., 1959, Introduction to geophysics, McGraw-Hill Book Co., Inc., New York.

Kendrick, T. D., 1956, The Lisbon earthquake, Methuen and Co., London.

Kuiper, G. P., and others, 1954, The earth as a planet, Univ. of Chicago Press, Chicago, Ill.

Lawson, A. C., and others, 1908, The California earthquake of April 18, 1906, Rept. of the State Earthquake Commission, Carnegie Inst. of Washington.

Leet, L. D., 1948, Causes of catastrophe, Whittlesey House, McGraw-Hill Book Co., Inc., New York.

Lovering, J. F., 1958, The nature of the Mohorovičić discontinuity, Trans. Amer. Geophysical Union, v. 39, p. 947-955.

Oakeshott, G. B., and others, 1955, Earthquakes in Kern County, California, during 1952, Calif. State Division of Mines, Bulletin 171.

Poldervaart, A., and others, 1955, Crust of the earth, Geol. Soc. Amer., Special Paper No. 62.

Reid, H. F., 1914, The Lisbon earthquake of November 1, 1755, Seismological Soc. of Amer., Bull., v. 4, p. 53-80.

Richter, C. F., 1958, Elementary seismology, W. H. Freeman and Co., San Francisco.

Shepard, F. P., 1933, Depth changes in Sagami Bay during the great Japanese earthquake, Jour. Geol., v. 41, p. 527-536.

Sutherland, Monica, 1959, The damndest finest ruins, Coward-McCann Book Co., New York.

Verhoogen, J., 1956, Temperatures within the earth, in Vol. I, Physics and chemistry of the earth, Pergamon Press, Inc., New York.

Witkind, J. S., 1962, The night the earth shook; a guide to the Madison River Canyon earthquakes area, Dept. of Agric., U. S. Forest Service, Misc. Publ. 907.

X

Weathering and Mass Movement

In the days of the Pharaohs a cherished status symbol was the obelisk. These hieroglyph-bedecked stone columns early became collector's items for a procession of conquerors of the Nile, beginning with the Caesars and ending with Napoleon. Or more properly speaking, ending with us, because we collected an obelisk in 1879. After prodigies of effort, involving among other things the cutting of a loading port in the bow of one of the primitive steamships of the time (whereupon it nearly foundered), our obelisk was finally set up in Central Park to take its place among similar far-wandering artifacts in cities such as Paris, London, and Rome—which alone holds twelve of them.

The climate of New York is considerably more stimulating than that of Egypt. A mixture of cold winters, sleet- and snow-laden winds, and hot, steamy summers, in addition to an atmosphere laden with coal smoke and gasoline fumes, is bound to add a certain amount of zest. No wonder that in about seventy years many of the hieroglyphs spalled off and the whole surface of the obelisk started to come apart, while its counterparts still standing in Egypt have survived nearly unscathed beneath the desert sun for almost 4,000 years (Fig. 10-1).

This brief story makes the point that climate is one of the leading factors in determining the rate and manner in which rocks disintegrate or decompose, or as we say *weather*—using the word in about the same way we do when we speak of a weather-beaten face. Another critical factor in determining the effectiveness of weathering is the kind of rock which is exposed to atmospheric attack. Evidence for this can be found in New England graveyards, where slate headstones carrying the salty epitaphs beloved by some of our forebears survive from the 1700's, while the words carved on limestone or marble markers of much more recent vintage may be wholly obliterated.

In general, limestone and marble are more susceptible than slate to weathering, because they consist of the soluble mineral calcite ($CaCO_3$). Many slates are made from recrystallized clay flakes, which are about as durable as any material can be. However, as with most general statements, there is the inevitable exception. Limestone and marble are extremely resistant rocks in an arid climate, where there is a lack of moisture or of plants to provide a source for carbonic acid (H_2CO_3). Limestone also may hold up surprisingly well even in a moderately semi-arid climate, as is demonstrated by Mayan temples and carvings, overgrown these many years by the jungles of Yucatan.

The obelisk of Thothmes III, from the Temple of Heliopolis, Egypt, now in Central Park, New York. The lower part of the column shows a loss of detail due to weathering. The monument was brought to New York in 1879. (Courtesy of the Metropolitan Museum of Art.)

Every observant traveler has probably noticed how different the surface of the ground appears in various parts of the world. In some, the soil may be dark colored and deep, in others there may be only the thinnest veneer of sterile, stony soil and original colors of the rocks dominate, as they do throughout the deserts of the southwestern United States.

Climate is perhaps the leading, although far from being the only, reason for many of these differences. In humid, warm regions where vegetation flourishes and organic acids are abundant, chemical processes are dominant and rocks are prone to *decompose,* or to decay. In harsher climates where frost action may dominate, rocks break up mechanically, or *disintegrate,* without undergoing chemical alteration. In other words, when rocks decompose, they are changed into substances with quite different chemical compositions and physical properties than they started with. If they disintegrate, they are simply broken up into smaller fragments, much as if they had been struck a hammer blow. There are few areas where only chemical weathering or only mechanical weathering operates to the exclusion of the other process, but there are many where one or the other rules.

Decomposition or disintegration of rocks produces a mantle of rock particles on the surface of the Earth thick in some places, thin in others, or even totally lacking in still others. Such a mantle is called the *regolith,* and the formation of a true soil is an end-product of its development. In fact, soil is by far the most valuable of all the mineral resources of the Earth. Without it, life—such as we know it—would be impossible. While we could survive without a number of other substances such as gold or diamonds, which are admittedly more attractive than plain, ordinary dirt, we would never make it without the latter.

FIG. 10-1 *The surface of this obelisk, still standing in Karnak, Egypt, is scarcely marred by four millennia of weathering. (Photograph by Jean B. Thorpe.)*

MECHANICAL WEATHERING

Some aspects of mechanical weathering are irritatingly familiar to all of us, such as the wedging apart of sidewalks, foundations, and walls by the roots of grass, trees, and shrubs (Fig. 10-2). The same thing goes on in mountains, and a common sight high on their slopes is an isolated pine clinging to a sheer granite ledge. With no soil in which to take hold, its roots succeed in forcing their way into crevices, springing the rocks apart. This is a process much like the one used millennia ago by Egyptian slaves, when they utilized water-soaked wooden wedges to pry out granite blocks to make obelisks.

Almost all rocks are cut by cracks, large and small; sometimes as closely spaced as a fraction of an inch, at other times they may be scores of feet apart, as they are in the stupendous cliff of El Capitan in Yosemite Valley. These cracks are called joints, and they provide an ideal path

FIG. 10-2 *The results of root wedging at Angkor Wat, Cambodia, where a temple built of laterite blocks is gradually being destroyed. (Photograph by Leonard Palmer.)*

for roots, organic acid-bearing solutions, and water to penetrate far into the rocks (Fig. 10-3).

FREEZING AND THAWING

Water, as we learned in Chapter I, is a highly unusual substance. The property of the greatest significance to us here is the expansion water undergoes when its temperature drops from 39.2°F. to 32.0°F., its freezing point. Water expands by about 9 per cent when it is chilled in this range of 7.2°F.

Should water freeze in a confined space, then it is capable of delivering an enormous outward thrust against its containing walls. Everyone who has glumly contemplated a cracked engine block or ruptured radiator knows this fact too well. Few realize, though, how great this force actually is. At the minimum, it probably is at least 2,000 pounds per square inch, which is 288,000 pounds per square foot. No wonder the need for repairs in the wake of water frozen in the plumbing can devastate a household budget.

This outward pressure continues to build up at temperatures below 32°F., since a certain amount of expansion continues to take place at subzero temperatures, at least down to −7.6°F. Here a pressure with a theoretical maximum of 30,000 pounds per square inch is possible (Taber, 1930). Probably this figure is never reached, because few rocks could stand up to

FIG. 10-3 *Vertical and horizontal joints in granite in the Sierra Nevada, Calif., provide avenues for moisture, which may aid in mechanical disintegration when it turns into ice, and also enable plants to send down their roots, which wedge apart blocks. (From the Cedric Wright Collection, courtesy of the Sierra Club.)*

FIG. 10-4 *The summit of Mount Whitney (alt. 14,495 ft.) is composed of frost- and ice-shattered granite which is closely jointed. Most mountain crests above timberline are blanketed with mechanically shattered blocks resulting from frost wedging. (Photograph by Tom Ross.)*

such a pressure without rupturing. In addition, for such a tremendous stress to build up it is necessary to have a completely enclosed system with air excluded, and this is seldom realized in an environment such as a crack in a rock.

Actually the pressure made available by the freezing of water is enough to sunder most rocks exposed in high mountains. Water freezing in an open crevice freezes from the top down and thus is sealed in with a cover of ice. Then, if confined in the lower part of the crevice, it can act as a wedge to spring rocks apart along planes of weakness such as joints.

The process of *frost wedging* is most effective when it is repeated the greatest number of times. In other words, if the temperature swings from 39°F. to 32°F. each day, the amount of frost riving will be many times greater than in the Arctic, where everything is in a deep freeze through the winter.

For this reason, freezing and thawing reaches its peak effectiveness above timber line on high mountains outside of the Arctic. Temperatures on them rise above the melting point by day and drop below at night. As a result summit uplands may be carpeted with a pavement of frost-shattered angular joint blocks (Fig. 10-4). Sometimes these are packed so tightly together they resemble an artificial pavement, and in fact will support a light plane for landings and take-offs.

The accumulation of joint blocks found in a long apron at the base of a steep slope is called

FIG. 10-5 *Accumulations of ice-shattered joint blocks at the base of steep slopes are termed talus or scree, shown here at the base of Kearsarge Pinnacles, in the Sierra Nevada, Calif. (Photograph by Tom Ross.)*

---

talus (Fig. 10-5), a term borrowed from medieval military engineering for the slope at the base of a fortification wall. In Scotland such an accumulation is called a *scree,* and this incisive word, derived from Old Norse, occasionally is used in this country (Fig. 10-6).

If a large mass of frost-broken rock accumulates on a moderately steep slope and contains enough interstitial ice, it may move downhill as a ponderously advancing lobe with a wrinkled, corrugated surface and steep sides, in which case it is known as a *rock glacier.* Such slowly moving rock streams are especially well developed in the southern part of the Rocky Mountains (Fig. 10-7).

Should water freeze in the pore spaces, or interstices of a soil, a surprising amount of damage may result. The principal effect of the growth of soil ice is a phenomenon known as *frost heave.* This is a familiar problem to people in northern lands, even though it may manifest itself in forms of no greater severity than garage doors that stick in winter. Frost heave may cause serious damage to concrete which contains water. Should this water freeze, it may lead to the breaking up of such things as runways, roads, and foundations. Agriculturally, frost heave is an unmitigated nuisance in areas with stony soil, such as New England, where each year it seems almost as though a new crop of boulders had been heaved out of the ground.

Frost heave is more effective in finely textured soils, such as clay and silt, than it is in coarse ones such as sand and gravel. For frost heave to operate, more is required than having the water initially contained in the ground freeze. To be more effective the ice should continue to grow in the ground; this is best achieved when water is added continuously and then frozen. This can be accomplished best where the pore spaces or interstices are thread-like, because then the force known as *capillarity* can operate. All of us are familiar with its workings —it is, for example, the force that draws water up into a sponge, or ink into a blotter. As an illustration of the effectiveness of capillarity, water will rise about 1 foot in a glass tube

1 mm. in diameter, but if the diameter is reduced to 0.1 mm. it can rise about 10 feet.

Ice wedging can be a most destructive process. Silt layers are wedged apart, the surface of the ground is heaved up differentially, and buildings, roads, etc., are cracked or thrown out of alignment.

Bad as this may be, things rapidly become worse in the spring when such ice wedges melt. Then the ground literally falls apart because the binding or cementing action of the ice is destroyed. A thawed silt becomes spongy, and if it is water-saturated it quickly becomes a boggy morass in which even four-wheel-drive vehicles flounder helplessly.

Permafrost

An important kind of ice widely distributed throughout the Arctic is in ground which remains frozen from one year to the next. The

FIG. 10-6 *A scree slope below a rocky summit in the Sierra Nevada. (From the Cedric Wright Collection, courtesy of the Sierra Club.)*

FIG. 10-7 *A rock stream or rock glacier is composed of frost- and ice-shattered rock filled with interstitial ice which slowly moves downslope, as illustrated here in the San Juan Mountains of Colorado, about 10 miles southeast of Silverton. (Photograph by John S. Shelton.)*

coined name of *permafrost* was applied to this ground ice during World War II, and all efforts to substitute terms that sound a little less like a trade name for a refrigerator have been successfully resisted.

Permafrost is more widely distributed than many people realize, since it underlies almost 20 per cent of the *land* surface of the Earth, including about 80 per cent of Alaska and perhaps half of Canada. The actual distribution of permafrost is shown on the accompanying map (Fig. 10-8). Interestingly enough, areas underlain by permafrost today are not the same as those glaciated during the Ice Age which presumably ended about 12,000 years ago.

Permafrost reaches its maximum thickness around the margins of the Arctic Ocean in Alaska, Canada, and the Soviet Arctic. It may extend to depths of as much as 1,000 feet below the surface of the ground along the northern margins of North America and Eurasia. In a general way the thickness decreases southward until finally it thins to zero about along the southern boundary shown on the map (Fig. 10-8).

Overlying the permafrost is a soil layer in which ground ice thaws in the spring and freezes in the fall to remain frozen throughout the winter. This is the so-called active layer, and in areas where permafrost is widespread it may be only 1 to 3 feet deep. The upper surface of the permafrost in the ground is called the *permafrost table,* and in many ways it is analogous to the water table, which is discussed in Chapter VIII.

Below the permafrost table the available pore spaces are filled with ice, and the surface water in the active layer cannot sink underground. This is one reason why much of the tundra in the Arctic is so boggy and water-soaked. Although precipitation over large segments of the Arctic is very slight, the country appears to be wetter than it actually is because, with a relatively low evaporation rate and no chance to sink underground, the available water stands in lakes and muskeg on the surface.

Before 1942 little attention was given in this country to permafrost and its manifold prob-

lems, although Russians had studied this phenomenon intensively for more than half a century. Visitors to the interior of Alaska, especially in the vicinity of Fairbanks, are invariably surprised at the tilted houses and the "drunken forests" with their tipsy looking trees, thrown out of line by melting of the permafrost or by upward growth of permafrost into the active zone.

Out of the scores of problems that permafrost can produce, only a few need be mentioned. Heated buildings in the Arctic are likely to thaw out the permafrost beneath them and melt their way down into the soggy, unstable

FIG. 10-8 *The area of permafrost, or frozen ground (coarse dots), covers about 20 per cent of the land surface of the Earth at higher northern and southern latitudes.*

After R. F. Black, Geol. Soc. Amer. Bull. 65, 1954. By permission.

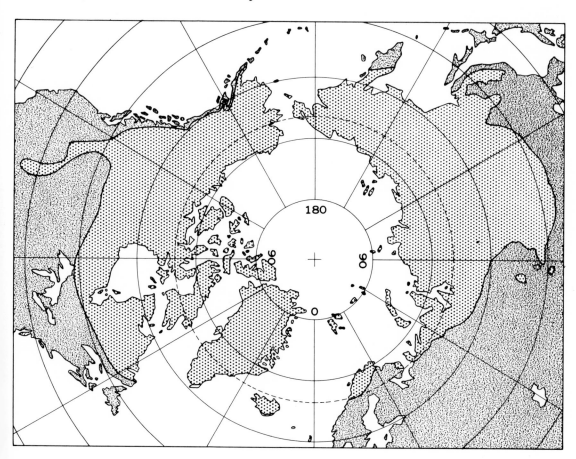

ground under the foundation. Usually such houses sink unevenly, so that floors sag, walls tip, and doors stick. The most practical answer to the problem seems to be to put houses and barracks up on stilts. This allows cold air to circulate under them and makes a minimum of disturbance of the permafrost.

Unheated buildings, especially large ones such as hangars or warehouses, insulate the ground surface below them so that the active layer does not thaw in the summer. The result is that the permafrost table rises, and may constitute a dam which blocks the flow of ground water through the active layer. If the ground water is forced out onto the surface where it freezes, this is the phenomenon known as *icing*. It may be spectacular indeed. For example, the interior of an unheated building into which ground water forces its way may be converted into a block of ice, with ice cascading out of the doors and windows.

Roads and airfields have about the same effect on the permafrost table as an unheated building. If ground water is forced to the surface it may form an ice field, or an "icing" to translate the Russian word, which can block the highway for thousands of feet. Two methods of alleviating this are (1) to extend broad aprons, called *berms,* on either side of the highway or airfield to prevent the permafrost table from rising abruptly under the highway, and (2) to excavate a broad, shallow ditch, perhaps 30 feet wide, on the upslope side so that ground water moving within the active layer will be intercepted. Ice sheets will form harmlessly in the ditch whose embankment keeps them from spreading across the pavement.

The list of problems permafrost can create seems endless; the degree to which Arctic pioneers have solved them is a testimonial to their ingenuity and perseverance. Even such a simple thing as developing a water supply in a permafrost area can become a major frustration. Ground water in the active layer is available only during the summer, and usually is at so

shallow a depth that it is readily contaminated by surface wastes. Although there may be ground water below the permafrost, it is deep, and the part of the well that is within the frozen ground is almost certain to freeze. If water pipes are buried underground, they freeze; if placed above ground, they freeze, too, and are likely to be thrown out of line as the ground under them either heaves when it freezes or sinks when it thaws. Fire fighting is an exceedingly difficult enterprise when all surface water freezes, and if buildings are destroyed by fire their occupants may freeze, too.

Sewage disposal is perhaps the ultimate problem. Septic tanks freeze, and in the absence of bacteria, decay does not dispose of waste as it does in warmer climates. At Point Barrow the unsightly, but practical, solution is to heap everything up in a pile on an ice floe in the winter. In the summer this cake of ice floats out into the Arctic Ocean, melts, and the waste sinks.

TEMPERATURE CHANGES

In textbooks of a generation ago much was made of the supposed disintegration of rocks resulting from alternate expansion and contraction induced by severe temperature changes. The favorite locale for such a performance was the desert. There, according to most versions, rocks expanded drastically under the noonday sun and contracted sharply with the fall of temperature at night. Presumably these dimensional changes would be greatest on the surface of a rock and least in its interior, because rocks are such notoriously poor conductors of heat. Such a process, called *exfoliation* from the Latin *exfoliatus*—stripped of leaves—was believed adequate to explain the onion-layered appearance of many rocks.

There is no doubt about the existence of exfoliated rocks; their number truly is legion, but there is uncertainty about the way in which they are formed. Peeling off of concentric rings by differential expansion of the heated surface layers from the cooler interior is an appealing solution, but there are a number of difficulties. For example, in deserts such as the Sahara and Arabia, stone monuments and buildings have survived for 4,000 years with scarcely any blurring of their inscriptions.

Perhaps the most conclusive evidence that temperature changes alone are incapable of disrupting rocks comes from an interesting experiment made by D. T. Griggs (1936). He placed a highly polished block of granite under a heat source so arranged that for 5 minutes the heat was on and then for 10 minutes the surface was air cooled by a fan. This ran the surface of the granite through a temperature range of 110°C., and the process was repeated 89,400 times, or the equivalent of 244 years of weathering, should each of these 15-minute cycles be considered a day. In even the fiercest desert the diurnal range is far less than 100°C.—equivalent to 212°F.; if we were to consider the experiment in more realistic terms, 1,000 years of actual weathering were more closely approximated.

What happened as a result of the punishment to which the rock was subjected? Nothing. The surface remained unblemished, retaining its original bright polish throughout the entire ordeal.

Griggs then introduced a little rain, as it were, into the environment by having a fine spray of water turned on during the cooling cycle. This was done for only 10 days, the equivalent of 2½ years of weathering, and in this brief time a number of notable changes occurred. The granite lost its polish, feldspar crystals clouded up with a film of clayey material on their surface, and exfoliation cracks started to appear. All this occurred in the equivalent of 2½ years, as compared with the absence of visible results after the laboratory equivalent of 10 centuries of total aridity and extreme temperature ranges.

This isolated experiment supports the observations made in Egypt by an American geologist, Barton (1916). He noticed that almost no discernible change was visible on granite inscriptions that faced the sun, while those that were in the shade and thus remained relatively damp showed much more spalling of rock surfaces and hieroglyphs.

The conclusion made from the experiment, as well as from evidence in arid regions all over the world, is that temperature changes by themselves are incapable of making a rock exfoliate, but that water plays an important role in the process. A plausible explanation is that in many deserts, no matter how arid they may seem, a little water may be available from sporadic showers or from nocturnal dew. When this water enters into chemical combination with the more susceptible minerals in a rock they swell. It is this increase in volume resulting from *hydration* that gives the needed shove to lift off the outer layers of a rock in concentric shells. To summarize, exfoliation appears to be essentially a mechanical or disintegrative process, accomplished, however, by a chemical means—hydration.

CHEMICAL WEATHERING

Chemical changes dominate in hot and humid lands where temperatures are high, a large amount of water is available, and vegetation flourishes. Organic acids, which are potent agents of rock decay, are readily generated and rocks that can stand up to their onslaught are rare. Carbonic acid (H_2CO_3) is a common acid of this type, and it results from a union of water (H_2O) and carbon dioxide (CO_2).

Of the manifold processes involved in chemical weathering, four of the more important are: (1) solution, (2) oxidation, (3) hydration, and (4) carbonation.

Solution

Among the multitude of rocks exposed on the Earth's surface, few are more susceptible to chemical attack than limestone; slow disappearance through dissolving into solution is more likely than not to be its fate. This simple equation illustrates the process:

$$CaCO_3 \quad + \quad H_2CO_3 \quad = \quad Ca(HCO_3)_2$$
calcite   carbonic   calcium
                         acid   bicarbonate

Calcium bicarbonate is soluble and, once introduced into water, above or below ground, is carried away in solution. Thus where a layer of limestone may once have been, there may well remain nothing, because its chief constituent, calcite, is now dissolved away. This explains the profusion of caverns, underground channels, and disappearing rivers in limestone regions, as we have seen in Chapter VIII, Ground Water.

Oxidation

Rusting is a process familiar to most of us. In anything but the most severe climates, such as the Antarctic Ice Sheet, all unprotected objects made of iron rust away within a lifetime. In a rainy tropical climate the struggle to maintain steel bridges, ships, rails, and automobiles is a relentless one.

The preponderance of rocks contain some iron-bearing minerals. When these are exposed to atmospheric attack, like an old Model T frame in an automobile graveyard, they rust. Such iron-rich rocks lose their original gray, and are stained a wide variety of colors, such as red, yellow, orange, red-brown, etc. The equation expressing this change is:

$$4FeO \quad + \quad O_2 \quad = \quad 2Fe_2O_3$$
ferrous iron oxide   oxygen   ferric iron oxide
  (gray-green)   (rust-colored)

Geologists of a generation ago were prone to equate the origin of red soil and rock colors with arid regions. Of course, red-colored rocks are dominant in such landscapes as Monument Valley, Grand Canyon, and the Painted Desert, and these are unquestionably desert areas. The

arid climate tends to preserve the iron oxides in the rocks, and the lack of moisture and vegetation means that organic compounds do not accumulate and thus carbon is not present to reduce (deoxygenate) the ferric iron oxide (Fe_2O_3) and change it back to drab, grayish-green ferrous iron oxide (FeO).

However, the red color of these sediments depends on their origin, not the accident of their preservation in a dry climate. Many of the red or reddish-brown sediments that are accumulating today are in tropical lands, especially those with pronounced wet and dry seasons, so that the ground is alternately thoroughly wetted and then dried out. We shall see the importance of this when we come to the discussion of lateritic soils.

Carbonation and Hydration

The two processes of chemical combination of minerals with carbon dioxide (CO_2) and water (H_2O), or carbonation and hydration respectively, are combined in this one reaction:

$$2KAlSi_3O_8 \quad + \quad 2H_2O \quad + \quad CO_2 \quad =$$
feldspar   water   carbon
                                       dioxide

$$H_4Al_2Si_2O_9 \quad + \quad 4SiO_2 \quad + \quad K_2CO_3$$
clay   silica   potassium
                                  carbonate

This is one of the important reactions in nature since it involves the most abundant of all minerals, feldspar, and such standard reagents as water and carbon dioxide. The end-products of the reaction are interesting because of their role in soil formation, as well as the part they play in agriculture and life processes in general. The equation shows that the chief result of the decomposition of feldspar is the formation of a clay mineral (kaolin). Clay is about as common a soil element as there is, and the formula for this particular variety shows it to be a hydrous aluminum silicate. An interesting feature of its composition is the presence of aluminum, a most abundant metal in the Earth's crust. Why, then, is it not less expensive and also more commonly used? The answer lies in its link with silica in the clay. Since this bond is one of the more difficult in nature to break, an immense amount of energy is required to achieve such a separation. Most aluminum actually comes from clay which has been subjected to weathering so intense that the silica has been leached out and only aluminum oxide (Al_2O_3), or alumina, is left. This is the mineral bauxite, and many of the world's commercial deposits seem to have originated in tropical lands which have about the same climatic regime as is responsible for the iron-bearing soil known as laterite, described further on.

Along with clay, the carbonation and hydration of feldspar frees silica which may remain dispersed throughout the deposit. Since the potassium carbonate is soluble, most of it is carried away in solution. Not all the potassium is removed from the site, however, because some of it is taken up by plants and some probably enters into combination with the clay.

The decomposition of feldspar yields a wholly different product from the original—in this case a sandy clay, quite unlike the strongly crystalline, rock-forming mineral from which it is derived.

Decomposition of Granite

The way in which granite decomposes is a good illustration of the way chemical weathering affects rocks. Granite, as we learned in Chapter III, is an intrusive igneous rock with a coarse-grained texture and consists of quartz, feldspar, and ferromagnesian minerals, such as hornblende and biotite.

Typically the feldspars decompose to sandy clay and soluble potassium-, sodium-, or calcium-carbonate, depending on their composition. The quartz survives largely unscathed, except under truly severe conditions. The ferromagnesian minerals, including biotite, break down to a rusty clay containing varying amounts of iron oxide, potassium carbonate, magnesium bicarbonate, and silica, dependent somewhat upon the composition of the original mineral.

Thus, in a warm, rainy climate, granite boulders, monuments, and buildings molder away in time to a mass of rust-stained sandy clay, or *loam*. Conversely, granite in a desert (Fig. 10-9) is more prone to disintegrate into separate sand grains, which consist chiefly of feldspar, since this is the dominant mineral; such a feldspathic sand if later cemented together to make a sandstone is called an *arkose*. In short, the same rock, granite, if placed in unlike climatic environments yields wholly unlike products.

SOILS

The result of the decomposition and disintegration of rocks and rock-forming minerals is the formation of soil. Because soil is so fundamental to life, it has been studied intensively for more than a century. Unfortunately, perhaps, the problems of the origin, nature, and use of soil have been attacked piecemeal by specialists with widely differing interests, with each discipline using a wholly different terminology. The geologist's concern with soil is primarily with its origin, and his interest is likely to be directed toward establishing the relationship between parent material and soil. For example, what kind of soil results from the weathering of granite in a dry climate, of limestone in a warm humid one, etc.?

Agriculturally, an emphasis in soil classification has been to relate the various types to climatic regions. This approach was begun in Russia around 1870 by V. V. Dokuchaiev, K. D. Glinka, and their successors. A climatically dominated origin for soils is an understandable emphasis in such a land as Russia with its endless sweep of open steppe. In other words, the latitudinal zoning of climates across such broad plains is of greater significance than local variations in topography or rock type. The Russian

FIG. 10-9 *Disintegration of granite in the desert region of Joshua Tree National Monument, southeastern California. A coarse granitic sand composed of individual mineral grains accumulates at the base of the rocks in this dry region because chemical weathering is greatly reduced and the effects of solution, carbonation, and hydration are largely minimized. (Photograph by Ansel Adams.)*

concept of the ascendancy of climate as a controlling factor in soil evolution was introduced into this country in the early 1920's by C. F. Marbut, then Chief of the Division of Soil Survey in the U. S. Department of Agriculture.

In a typical *mature soil,* according to Marbut and his associates, three distinct layers should be present in a complete soil *profile.* These layers are called horizons, and in order from top to bottom are the A-, B-, and C-horizons (Fig. 10-10). The surface layer, or A-horizon, has had its soluble constituents very largely leached out or washed out, and is the so-called *eluvial zone,* from the Latin word *eluere,* which means just that—to wash out. Although soluble material very largely has been removed from the A-horizon, organic matter has been added in its place, and in some climates this is quite a bit, especially where soils are black and humus-laden.

Some of the material dissolved from minerals of the A-horizon is carried by percolating water down into the B-horizon, where it may then accumulate. Largely for this reason the B-horizon is sometimes termed the *illuvial zone,* or the layer into which material is washed. Iron oxide is especially prone to collect in the B-horizon, as is finer solid material such as clay. Should enough iron oxide be precipitated, it may form a cemented layer called *hardpan* by farmers, which is hard enough to turn aside an ordinary plow. In some arid regions, as in the Llano Estacado of Texas, a limy encrustation, *caliche,* may build up in the soil. In part it may be $CaCO_3$ dissolved out of the A-horizon and washed down into the B-horizon, and in part it may be lime brought up from below by capillarity and then precipitated in the B-horizon.

The C-horizon is essentially a transitional zone between the true soil horizons above and the unaltered parent material below. Thus it is a mixture in varying proportions of altered and unaltered rock fragments and soil particles. Unaltered bedrock is likely to be dominant near the base of the horizon and maturely weathered soil will be the leading constituent in the upper part. Crevices filled with soil particles characteristically will extend down into the bedrock, while higher up in the C-horizon unaltered fragments of bedrock may be isolated and completely free-floating like seeds in a watermelon.

ZONAL SOILS

Mature soils with fully developed profiles and with characteristics that appear to be determined by the prevailing climate over a wide region are called *zonal soils*. Tropical soils, for example, are markedly unlike those of the Arctic, and even within a temperate climate there

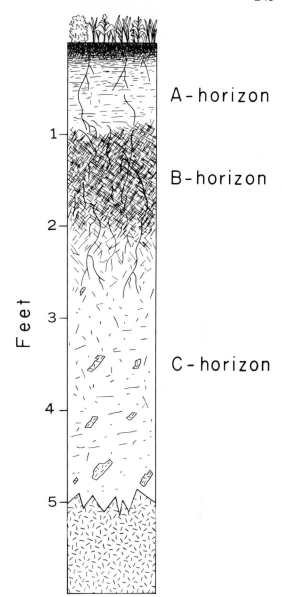

From C. E. Kellogg, "Great Soil Groups," 1936. By permission of U.S. Dept. of Agriculture.

FIG. 10-10 *A mature soil shows three distinct layers or horizons, A, B, and C. The A-horizon has its soluble constituents largely leached out, and organic matter is added. The B-horizon is often a zone of accumulation of materials leached downward from the A-horizon, and may form a hardpan composed of iron oxide or carbonate calcium (caliche) The C-horizon is a transitional zone to the parent rock below.*

are wide differences which are controlled by local patterns of temperature, amount and distribution of rainfall, and nature of vegetation. *Intrazonal soils* are atypical and are not representative of a particular climatic zone. These are soils whose nature is determined by some local environment, such as the bottom of a bog or marsh or similar undrained area.

In a very general way the soils of the world can be placed in two great categories, the *pedocals* and *pedalfers*. Each word is derived from the Greek, *pedo(n)* for ground, plus an abbreviation for calcium in the first of these soil types and the symbols Al and Fe for aluminum and iron in the second. Pedocals are soils which contain such soluble substances as calcium and magnesium, usually in combination with carbonates and sulphates. These are soils which are typical of much of the arid and semi-arid West beyond the 100th Meridian, and in extreme cases they are the alkali soil which is so lethal for agricultural plants.

Pedalfers are more thoroughly leached soils than pedocals, and occur in the United States mostly east of the 100th Meridian. These are soils in which soluble material does not accumulate, and in extreme examples they may be so degraded that only such insoluble residues as aluminum oxide (Al_2O_3) and iron oxide (Fe_2O_3) survive.

Chernozems

These are the black prairie or steppe pedocal soils of Russia and of the dry-farming belt of the western plains of the United States and Canada. Although these soils form in semi-arid regions, they have a high content of organic matter, from which they derive their Russian name, which means black earth.

How does it happen that under a dry climate in such a treeless land as the Dakotas an abundant supply of black, organic matter can be present in the soil? The answer apparently lies in the nature of the distinctive vegetation of these open plains. These are the tall-grass lands of much of the temperate world. When this sea of grass in the early West was first opened to settlement it must have been a magnificent sight. Today this Chernozem soil in North America is one of our greatest natural resources, since it is the heart of one of the world's leading wheatlands.

The black color is supplied by partially decomposed grass roots; this is the organic content responsible for the high fertility of these soils. An additional characteristic of Chernozem is the presence of a limy zone close to the base of the grass roots. This represents calcium removed by plants from soil minerals and deposited after the roots decay, whereupon it combines with carbonate ions to make calcium carbonate ($CaCO_3$).

Podzols

These grayish pedalfer soils are widespread throughout the cooler parts of the Earth, especially where coniferous and hardwood deciduous forests flourish. Almost every person who has walked through such a forest is likely to be impressed by the litter of organic matter, such as pine cones, branches, and needles, that covers the ground. Beneath this so-called duff, the A-horizon characteristically is a white or gray, platy, leached-out soil layer. In fact, it is the ashen color in the bleached surface layer which is responsible for the soil name, podzol, taken from the Russian words for under and ash.

Below the bleached A-horizon is a dark, normally brown or grayish-brown B-horizon stained a rusty color from iron dissolved out of the upper layer and concentrated in the lower. Enough iron may accumulate so that a true hardpan develops, making this soil less attractive for agriculture than it otherwise might be. The soluble salts, including calcium and magnesium carbonate, are leached out of podsolic soils. Trees are less dependent on alkalis for food than grasses are, and hence not enough bases are returned to surface layers to prevent acids from accumulating. The result is that podsolic soils are acidic in the typically moist and cool environment of a coniferous and hardwood deciduous forest. Clearing such a forest with the hope of converting it to agriculture often results in only the most modest yields.

Laterites

In 1807, Buchanan Hamilton, an observant Scotsman, was traveling in India, then a virtual monopoly of The Honorable The East India Company. He was greatly impressed by the sight of Hindu laborers excavating the red-brown tropical clay, shaping it into bricks, and using these for building material after case-hardening in the sun. In this respect, these clay blocks were much like the sun-dried bricks, or adobe, of the arid Southwest, although they differed by being taken directly from the ground and not manufactured out of mud which had been shaped in molds.

Because this tropical clay could be used so readily as a construction material, Hamilton called it laterite from the Latin word *latere,* or brick. Its origin was a source of wonderment to him, and has remained a puzzle to soil scientists ever since. As a construction material, laterite has served to build enduring monuments, since, among others, much of the long-forgotten city of Angkor Wat in Cambodia is built of laterite (Fig. 10-11). This alone is an indication that laterite consists of material which is virtually insoluble.

Laterite might be regarded as the skeleton of

FIG. 10-11 *The building blocks of laterite that compose this temple at Angkor Wat, Cambodia, are highly resistant because they are composed chiefly of residual iron oxide, all the other minerals having been removed by chemical weathering. By contrast, note the difference in weathering of the sandstone columns and statues which are composed of minerals that are being removed by solution, carbonation, hydration, and oxidation. (Photograph by Leonard Palmer.)*

a soil, since the soluble elements, such as calcium, sodium, and potassium, are leached out, and even such a normally insoluble substance as silica (SiO_2) has been removed. This means that a typical laterite is mainly iron oxide (Fe_2O_3). Should the source rocks from which this soil is derived have a high content of aluminum, then these residual tropical clays grade into *bauxite* ($Al_2O_3 \cdot 2H_2O$), which is the chief ore of aluminum.

Laterites characteristically are found in tropical terrain that has adequate slope drainage; they do not form in continuously wet areas, such as swamps. In fact, they develop best in the monsoon or savanna tropical climate, which is one with pronounced wet and dry seasons. Essential for the formation of laterite is the alternation of heavy rainfall, which supplies the ground water to carry iron oxide in solution down from the A-horizon to be concentrated in the B-horizon, and drought, which permits the soil to aerate and allows the soil minerals to oxidize.

Laterites begin to form through the deposition of iron oxide around nuclei, such as individual mineral grains. The iron-rich nodules grow until finally they may unite to form a cement-like, concretionary layer, probably comparable to the hardpan layer of temperate-climate soils. When this happens, water percolates downward with difficulty, if at all, and the surface layers of soil, the probable equivalent of the A-horizon of temperate regions, then are readily swept away under the driving rains of the monsoon.

The result is the nearly total destruction of a region for agriculture, and in a densely populated area such as a large part of Southeast Asia, this is disastrous. Little of value can grow in a lateritic soil whose A-horizon has been stripped away so that a ferruginous clay, devoid of plant nutrients, makes up the ground surface. Such a blanket of iron-rich soil in Australia is called by an appropriate name, *duricrust,* and it spreads over an entire countryside much like an undulating pavement that covers hill crests and valley bottoms alike.

The iron content of laterite in some parts of the tropics may be high enough for this blanket of regolith to be mined as ore. The iron mines of Cuba and of the Surigao Peninsula in Mindanao are examples. Bauxite shares a nearly common origin, except that it has been formed from the weathering of rocks that were richer in aluminum than iron. This appears to have been the story of the bauxite ores of Little Rock, Arkansas, which are in sedimentary layers deposited under what probably were climatic conditions very much like those of the tropical savanna today. In fact, most of the aluminum ore now processed in North America no longer comes from Arkansas, but comes from the high-alumina clays of Surinam, Jamaica, and other South American and Caribbean lands.

MASS MOVEMENT

The breakdown of rocks at the Earth's surface through decomposition and disintegration yields a mass of unstable material that may shift downslope in response to gravity, especially where hillsides are steep. Such a transfer, sometimes involving both the regolith and the bedrock, may be so slow as to be imperceptible. Sometimes it may be as catastrophically violent as a landslide that plunges down a mountain to overwhelm a village at the base.

This mass movement of surface material adds enormously to the effectiveness of streams in shaping the surface of the Earth. Mass movement is responsible for the downslope transfer of material to rivers which then act as continuously moving conveyor belts to carry it away. The way in which the walls of the Grand Canyon flare outward from the Colorado River is largely the result of transfer by gravity of rock fragments and mineral grains downslope to where they can be carried out of the entire Colorado Plateau region by the river and its intricate network of tributaries.

How much or how little material will be shifted downhill by gravity and how rapidly or how slowly it will move are a consequence of a multiplicity of factors such as (1) climate, (2) nature of the bedrock and its attitude, (3) vegetation, (4) the principal types of weathering that are active, (5) steepness of slopes, and (6) local relief, to name some of the more obvious. Few landscapes consist solely of bare rock, and most hill slopes show some degree of rounding. Soil cover serves to alleviate the starkness of a rock-dominated landscape, and soil-blanketed and smoothed slopes are an indication that the regolith is not stationary but has a motion of its own.

This gravity-induced, downslope transfer of material is difficult to segregate into neatly compartmented little packages. The transition from gradual, virtually imperceptible movement at one end of the scale, to a free-falling mass of rock avalanching down a mountain face and filling all the valleys with thunderous echoes at the other, is blurred. In fact, these distinctions are nonexistent, since this is an entirely gradational series. A practical solution to the problem of classification is to divide mass movement into two obvious categories: slow and rapid. This is a highly subjective division, because no two people are likely to agree on their meaning. We are constantly confronted, for example, with the problem of their definition in occasional little controversies involving interpretations of traffic speeds.

SLOW MOVEMENT

Creep

This descriptive word is used for the slow, glacier-like movement of the soil mantle downslope. We are likely to be quite oblivious of its existence, except to observe with dismay that building foundations may be thrown out of line, power and telephone poles tilted, and sidewalks and retaining walls cracked.

Should roadcuts be made in such shifting ground, they may reveal strata that are turned back on themselves, or thrown into a maze of convolutions where they have been dragged downslope. Soil creeping down a hill very often will drag with it fragments of the underlying rock. These commonly will decrease in number with increasing distance downslope from the outcrop, but may also form a continuous, although attenuated, line when seen in a roadcut. This so-called *stone line* generally will be at the boundary between the undisturbed ground below and the moving regolith above. This very often is a conspicuous feature in areas where creep is prevalent—look carefully for it should you ever think of building a hillside house.

Creep is an especially drastic problem in cold climates where water freezes in the ground. Here soil layers and particles may be lifted up by the expansion of freezing water, and then shifted a little farther downslope when their support is removed through melting.

Solifluction

Solifluction is an extreme sort of creep that reaches a maximum development in cold climates. Hilly terrain underlain by permafrost exemplifies it best, for while the surface layers freeze and thaw, the permafrost table remains constant. Surface water cannot sink into the permafrost, so that water which would normally percolate far down into the ground is concentrated in the active layer. The active layer, then, is far more susceptible to creep than similar terrain would be in a more temperate climate because (1) the opposing forces of ice crystallization and melting of ground ice are most active here, (2) the active layer holds more water than it would under a similar precipitation regime elsewhere, and (3) this water-saturated, unstable ground rests on a frozen base over whose surface it can slide readily.

Active solifluction produces a landscape that bears some resemblance to the wrinkled hide of

FIG. 10-12 *Active slump-earthflows (1) and new scarplets (2) about one foot high within an old landslide area (3) on the west side of Pleitito Canyon, San Emigdio Mountains, Calif. The large, hummocky area of the old slide (3) is one mile long and about 1,200 feet in altitude from head to toe. (Photograph by John T. McGill.)*

an aged elephant. Different parts of the water-saturated surface layer creep downslope at different rates, so that hillsides where solifluction is active are festooned with soil lobes or tongues, some of which advance rapidly and some slowly.

Another bizarre manifestation of ice-churned ground in the Arctic is curiously regular patterned ground. Sometimes from the air the tundra looks like a gigantic tiled floor. These geometrically shaped polygonal areas are thought to be the result of frost heave, which is much more effective in fine-grained soils than in coarse. When this process of frost heaving is applied repetitively over many years to a soil of

mixed composition, the coarse material, such as boulders and gravel, is gradually shoved radially outward from the central area, and the finer materials lag behind and become concentrated.

Earthflows

This type of earth movement is transitional between slow and rapid varieties. It is a more visible form of movement than creep, yet slower than a mudflow or a landslide.

Earthflows are characteristic of grass-covered, soil-blanketed hills (Fig. 10-12). Although they are commonly minor features, some may be quite large and cover many acres. Earthflows usually have a spoon-shaped sliding surface (Varnes, 1958) with a crescent-shaped cliff at the upper end and a tongue-shaped bulge at the lower. They involve the soil mantle and are most likely to occur when the ground is saturated with water. This interstitial water not only increases the weight of the mantle but drastically reduces its stability by lowering its resistance to shear.

RAPID MOVEMENT

Mudflows

With increasing velocity this type of mass movement grades into ordinary stream flow, and with decreasing velocity it merges with earthflows. A typical mudflow is a streaming mass of mud and water moving down the floor of a stream channel, such as a desert arroyo. Such a viscous mass, with a specific gravity much higher than clear water, very often carries along in it a tumbling mass of boulders and rocks, some of which may be as large as automobiles.

Mudflows are a most impressive feature of many of the world's deserts. In arid lands the normally empty stream courses occasionally may fill almost at once with a racing torrent of chocolate-colored mud, following a cloudburst. Where arroyos are shallow, the mudflow may exceed the channel's capacity and spill out over the desert surface.

Mudflows, because of their greater density, are more efficient transporters of large rocks for short distances than normal streams are. They carry the large blocks and boulders often found on the floor of desert basins far beyond the base of a bordering mountain range. There they linger, long after the enclosing mud which once rafted them out beyond the mountains has been eroded away.

Mudflows not only are capable of transporting large natural objects, such as house-size boulders, but may sweep along trucks, buses, or even locomotives trapped in such a debris flow. Houses inundated by such mud streams may be buried all the way up to the eaves. When the mud has dried out, they look for all the world like so many doll houses scattered about by children and pushed by heedless hands deep into the ground.

Mudflows are by no means restricted to arid or semi-arid lands. They are characteristic of alpine regions, too, and are likely to be exceptionally destructive where a combination of steep slopes, a large volume of water freed by melting snow, and a great mass of loose debris are all available (Fig. 10-13). These mud avalanches

FIG. 10-13 *A small village in the St. Moritz area, Switzerland, clustered about an old mudflow which shows the comparatively large size of the blocks transported from upslope. Additional building on the site may lead to further instability, causing damage in the central part of the village.*

FIG. 10-14 *This rockfall from the Flimserstein, Switzerland, occurred on April 10, 1939. It buried not only forests and arable land but also a building and eleven persons, all in a moment of time. (Photograph by Swissair-Photo A G.)*

are especially impressive when they overwhelm a forest. A lava-like mud stream may cut a swath through the forest smashing and splintering trees and branches, which then are strewn about like so much straw in an adobe brick.

A rarer sort, fortunately unknown in the continental United States in recent years, is the volcanic mudflow. The only exception to this was a relatively minor one on the flanks of Mt. Lassen, California, in 1915. Herculaneum was destroyed in A.D. 79 by such a viscous flow of water-lubricated volcanic ash that coursed down the flanks of Vesuvius. The most impressive of such cement-like mixtures of volcanic ash, bombs, and cinders, steam, and water are those of Indonesia, where such torrential outbursts are known as *lahars*. One of the more destructive of these occurred in 1919 in the volcano Gunong Keloet, whose crater had been occupied by a lake. When an eruption occurred on the lake floor, the waters overflowed, were mixed with volcanic debris, and swept in mud avalanches down the slopes to overwhelm 104 villages and take more than 5,000 lives.

Rockfalls and Rockslides

Many attempts have been made to develop workable classifications or acceptable definitions of various kinds of mass movement. Because of the complex nature of most landslides —few have a single cause, or even a single aspect—and because the terminology used to describe them comes from ordinary, everyday words, and thus is susceptible to widely differing interpretations by different users, none are wholly satisfactory.

A good solution for our purpose is to utilize in simplified form the terminology employed by Varnes (1958), in a classification designed primarily to aid highway engineers.

In this classification, material that drops at very nearly the velocity of free fall is called either a *rockfall* or *soilfall,* depending on its composition. Rockfalls can range in size from the dropping of individual blocks on a mountain slope to the failure of masses weighing hundreds of thousands of tons and avalanching down a mountain face (Fig. 10-14). In the first example, such individual blocks commonly come to rest in a loose pile of angular blocks, or a talus, at the base of a cliff. Should large blocks of rock drop into a standing body of water, such as a lake or fjord, immensely destructive waves may be set in motion with no warning at all. This is a hazard particularly feared in Norway where small deltas may provide the only available flat land at sea level. Should such a rockfall-induced wave burst through the village streets and houses, destruction is likely to be as complete as it is sudden, since these waves may range all the way from 20 to 300 feet high.

A much greater mass of rock that starts as a freely falling body high on a mountain face may avalanche on downslope and sweep completely across a valley floor with a velocity as great as 130 miles per hour (Fig. 10-15). At such high speeds the shattered mass of fallen rock flows much as a liquid would. With entrained air acting as cushion and thus reducing internal friction, such a mass of debris behaves a great deal like the glowing, gas-charged *nuée ardentes* of Mount Pelée (Chapter III).

The most celebrated example of such a rockfall in North America is one that occurred at Frank, Alberta, in 1903. There, a mass of strongly jointed limestone blocks at the crest of Turtle Mountain, possibly undermined by coal mining carried on below the thrust fault at the base of the mountain, broke loose and plunged down the steep escarpment. Something like 35 to 40 million cubic yards fell, and then washed in one gigantic wave through the little coal-mining town of Frank—killing 70 people on the way —and swept to a high point 400 feet above the valley floor on the slope facing toward the source (Daly, et al., 1912).

The great rockfall-rockslide at Gohna, India, in 1893 (Griggs, 1922) remains as one of the more impressive examples of modern times.

FIG. 10-15 *The Blackhawk slide, on the north slope of the San Bernardino Mountains, Calif. This slide, which moved five miles from the scarp in the middle distance, started as a rockfall in the mountains. (Photograph by John S. Shelton.)*

There a stupendous mass of rock, loosened by the driving monsoon rains, dropped 4,000 feet into one of the narrow Himalayan gorges. A great natural dam was formed by this mass of detritus—perhaps 900 feet high, 3,000 feet across the gorge at the crest, and extending for 11,000 feet up and down stream. This pile of broken rock, involving about 5 billion cubic yards, impounded a lake 777 feet deep when the waters of the river were dammed.

The British engineers, then in India, proved to be a remarkably foresighted lot. They predicted the date of the dam's failure within ten days of the time that it actually occurred, over the two years of its span of life. All bridges were removed downstream while the dam was in existence, the river channel was cleared of obstacles, a telegraphic warning network was set up, and everything was prepared for the imminent flood. When it came it set a world record. Around 10,000 million cubic feet of water were discharged in four hours and made a flood whose crest was 240 feet high. Interestingly enough, after the flood was over, the river channel close to the dam, instead of being deepened, was raised 234 feet by the sand and gravel deposited after the flood crest had passed and the river flow had returned to normal.

Landslides

A multiplicity of downslope movements is included in this broad general term, and no useful purpose is served here by reviewing the many schemes that have been proposed by geologists, engineers, and other specialists. That so many people are concerned indicates in itself the important role landslides play in everyday life. The difficulties they make for us—and they are considerable, as well as being expensive—are very largely our own doing. Without our disturbance of natural slopes, landslides would be important chiefly in remote mountainous terrain or on hillslopes underlain by notably unstable rocks. Today, landslides are a problem of increasing magnitude as a result of growing urbanization and the mounting demand for high-capacity freeways. Both trends require larger excavations for building foundations and deeper cuts and higher fills for highways. Oversteepening of slopes is a likely cause to start the ground moving.

Landslides may involve the bedrock alone, or they may be limited to the overlying soil

FIG. 10-16 *A landslide in the Palos Verdes Hills, near Los Angeles, Calif.* (*Photograph by George Cleveland.*)

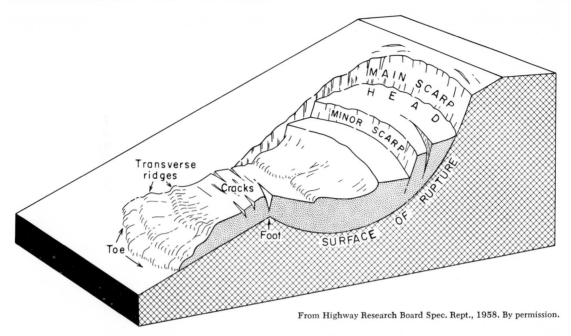

From Highway Research Board Spec. Rept., 1958. By permission.

FIG. 10-17 *The principal parts of a slump-type landslide.*

mantle, especially if it is deep and water-saturated. More typically, perhaps, they involve both soil and rock. Varnes (1958) recognizes two major categories of landslides: (1) glides and (2) slumps. In the first, the slippage is dominantly planar; that is, a large mass of rock may become separated from its fellows and glide outward and downward along the surface of an inclined bedding plane. In slumps, the motion is rotational—usually along a concave-upward slip-plane, so that the upper part of the landslide is dropped down below the normal ground level and the lower part is bulged above it.

The diagram (Fig. 10-17) shows the principal parts of such a slump-type slide, and since by far the greater number of landslides are variants of this form, some of its details are worth noting.

Most of these slides start abruptly with a crescent-shaped *scarp,* or cliff, at their head, sometimes known as a breakaway scarp. Downslope from this may be a number of lesser scarps, and in plan these are almost always concave downhill. Between the individual scarps the surface of the slide customarily is tilted or

rotated backward against the original slope of the ground. This causes more instability since these backward-rotated wedges on the surface of the slide make collecting basins in which small lakes or ponds can form. With the slip surface leading downward from the marginal scarp, a channel is available for water to seep into the slide, greatly increasing its instability.

The concave-upward slip plane down which the jumbled mass of soil and rocks moves may approximate a cross section of a cylinder whose axis parallels the ground surface, if the slide is sufficiently broad. Otherwise, the pattern of the surface of rupture is likely to be spoon shaped.

The slide may advance downstream from the point where the surface of rupture intersects the ground (Fig. 10-17), as a glacier-like lobe of jumbled debris whose surface typically is a chaotic pattern of hummocks and undrained depressions. If the slide moves down a forested slope it often presents a desolate scene of broken trunks and trees. The inexorable thrust of the foot of such a slide against man-made structures almost invariably leads to their collapse,

FIG. 10-18 *A landslide on April 4, 1958, at Pacific Palisades, Calif., blocked State Highway 101. Note the bulldozer on the beach just beginning to cut around the toe.* (*Photograph by John S. Shelton.*)

and it is this part of the slide that commonly is responsible for blocking canals, highways, railroads, and engulfing other types of excavations.

Among such slides, the immense ones that closed the Panama Canal at Culebra Cut shortly after it was opened in 1914 and that kept it closed more or less continuously until 1920 are impressive examples. Of the 168 million cubic yards excavated in the Gaillard Cut, landslides made necessary the removal of at least 73 million cubic yards. Great masses of loose, unstable volcanic ash, shale, and sandstone slid on

a gently inclined rupture surface toward the canal excavation. One unexpected result was that the bottom of the canal was heaved upward —once as much as 30 feet—until what had been the canal bottom appeared as an island in mid-channel.

Water is the hidden devil in the ground in many landslides. Keeping water out, or draining it away once it has entered, may become the primary task of the engineer charged with halting the continued progress of such a slide. An outstanding example of the heroic efforts that may be required to achieve this is the history of the large slides that interrupt the hilly terrain of the Ventura Avenue oil field in southern California. Some of these landslides cover 160 acres, and in the rainy winter of 1940-41 one block of

60 acres slid as a single unit for a distance of approximately 100 feet.

Since these slides sheared through oil wells when they moved (in this particular episode twenty-three of them were cut off at depths of as much as 100 feet below the ground surface), unusually extensive and expensive efforts were made. Continued slide movement was partially curbed by covering the surface with tar and by drilling horizontal drainage holes into the slides —40 miles of them. Vertical wells were also drilled through the slides to a porous layer of sandstone beneath it. This sandstone then served as a conduit to carry water away from the slides and into adjacent solid ground where the excess flow could then be pumped out.

Landslides are the bane of nearly all highway departments (Fig. 10-18) and can wreak all sorts of havoc on a construction budget, if not actually producing financial hemophilia. The next trip you take through mountainous country, look at the hillslopes as they flash by, and you may be impressed by the extensive defensive measures highway engineers must take. These are likely to be visible as terraced slopes, with concrete, stone, or cribbed retaining walls, and all but hidden from view may be elaborate drainage systems of which the culverts at the ends are the only visible elements.

Suggested References

Anonymous, 1960, Bank and shore protection in California highway practice, State of Calif., Dept. of Public Works, Div. of Highways, Sacramento, Calif.

Black, R. F., 1954, Permafrost—a review, Geol. Soc. Amer., Bull., v. 65, p. 839-856.

Cleaves, A. B., 1961, Landslide investigations, Bur. of Public Roads, U. S. Dept. of Commerce, Washington, D. C.

Daly, R. A., Miller, W. G., and Rice, G. S., 1912, Report of the commission appointed to investigate Turtle Mountain, Frank, Alberta, Canada Geol. Surv., Memoir 27.

Eckel, E. G., and others, 1958, Landslides and engineering practice, Highway Research Board, Spec. Rept. 29, Washington, D. C.

Glinka, K. D., 1927, The great soil groups of the world and their development, translated by C. F. Marbut, Ann Arbor, Mich.

Goldich, S. S., 1938, A study in rock weathering, Jour. Geol., v. 46, p. 17-58.

Griggs, R. F., 1922, The Valley of Ten Thousand Smokes, Natl. Geog. Soc., Washington, D. C.

Handy, R. L., 1957 to date, Various articles in Screenings from the Soil Research Lab, Iowa Engr. Exp. Sta., Iowa State Univ., Ames, Iowa.

Howe, Ernest, 1909, Landslides in the San Juan Mountains, Colorado, U. S. Geol. Survey, Prof. Paper 67.

Jenny, Hans, 1941, Factors of soil formation, McGraw-Hill Book Co., Inc., New York.

Keller, W. D., 1955, The principles of chemical weathering, Lucas Bros., Columbia, Mo.

Kellogg, C. E., 1936, Development and significance of the great soil groups of the United States, U. S. Dept. of Agriculture, Misc. Publ. No. 229.

———, 1950, Soil, Scientific American, July.

Knight, H. G., and others, 1938, Soils and men, U. S. Dept. of Agriculture, Yearbook of agriculture, 1938, Washington, D. C.

Krynine, D. P., and Judd, W. R., 1957, Principles of engineering geology and geotechnics, McGraw-Hill Book Co., Inc., New York.

McDowell, Bart, and Fletcher, J. E., 1962, Avalanche! 3,500 Peruvians perish in seven minutes, National Geographic, v. 121, p. 855-880.

McGee, W. J., 1897, Sheetflood erosion, Geol. Soc. Amer., Bull., v. 8, p. 87-112.

Marbut, C. F., 1935, Soils of the United States, Part III, Atlas of American agriculture, U. S. Dept. of Agriculture, Washington, D. C.

Muller, S. W., 1947, Permafrost, or permanently frozen ground and related engineering problems, Edwards Bros., Ann Arbor, Mich.

Pewe, T. L., 1957, Permafrost and its effect on life in the North, 18th Biology Colloquium, Corvallis, Oregon.

Reiche, Parry, 1950, A survey of weathering processes and products, Univ. of New Mexico, Publ. in Geology, Albuquerque, N. Mex.

Sharpe, C. F. S., 1938, Landslides and related phenomena, Columbia Univ. Press, New York.

Varnes, D. J., 1958, Landslide types and processes, Chap. 3, in Landslides and engineering practice, Highway Research Board, Spec. Rept. 29.

Wahrhaftig, Clyde, and Cox, Allen, 1959, Rock glaciers in the Alaska Range, Geol. Soc. Amer., Bull., v. 70, p. 383-436.

Wechsberg, Josef, 1958, Avalanche, Alfred Knopf, New York.

Wooley, R. R., 1946, Cloudburst floods in Utah, 1850-1938, U. S. Geol. Survey, Water-Supply Paper 994.

A stream in the Sierra Nevada, California.

(From the Cedric Wright Collection, courtesy of the Sierra Club.)

XI

Stream Transportation and Erosion

Few natural phenomena are more intimately involved with human affairs than rivers. In centuries past such streams as the Nile, the Tigris, and the Euphrates literally were the givers of life as they threaded their way across a weary desert land (Fig. 11-1). The ancient civilizations depended on this water for irrigation; it was through this communal enterprise that many of the attributes of modern urbanized society arose. The beginnings of mathematics, surveying, and hydraulics developed in the designing of dams and canals. One of the earliest was a long dike built about 3200 B.C. on the west bank of the Nile with cross dikes and canals to carry flood waters into basins adjacent to the river.

Boundary disputes and ownership problems logically led to a system of codes and usages that evolved into a pattern of laws and courts much like ours today. The Code of Hammurabi (c. 1900 B.C.) includes a provision that if a landowner damages his neighbor's land through neglect of a portion of a canal that was his responsibility, he was liable for all the damage (Merdinger, 1959).

Rivers have long played a role as natural barriers—two that were of decisive importance in Roman times were the Rhine and the Danube. The crossing of the Danube by the barbarians commonly is cited as one of the events heralding the fall of the Roman Empire.

Contrasting with their role as barriers is the function that rivers serve as communication routes. The Mississippi packet boat, with its flashing wheels and double columns of smoke, is gone forever, to linger on only in memory, or in the pseudoreality of Disneyland. Its place is usurped by the vastly more powerful diesel-propelled towboat (which actually pushes its load), and its broad acreage of heavily laden barges driving against the current. The endless parade of diesel-powered barges that surges up and down the Rhine is an impressive sight to the European traveler.

Rivers from time immemorial have been routes from the sea to the interior. Explorers have followed them; most of the world's leading cities are built on their banks. They are identified indissolubly with the history and national aspirations of almost all the lands that border them. It would be difficult to conceive of a Germany without the Rhine, a Vienna without the the Danube, or a Russia without the Volga or the Don. How powerful the emotional tie can be between such a city as London and its river, the Thames, is brought to life by Joseph Conrad in *Heart of Darkness:*

The tidal current runs to and fro in its unceasing service, crowded with the memories of men and ships it had borne to the rest of home or to the battles of the sea. It had known and served all the men of whom the nation is proud, from Sir Francis Drake to Sir John Franklin. It had borne all the ships whose names are like jewels flashing in the night of time, from the *Golden Hind* returning with her round flanks full of treasure, to be visited by the Queen's Highness and thus pass out of the gigantic tale, to the *Erebus* and *Terror*, bound on other conquests—and that never returned. It had known the ships and the men. . . . Hunters for gold or pursuers of fame, they had all gone out on that stream, bearing the sword, and often the torch, messengers of the might within the land, bearers of a spark from the sacred fire. What greatness had not floated on the ebb of that river into the mystery of an unknown earth! . . . The dreams of men, the seed of commonwealths, the germs of empires.

STREAM FLOW

Although streams play so vital a role in our lives, and their control had engaged the efforts of men for centuries, many aspects of their behavior remain as mysterious today as they have always been. Great impetus has been given in

FIG. 11-1 *A river meanders across the Iranian desert in the land of Elam and flows past the ancient city of Susa, where Esther was chosen queen. (Photograph by Aerofilms and Aero Pictorial Ltd.)*

recent years to the study of stream flow because of its importance in the design of high-head hydroelectric plants, dams and spillways, and increasingly complex irrigation systems. Every leading nation is actively engaged in research into the nature of stream flow, and the majority of them maintain large and well-equipped hydraulics laboratories. The largest in this country is the U. S. Waterways Experiment Station, operated by the Corps of Engineers, U. S. Army, at Vicksburg, Mississippi. Here, elaborate models of the Mississippi River have been constructed (Fig. 11-2), and an immense amount of data collected and analyzed in order to find ways to bring this unruly river and its tributaries under control.

From laboratory studies and field investigations around the world, a number of observations can be made about the nature of stream flow. Water appears to move principally in two ways: by *laminar flow* and by *turbulent flow*.

Laminar Flow

This can best be thought of as streamline flow, and is characteristic of viscous fluids such as corn syrup, tar, and mud. In a stream of water it exists only as a thin film on the bottom and sides of a channel. Within this film the water particles glide past one another on parallel paths, their paths not crossing one another nor merging. Such a flow pattern probably exists only at very slow velocities in fluids of such low viscosity as water. Very likely laminar flow is characteristic of the flow of water underground through pore spaces between sand and silt grains, rather than of the flow of water in open channels at the surface. However, the skin of laminar flow along the bottom and sides of a stream channel possibly is significant when we are concerned with the erosion and transportation of fine-grained versus coarse-grained material; clay versus silt and sand, for example.

Turbulent Flow

Turbulent flow is of vastly greater importance in the motion of water in natural streams. Individual water particles, instead of gliding past

FIG. 11-2 *A section of the Mississippi Basin Model at the U. S. Waterways Experiment Station, Vicksburg, Miss. (Courtesy of U. S. Waterways Experiment Station.)*

one another as in a beautifully arranged ballet, thrash about in the most irregular fashion imaginable (Fig. 11-3). Familiar examples of turbulent flow are the tumultuous rush of water through Niagara Gorge downstream from the plunge pool at the base of the Falls, or the surging maelstrom of white water at the bottom of the spillway of the Grand Coulee Dam. Other less awesome examples are the mass of swirling white water in a breaker, the whirlpools that endlessly shape and reshape themselves in the wake of a ship, or even the eddies that slip by one another along the dark, willow-shaded bank of a trout stream.

In turbulent flow, the main component of motion of the water is forward, downslope in the direction that the stream is flowing, but in addition there is a vast amount of purely random movement of water particles. Sometimes they swirl upward like autumn leaves, or like dust devils in the desert—at other times they descend just as violently in the vortices of whirlpools and eddies. In part, it is this erratic flow pattern that makes the actual velocity of a stream such a difficult parameter to measure.

Velocity

In very general terms, the velocity of a stream can be defined as the direction and magnitude of displacement of a point per unit of time. When we speak of speed, we really mean only the magnitude of the displacement. Customarily we measure this in miles per hour. Few streams, however, attain velocities in excess of 10 miles per hour, and velocities of less than 5 are more likely to be the rule.

Where is such a thing as an average velocity likely to be located within a stream? Different parts of the water in a stream advance at different rates. The velocity front is essentially curved from the stream surface down to a point a short distance above the bed. Then the velocity gradient becomes very steep from this in-

flection point down to where it becomes zero at the stream bottom. The sharp break in the stream profile is considered to be at the boundary between the zones of laminar and turbulent flow (Fig. 11-4). This is the critical point on the curve, and the rather inappropriate name of *bed velocity* is given to it. The inappropriateness stems from the fact mentioned immediately above—that the velocity is zero directly on the bottom of the stream. The so-called bed velocity is of the greatest importance in determining the size of sediment particles a stream picks up in the process of eroding its channel, as we shall see later. The average velocity of a stream depends on such factors as the volume of water, the gradient (or *forward* slope), the cross-sectional shape of the channel, the roughness of the channel surface, and the quantity of sediment the stream is carrying.

In general, an increase of the volume of water in a stream, coupled with an increase in depth and width, increases the velocity, according to Leopold and Maddock (1953). Observational data for the middle reaches of the Mississippi

FIG. 11-3 *Turbulent flow patterns in the Colorado River. (Photograph by Martin Litton.)*

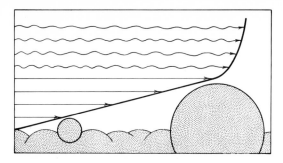

After W. W. Rubey, 1937. By permission of U.S. Geological Survey.

FIG. 11-4 *Velocity gradient near a stream bed. The swift and turbulent flow slows and becomes laminar near the bed.*

River and its tributary system, the Missouri, support this view.

Increased gradient obviously speeds up a stream's flow. Where its gradient becomes zero, as when a river empties into a river or lake, then its velocity quickly becomes zero. Where slopes are vertical, as in a waterfall, the velocity approaches that of free fall. These effects of differing slope are impressively demonstrated at Niagara. The river above the Falls idles along, by comparison, because its gradient is hung up by a gently dipping stratum of resistant rock. When the water plunges over this ledge it drops almost vertically, attaining its peak velocity. Below the Falls, where the river is cutting the Gorge down to the level of Lake Ontario, it races along much more purposefully than where its downcutting had been retarded above the Falls.

So it is in principle with almost all other streams. Where the gradient is low, a stream lazes along; where the gradient is high, the water leaps and quickens in a headlong dash to the sea.

Ideally, the stream gradient should be a beautifully sweeping curve, concave upward to the air, steeper at the head and gentler at the seaward end. In actuality, though, few streams achieve this ideal. The cross-sectional shape of the channel has an effect on the velocity, too. If

this approaches a semicircle, then the stream has achieved the shape that includes the maximum area within the shortest perimeter.

A stream flowing in a channel with an extremely narrow cross section tends to erode the banks and increase the width until a more equable balance is reached between velocity and channel width (Rubey, 1952). In a flattened channel, the current slows near the banks where the velocity is least, and as a consequence deposition occurs there. The result is a narrowing of the channel until the best hydraulic fit is achieved between channel cross section and discharge.

Curiously enough, streams seemingly are sufficiently perverse not to prefer what theoretically might be the ideal channel—one with a semicircular cross section. Instead, since the maximum velocity is near the surface, lateral, or sideward, erosion is likely to dominate, with the result that a hydraulically adjusted stream resembles more closely a very broad, flat-floored trough in cross section. The Mississippi River is a good illustration since the dimensions of its channel in the lower part of the river may be a mile across and 100 feet deep.

The effect of roughness on velocity is obvious. A smooth, clay-lined channel will promote an even, uniform flow, while an irregular, bumpy, boulder-filled one induces enough turbulence within a stream to significantly retard its velocity.

An increase in the sediment load, and a corresponding decrease in the percentage of water, has a strong braking effect on the velocity. This is readily understandable because the more sediment is mixed in with the stream, the muddier it becomes, until finally it may become a mudflow. Such a muddy, viscous stream may come to a halt when the ratio of solids to fluid becomes so high that the viscosity is so great that the stream can no longer flow. This is sometimes demonstrated by the ephemeral streams produced by short-lived thunder showers in the desert.

Discharge

Another important property of streams is their discharge. This is a measure of the quantity of water that passes a point in a given interval of time. A widely used unit of measurement in the United States is the *second foot,* which means that one cubic foot of water passes a given point per second. This same unit may also be expressed by the abbreviation c.f.s., or cubic feet per second.

The discharge of most rivers is far from constant. The flow of northern rivers fluctuates with the melting of snow and ice—those that drain northward to the Arctic are likely to have especially serious problems because their lower courses are still frozen when the headwaters have thawed out and are in flood. Tropical rivers, too, especially those in monsoonal regions, show large seasonal variations, determined by the rhythm of wet and dry seasons throughout the year. Streams of the arid southwestern United States show as great a range as any. Throughout much of the year they may have no surface flow at all. During a sudden cloudburst they may be converted into raging torrents filling the channels from bank to bank.

These variations, as well as the actual amount of the discharge, are of great importance in determining the velocity of a stream. The velocity as much as any single factor is responsible for determining the size of particles that a stream can transport, as well as the way in which it carries its load.

STREAM TRANSPORTATION

The roiled cloud of sediment brought down by the Mississippi River stains the waters of the Gulf of Mexico far seaward of the river mouth. In the Southwest, within a generation some fairly large reservoirs have silted up completely, and the lakes once backed up behind the dams are converted into dreary expanses of muddy or dusty silt, depending on the season. After a heavy rain, many streets and sidewalks are slippery with a coating of mud, or have a scattering of stones over their surface. Scores of other examples from everyday life are enough to convince an observant person that the land is inevitably wasting away, and that much of its substance is being swept to the sea.

This annual wastage can be an imposing amount and is demonstrated by a single example, the Mississippi, which every day carries around 2,000,000 tons of sediment to the Gulf of Mexico. When the river is in flood, this may rise to as much as 4,000,000 tons. This colossal drain on the central lowlands of the United States has resulted in the construction within the past million years or so of a broad platform of sand, silt, and clay that covers an area of around 12,000 square miles at the river's mouth, with a central thickness of at least a mile.

Most people know that streams carry a heavy burden, but they may be uncertain as to how it is moved. Even experts in hydraulics are uncertain as to the actual way in which a stream moves its load. The attempt to answer this problem justifies a vast amount of research and the publication of scores of papers.

There is, nevertheless, a broad spectrum of agreement that a river moves its load in three major ways—in part by solution, in part by suspension, and in part by rolling, sliding, and moving it bodily along the bottom of the channel.

Solution

This is the load of dissolved material in a river that has been supplied largely through the leaching out of soluble minerals in rocks. An outstanding example, as we saw in Chapter X, is the solution of limestone, which is achieved by the change of the insoluble carbonate, $CaCO_3$, to the soluble bicarbonate form, $Ca(HCO_3)_2$, through reaction with carbonic acid.

It is the invisible dissolved load which gives some river water its distinctive taste. This is especially true of western rivers which cross arid or semi-arid regions. When such water evaporates it leaves behind a white residue that blankets the entire surface of the ground; from a distance extensive patches of it may look like fields of snow. Such accumulations of alkali are fatal to nearly all crop plants, and are the bane of many irrigation districts. Keeping these soluble residues from accumulating in the soil is an unceasing struggle, and one that has been lost in a number of reclaimed areas.

The solution load in a stream, although it is invisible, is imposing. A plausible estimate (Clarke, 1924) is that rivers carry around 2,500,000,000 tons of dissolved material to the sea each year; this amounts to a contribution of 62 tons from each square mile of land that drains to the sea. This loss of soluble chemicals is so great that the lands of the world would be lowered by about 1 foot in 30,000 years through solution alone.

Suspension

The contrast between a limpid trout stream in the high mountains and the muddy, roiled water sluicing through an arroyo as the aftermath of a desert cloudburst is largely a function of the suspended load. This is the visible cloud of sediment suspended in the water above the stream bottom. If the sediment is so finely subdivided that it approaches colloidal dimensions, it may remain buoyed up in the moving water almost indefinitely. This is likely to be true for such particles as clay flakes; it is not so true for silt or sand, or for larger particles. How long such fragmental material keeps afloat depends on many factors: (1) the size, (2) the shape, (3) the specific gravity of the sediment grains, (4) the velocity of the current, and (5) the degree of turbulence.

The effect of these factors is obvious. Flat mineral grains, such as mica flakes, will sift down through the water much like confetti, when compared with the more direct way in which nearly spherical grains settle out. Specific gravity is important, too, because denser substances such as gold nuggets, with a specific gravity of 16-19, are deposited far more rapidly than feldspar grains of the same dimensions, but with a specific gravity of about 2.7.

One of the more important factors in keeping particles in suspension is turbulence. If a particle is about to settle out and then is caught in an upward swirl of water, it may be whisked up suddenly in much the same way that tumbleweeds spiral upward in a swirling wind eddy in the desert. This means it is most unlikely in a stream for a grain of sediment to settle out at a uniform velocity all the way down from the top to the bottom of a river. Rather, such a particle follows a complex path. In part, it drifts forward down the river with the moving current, and in part it swirls erratically up or down much like a sheet of paper caught in a vagrant wind.

Typically, not all of a stream's suspended load is distributed uniformly throughout a stream. Uniform distribution is likely to be true of the finer grain sizes, such as silt or clay, but the greatest concentration of larger grains, such as sand, is closer to the bottom. A stronger current is required to keep sand in suspension, more turbulence is needed to get it up off the bottom, and sand-sized grains settle out more rapidly than do clay-sized particles. In fact, this basal concentration of sand grains may be in suspension briefly, only to sink back to the bottom of the channel, whereupon it becomes part of the so-called bed load.

Bed Load

Part of the river's burden is transported by rolling or sliding, either as individual particles or collectively along the bottom. This is the bed load. In terms of work accomplished by a stream in cutting down or widening its channel, this is the part that does the lion's share. The bombardment of sedimentary particles against the sides and bottom of the channel wears it away as effectively as though it had been worked over by an abrasive such as carborundum.

The bed load is a virtually impossible quantity to measure in a natural stream as compared to the dissolved or suspended load. Both of these are diffused through the main body of the river. The bed load not only is moving along the most inaccessible part of a stream—the bottom—but it is not measurable by any ordinary sampling devices.

The magnitude of the problem of measuring the bed load is illustrated by the Colorado River in Black Canyon. When the river was temporarily diverted during the construction of Hoover Dam, a sawed timber was found on the bedrock of the channel bottom under a cover of approximately 100 feet of stream gravel. This was a clear indication that the entire mass of boulders and gravel normally covering the river floor had been in motion, at least since the advent of the steam sawmill. We know very little of how such a mass of sand, gravel, and boulders moves, but enough observational evidence has been collected to suggest that, in great floods, the whole body of sediment on the floor of the Colorado flows bodily downstream. The result is that large, angular rock fragments soon are worn round and smooth, and are also reduced to smaller size. One has only to listen to the roar of boulders bumping and grinding along the channel in the Grand Canyon to carry away a lasting impression of the enormous effectiveness of such a gigantic rasp endlessly filing away at the continental framework.

Evidence from other streams, too, is convincing that much of the bed load is moved during floods. Then the channel bottom may be scoured to roughly the same depth that the river surface crests above the normal level. This is shown by the accompanying diagram (Fig. 11-5), illustrating how the flood discharge of the Rio Grande swept the bedrock channel free of stream gravel, only to have it redeposited as the flood waters subsided and the average velocity of the stream decreased (Leopold and Maddock, 1953).

Although the way in which the bed load

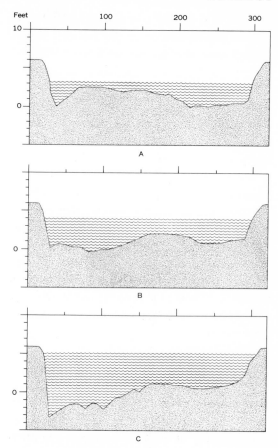

After L. B. Leopold and T. Maddock, Jr., 1953. By permission of U.S. Geological Survey.

FIG. 11-5 *Changes in the shape of the channel of the Rio Grande, near Bernalillo, New Mexico, during the progress of a flood in the spring of 1948. A, May 15, discharge 1,540 c.f.s.; B, May 22, discharge 4,920 c.f.s.; C, May 28, discharge 12,400 c.f.s.*

moves is not known, some knowledge of what may be happening is gained from laboratory studies with controlled conditions of velocity, channel shape and cross section, and amount and size of sedimentary particles.

Individual particles may move by sliding, rolling, or saltation (from the Latin word, *saltare,* to jump). This last process is somewhat analogous to playing leapfrog. A sand grain may be rolling along the bottom, or even may be stationary, when it is caught up by a swirling eddy of turbulence. Then it bounds or leaps through the water in an arching path. Should the velocity be great enough, it may be swept upward to become part of the stream's suspended load; if not, the particle sinks again, either to remain stationary, or perhaps to continue its downstream progress by leaps and bounds.

At moderate velocities the entire bed load may start to move collectively, and almost at once a rhythmic pattern of ripples, much resembling the corrugations on a sand dune, will appear. The reason for this is not known, but may be related to some sort of pulsation in the current. These ripples commonly are closely spaced, and have a gentler slope on the upstream side, a steeper one on the downstream side.

With increasing velocity, the current ripples are erased, and the whole mass of sediment on the stream bottom starts to move. Smaller grains swirl up into suspension, larger ones saltate, and still larger ones roll and slide. The surface of the entire mass of moving debris flattens out, the original corrugations disappear, and the bed load enters the so-called smooth phase.

Should the velocity continue to increase, then with surprising rapidity a pattern of large, asymmetrical ripples—the so-called *antidunes,* or regressive sand waves—appear. Their crests usually are gently rounded and are spaced more widely apart than normal current ripples. The change-over from the smooth phase to the antidune phase commonly is abrupt. The antidunes appear suddenly and grow in a completely opposite way from the manner in which ripple marks form. Sediment is deposited on their upstream face while the downstream face is the one which is being scoured. Thus antidunes march upstream against the current, rather than migrating slowly downstream with it as is characteristic of the more orthodox ripple marks.

Standing waves that curl and break, sometimes violently, mark the presence of antidunes on the stream floor below (Fig. 11-6). As the regressive sand waves march upstream, the standing waves on the surface also migrate against the current—a most impressive sight in a swiftly moving torrent.

FIG. 11-6 *Regularly spaced standing waves on the Colorado River. (Photograph by Martin Litton.)*

In a typical case, when the flood diminishes, the velocity drops, and the process reverses itself. The antidunes flatten, the standing waves disappear, the bottom smooths out, and as the velocity decreases still further toward the normal rate, asymmetrical ripple marks of the first phase reappear.

Competence

The size of sedimentary particles a stream can transport, or its *competence,* depends primarily upon the velocity. At low velocities a typical stream may run clear, and sediment grains on the floor may rest relatively undisturbed. With rising velocity the water becomes increasingly roiled and larger and larger particles are set to moving. Finally, even such impressive loads as railroad locomotives may be swept along—several were rafted away, out of the roundhouse and into oblivion, during the Johnstown Flood of 1889. In a cloudburst in the Tehachapi Valley of California in 1933, a far larger behemoth of the rails, a Santa Fe steam freight locomotive and its fully loaded tender, was swept several hundred yards downstream from the tracks and completely buried in the stream gravels.

The most stupendous example in the United States of the transporting power of running

FIG. 11-7 *A field of boulders swept here by flash torrents from the distant canyon. Near Manzanar, Calif. (Photograph by Ansel Adams.)*

water probably was provided by the failure of the San Francisquito dam in California in 1928. When this 205-foot-high concrete structure collapsed in the darkness, a wall of water 125 feet high swept down the canyon with a velocity of perhaps 50 miles per hour. This was enough to raft individual blocks of concrete weighing as much as 10,000 tons half a mile downstream. Partially buried in the gravel and boulders swept down river by the same torrent, they much resembled gray icebergs stranded on an arctic beach.

Experimental data and observations in natural streams indicate that for sedimentary particles the size of coarse sand or gravel, or even larger, the diameter of the larger particles the stream can move varies as the sixth power of the bed velocity. This means that the size of particles moved by running water increases with astonishing rapidity with seemingly slight increases of velocity, as might be anticipated from a progression as rapid as this. For example, doubling the velocity means that a stream can move a rock not twice as large as before the increase, but one that is 64 times as large; 2 x 2 x 2 x 2 x 2 x 2 = 64.

This effect of a geometric progression is especially impressive in desert stream washes which may be completely dry and then have a velocity increase of a hundredfold when they are filled from bank to bank by a turbid flood—the result of a sudden cloudburst (Fig. 11-7).

One reversal of the general rule, that large-sized particles are picked up by strong currents and only small ones are moved by feeble currents, is illustrated by the accompanying graph (Fig. 11-8). It shows that while a current with a velocity of 10 feet per second is needed to erode gravel, the same velocity also is required to pick up clay flakes and small silt particles. In fact, fine sand is the sediment size most readily set in motion by a moving stream. This effect very likely explains the strong resistance to erosion of stream channels with clay banks and bottoms.

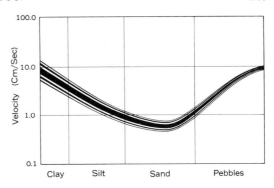

After F. Hjulstrom, *Recent Marine Sediments,* Ed. by P. Trask, American Association of Petroleum Geologists, 1939. By permission.

FIG. 11-8 *Graph showing how swiftly a current must flow to erode material of various sizes.*

Among the explanations for the tenaciousness of clay banks may be the flaky nature of the clay minerals and the strength of the forces that make them adhere to one another. The fact that the clay minerals are too small to project through the thin film of relatively slower moving laminar flow at the bottom of a stream up into the layer of swifter moving turbulent water may be important, too. This stability of silt and clay banks is significant in the far downstream sector of a river such as the Mississippi, and in part may be the reason for the unusually straight course of the river below New Orleans, as contrasted to the broadly sweeping meanders, or bends, in the channel farther upstream.

Capacity

This is a term for the potential load that a stream can carry. Like competence, it is dependent upon the velocity with which a current is flowing, but it is also dependent upon discharge, too. Obviously, a rivulet of water moving with the same velocity as the mile-wide Mississippi can move but a fraction of that river's immense burden.

The role of velocity is significant in determining the capacity of a stream. A sluggish stream meandering across a swamp is capable of moving very little in comparison with a boulder-rolling mountain torrent. Although the direct relationship between velocity and capacity is less certainly known than the relationship between competence and velocity, some such relationship as the following seems to hold—the capacity of a stream varies approximately as the third power of the bed velocity (Rubey, 1938).

Grade

If we remember that *capacity* is a measure of what a stream theoretically can do and *load* is a measure of what a stream actually is doing, then we can keep these two terms straight. For example, a Lackawanna boxcar may have such a figure as "Capacity 100,000" stenciled on its side, yet actually be carrying a load of 80,000 pounds of automobile frames.

A stream whose capacity is less than its load is not likely to be spurred on by excess of zeal into carrying more than is expected of it. Instead, the overload is dropped as abruptly as a Peruvian llama deposits its burden if it is convinced that its carrying capacity of around 100 pounds has been exceeded. When a stream deposits its excess load we say that it is *aggrading* its channel and this may happen when too much sediment is supplied or when the particle size exceeds the competence. Conversely, an underloaded stream—one whose capacity is greater than its load—is likely to pick up an additional quantity of material and thus erode its channel, or *degrade* it.

When a stream is balanced between these extremes, and has achieved equilibrium, so that its slope and discharge give it a current which is balanced for its load, it is at *grade*. A *graded stream* is defined by Mackin (1948), and his statement includes all the essential elements:

A graded stream is one in which, over a period of years, slope is delicately adjusted to provide, with available discharge and with prevailing channel characteristics, just the velocity required for

transportation of the load supplied from the drainage basin. The graded stream is a system in equilibrium; its diagnostic characteristic is that any change in any of the controlling factors will cause a displacement of the equilibrium in a direction that will tend to absorb the effect of the change.

A word often confused with grade is *gradient,* which means slope. The two are interrelated because a graded stream will have developed a gradient whereby it will be able to maintain this delicate balance between velocity, load, channel cross section, and size and amount of load. Such a gradient constitutes the so-called *profile of equilibrium,* and ideally it would be a concave-upward curve—nearly horizontal at the river mouth and steeper near the head. The reason for this is that there is a progressive change in conditions downstream, such as increasing discharge and volume of water as successive tributary streams make their contribution, a decrease in size of sedimentary particles constituting the stream's load as they undergo the wear and tear that is a necessary accompaniment of their journey to the sea, as well as a decrease in the proportion of actual load to discharge, and commonly a greater erodibility of the channel where a stream is flowing on its own deposits near the mouth than where it is carving its way through resistant bedrock in the headwaters zone.

STREAM EROSION

Today virtually everyone recognizes that valleys, even such imposing ones as Hells Canyon in Idaho, Grand Canyon in Arizona, or Kings Canyon in California—all of them more than a mile deep—were cut by the narrow ribbon of turbid water in the stream at the bottom, barely visible thousands of feet below the canyon rim (Fig. 11-9).

This belief, so obvious now, was disputed by our predecessors, and was not fully acceptable even to such illustrious figures as Sir Charles Lyell and Charles Darwin. As late as 1880 many geologists were content to believe that while streams were capable of some downcutting, nonetheless the deeper and more impressive gorges, such as Grand Canyon, resulted from a violent sundering of the Earth's crust. The presence of such a river as the Colorado

was purely fortuitous—instead of cutting the canyon it simply followed the course it does because that was predetermined as the lowest and easiest route to follow.

Although a belief in a cataclysmic origin unquestionably has greater appeal to the imagination, it simply means that many geologists of a century ago had overlooked the succinct and eloquent statement made in 1802 by a Scottish mathematician and amateur geologist, John

FIG. 11-9 *The Snake River, here nearly a mile below us, has cut Hells Canyon, Idaho. (Courtesy of Oregon State Highway Dept.)*

Playfair. Although this essay of his is now widely quoted, it is worth repeating because of the clarity of his style—an attribute not always characteristic of scientific writing today—and because his choice of essentially simple, straightforward words made the point so long ago that streams do in fact excavate the valleys they occupy.

If indeed a river consisted of a single stream, without branches, running in a straight valley, it might be supposed that some great concussion, or some powerful torrent, had opened at once the channel by which its waters are conducted to the ocean; but when the usual form of a river is considered, the trunk divided into many branches, which rise at a great distance from one another, and these again subdivided into an infinity of smaller ramifications, it becomes strongly impressed upon the mind, that all these channels have been cut by the waters themselves; that they have been slowly dug out by the washing and erosion of the land; and that it is by the repeated touches of the same instrument that this curious assemblage of lines has been engraved so deeply on the surface of the globe.

We saw in Chapter X that in such a chasm as the Grand Canyon, the Colorado River is responsible for cutting its channel to a depth of a mile below the plateau, but is not responsible for the excavation of the full 13-mile-wide trough. The widely flaring portion of the valley, outside of the narrow slot actually cut by the Colorado, is the result of mass movement downslope, of weathering, and of slope wash. The role of the river has been to serve as a gigantic conveyor belt, running without cessation, sweeping away most of the debris supplied to it, and cutting downward to maintain the gradient of the sides.

VALLEY WIDENING

The long-term goal of all rivers is to wear the land down to a nearly featureless plain virtually at sea level. Stream erosion for all practical purposes ceases at sea level. This was called the *base level of erosion* about seventy-five years ago by Major John Wesley Powell, pioneering geologist of the far western United States and leader of the first party to explore the Grand Canyon of the Colorado. In his thinking this included much more than merely carving a narrow, water-filled stream channel down to sea level; it also involved the reduction of all the interstream areas until an entire region was worn down nearly to sea level.

How, then, is such a concept to be reconciled with the statement that most of the width of the Grand Canyon is the product of mass movement, rather than stream erosion?

The two ideas are not so irreconcilable as might appear at first, although there is disagreement among geologists as to how the goal of landscape reduction is reached. One way that it may be achieved is by *downwasting,* a process through which the steepness of slopes adjacent to a stream valley gradually diminishes through soil creep, gravitative transfer, and the decomposition of rocks.

The effect of this slow wasting away of the area between streams is shown in the accompanying diagram (Fig. 11-10). A once broad and nearly level upland, trenched by narrow canyons, may over many years decline until ultimately it is reduced to a nearly level plain not very far above sea level. To such a broad, nearly featureless plain the term *peneplain* is applied, from the Latin, *paene,* meaning almost, and the English, *plain*.

A peneplain, since it is a product of widespread degradation by streams and mass wasting, can never have a perfectly level surface, although it may come very close to it. Since it is a product of erosion rather than deposition, the surface of the plain truncates the underlying bedrock. This bedrock surface may not be worn down everywhere to the same monotonous level; portions underlain by more resistant material may stand higher than their surroundings. Such isolated, residual hills, or even mountains, are

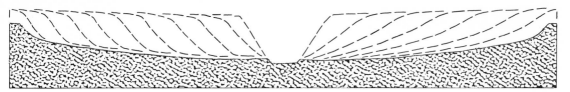

FIG. 11-10 *The successive cross-profiles of a valley, beginning with a narrow canyon and progressing toward a peneplain. On the right, the slopes are diminished by downwasting; on the left, the slope angles are parallel and the valley walls retreat by backwasting.*

called *monadnocks,* after Mount Monadnock in New Hampshire.

Few incontestable examples of peneplains have been described from around the world, although many partial peneplains, or partially convincing examples, have been described. Many expanses of nearly level plains of barren rock, such as the Hudson Bay region of Canada or much of the Scandinavian Peninsula, have complex histories, in each of these cases involving widespread glacial stripping.

Actually, there is less than general agreement among geologists about the way in which a combination of stream erosion and mass wasting operates to produce these broad plains. The process of downwasting described in an earlier paragraph might be regarded as a point of view based on the work of W. M. Davis, a pioneer American scientist. A different solution was advocated by an Austrian, Walther Penck, and according to him would yield the same end product, a nearly level, stripped plain, but produced by *backwasting.*

For this process to operate, an equilibrium slope has first to be established on the canyon walls, as in Fig. 11-10, and once the proper inclination of this slope has been reached for a particular climate, dominant sort of weathering, vegetative cover, and kind of bedrock, then the slope will continue to retreat essentially parallel to itself. As it recedes, a graded, stripped rock

surface develops at the base, and as the slope above it retreats, the platform widens. Ultimately, all land above the level of the widening platform will be stripped off as separate retreating equilibrium slopes meet, and then an entire region will be worn down to a base level of erosion with a very gentle gradient toward the sea.

A final choice between these two explanations would be premature in view of the state of knowledge today. The answer to the problem of the wearing away of the land between the rivers, just as to many problems in the real world, is complex, and rather than being all one or all the other, involves elements of each. If any differentiation can be made, the possibility seems strong that backwasting may be a leading process in the more arid lands of the world, and downwasting may be paramount in lands where vegetation blankets slopes, soil is deep, and mass movement plays a strong supporting role.

Regardless of the details of the mechanism of its accomplishment, geologists today are in essential agreement that the running water of streams—given time—can wear away the highest mountain made of the most resistant rocks, until it is reduced to a nearly featureless plain. That so much of the land surface of the world fails to conform to this drab description is a testimonial in itself of the recency and continuing nature of the forces of deformation affecting the rocks of the Earth's crust.

In other words, seldom does a portion of the crust remain stationary long enough for erosion to run its course. More often than not the Earth's surface may be re-elevated, as in the Grand Canyon region, and a plains area, once near sea level, may then become a plateau

FIG. 11-11 *The gauge that measures the height of the Nile at Elephantine Island, Egypt. The records of floods along this river extend back thousands of years. (Photograph by Jean B. Thorpe.)*

hoisted thousands of feet above its former base level. This process probably has been repeated again and again through the long antiquity of the Earth. The forces of crustal deformation are ranged in never-ceasing opposition to those of erosion. When erosion prevails, extensive degraded rock plains develop. With a reversal of the forces, such a peneplain, broadly uplifted, may survive after many millennia only in tattered remnants of upland surfaces, or accordant ridge crests, high in the alpine zone of some lofty mountain range.

FLOOD PLAINS AND DELTAS

The broad plains bordering many of the large rivers of the world have been tempting sites for settlement since the beginning of history. Both the Egyptian and Babylonian civilizations were essentially riparian, and the life of their people was bound to the river, be it the Nile or the Euphrates, the giver of life in an arid land.

Across the wide expanse of lowland bordering a river, a stream such as the Nile is free to spread its waters in time of flood. In fact, the annual flood was an event of such importance in the survival of Egypt that a whole pantheon of deities centered their activities around whatever divine force was responsible for this phenomenon (Fig. 11-11).

A plain, such as the one flanking the lower Nile, quite appropriately is called a *flood plain*. In the United States the region adjacent to the lower Mississippi River is a superb example. This is probably the most thoroughly surveyed of the world's largest rivers, both with regard to the configuration of the river itself—its bends and channel patterns—and with respect to the thickness and character of its deposits as well. A leading reason for this extensive investigation is the enormous exploratory effort made in the search for oil in the Mississippi Delta, and the active drilling campaign that has been waged there.

Characteristic Flood Plain Features

From the nature of the term itself, we should logically expect the surface of a flood plain to be covered with deposits made by the river in time of flood. This is true for the lower Mississippi River, whose channel from a short distance below the junction with the Ohio down to the Gulf of Mexico lies wholly upon its own alluvium.

Such a flood plain normally is bordered by low bluffs (Fig. 11-12) which mark the outer limits of the band of swampy ground that the river has been free to wander across. Most such rivers, and the lower Mississippi is typical, are confined by low embankments, or *natural levees,* which slope gently away from the river. A section of low-lying ground, the *backswamp,* may be found between the bluff and the natural levee. This may be a swampy, ill-drained, boggy section whose surface waters cannot flow back into the river because the slope of the natural levee is against them.

Natural levees are built by the river when it overtops its banks during a flood. Rather than surging violently over its banks at a single outlet, the typical flood moves away from the river toward the backswamp as a sullen, tawny, inexorably spreading tide of muddy water. The greatest check to the velocity of the flood waters comes when they leave the relatively compact hydraulic configuration of the stream channel and first encounter the lake-like expanse of flood waters that have inundated the backswamp. The bulk of the suspended sediment is deposited forthwith where the sudden velocity drop occurs at the channel edge. The result, then, is the gradual building up of a narrow embankment, chiefly of fine sand and silt on either side of the lower Mississippi River. Because their water content is less than the immediately adjacent, ill-drained backswamp, and the grain size of their sediment is larger than that of the swamp muck, the natural levees provide the only solid ground in such a saturated region as the lower Mississippi flood plain, and for this reason, roads, settlements, and farms are clustered along the higher and firmer ground of the levee immediately ad-

jacent to the river. The backswamp with its intricate pattern of bayous, branching channels, and lakes is virtually uninhabited, with the exception perhaps of birds and muskrats and their hunters, and isolated drilling crews living on barges towed from one well site to another.

A bird's-eye view of a flood plain is likely to look like the aerial photograph of Fig. 11-13, which shows the river swinging in broad curving bends, or *meanders.* The word comes from an actual river, the Menderes, in western Turkey, and the derivation of the word is from the Greek *maendere,* to wander.

Before speculating about the origin of these beautiful but perplexing sinuosities in a river's course we need to know something of their geometry, as well as their nomenclature. Fortunately, the names we give their various parts are taken from the American vernacular; they are the same ones that were in use along the Mississippi by the river men of a century or so ago.

The common name for a broadly curving part of a river is a *bend.* The convex bank in such a curve is a *point.* A straight stretch of the river is a *reach.* A now abandoned and partially filled river channel—ordinarily sited just inside a point—is called a *chute.* The level of the stagnant backwater might rise during a flood, and in the days of steamboat racing a chute would provide a short cut for a daring pilot trying for a fast upriver passage. Here the danger for a

FIG. 11-12 *Diagram of a flood plain.*

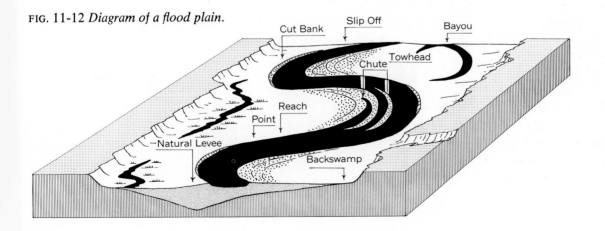

packet boat was impaling the hull on the roots of a waterlogged tree, or snag.

Oddly, there is no common term for the path followed by the thread of maximum velocity of a stream. In general, the main current clings to the outer side of a bend where it is shunted by centrifugal force. In such a bend, where the current is strong, the bottom of the channel is scoured more deeply than elsewhere, and this section of deeper water close to the bank is given the old-fashioned name of *pool*.

When the current leaves a bend, it normally does so on a tangent and may occupy a variety of positions while in a reach. On entering the next bend downstream it crosses over to the opposite bank, and such a place was known as a *crossing* to the steamboat pilots. They disliked crossings because here the current was diffused,

FIG. 11-13 *Meanders on the Lyell Fork of the Tuolumne River, in Yosemite National Park, Calif. The river flows toward the right.* (*Photograph by Hal Roth.*)

its strength dissipated when compared to where it ran deep and strong along the outer curvature of a bend. A crossing, then, was beset by shoals and shallows, or sand bars, and at low water it was necessary to take a steamboat across under slow bell, sounding all the way. The leadsman's cry could be heard echoing along the river through the stillness of a summer noon, "By the mark five, by the deep four, by the mark three, Mark Twain!" The last is a depth of two fathoms (12 feet).

At a truly low stage of the river some of the bars appear above the water surface as low, tawny sand islands, appropriately known as *tow-heads*.

If we draw two profiles across the channel of such a river as the Mississippi, the first in a reach, where the current is approximately in midstream, and the second in a bend, the two channel cross sections will be quite unlike. In the reach, the Mississippi flows in a broad, shallow, nearly flat-floored trough. Typical of such

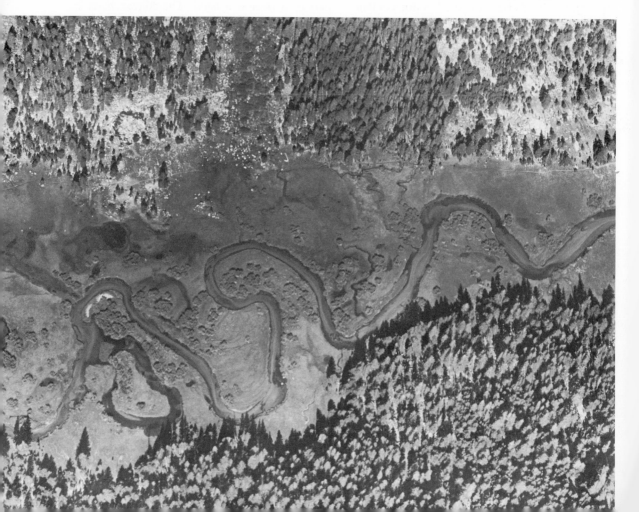

a pattern are the river's dimensions in the delta just before it breaks up into separate distributary channels. There the river is around 4,000 feet wide and roughly 50 feet deep, with an approximately trapezohedral shape; that is, a flat bottom and comparatively steep, flaring sides.

The form is quite different in a bend. The channel nearest the concave, or outer, side of the bend is deep and nearest the point it is shallow. In short, the cross-sectional pattern is wedge-shaped, with the deep part of the triangle being the pool. The parts of the profile that stand above the water surface have distinctive names, too. The concave side is the steeper, since it is continuously being undermined by the river, and commonly it is known as the *cut bank*. The gentler, or convex, point is a site of deposition and has been built up gradually through the accumulation of sand and silt. It is called the *slip-off slope*. In a metaphorical sense the river appears gradually to have slipped away from it as the diameter of the meander has enlarged through undermining of the cut bank.

How meanders enlarge is a question that has been long debated. The most generally accepted belief is that the cut bank is undermined by the river, especially when in flood, by deep scouring in the pool, thus over-steepening the cut bank and slicing away its foundations. Commonly, the bank fails by slumping into the stream through this removal of support at the base, rather than being sawed horizontally by the river.

How the slip-off slope grew—so that additions to it just about keep pace with the retreat of the cut bank, with the result that the river always maintains about the same width—puzzled investigators for many years. Where does the sand come from to keep the slip-off slope advancing as the cut bank recedes? At one time it was believed that there was a cross-channel transfer of material from the cut bank to the slip-off side—which in a sense maintained a balance between cutting on one side of the river and filling on the other.

An impressive series of large-scale laboratory experiments was made by the U. S. Waterways Experiment Station in Vicksburg (Friedkin, 1945). These demonstrate very convincingly, by using models with river lengths ranging from 50 to 150 feet and widths of from 1 to 5 feet, that much of the contribution of sand and silt to a slip-off slope comes from the erosion of the cut bank next upstream. This is a fully expectable process since the current is at maximum efficiency in the pool, and when material from a cut bank slumps into the river through undermining, the sedimentary material is delivered at the point where it can be most effectively transported. As a result, most of it is swept away from the concave part of the bend in short order.

A careful study of the course taken by the current shows that its erosive effectiveness is directed against the outside of the curve, the bends tending to enlarge in diameter rather than contract. The neck of land between adjacent bends narrows correspondingly. This narrowing may continue until finally the neck is cut through, the former channel becomes a crescentic lake, and the land area of the point is converted to an island.

The new and more direct channel of the river is known as a *cut-off*, and the abandoned channel, whose entrances soon silt up, becomes a crescent-shaped lake, or *bayou*, as it is known along the Gulf Coast. All told there have been something like twenty naturally occurring cut-offs on the lower Mississippi since 1765. About fifteen have been made artificially by the Mississippi River Commission since 1932 to straighten out the river's course, thereby increasing the gradient and thus the velocity, and as a consequence diminishing the flood hazard by improving the hydraulic efficiency of the channel.

Historically, one of the more interesting cut-offs of the Mississippi occurred at Vicksburg in 1876. Before that date the river made a broadly sweeping curve past the city, now isolated from the main stream by the cut-off that created Centennial Lake (Fig. 11-14).

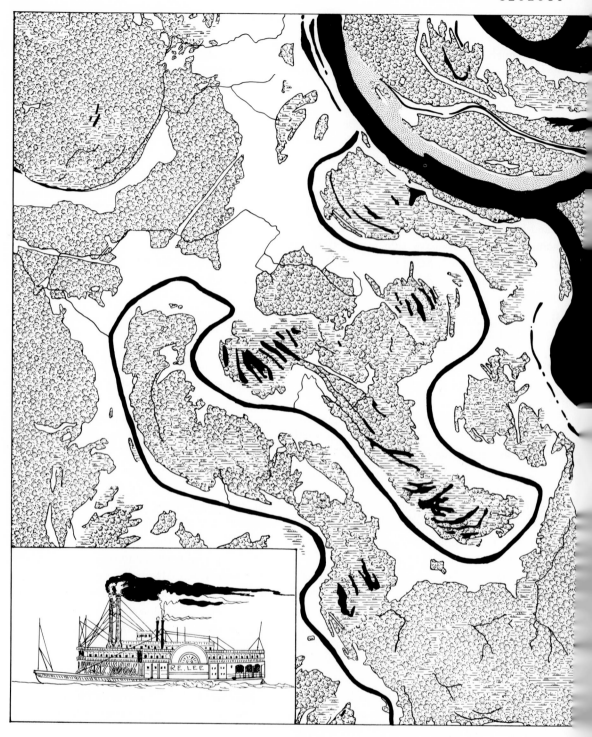

FIG. 11-14 *Before 1876 the Mississippi River flowed around the meander that is now Centennial Lake.*

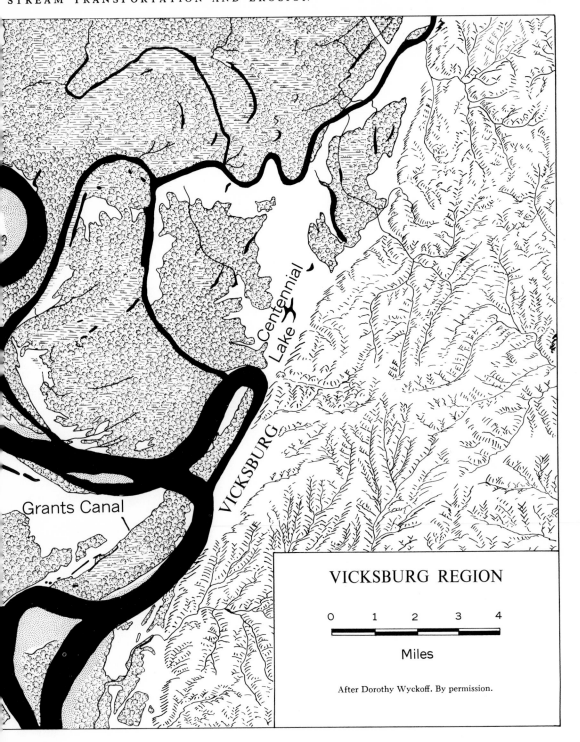

VICKSBURG REGION

0 1 2 3 4

Miles

After Dorothy Wyckoff. By permission.

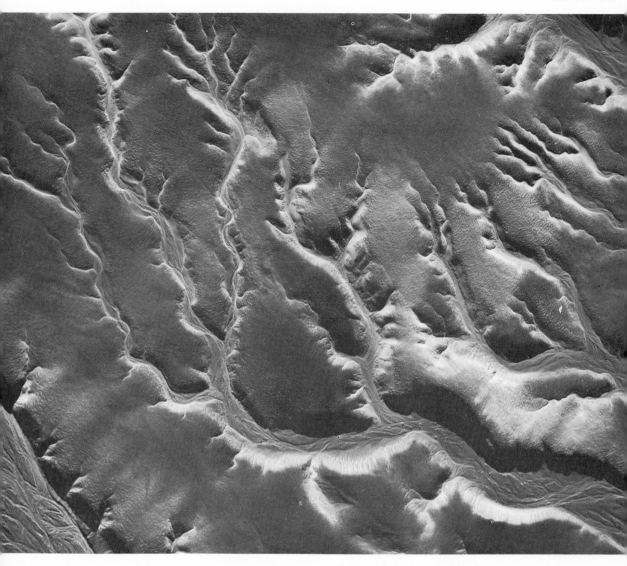

FIG. 11-15 *Dry stream beds in Death Valley, California, show a braided pattern of small channels. The width of the channel at lower right is about 75 feet. (Photograph by William Garnett.)*

The river then achieved by itself what General U. S. Grant failed to do in 1863 when the Union Army made an abortive attempt to dig a short canal across the neck to divert the river and thus bypass Vicksburg. It is too bad that the effort failed—perhaps because Grant was not fully persuaded of its merit—because had it succeeded it would not only have made Admiral Porter's lot much easier by not having to run his fleet of Union gunboats past the Confederate batteries, but such an artificial diversion would have been a signal achievement for the branch of the science recognized today as military geology.

The final word on the fundamental causes of meandering is far from the writing. Because of the great economic significance of flood control and navigation on the Mississippi, more study has probably been given to the problem there than for any other river. At least a few of the generalizations made for the Mississippi appear to be valid for other rivers, too.

Meanders seem to develop best when river banks are eroded with relative ease; if they are too resistant, the stream cannot establish a rhythmically swinging pattern. There also needs to be some degree of inhomogeneity in the composition of the stream banks, such as a mixture of sand and silt. If the material is too uniform in size, and relatively resistant to erosion—such as clay—then the channel very likely will remain essentially straight, as the Mississippi does below New Orleans.

If the banks consist of readily erodible material, there is a tendency for the channel to widen appreciably, and perhaps locally to develop a *braided* pattern (Fig. 11-15). This is a channel pattern where the stream instead of flowing in a single channel divides and subdivides in a complex fashion. The actual size of the river is not a factor in determining whether or not a stream meanders or braids—the lower Ganges and the Amazon, for example, have braided channels (Leopold and Wolman, 1957)—and the same stream may show both types of patterns at different places along its length. In a general way, braids seem to be characteristic of those reaches of a stream with steeper gradients, while meanders apparently typify those with gentler slopes.

The same river may go from one pattern to the other at different times and under different circumstances in its history. The Mississippi, for example, had a braided channel for a brief time at the close of the Pleistocene glaciation (Fisk, 1944). Then, the river had a vastly greater volume of debris to transport, and a load made up of coarser material than is being moved today.

After this excess load was worked out of the way, the river achieved its present meandering habit—the result in part of a large volume of water, relatively small bed load, gentle gradient, and moderately uniform and fairly erodible banks. The meandering, rather than the braided,

configuration became dominant for the river, and this pattern has been maintained for at least the last 10,000 years. The principal change that has occurred in historic times has been a migration of the river channel, in general from the western side of the flood plain across to the eastern. The individual channel changes that mark the stages in this march across the flood plain are more likely to involve several hundred miles of river length rather than to be isolated minor episodes, such as the cutting off of individual meander loops.

Such a change appears to be a real possibility in the foreseeable future. Around 25 per cent of the Mississippi River discharge is intercepted a short distance above New Orleans by the Atchafalaya River and is diverted into the Gulf of Mexico. Should this diversion increase progressively into the future, then before long nearly half the discharge of the Mississippi will be following the new course to the sea and the deterioration of the old channel by New Orleans will be rapid. Substantial efforts are being made to prevent such a disaster—from the point of view of New Orleans—from occurring. It will be interesting to see what the future may unfold.

Deltas

Herodotus, in the fifth century B.C., impressed by the branching pattern of the distributaries of the Nile, compared the form of the watery, muddy region between Cairo and Alexandria to the Greek letter *delta,* △. The comparison is so apt that it has won acceptance in most of the languages of western Europe from that day to this.

The Nile delta is a nearly ideal example of this particular landform, so much so that few others measure up to its perfection. The map shows how the main channel of the Nile separates into a host of branching lesser arms, called quite appropriately *distributaries* (Fig. 11-16). Another interesting feature of the Nile delta is

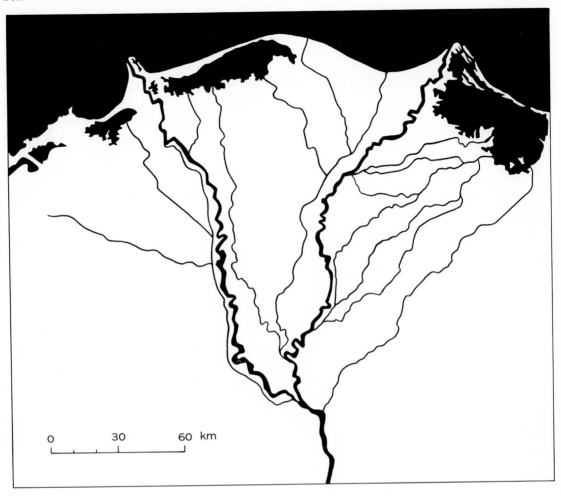

FIG. 11-16 *The delta of the Nile.*

the bordering bays and lakes, of which one, Abu Qir Bay, is a good example. This was the site of the Battle of the Nile where the French Fleet was destroyed by Nelson, thus ending Napoleon's hopes for an Eastern empire. Similar *delta-flank depressions,* as such water bodies are called, border many of the other deltas of the world. Well-known ones are Lake Pon-chartrain by the Mississippi delta, the Zuider Zee (Ijsselmeer) and marshes of Zeeland adjacent to the Rhine, and the lagoon surrounding Venice at the mouth of the Po.

Not all the world's rivers have deltas where they enter the sea. Two large ones that do not are the St. Lawrence and the Columbia—the St. Lawrence because it has little chance to pick up much sediment in the short run between Lake Ontario and the Gulf; the Columbia because it discharges directly into the open sea whose powerful waves and currents quickly redistribute the river's burden of sand and silt.

The best-developed deltas are most likely to be constructed where a river moves a large load of sediment into a relatively undisturbed body of water. Examples of such impressive accumulations of riverine deposits are the great deltas at the mouths of the Ganges-Brahmaputra in India and East Pakistan, the Indus in West Pakistan, the Tigris-Euphrates in Iraq, the Niger in Nigeria, the Yangtze Kiang and Hwang Ho in China, the Mississippi in the United States, the Danube in Romania, and the Volga in the Soviet Union. One of the most picturesque of the deltaic worlds is the Camargue, the land of cowboys and semi-wild cattle at the mouth of the Rhone in southern France.

In America, the Mississippi is by far the best known geologically, not only because of the long record of channel changes but because something like 90,000 oil wells have been drilled in its sediments, and because repeated geophysical surveys have been made up and down its length. All this information combined gives us a uniquely detailed, three-dimensional picture, not only of the 12,000 square miles of delta surface but of the mile-deep thickness of sediments below the waters of the Gulf of Mexico as well.

The Mississippi differs a bit from many other deltas in the remarkable extensions of its distributaries and their bordering natural levees out beyond the normal delta margin. It is this distinctive pattern that causes the Mississippi to be described as a *bird's-foot delta*.

The great delta of the Mississippi is not a single simple structure, but is a compound feature built up through a complexly overlapping pattern of so-called *subdeltas*. The relative succession in which these appeared is shown on the accompanying map (Fig. 11-17) which also gives the estimated dates at which the river held the positions shown. From these it can be seen that the river established its present course only very briefly before the arrival of the first white men, Cabeza de Vaca in 1528(?) or de Soto's followers in 1544.

The toes of the bird's foot actually are natural levees bordering the channels of distributaries that are growing outward into the Gulf. The height of the natural levees increases gradually inland from the Gulf until they are around

13 feet high at New Orleans, a distance of 103 miles from Head of the Passes. Incidentally, the average flood height of the river at New Orleans is about 17 feet, which gives a hydraulic gradient of around 0.11 foot per mile.

Head of the Passes is where the present-day river breaks up into three major and a number of minor distributaries (Fig. 11-18), and here the river depth is around 40 feet. The slope of the channel bottom in these distributaries is upstream against the gradient of the river surface, because most deposition occurs at the mouth of the distributaries, and here, without the modern interference of dredging and jetty construction, the river builds up a shallow sand bar where it enters the Gulf of Mexico. Thus, the normal low water depth at the mouth of a distributary was as little as 10 to 15 feet—before improvement—and in some of the minor, less frequently used channels, as little as 3 to 5 feet.

This shoaling at the mouth and upstream inclination of the river bottom is part of the reason why the Mississippi breaks up into branching and rebranching distributaries. The upstream slope of the river bottom makes the river unstable, as it were, and if it spills over or breaks through a levee in a so-called *crevasse*, a new channel may form and drain away an increasing share of the river's discharge.

Such a new channel developed at Cubits Gap in 1862 when Mr. Cubit's daughters cut a short ditch to connect the river with the Gulf of Mexico, then only a few hundred yards to the east (Welder, 1959). In the century since then, the river has extended a complex of distributaries, natural levees, and delta land for 12 miles eastward into the Gulf of Mexico.

Because the mouth of a distributary is almost always partially blocked by a sand bar, this is a place where a channel is especially prone to split around such an obstacle in its path. Once it has divided, the two arms may compete on a basis of equality, but more frequently one branch gains advantage over the other. The de-

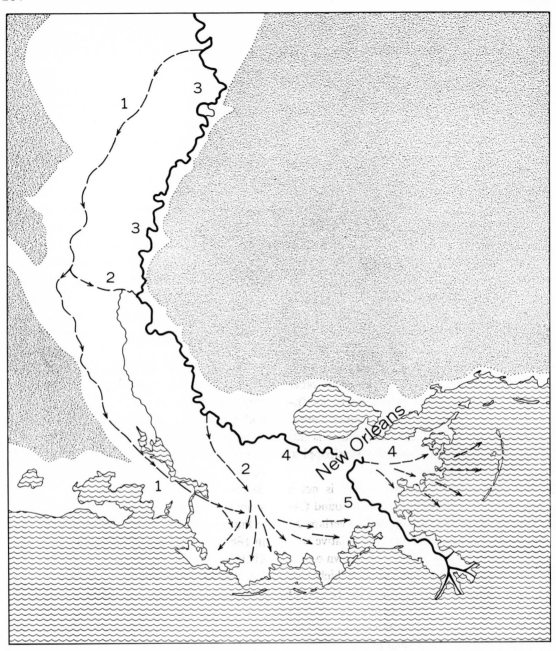

FIG. 11-17 *Various courses of the Mississippi River.*

From J. H. Zumberge (after H. N. Fisk, "Geological Investigations of the Atchafalaya Basin and the Problem of Mississippi River Diversion," 1952) *Elements of Geology*, 1958. By permission of John Wiley & Sons, Inc. and U.S. Army Corps of Engineers.

COURSE	WHEN ESTABLISHED
1	100 A.D.
2	300–400 A.D.
3	1000–1100 A.D.
4	1100–1200 A.D.
5	1500–1600 A.D.

FIG. 11-18 *At Head of the Missis-sippi River divides into several distributaries which lead out to the Gulf of Mexico. (Courtesy of Humble Oil and Refining Company.)*

feated channel may survive as an attenuated shadow of its successful rival, or it may even be deserted by the river, ultimately to silt up completely.

This strange deltaic world—half water and half land, the abode of water birds of great variety, with a continuously changing pattern of lakes, swamps, marshes, and constantly shifting streams—is one of the more important environments for man on Earth. From the beginning of historic time their fertile soil, their network of waterways, and their position as a meeting ground between seafarers and those who make their living along the rivers of the world have made deltas tempting sites for coastal cities. Such a bewildering maze of channels, large and small, was made to order for piracy, as witness the successful operations for many years of the brothers Lafitte at Barataria in the Mississippi delta.

Quite a price is exacted, however, from a delta city in return for its communication advantages. Such a city is under constant threat of inundation by flood, building foundations are insecure—a visit to Venice is an impressive illustration of what differential settling can do to structures built on delta mud. Even such a shallow excavation as a grave may fill with water (the vaulted sepulchers of New Orleans are an answer to this problem), and the development of an unpolluted local water supply is a difficult task. Overriding these many adversities is the greatest threat of all, that the river may change its course completely or the channel may silt up. A good example of this latter fate is the ancient city of Ravenna; in the days of Justinian and Theodora it was a leading seaport on the Adriatic, now it is something like 6 miles from the coast.

The low country bordering the mouths of the Rhine provides an impressive example of the problems besetting the inhabitants of a delta. This is one of the more densely inhabited regions of the world, and one where an immense volume of seaborne and riverborne trade moves through such ports as Rotterdam and Amsterdam. As we saw in Chapter VI, these cities, already below sea level, throughout their entire existence have not only had to endure attacks overland—a hazard to which delta cities are peculiarly vulnerable—but have had to labor valiantly to hold back the sea. The explanations of all the difficulties faced by the people of the Rhine delta are complex, but they certainly include the currently rising level of the sea, the compaction of the water-logged clays on which these cities stand, and the apparently geologically active subsidence of this part of the European coast.

Many of these same difficulties plague New Orleans, not the least being the problem of subsidence. Indications of a relative lowering of the land with respect to the sea are everywhere. Among these are the presence of what were once Indian settlements far out on the bottom of Lake Ponchartrain, drowned cypress trees and inundated farmland around the lake margin, and the sunken streets and graves of the deserted settlement of Balize near Head of Passes. The now silent, shell-paved streets are buried under the marsh about four feet below sea level.

There is little disagreement over the evidence of subsidence in many of the world's deltas, but there are strong differences of opinion as to its cause. There are those who believe the addition of perhaps as much as 2,000,000 tons of sediment a day, as in the Mississippi delta, makes for an excess load on the Earth's crust, which bows down as a consequence. Opponents of this belief point out that the excess load is not so great as might appear at first since the weight of the displaced sea water has to be considered, too. Thus, the material added to the crust may have a net density of about 1.8, or so, and how this lighter material displaces heavier subcrustal material with a specific gravity of perhaps 3.3 is a tricky question to answer.

The answer probably is not a simple one, but certainly involves many of the factors operating in the Netherlands. The addition of an extra burden of sediment, as in the Mississippi delta, may not be adequate in itself to bring about a broad crustal downwarping, but if a load such as the Mississippi's accumulates in a region where subsidence is the dominant geological process, this additional weight certainly is not going to work in an opposite direction.

Suggested References

Bryan, Kirk, 1940, The retreat of slopes, Assoc. Amer. Geographers, Annals, v. 30, p. 254-268.

Clarke, F. W., 1924, The data of geochemistry, U. S. Geol. Survey, Bull. 770.

Davis, W. M., 1902, Base-level, grade, and peneplain, in Geographical Essays, Ginn and Co., Boston, Mass.

Fisk, H. N., 1944, Geological investigation of the alluvial valley of the lower Mississippi River, Corps of Engineers, Mississippi River Comm., Vicksburg, Miss.

———, 1952, Geological investigation of the Atchafalaya Basin and the problem of Mississippi River diversion, Corps of Engineers, U. S. Army, Waterways Exp. Station, Vicksburg, Miss.

———, 1952, Mississippi River Valley geology in relation to river regime, Amer. Soc. Civil Engrs., Trans., v. 117, p. 667-682.

Friedkin, J. F., 1945, A laboratory study of the meandering of alluvial rivers, Corps of Engineers, U. S. Army, Waterways Exp. Station, Vicksburg, Miss.

Gilbert, G. K., 1914, The transportation of debris by running water, U. S. Geol. Survey, Prof. Paper 86.

Hjulström, Filip, 1939, Transportation of debris by running water, in Recent Maritime Sediments, Amer. Assoc. Petroleum Geologists, Tulsa, Okla.

Kuenen, Ph. H., 1955, Realms of water, John Wiley and Sons, Inc., New York.

Leopold, L. B., 1962, Rivers, American Scientist, v. 50, p. 511-537.

Leopold, L. B., and Maddock, Thomas, Jr., 1953, The hydraulic geometry of stream channels and some physiographic implications, U. S. Geol. Survey, Prof. Paper 252.

Leopold, L. B., and Wolman, M. G., 1957, River channel patterns: braided, meandering, and straight, U. S. Geol. Survey, Prof. Paper 282-B.

Leopold, L. B., and Langbein, W. B., 1960, A primer on water, U. S. Geol. Survey, Washington, D. C.

Mackin, J. H., 1948, Concept of the graded river, Geol. Soc. Amer., Bull., v. 59, p. 561-588.

Matthes, G. H., 1951, Paradoxes of the Mississippi, Scientific American, April.

Merdinger, C. J., 1959, Hydraulics through the ages, Military Engr., v. 51, p.379-384.

Playfair, John, 1802, Illustrations of the Huttonian theory of the earth, Edinburgh.

Rubey, W. W., 1938, The force required to move particles on a stream bed, U. S. Geol. Survey, Prof. Paper 189-E.

————, 1952, Geology and mineral resources of the Hardin and Brussells quadrangles (in Illinois), U. S. Geol. Survey, Prof. Paper 218.

Russell, R. J., 1936, Physiography of the Lower Mississippi River Delta, in Lower Mississippi River Delta, Dept. of Conserv., Louisiana Geol. Surv., Bull. 8.

————, 1958, Geological geomorphology, Geol. Soc. Amer., Bull., v. 69, p. 1-22.

Shimer, J. A., 1959, This sculptured earth, the landscape of America, Columbia Univ. Press, New York.

Twain, Mark, 1874, Life on the Mississippi, Harper and Bros., New York.

Welder, F. A., 1959, Processes of deltaic sedimentation on the lower Mississippi River, Tech. Rept. No. 12, Coastal Studies Inst., Louisiana State Univ., Baton Rouge, La.

Arroyo de la Parra, between San Xavier and Loreto, Baja California.
(*Photograph by William Aplin.*)

XII

Deserts

Least familiar of land areas, aside from the extreme arctic, are the world's deserts. Perhaps their seeming mystery lies in their relative remoteness from lands such as western Europe and the Atlantic coast of North America, where the modern pattern of western civilization developed. Had western life remained centered on the Mediterranean, deserts would be much closer to our daily lives because the limitations imposed by aridity bear heavily on such bordering countries as Spain, Morocco, Algeria, Libya, Egypt, and Israel. In earlier days much of the southern shore of the Mediterranean was the granary of Rome, and once-flourishing cities, such as Leptus Magnus in Libya, are now stark ruins half buried in the sand. One of the problems in studying deserts is that the boundaries are not fixed inexorably, but may expand or contract through the centuries. In fact, there is much evidence from paleobotany—the study of fossil plants—that deserts are relatively late arrivals among the Earth's landscapes. Deserts require a rather specialized set of circumstances for their existence, and in a moment we shall inquire into what some of these are.

First of all we need a working agreement as to what constitutes a desert. Temperature is not the only factor; some are hot almost all the time, others may have hot summers and cold winters, and some are cold throughout much of the year. Since drought is their common factor, in a general way we might call those regions deserts where more water would evaporate than actually falls as rain. In other words, the criterion

we are using is relative rather than absolute, such as saying all regions are deserts that have less than 10 inches of rainfall in a year.

Drought is their prevailing characteristic, and deserts notably are regions of sparse vegetation. Few are completely devoid of plants, but some come very close to this ultimate limit. Typically, desert plants are widely spaced. Their colors tend to be subdued and drab, blending with their surroundings. Their leaves may be small and leathery in order to reduce evaporation. In fact, some, as the *saguaro* of Arizona or the barrel cactus of the Sonoran Desert, may have no leaves at all. Other desert plants, such as the ubiquitous sage, may develop an extraordinarily deep root system in proportion to the part of the plant that shows above ground. Plants with these adaptations of extensive roots, leathery leaves, and large water-holding capacity are called *xerophytes,* from a combination of Greek words meaning dry + plant.

Every gradation exists in deserts, from those that are completely arid and that are essentially barren expanses of rock and sand, devoid of almost all visible plants, to deserts which support a nearly continuous cover of such plants as sagebrush and short grass. Dry regions with such a characteristic seasonal cover are best referred to as *steppe,* and commonly are marginal to the more desolate wastes.

The accompanying map of the world (Fig. 12-2) shows that the dry regions are concentrated in subtropical and in middle latitude parts of the Earth's surface. For example, there is nearly continuous desert from Cape Verde on the west coast of Africa, across the Sahara, the barren interior of Arabia, the desolate mountains of southern Iran, and on to the banks of the Indus in Pakistan. All told, 18 or 19 million square miles, or 36 per cent of the land surface of the Earth, might be classed as arid.

This statement brings us to the problem of definitions once more. Many regions marginal to the tropics and having a monsoonal climate are arid and drought burdened during the dry season, yet are rain sodden and soaked during the wet season. In the dry season many trees shed

their leaves, thorn-bearing plants with woody, unyielding branches are a genuine obstacle to travel, and the ground is baked and sun-dried to the point where agriculture is impossible.

Another region of deficient precipitation that is difficult to classify is the barren land of the Arctic. The precipitation may be 10 inches a year or less, yet with a low evaporation rate, the tundra appears to be far better watered than it is. This illusion is aided by permafrost which keeps surface water from sinking very deep into the ground.

These cold deserts are so unlike the more typical dry lands of middle and low latitudes that we shall leave them out of this chapter in order to concentrate on the familiar sort of desert. The map (Fig. 12-2) shows that the pre-

FIG. 12-1 *The desert crowds the edge of the irrigated flood plain of the Nile, near Giza, Egypt. (Courtesy of Trans World Airlines.)*

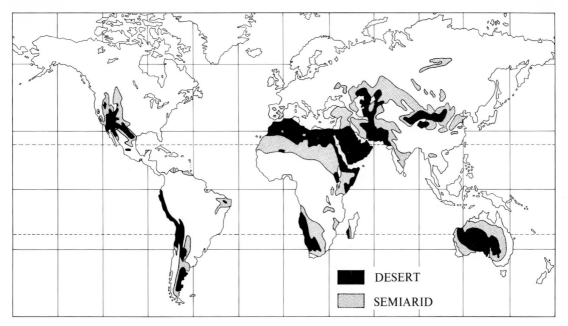

After P. Meigs, "Future of Arid Lands," 1956. By permission of the American Association for the Advancement of Science.

FIG. 12-2 *Dry regions are found chiefly in the subtropics and the middle latitudes. They occur (1) below the high pressure cells in the atmosphere where descending air is being heated, (2) along cold-water coasts where moisture-laden air (fog) is transported to the warmer land, and (3) to the lee of high mountain ranges where descending air is being warmed.*

ponderance of the dry areas of the Earth—exclusive of the Arctic—are on either side of the equator, chiefly around latitude 30°, and that they tend to favor the western side of continents.

Contrary to the popular image, most deserts are not vast shimmering seas of sand across which such picturesque characters as Foreign Legionnaires slog along while sheiks on spirited stallions sweep by. Although many deserts are sand covered, the majority are not. Most desert regions are more likely to be broad expanses of barren rock, or of stony ground with only a rudimentary soil profile developed. Ground colors are largely those of the original bedrock. They lack the red colors of tropical soils, especially those that are alternately wetted and

dried, or the blacks and dark grays of humid temperate regions where the organic content in soil may be high. The bright red color that we associate with such places as Grand Canyon and Monument Valley comes in large part from coloring matter within the rocks themselves, rather than from red-soil forming processes active there today.

It is typical of many desert regions, especially those in continental interiors, that streams originating within the desert often falter and die within the desert's boundaries. This pattern of streams that do not reach the sea is called *interior drainage,* and is an unusual feature to a visitor from a well-watered region with through-flowing streams. Some desert streams simply wither away and sink into the sand. Others may carry enough water to maintain a lake at the end of their course. Since this will be a lake without an outlet, it is almost universally salty or brackish—the Dead Sea, about 1,300 feet below sea level at the end of the River Jordan, is a renowned example. A larger water body without an outlet is the Caspian Sea, covering about 164,000 square miles, and even though it is supplied by such a mighty river as the Volga not enough water reaches it to overcome the inexorable losses of evaporation and to allow the lake to spill over the low divide separating it from the Don River and the Black Sea.

At many arid parts of the world, where the water brought in by streams cannot hold its own against evaporation, desert lakes may be only short-lived seasonal affairs, or may be completely dry for decades. Such ephemeral lakes, so characteristic of drought-burdened lands, are called *playas* in the southwestern United States. This is an extension of the meaning of the original Spanish word for beach or sandy bank of a river. Some playas may be glaring expanses of shimmering salt, such as the Bonneville Salt Flats near Great Salt Lake in Utah, or they may be broad, dead flat, clay-floored dry lakes— seemingly created for landing fields, they have such an ideally level surface.

CAUSES OF DESERTS

Before we launch into a discussion of the landforms in deserts and the nature of processes that operate there, it might be well to consider briefly what some of the special circumstances are that are responsible for causing some parts of the Earth's surface to be deprived of normal rainfall. Omitting the polar regions of deficient precipitation, there are three major types of arid regions. These are: (1) subtropical deserts, (2) deserts produced by cold coastal currents in tropical and subtropical regions, and (3) rain-shadow deserts.

The broad band of drought reaching across Africa and into India belongs in the first category, as do other similar dry subtropical lands. In part these deserts owe their existence to the presence of persistent high pressure cells in the atmosphere on both sides of the equator and centered approximately on the Tropic of Cancer and the Tropic of Capricorn. Since these cells are centers of descending, and therefore heating and drying air, land areas beneath them are burdened by persistent drought and exception-

ally high evaporation rates. Years may pass between rains in such a desert as the interior of Arabia. Infrequent rains, when they do occur in these tropical deserts, may be violent and commonly result from a weakening of the pattern of high pressure and a resulting invasion of moisture bearing maritime-tropical or equatorial air.

In other parts of the tropics, dry lands are caused by the planetary air circulation toward the equator. This nearly constant current of air, better established over sea than land (where local differences of temperature may be pronounced), is given the old name of the *trade winds*. These winds were a boon to the masters of sailing ships of a century ago because they could be relied upon to blow almost constantly with about the same force and from the same direction. They blow in both the Northern and Southern Hemispheres toward the equatorial belt of calms. Because of the Earth's rotation these streams of air are deflected to the right in the Northern Hemisphere (looking in the direction the current flows), as other moving things such as ocean currents, or projectiles, or missiles are, too. This means that instead of blowing from due north or due south, at right angles to the equator, these winds come from the northeast, north of the equator, and from the southeast, south of it.

The trade winds, or others like them, blowing across land are drying winds because they are blowing from colder to warmer regions. The ability of air to hold water increases with temperature; it decreases as the temperature drops. As a current of air is forced to climb a mountain front which lies athwart its path, it is chilled and rain falls. This is strikingly shown by the high islands in the trade wind seas. Windward slopes, as in Hawaii, may receive 450 inches of rain (in one instance, 600 inches), while leeward slopes may have as little as 10 inches fall in a year.

Deserts formed because of cool coastal currents are perhaps the least familiar type to Americans. Such deserts flourish along the

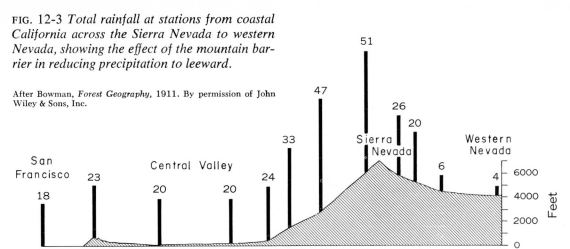

FIG. 12-3 *Total rainfall at stations from coastal California across the Sierra Nevada to western Nevada, showing the effect of the mountain barrier in reducing precipitation to leeward.*

After Bowman, *Forest Geography,* 1911. By permission of John Wiley & Sons, Inc.

middle latitude coasts of continents whose shores are bathed by cold coastal currents, such as the Humboldt Current off the Atacama Desert of Chile and Peru, or the Benguela Current off the Kalahari Desert of southwest Africa.

These deserts are exceptionally impressive for the very dramatic climatic contrasts encountered within extremely short distances. The Atacama Desert, for example, is among the drier lands on Earth, yet its seaward margin is concealed in a virtually unbroken gray wall of fog. Winds blowing across the cold waters of the coastal current are chilled, their moisture condenses and thus a seemingly eternal blanket of fog stands over the sea. Once this fog drifts landward to where the air temperature is higher, the fog burns off almost immediately, and the water-holding capacity of the air current increases rather than decreases as it moves across the heated land. A high, thin cover of fog may build up once more high on the Andean slopes, with the result that Lima, for example, is a sober, austere-looking city with a thin, unbroken pall of gray high-altitude fog spreading above it. The sun rarely shines, yet rain is equally rare, averaging perhaps 2 inches a year.

A third cause of aridity is the interposition of a mountain barrier in the path of a moisture-bearing air current. We have a striking example in western North America with the desert stretching eastward in the so-called rain shadow of the Sierra Nevada of California. The profile (Fig. 12-3) across this part of central California at the latitude of San Francisco shows the great disparity between precipitation on the western slope of the Sierra Nevada and the floor of the Nevada desert.

Few deserts are the product of a single cause operating to the exclusion of all others. The high deserts of Asia do not fit into the categories outlined above. They could scarcely be more remote from coastal currents, hot or cold, and they lie well outside the subtropical high pressure belt. The factors entering into their origin certainly involve the enclosing ring of mountains, the great distance this so-called roof of the world lies from the sea—the ultimate source of water to be precipitated—and the northern location of this desert land which places it climatically in a part of the Earth where the barometric pressure is relatively high, and where cool, drying air descends from the higher levels of the atmosphere. This last reason also applies to many of the subtropical deserts.

In summary, we can say that deserts do not have a simple reason for their existence. Their origins are complex, but they are well worth trying to understand, not only for their own sake as an intellectual challenge but also because so much of the future of mankind is de-

FIG. 12-4A *The present desert regions of North Africa and the Near East were the sites of flourishing civilizations only a few thousand years ago, as Leptus Magnus in Libya, which is now isolated in a sand sea. (Photograph by A. E. L. Morris.)*

FIG. 12-4B *Another example of desert encroachment is Mirgissa, Sudan, near the second cataract of the Nile, which dates from 1500 to 1300 B.C. (Photograph by C. W. Meighan.)*

pendent upon the utilization of arid lands. An equally intriguing question is whether the boundaries of deserts are stationary, or whether they are contracting or expanding. As we shall see in Chapter XIII, the climate of the world has slowly changed in historic time. This is strikingly true of deserts, and much of the most compelling evidence comes from the Sahara and the Middle East (Fig. 12-4). Artifacts, stone implements, and rock paintings of extraordinary subtlety and sophistication testify to the presence of early man in what are desolate expanses of the Sahara today. At a later date much of this barren region was the granary of Rome, and colonial cities of that day as well as roads along which the legions marched are now overrun by drifting sand. The expansion of the desert broke the slender thread of communication lines linking the cultures of the Mediterranean and African worlds. Apparently thereafter the two had a vague and uncertain awareness of each other over the centuries, but it was not until the introduction of the camel caravan that the land connection was re-established. By this time each culture had evolved along a different path.

STREAM EROSION
IN AN ARID REGION

What are some of the things, other than drought, that set the deserts of the world apart from more favored lands? Paradoxical as it may seem the leading agency responsible for sculpturing the landforms of a desert is running water, just as it is in humid regions. Puzzling indeed is how all the work was done of removing the enormous volumes of rock that once filled the canyons of desert mountains, or of shaping the mountains themselves, or even of wearing them away completely to bare rock plains stretching endlessly to the empty horizon, when there appear to be no streams at all in this seemingly timeless land.

Part of the answer may lie in the brief discussion in the immediately preceding section. Not all landforms in all deserts were necessarily formed under the climatic regime we see today; they may be fossil landscapes in a sense, survivals of erosional patterns carved during a time more humid than ours. We shall see one result of a recent climatic shift a little farther on when we talk about the Pleistocene (ice-age) lakes of the desert. Their abandoned shorelines contour the slopes of many of the mountains and their saline deposits whiten the floors of many of the western desert basins.

Not all the erosion of desert landscapes, however, was done in the remote geologic past and under climatic controls alien to the contemporary world. Almost all deserts have some rainfall, even though ten to fifteen years may elapse between showers.

Nature of the Run-off

Contrary to popular belief, cloudbursts are relatively rare in arid lands—they are much more common where rainfall is greatest, as for example, the rainy tropics, or the southern Atlantic coastal states. When a moderate rain does fall on the desert, it is likely to assume the apparent proportions of a cloudburst in a more humid region and also to do a very effective job of erosion, because there is no vegetation to protect slopes from the spattering effect of rain drops, from rill wash, and from the rapid cutting of the ravines and arroyos that are so typical an aftermath of desert cloudbursts.

Anyone caught in one of these sudden downpours is likely to have an unforgettable experience should he fail to make his way to higher ground in a hurry. In a matter of moments, a dry sandy arroyo, bordered by low but steep cliffs, is filled with a surging, mud-laden flood. Such a stream swirls and churns forward violently, sweeping a great mass of debris along with it. Such flash floods make deserts impassable, until the arroyos drain. This they do almost as rapidly as they filled, because there is no con-

tinuing source of water supply for them as there is in regions of plentiful rain and perennial springs. In a matter of a few hours beneath the desert sun, an arroyo floor covered by 10 feet of water may be dry sand again, interrupted by only occasional pools of muddy water.

Such torrential floods as these short-lived desert ones may on occasion overtop the low banks of desert dry washes and spread out as a sheet of muddy, turbulent water over the desert floor. Such a *sheet flood* is vastly effective in picking up loose sediment and shifting it around the landscape.

Thus, deserts strike a curious balance when their rates of erosion are contrasted with those of humid regions. Much less rain falls in arid regions, but slopes are correspondingly more vulnerable because they lack the stabilizing effect of vegetation. Badlands, or slopes scored with great numbers of gullies, large and small, are characteristic desert landscape elements.

Depositional Forms

Wherever erosion occurs, there is deposition close by. This is especially true in arid regions because here ordinary streams cannot escape beyond the confines of the desert. Their water sinks underground into sandy stretches of their own normally dry stream beds, or it evaporates, or it may be withdrawn by the fiercely competitive water-seeking plants, such as mesquite and tamarisks that line the banks of many desert watercourses. Much of the desert landscape is dominated by stream deposits, in large part because of the inadequacy of running water to move great quantities of debris out of a desert basin and on to the sea.

A most characteristic desert landform is the alluvial fan. These are accumulations of boulders, gravel, and sand deposited by dry-climate streams which begin at the point where such a stream leaves the rock-walled defile it has eroded in the mountains and starts out across the basin at their feet. The stream velocity is

FIG. 12-5 *The surface of an alluvial fan in Death Valley, Calif., is marked by a braided pattern of small channels. Drying patches of mud have begun to crack and curl. (Photograph by Philip Hyde.)*

further reduced because much of the water sinks into the porous, sandy subsurface layers of the fan, thereby decreasing the volume which is one of the factors controlling the velocity. The stream quickly becomes overloaded where it starts across the fan. Its load does not diminish, but its volume fades rapidly. The main channel very soon separates into a score of distributaries, and it acquires a braided pattern resembling the one described in Chapter XI.

Streams may be able to cross the fan in time of flood, but under normal conditions they sink into the sandy ground almost as soon as they leave the bedrock of the mountains. This is almost always a surprise to visitors to a dry country—to see a stream waste away, growing thinner and thinner downstream and then vanishing completely—quite the reverse of humid climate streams, whose volume commonly increases downstream.

Actually the water has not vanished but is percolating slowly through pore spaces in the fan. Far down the fan where the material is finer—chiefly sand and silt—the permeability is less. The gradient is diminished, too, and the thickness of the fan is correspondingly reduced. The result of all these factors is that water which was deep in the ground in the mid-section of the fan is forced to the surface at the toe, or lower end. Here it may seep out in springs, or *cienegas* (from a Spanish word for swampy ground), commonly marked in the desert by clumps of mesquite trees—one of the best guides to water in the arid Southwest.

If there is a single alluvial fan at the base of a desert range, probably there will be others—in fact, there probably will be one at the mouth of each principal canyon. These fans overlap like palm fronds, to make a nearly continuous apron sloping away from the mountain front to the basin floor (Fig. 12-6). Such a constructional surface built up by overlapping, or coalescing alluvial fans is called a *bajada* (pronounced as though it were spelled bahada), from a Spanish word meaning a gradual descent. We use the same root when we speak of Baja California for the peninsula in Mexico on the west side of the Gulf of California.

Driving across a bajada on a road paralleling

a mountain front and near the base is a singular experience. The road continually rises and falls, much as though it were laid across an immense ground swell at sea. The high points are opposite canyon mouths where the road is on the axis of the fan, and the low points are about midway between canyon mouths where the road is in the swale separating two fans.

A desert basin bordered by mountains whose lower slopes are partially buried in their own

FIG. 12-6 *The gently sloping constructional surface along the east front of the Sierra Nevada, Owens Valley, Calif., is composed of a series of overlapping alluvial fans which form a* bajada. *Note the size of the boulders in the foreground, about two miles from the mountain front; to the east (left) they give way to finer sediments. (From the Cedric Wright Collection, courtesy of the Sierra Club.)*

FIG. 12-7 *A desert bolson near Jean in southern Nevada, showing the closed nature of the basin, bordering mountains partially buried in their own debris, and the playa in the center of the basin. (Photograph by John S. Shelton.)*

debris is called a *bolson* (Fig. 12-7). This is a Spanish word meaning purse, but used locally in the southwestern United States for a mountain-girt desert basin or valley without an outlet, in other words a closed basin with interior drainage. In a humid region—where precipitation is greater than evaporation—such a basin would be occupied by a lake whose waters would rise until they spilled over the lowest point of the basin rim.

This will not happen in a desert. There, since more water evaporates than falls as rain, a large permanent and continually expanding lake cannot form. There are lakes in deserts, though, and some, such as Great Salt Lake, are well known. Characteristically, their shorelines fluctuate with climatic variations, and their waters are saline. Sometimes, as in Great Salt Lake, when the surrounding region is underlain chiefly by sedimentary rocks, the leading dissolved constituent in the water is NaCl. In others, where the principal source of soluble material has been the erosion of volcanic rocks, the water may hold a much higher content of Na_2CO_3 (sodium carbonate). Since everything soluble in the rocks of a desert region may be carried into such a lake, no wonder some desert lakes are natural chemical factories. Saline lakes in volcanic areas are likely to be especially prolific sources of unusual substances, including potash, potassium salts, and in the eastern desert of California, boron compounds.

During a dry climatic cycle such a saline lake

may evaporate completely, leaving an achingly white residue of salts, as complex chlorides, sulphates, and carbonates. The surface of such a salt layer may be smooth, or if it is undergoing solution, it may be very rough. The incredibly jagged terrain of salt pinnacles on the floor of Death Valley (Fig. 12-8), nearly 300 feet below sea level, was a fearsome stretch for the first party of emigrants to cross, with their battered wagons and patient, long-suffering oxen.

The playas we have just been discussing are saline, and these chemically complex accumulations of soluble salts commonly are (1) the residue left behind through the evaporation of a once larger lake, or (2) the salt accumulation that gradually builds up at the end of an essentially continuously flowing desert stream system. There are some desert rivers that do have a fairly continuous flow of water throughout the year, even though they are underground through the porous sand and gravel of the stream bed, and thus not visible from the surface at all. Actually, most saline playas are combinations of the two types. A large number of them are the floors of dessicated lakes and are also at the end of a salty, perennial stream. This is true, for example, in Death Valley, which once held a lake about 120 miles long and whose surviving saline playa is also at the end of the Amargosa River, which name appropriately enough means bitter.

Clay playas are more likely to be found in smaller isolated bolsons, rather than in larger basins at the end of a long and integrated drainage system. Most of the year they are dry and their surface is baked as hard as a brick; in fact, they make ideal emergency landing fields. Or the whole lake floor may be converted into a gigantic multidirectional landing ground, as at 15-mile-long Rogers Dry Lake at Edwards Air Force Base in eastern California.

When a typical short-lived downpour is over, desert streams waste away as suddenly as they sprang into being. Then the arroyo bottoms quickly return to their seemingly unchanging state of dry, shifting sand enclosed between steep arroyo or canyon walls. The playa may endure a bit longer, but ultimately its murky, dark-hued water evaporates or sinks underground. Before this happens, the suspended load of finely divided silt and clay particles has been disseminated throughout the entire body of the ephemeral lake. Thus, when the lake is gone its newly revealed floor is a dead flat expanse of uniformly distributed, tan-colored, fine-grained sediment. Very often, too, the surface layer of playa clay shrinks as it dries, cracking into thousands of small polygonally bounded blocks. These have much the same sort of pattern one sees on the tops of basalt columns, such as those in the Devil's Postpile. Both patterns are the result of shrinkage. In the case of basalt, it is the loss of volume on cooling; and in playa clays it is the loss of water.

Erosional Forms

A curious landform, typical of the arid southwestern United States, and especially of the Gadsden Purchase part of Arizona south of the Gila River, is the *pediment*. Pediments are bedrock surfaces, stripped bare, gently sloping away from low desert mountains toward the lower central part of the bolson. From a distance these broad encircling surfaces look like a uniformly sloping bajada or a constructional apron of overlapping alluvial fans, rather than a product of long-continued degradation and removal of many thousands of cubic yards of bedrock.

Pediments were first described in this country by one of America's more picturesque exploring geologists, W. J. McGee (1897). He was as surprised as anyone by their true nature:

During the first expedition of the Bureau of American Ethnology (in 1894) it was noted with surprise that the horse shoes beat on planed granite or schist or other rocks in traversing plains 3 or 5 miles from mountains rising sharply from the same plains without intervening foothills; it was only after observing this phenomenon on both

FIG. 12-8 *The Devil's Golf Course, Death Valley, Calif., is composed of salts—complex chlorides, sulphates, and carbonates—which were concentrated in Lake Manley at the end of a long drainage system. The salts were then precipitated as the lake disappeared. (Photograph by Ansel Adams.)*

sides of different ranges and all around several buttes that the relation (between the size of planed bedrock and of thick alluvium) was generalized, and then the generalization seemed so far inconsistent with facts in other districts that it was stated with caution even in conversation.

It was to these broadly graded rock surfaces that McGee gave the name of pediment. No one today knows what he had in mind in applying the term. Perhaps he meant in the sense of pedestal, for these broad surfaces of eroded bedrock are pedestals upon which the surviving soon-to-be-consumed remnant of a desert mountain range stands. With this connotation the word might be derived from the Latin *pes, pedem,* meaning foot.

FIG. 12-9 *The gentle slope leading upward to the base of the Oro Grande Mountains, near Mojave, California, is largely a bare rock surface. (Photograph by John S. Shelton.)*

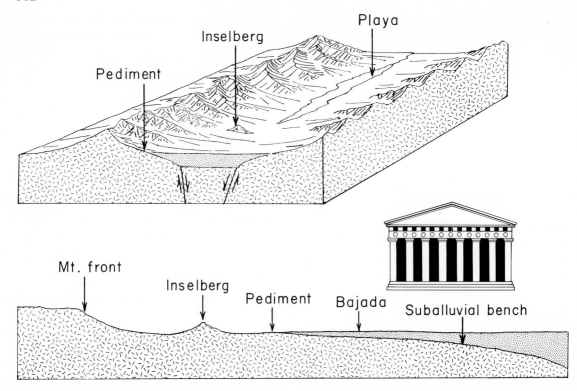

FIG. 12-10 *The position of the bare bedrock surface, or pediment, in relation to the principal geomorphic features found in closed basins of arid regions such as the American Southwest. Note that the sediments derived from the bordering hills are largely trapped in the basin; only the finest sized particles are removed by wind.*

The term pediment is used in another way in architecture, and possibly it may have been borrowed from that profession. On a Greek temple the pediment is the triangular part of the building under the roof and over the columns (Fig. 12-10). The word has been used in modern architecture in this sense since the seventeenth century, and this meaning is derived from the Greek and ultimately the Egyptian word, pyramid. In a way desert pediments do have a pyramidal form—a counterpart of the façade of a temple where the fruits of victory and the trophies of the chase were once so graphically displayed. The diagram (Fig. 12-10) shows how the pedestal-like bedrock surface between the

mountain remnant and the playa does in fact have a pyramidal form in cross section.

Not only is the origin of the word itself uncertain, but over the last sixty years a considerable amount of energy has been spent in debating the origin of pediments. To greatly simplify the complex story of pediments, we should briefly define some of their elements before launching into a debate concerning their origin. The diagram (Fig. 12-10) is a cross section of a typical pediment. The mountains, or *sierra,* stand as a serrated remnant in the midst of a broad expanse of planed-off bedrock. Above the bedrock surface may rise a few surviving isolated outliers of the central sierra, and to these are given the appropriately descriptive German name of *inselbergen,* which means island-mountains.

Notice, too, how the concave-upward slope of the pediment gradually changes form as it passes basinward beneath the thickening wedge of the bajada. There the bedrock surface is thought by some to become convex upward, and to this buried portion of the bedrock surface is given the somewhat involved name of *suballuvial bench*. Its existence has not been proved, but the arguments advanced in 1915 in favor of its origin by a pioneer California geologist, A. C. Lawson, run as follows:

As a steep mountain front recedes through erosion, the waste supplied by its retreat accumulates in the desert basin at its feet. Because, as we saw earlier in this chapter, such a basin has no outlet—that is, it has an interior drainage—the pile of sediment builds up as the mountain front recedes. However, the rate of supply diminishes as the mountain mass dwindles through retreat on all sides, and the rate at which the basin fills decreases, too. The buried part of the pediment, the suballuvial bench, develops a convex-upward curve as this systematic decrease in increments of fill produces an exponential curve.

In summary, two elements are necessary if this explanation is really true. One is a rising base level and burial of the basinward edge of the pediment. The other is that the mountain front retreats roughly parallel to itself, maintaining essentially the same steepness of slope throughout its history. In other words, once an equilibrium slope is developed for a given rock type in an environment, such as a desert, the slope tends to maintain the same angle as it recedes. This is quite a different matter from the way in which mountains are believed to fade away in more humid regions, as we shall see at the close of this chapter in the section describing the arid cycle of erosion.

The critical question, then, is: how does the mountain front recede? According to Lawson and his followers through the years, this wearing back is the product of the work of a multitude of small ravines combined with the peculiarities of desert rainfall. Rocks, such as granite, which disintegrate directly from solid rock to mineral grains, are unusually susceptible to rapid removal and at the same time preservation of steep mountain fronts.

The chief opposition to Lawson's theory came from D. W. Johnson (1932), then a professor at Columbia University, whose belief it was that pediments owe their origin to sideward cutting, or lateral planation, of streams in the sector between the mountain front and the playa. The pediment essentially was planed off smoothly by such sideswinging streams, instead of being carved by a multitude of closely spaced, shallow ravines. According to Johnson, the mountain front is snubbed back, or undercut by sideward sweeping streams at the time they are at the ends of the arc through which they are free to swing. Were Johnson's theory to be true, such streams would plane off a pediment surface that would be convex upward on a profile parallel to the mountain front, in the same way that an alluvial fan is, and for this reason he called such a landform a *rock fan*. The important distinction here is that a rock fan does not consist of rocks, as an alluvial fan does, but of bedrock, and is a wholly stream-eroded feature rather than a stream-depositional one.

According to Johnson, a pediment should have a longitudinal cross section parallel to the streams crossing it as shown in Fig 12-11 A. Notice that it lacks the convex-upward, suballuvial bench that Lawson postulates (Fig. 12-11 B). As the mountain front is cut back by laterally swinging streams, the bases of ridges sloping down to the bolson will be sliced off and continuously steepened.

Compare the two diagrams (Fig. 12-11, A, B). They are an interesting example of the problems we are continually confronted with in geology. Along the ground surface both cross sections look alike. It is underground that they differ significantly. One cross section has a convex-upward bedrock surface, the other does not. Both show the shingling effect of gradual overlapping of the gravels of the bajada on the pediment as a direct consequence of the rising base level which in turn is a consequence of an interior drainage pattern.

In order to choose between the two hypotheses

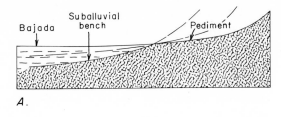

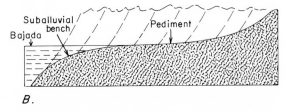

After Yi-Fu Tuan, *Pediments in South East Arizona*, Vol. 13, Univ. of Calif. Publ. in Geology. By permission of University of California Press.

FIG. 12-11 *Comparison of interpretations* of *the origin of pediments by W. D. Johnson (above) and by A. C. Lawson (below). Is the suballuvial bench concave or convex?*

for the origin of pediments, a simple test would be to drill a line of holes outward from the sierra, and thus determine not only the depth to the suballuvial bench but also its form. This would help to settle the argument as to whether or not it actually is convex upward. Oddly enough, this has not been done, perhaps because too much money is involved for the solution of a problem primarily of scientific interest; nor for that matter have any extended geophysical studies been undertaken at a variety of places to determine the configuration of the bedrock surface. Perhaps at some future date we may have an answer, but this apparently simple, yet unsolved, riddle is crucial to an understanding of how these landforms were produced.

WIND EROSION

Over many of the dry lands of the world the wind blows seemingly without restraint, adding a note of harassing melancholy to an already unbearably lugubrious scene. Such a desolate region, with the wind keening ceaselessly across

it, is the drier part of Patagonia in the far southeastern reaches of Argentina. Other deserts are perhaps as windy on occasion, but in most of them times of extreme windiness alternate with times of calm.

During the intervals the wind blows, its erosional effectiveness is likely to be greater than in humid regions. In the latter, the ground surface is protected by vegetation and by a more tenacious mantle of weathered soil which also may be damp throughout most of the year. Vegetation plays an important role indeed because the potency of the wind drops off very rapidly at the ground, the plants acting as an extremely effective baffle.

The wind is a most effective agent of transportation for certain sizes of rock particles, and scarcely at all for others. It is this high degree of selectivity that makes the wind such an unusual agent of erosion.

Obviously there is an upper limit to the size of particles that the wind reasonably can be expected to move. Very few boulders of the size that are handily transported by streams, waves, or glaciers will be moved by the wind—even by a Middle West tornado. This immobility is true for rocky material down to the size of gravel and, in all but exceptional cases, of pebbles. This means that many desert surfaces are sheathed with a protective armor, as it were, of rock fragments. This lag gravel, or *desert pavement,* as it is called, is a blanket of pebbles and gravel left behind while the finer material was winnowed out and whisked away by the wind. If for some reason a chink in the armor develops, perhaps by having individual gravel fragments shouldered aside by a jeep breaking a trail across the desert, then the newly exposed sand will be blown away by the wind (Fig. 12-12). The immediately adjacent surface is lowered by wind scour down to a level where new rock fragments are exposed. Then the desert pavement is stabilized once more.

Odd as it may seem, very fine-grained particles, such as silt or clay flakes, are difficult for the wind to start in motion. In general, the same principles are operating here that also operate in streams of water. Silt and clay, with their small dimensions and strong cohesiveness, are difficult for a moving current of air to pick up. Once lifted out of place, however, they remain in suspension many times longer than sand. Their tenacity when in place is demonstrated when the wind blows full strength across the surface of a clay playa. Very little dust is stirred up as a rule, the hard-packed clay particles stand firm, although some of the looser sand and silt around the margin may be picked up—especially if the playa surface is sun-cracked.

This difficulty of the wind in picking up fine material is no longer true once the natural tenacity of these small particles is overcome. The way in which such particles may be loosened is illustrated by such familiar examples as the running of a band of sheep across clayey ground, or the driving of a car along the dusty tracks of a desert road, or above all else, the plowing of dry and dusty soil in advance of the windy season. To anyone flying over an arid or semi-arid region on a windy day, it is most impressive to see the dust blowing in long streamers from some fields while others are dust free.

Once silt- or clay-sized particles are picked up by the wind, there are no restraints imposed on their travel comparable to the lot of their waterborne contemporaries, which are limited to the drainage pattern of some stream or to some glacier's course. Windborne dust swept from the fields of Colorado in the *Grapes of Wrath* days of the 1930's was carried as far east as the New England states. In fact, some dust was blown far beyond, out over the North Atlantic.

There are scores of other examples of the efficacy of air currents in moving fine particles over vast distances. Eruptions of the explosive sort are the most telling kind because they constitute a point source for the volcanic dust, and also, because of the unique nature of this material, it can be traced over vast distances all the way back to the origin. Krakatoa, as we saw in Chapter III, hurled dust into the upper atmosphere to circle the Earth several times and to produce an appreciable fall in regions as remote from the source as western Europe. Icelandic eruptions have made appreciable deposits in Europe, too, as well as in eastern North America.

FIG. 12-12 *The surface of the stony desert in Jordan is composed of a blanket of pebbles and gravel which were left behind after the finer sand had been blown away by the wind. (Photograph by A. E. L. Morris.)*

More typical, however, of the aspect of dust transport with which we are concerned here is the dust whirled high into the air by turbulent winds of the Sahara and broadcast far and wide over the Mediterranean, southern Europe, and on occasion as far as England, 2,000 miles away.

The sheer quantity of material that can be in the air at any given time is surprising. According to Lobeck (1939), in a dust storm of average violence a cube of air 10 feet on a side might well have 1 ounce of dust suspended in it. This seems trifling, but if we increase the size of our cube of air until it is a mile on each side and maintain the same saturation of dust, then each cubic mile of air is supporting 4,000 tons of solid material. Thus, a storm 300 or 400 miles across might well be sweeping 100,000,-000 tons of solids along with it.

All this is strong evidence that the wind can be an effective erosional agent and one of especially great significance in arid regions. It is the only agent that can transport material beyond the confines of the typical desert. Not only can the wind carry sediment beyond the rim of a desert basin, but it is also the one agent that can overcome the rising base level imposed on desert streams as desert bolsons gradually fill up with their own debris.

Some of the closed basins in the desert supposedly excavated, or, as we say, *deflated,* by the wind reach very large dimensions. A famous example is the great oasis of Kharga in the Sahara west of the Nile. This depression is about 120 miles long by 12 to 50 miles wide and 600 to 1,000 feet deep. The walls are flat-lying layers of readily eroded sandstone, apparently unbroken by any sizable faults. A series of longitudinal sand dunes trails off downwind from this great depression whose sandy floor has almost certainly been the source of supply. This is not to say that the wind hollowed out the whole basin; its origin unquestionably is more complex. Rain wash and streams may erode the friable sandstone and sweep the loose sand down

to the floor of the trough. There the sand rests until it is picked up by the wind to accumulate in dunes to the leeward of the basin.

Ground water sets a lower limit to wind erosion. Once the desert surface is deflated to where the water table is reached and the ground is kept damp, then the wind can no longer pick up loose material with the same ease, and deflation slows to a virtual halt. In Kharga the beneficial effect of this has been the appearance of springs around the margins of the great depression. The springs appear at the level that the water table intersects the ground surface at the base of the escarpment. Such springs are the source of water for the true oases, for with only a little ground water to draw on, date palms flourish and make a startlingly green contrast to their stark surroundings.

Another impressive closed basin in the Sahara is the Qattara, 185 miles long with a floor that is a searingly forbidding quagmire of salt and shifting sand covering about 7,500 square miles. Whatever the origin of the Qattara Depression may be, the wind almost certainly played a prominent role in enlarging it and in deepening it to the water table. Evaporation of this water through centuries is responsible for the accumulation of the salt deposits. This immense, impassable saline trough acted as a barrier in World War II that made it impossible for Rommel's Afrika Korps to turn Montgomery's flank and compelled the Germans to attack where the British forces were concentrated at El Alamein on the narrow neck of land separating the Qattara from the Mediterranean.

At some future date this sink may have surprising utility if an unorthodox proposal should be developed of leading Mediterranean water to it through canals and a tunnel, and then using the 1,500-foot drop available from the rim of the depression to generate power from the unlimited supply of water available in the sea. Gradually the depression would fill with water to form a concentrated saline lake whose surface it is estimated would stabilize around 150 feet below the level of the Mediterranean when the input of sea water balanced the loss of lake water through evaporation beneath the Saharan sun.

WIND DEPOSITION

Loess

Dust lofted out of the desert by winds may be swept for scores of miles before it sifts down to accumulate in a tawny blanket spread far and wide over an area which may be enormously distant from the source. Such a deposit of airborne silt is called *loess,* from the German *löss* or *lös,* a fine, yellowish-gray loam characteristic of the Rhine and other river valleys.

The most renowned of such deposits are those of northeast China, and it was to these that Baron von Richthofen, a leading German geologist, gave the name of loess while on an exploring expedition to the outermost parts of the Russian and the Chinese empires.

The loess of China has been exported by the wind out of the Gobi and across the Kalgan Range whose barren ridges carry the Great Wall. Deposited on the North China plain by the dust storms of centuries, loess lies deep in the valleys of this ancient land, often to thicknesses of hundreds of feet, although it lies much thinner on the crests of divides. This tan-colored silt when picked up by the Yellow River gives the stream its name, as well as the Yellow Sea whose waters are stained for hundreds of miles from shore by suspended dust particles.

There are many other parts of the world where loess is found; among them are the Mississippi Valley and Central Europe, neither of which possibly can be construed as an arid region. This widespread distribution is simply an indication that like other things in nature, loess has more than one origin. Presumably these widely distributed blankets of dust were spread far afield by strong winds sweeping across the barren ground that was marginal to the glaciers

once covering northern North America and Europe.

Sand Dunes

A characteristic result of the work of the wind in arid lands is the sand dune. More misconception than understanding surrounds these intriguing features. For one thing they are by no means limited to deserts. Many of the larger and more renowned of the world's dunes are along shorelines, such as those on the shore of Lake Michigan, the length of Cape Cod, and the coast of Somalia. Dunes also border the sandy plains of some large rivers—the Volga is an outstanding example.

Few deserts are completely sand-covered. Most, as we learned earlier, have surfaces of stripped, planed-off bedrock, or else are protected with a carapace of stones, each touching the other, the so-called desert pavement (Fig. 12-12).

Nevertheless, there are sandy areas in almost all deserts; the south-central part of Arabia and the western part of the Sahara are among the better known. Broad areas in the Sahara which are covered with sand dunes are called *ergs,* and this curious name is now used rather generally for similar sand seas elsewhere (Fig. 12-14).

Sand dunes, whether coastal or desert, share many characteristics. Since they normally consist dominantly of sand-sized grains they are a testimony to the extraordinary sorting ability of the wind. Finer material such as silt may be blown far away, while coarse rock fragments, such as pebbles and gravel, may lag behind the sand which has been moved some intermediate distance. To a statement as simplified as this widely traveled geologists will recall scores of exceptions. Perhaps among the more striking departures from the norm are dunes made of clay flakes alone. These very often are found on the downwind side of clay playas whose surface, when dry, dusts up readily before the wind.

Dunes are neither stable nor permanent fea-

FIG. 12-13 *Small ripple marks make intricate patterns on the surface of sand dunes in Death Valley. The wind that formed these ripples blew from the right, but the wind that shaped the dunes in the background, at the right, blew from the left. (Photograph by William Aplin.)*

FIG. 12-14 *Great sand seas called ergs, shown here in eastern Rub' al-Khali, are typical of the desert of Arabia, as well as parts of the Sahara and other deserts of the world. In the foreground is the camp of a self-sufficient geophysical party exploring for petroleum. (Courtesy of Aramco.)*

tures of the landscape, but may be continuously on the march. Sand drifted or saltated by the wind streams over the gentler upwind slope of a sand dune. When it reaches the crest it may be carried a short distance over it—the tops of dunes when the sand is driving across them sometimes seem to be smoking. Behind the crest the sand drops out of the wind stream, much like flakes of snow, to accumulate on a steeper slope, the *slip face*. With dry, well-sorted sand, the inclination of the slip face may be as much as 34°. Should the slope become steeper, the sand becomes unstable and shears

along a slightly gentler plane with the result that a small avalanche of dry sand glides to the base of the dune. When new sand falls on the slip face, the slope steepens once more, and so the process repeats itself again and again. The net result is a transfer of sand from the upwind to the downwind side of the dune with the consequence that the dune slowly migrates, in a sense rolling along over itself, a process resembling the way in which a caterpillar tractor moves along on its own tracks.

Dunes show a fascinating variety of shapes and patterns (Fig. 12-15). Where the wind is

FIG. 12-15 *Long lines of dunes stretch across the Arabian Desert. The dunes are shaped by winds blowing diagonally across the lines. (Courtesy of Arabian American Oil Company.)*

variable in strength and inconstant in direction sand may be heaped up in ever-changing forms, although in most dunes the general rule persists that the downwind slope is steeper than the upwind one.

Where the wind holds more constantly from a single direction, as it may along a sea coast, dunes are likely to have a more persistent geometry. For example, they may be aligned at right angles to the wind in which case they are called *transverse dunes*. These are likely to be quite short and to flourish where an abundant supply of sand is available and where the winds are strong. Typically, many coastal dunes are in this category. Or if dunes are lined up parallel to the prevailing wind they are known as *longitudinal dunes*. These are most likely to

FIG. 12-16 *Crescent-shaped dunes, or barchans, form when there is a nearly constant wind direction, a limited supply of sand, and when wind velocity is not too high. Barchans migrate slowly, and the horns of the crescent point downwind. The beautifully symmetrical dunes pictured here are along the west shore of the Salton Sea, southern California. (Photograph by John S. Shelton.)*

form when the wind blows strongly out of a single quarter, the supply of sand is sparse, and vegetation is virtually absent. These conditions are fulfilled admirably in the remote Great Sandy Desert of Australia. Some of the individual longitudinal dunes there are said to be more than 60 miles long.

A curious and esthetically appealing sand dune is the *barchan* (Fig. 12-16). These are beautifully symmetrical, crescent dunes—sometimes as perfectly proportioned as the crescent moon, symbol of Islam. In a barchan the horns of the crescent point downwind and the steeper slip face lies between them. Barchans, too, need a nearly constant wind direction, and also a wind with not too high a velocity. For these reasons barchans flourish in the trade wind deserts, or in coastal deserts such as the Atacama. Barchans are migratory dunes, as a rule, and may march across the desert landscape at a rate of as much as 50 feet per year. This is done by sand streaming up the gentle upwind slope of the crescent and sliding down the steeper slip face—a procedure typical of most dunes. The chief variation here is that sand swept around the ends of the dune tails off downwind to make the tips of the crescent. As the dune migrates these points continue to pace its progress.

The desert surface between the individual barchans is more likely than not to be barren bedrock, almost completely devoid of sand. The

wind is a remarkably tidy housekeeper, whisk-
ing up the loose sand from the bedrock surface
of the desert between the dunes. Part of the reason seems to be that grains bounce along much
more readily over a bare rock surface than they
do over sand. Sand has a retarding effect on
bouncing grains, and once they strike an accumulation, such as in a dune, their independent
free-roving days temporarily are ended.

THE BASIN AND RANGE PROVINCE
OF THE WESTERN UNITED STATES

We have a broad desert of our own in western America, one well worth studying in its own
right. Geologically it provides us with a superb
sample of a desert environment and, although
it might be more exciting to go to Tombouctou
in the Sahara to study deserts, we can see almost
every desert landform displayed in our own
country. Only within recent years has the desert
become a place to be visited instead of avoided.
Now, for example, motels and swimming pools
flourish where once dust-plumed wagon trains
were targets for the Apache.

The mountainous landscapes of our own
Southwest perhaps are not fully representative
of the great deserts of the world—many of these
are vast empty plains. Our desert possibly has
more relief than most, and the mountain-girt
bolson with a playa in its lowest part is a typical
landform.

This alternation of mountains and basins was
a most bewildering pattern for the pioneers.
Since many of them came from more humid
lands, most knew of the normally effective procedure when lost in well-watered lands, of walk-
ing down a stream valley until one came to a
settlement, a lake, or the sea. In the American
desert such a course of action more times than
not led the wanderer to a barren sink with an
alkali flat in its midst, across which the elusive
mirage shimmered with its false promise of
deliverance.

Lieutenant Colonel John C. Fremont had a
reasonably sharp eye for terrain—especially
when assisted by such redoubtable mountain
men as Kit Carson. Fremont was one of the first
to appreciate that the desert of eastern California, most of Nevada, and western Utah has an
internal rather than external drainage, and a
well-defined mountain rim partially encircling it
—the Sierra Nevada to the west and the Wasatch
to the east. Because of this unique geometry he
coined the term *Great Basin* for the entire region. While the name is far from accurate, it is
wonderfully descriptive and much more pictorial than the geologically more precise name
of Basin and Range Province.

This last name does bring out the point that
the Far West is a more mountainous realm than
many other deserts of the world, and that these
mountains are not linked together in such nearly
continuous chains as the Alps and the Andes.
Rather, the desert mountains rise as nearly separate islands above a sea of their own waste
products.

The diagram (Fig. 12-17) of the characteristic features of the desert landscape, such as the
bajada, pediment, and playa, is modeled on the
typical terrain of the American Southwest. This
is the landscape to be seen at Death Valley and
in the vicinity of Las Vegas, as well as at such
places as Reno and Salt Lake City. These desert
mountains look curiously pale and bleached
from the air, and their slopes, which are barren
of vegetation, are deeply scored by ravines. The
apices of alluvial fans head into every canyon
and their radial streams may join at the base of
the fan into a single trunk stream which leads
to the playa (Fig. 12-7). Time and again this
pattern is repeated for the transcontinental traveler beating his way across the country. He may
wonder at times why this region presents so corrugated an appearance, with isolated, narrow,
nearly parallel mountain ranges alternating with
broad, waste-filled depressions. He may take
comfort in the fact that he is not alone in this

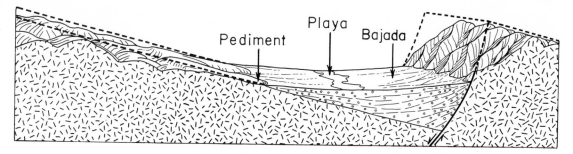

After P. B. King, *The Evolution of North America*, Copyright ©
1959. By permission of Princeton University Press, Princeton,
N.J.

FIG. 12-17 *Diagram showing the characteristic
features of a desert bolson in southwestern
North America, with heavy dashed lines indicating the inferred reconstruction of mountain
blocks prior to erosion.*

wonderment, because geologists have speculated about the origin of these desert mountains
for nearly a century without reaching a definitive answer.

We shall examine the problem of their origin
more thoroughly in the chapter on mountains,
but one of the hypotheses is that they owe their
origin in part to faulting along their margins.
Contributing support to this belief is the frequency of earthquakes in the western desert and
the presence of scarps—many of them tens of
feet high—which have appeared overnight as the
result of displacement on active faults.

Desert Lakes

Whatever its origin, the alternation of mountains and basins of interior drainage in the Far
West makes for unusual drainage patterns as
contrasted to the more familiar terrain of well-
watered regions. Among the many distinctive
features of such a dry and furrowed landscape
are the desert lakes. They owe their existence in
large part to the inability of desert streams to
develop through-flowing courses. Where such
streams are blocked, even though by no more
than the advancing toe of an alluvial fan, their
water is ponded and a lake results. Some of

these, such as Great Salt Lake with a surface
area of about 2,000 square miles, are quite
large. Others are little more than saline ponds.

Almost all desert lakes have the common attribute that their water is brackish or saline to
a greater or less degree. The concentration of
salt in Great Salt Lake ranges from as little as
13 per cent to as much as 27 per cent of the
weight of the water and is roughly four times
greater than in the sea.

Desert lakes are extremely sensitive climatic
indicators. In a dry cycle their water wastes
away through evaporation and the drought-
diminished streams are not able to hold their
own against the loss. The lake level drops and
the shores are bordered by an ever-widening
band of salt. Most famous of such expanses is
the Bonneville Salt Flat adjacent to Great Salt
Lake, the scene of many a determined assault
on land speed records.

Another interesting feature of deserts is the
evidence that they were once the site of far
larger lakes than the shrunken remnants that
survive today. The most redoubtable of these
now vanished inland seas in the United States
was Lake Bonneville. This was the precursor of
present-day Great Salt Lake, and shorelines of
this one-time inland sea now scar the higher
slopes of the Wasatch Mountains up to 1,000
feet above the modern lake. The area flooded
by Lake Bonneville was close to 20,000 square
miles, compared to the 2,000 or so of Great Salt
Lake. During part of its history, Lake Bonneville had an outlet north to the Snake River and
thence to the Pacific by way of the Columbia.

An interesting contemporary of Lake Bonneville was Lake Lahontan, located mostly in western Nevada not far from Reno. Since this is a strongly mountainous area today and all the intervening valleys were filled with long narrow arms of the lake, the terrain pattern in some ways resembled the Norwegian fjords of today. Pyramid, Walker, and Winnemucca lakes are the chief surviving remnants of Lake Lahontan, but both Lahontan and Bonneville left their imprint on the landscape in an impressive array of wave-cut and wave-built landforms. Among these are wonderfully well-preserved beaches, gravel bars, sea cliffs, deltas, and limy tower-like deposits knows as *tufa*. These last are built up underwater by lake-dwelling calcareous algae. In the arid climate of the western states these relics of a more humid time in the immediate geologic past are almost as perfectly preserved as though the lakes were in existence only yesterday. Radio-carbon dates indicate that indeed they were, since their lower levels were

at the sills of caves occupied by human beings who lived there approximately 11,000 years ago.

A remarkable set of ice age lakes briefly was a part of the California landscape in the desert east of the Sierra Nevada. Individually these lakes, far smaller than such giants as Lahontan and Bonneville, were part of a whole system of connected lakes and streams. One series extended north from the site of modern Lake Arrowhead in the San Bernardino Mountains out across one of the driest of North American deserts to Death Valley. This now dessicated depression then held a lake perhaps 120 miles

---

FIG. 12-18 *Old shorelines at Mono Lake, at the eastern base of the central Sierra Nevada, Calif. The level of the lake was highest during the last glacial age, for in nearby areas the old lake and glacial deposits interfinger. (Photograph by John Haddaway.)*

long and nearly 400 feet deep, to which the name Lake Manley is given. This honors the memory of Lewis Manley, a mountain man of tremendous strength and resolution, who saved the first party of pioneers to reach Death Valley. In a period of six weeks he hiked all the way to the coast and back again, and then back to the coast, in order to bring supplies and to lead the survivors out of their trap.

To the west of Death Valley a similar set of lakes and streams led from Mono Lake (Fig. 12-18), at the base of the Sierra Nevada, down the length of Owens Valley to at least the basin of Searles Lake (Fig. 12-19) and possibly on to Death Valley—although this last connection has not been positively demonstrated. At any rate,

FIG. 12-19 *Panamint Mountains and Panamint Valley, eastern California. This valley, like others nearby, held a large lake during the last ice age when precipitation was higher than at present. Lake shorelines can be seen at the base of the mountains and below them are large fan-deltas built out into the lake. The white materials of the playa are salts concentrated as the lake dessiccated. At nearby Searles Lake, a large chemical plant is based on mining such salts. (Photograph by Roland von Huene.)*

Searles Lake acted as a gigantic chemical processing plant, concentrating an enormous tonnage of dissolved material which is now being recovered from the dazzlingly white expanse of the saline playa.

The American desert has no monopoly on lakes, past and present, as they are equally characteristic of other arid regions throughout the world. Among well-known examples are Lake Chad in Africa, Lake Eyre in Australia, and Lop Nor, Lake Balkhash, and the Aral Sea in Central Asia. Not only were the Aral and Caspian seas larger in the recent geologic past than they are today, but they were connected with one another as well as with the Black Sea. Many others, such as the Dead Sea, are rimmed by abandoned shorelines that scar the barren slopes of the bordering desert hills much like gigantic flights of steps.

The obvious recency of these expanded lakes, coupled with the fact that their shorelines in a few favored locations, such as the flanks of the Wasatch and the Sierra Nevada, actually cut glacial moraines, leads many geologists to conclude that the last high stand of the lake coincided with the time of ice advance. The meltwater increase appears also to have been the cause of lake expansion, and as the glaciers of the world receded to their present diminished extent, the level of the desert lakes of North America fell. Many of them vanished almost entirely, leaving a barren expanse of salt or shrunken alkaline ponds as relics of what once was an inland sea.

Arid Erosion

In Chapter XI we discussed how streams widen their valleys, and how many geologists believe that through combinations of downwasting and slope retreat a hilly or mountainous land may waste away until all that remains is a broad and featureless stripped plain nearly at sea level. Such a product of long-continued degradation, as we learned, is called a peneplain.

Do peneplains form in deserts? At the moment the answer appears to be that no one really knows. There are many reasons for this ignorance. Among them is the fact that scientific investigation of deserts is a very recent activity.

Almost all our experience with various kinds of erosion, with the operation of geologic processes, and with inferences as to their relative efficiency are derived from western Europe and the eastern United States. Both these regions have abundant precipitation with much of it falling as summer rain. Both as a rule have through-flowing streams, a nearly continuous mantle of vegetation, deep soil, and well-rounded hill slopes.

Yet the perplexing question remains with us that most of the landforms in deserts appear to have been shaped by running water, rather than, for example, by the wind.

The answer, at least in part, may be that much of what we see in a modern desert is in a sense a fossil landscape. A great deal of it may have been shaped by running water at a time when precipitation was greater than it is today. This is shown by the shorelines and other lake features which are (1) survivals of another climatic regime, and (2) preserved so well in a dry climate that they are an integral part of the present-day landscape.

Obviously this cannot be the sole explanation, because as we learned earlier it is a rare desert in which no rain ever falls. How effectively the resulting run-off erodes when compared to an equivalent amount in a humid region is debatable. Some believe more, some less, but all agree that some erosion does result. The truth is that far too little is known because we have so short a base line of experience from which to extrapolate with regard to the rates of erosive processes in deserts, or even relative efficacy of stream and wind abrasion.

Admitting, then, that stream erosion does operate in arid regions, it faces the peculiar limitation that many of the streams fail to reach the sea, and as a consequence of the resulting pattern of interior drainage the base level in each bolson rises. This is because debris washed down from the encircling hills has nowhere else to go and thus accumulates in the basin at the foot of the desert mountain range.

Streams which scar the flanks of these bordering hills are not idle either, and by eroding headward the more vigorous may succeed in cutting through a watershed separating two basins. Should this occur, the higher of the two troughs is very likely to be captured and the central playa as well as the tributary streams of the higher basin will then be diverted to the lower basin. Should this process of headward growth and capture continue long enough, then much of a desert region may have its drainage integrated and instead of having a multiple base level, with as many base levels as there are independent basins, the whole region will be tributary to the basin whose floor is at the lowest altitude.

This line of argument, although actually untested, seems reasonable enough for the early stages in the evolution of deserts with a ridge and basin topography resembling that of the Far West. How the level of an entire desert region is lowered, and how it can be reduced to a nearly level plain, such as the broad expanses in the interior of Australia, are unanswered problems.

One of the questions at issue here is one that was raised earlier, and that is the possibility that some arid plains may have been shaped under a climatic regimen which is no longer operable. A time of greater rainfall and less local evaporation might be such a possibility. At any rate a leading modern view holds that many of these broad, stripped bedrock plains in the desert are the consequence of the gradual encroachment of pediments into the mountainous terrain at their heads. That is, as the pediments expand, the mountains are consumed and ultimately disappear. But in the final analysis the process of desert plain formation remains a

mystery. So many are of such vast extent and the means available for their cutting seem so inadequate.

Suggested References

Bagnold, R. A., 1942, The physics of blown sand and desert dunes, Wm. Morrow and Co., New York.

Berkey, C. P., and Morris, F. K., 1927, Geology of Mongolia, Amer. Mus. of Natural History, New York.

Bryan, Kirk, 1922, Erosion and sedimentation in the Papago Country, Arizona, U. S. Geol. Survey, Bull. 730.

Cooper, W. S., 1958, Coastal sand dunes of Oregon and Washington, Geol. Soc. Amer., Memoir 72.

Cotton, C. A., 1942, Climatic accidents, Whitcombe and Tombs, Ltd., Wellington, N. Z.

Davis, W. M., 1938, Sheetfloods and streamfloods, Geol. Soc. Amer., Bull., v. 49, p. 1337-1416.

Gautier, E. F., 1935, Sahara; the great desert, Columbia Univ. Press, New York.

Jaeger, E. C., 1948, The California deserts, Stanford Univ. Press, Stanford, Calif.

King, L. C., 1962, Morphology of the earth, Oliver and Boyd, Edinburgh and London.

Leopold, A. S., and the Editors of Life, 1962, The desert, Time, Inc., New York.

Lobeck, A. K., 1939, Geomorphology, McGraw-Hill Book Co., Inc., New York.

McGee, W. J., 1897, Sheetflood erosion, Geol. Soc. Amer., Bull., v. 8, p. 86-112.

Rich, J. L., 1938, Origin and evolution of rock fans and pediments, Geol. Soc. Amer., Bull., v. 46, p. 999-1024.

Tator, B. A., 1952, 1953, Pediment characteristics and terminology, Assoc. Amer. Geographers, Annals, v. 42, Pt. I, p. 293-317; v. 43, Pt. II, p. 47-53.

Thomas, H. E., 1962, The meteorologic phenomena of drought in the Southwest, U. S. Geol. Survey, Prof. Paper 372-A.

Tuan, Yi-Fu, 1959, Pediments in southeastern Arizona, Univ. of Calif. Publ. in Geography, v. 13, p. 1-163.

White, G. F., and others, 1956, The future of arid lands, Amer. Assoc. Adv. Science, Publ. 43, Washington, D. C.

Yosemite Valley, Sierra Nevada, California. (Photograph by Ansel Adams.)

XIII

Glaciation

Scenically, the world is more indebted to glaciation than to any other process of erosion. Without glaciation there would be few of the serrated peaks standing in isolated splendor along the crest of many of the world's lofty mountain ranges. Such a resplendent peak as the Matterhorn is an example, so familiar through endless repetition in calendars and travel posters as to verge on the trite until it is seen shining forth in reality.

Steepening of slopes in the summit regions of the Alps, the northern Rockies, Alaska, and the Sierra Nevada is but a single aspect of glaciation. The fact that a glacier can erode more deeply in some parts of its channel, less deeply in others, is responsible for the multitude of lakes that add such interest to the landscape of the north-central states and to Scandinavia. Deep valleys whose outlines have been sharpened by the glacial file—such as Yosemite Valley, the Lauterbrunnenthal of Switzerland, and the Norwegian fjords—are sufficiently spectacular to support large and flourishing tourist industries. These and many other testimonials to the effectiveness as well as the uniqueness of the glacial processes are widespread throughout the northern countries of the world.

No wonder many of the evidences of past glaciation attracted the attention of observant men in Europe and New England in centuries past. The lavish supply of boulders in the farms of New England was a source not only of wonderment to the early settlers but also of wearisome, backbreaking toil. So much labor was involved in clearing fields strewn with glacially transported stones that more than one young man was readily convinced that a life at sea could be no harsher—even on a New Bedford whaler.

For many, the presence of these stranger-stones found far from their place of origin and very often completely out of harmony with their new environment—for example, granite blocks resting on a limestone terrain—was adequately explained as the work of that "vindictive affliction," the Great Flood of Noah.

In Great Britain, much of which was covered by only recently vanished glaciers, the unstratified, widely scattered glacial detritus was called the *drift,* a name betraying the belief that it originated as a deposit spread far and wide by an all-encompassing sea. In England there has been a tendency to assign a leading role to the sea as an agent shaping the surface of the Earth. This is not surprising in view of England's insular position and the strength of the currents and waves that batter its coast. Some even accepted the idea that icebergs and ice floes may have transported these *erratics,* as such out-of-place rocks are called, for British whalers working off the coast of Greenland had seen such debris embedded in sea ice there, as had explorers elsewhere in the arctic.

Persuading English geologists that it was glaciers which had scoured the inland surface and transported rocks the size of small houses for scores of miles was a difficult task, for there were no existing glaciers to serve as models.

Therefore, it is not surprising that the most eloquent advocates of the notion that ice could perform prodigies of work in shaping mountains and excavating valleys were Swiss. There are about 2,000 glaciers in the Alps, and through the centuries their snouts have advanced or retreated, and alpine passes have been alternately ice-free or ice-blocked. Some villages, occupied in medieval times, are now buried by ice. The silver mine of Argentiere, active in the Middle Ages, is now covered by a glacier of Mont Blanc near Chamonix in alpine France.

Many alpine villagers must have been aware that when a glacier receded it left behind it a trail of barren, stony ground, interrupted by low, rocky ridges, diversified by lakes and ponds, and strewn freely with rock fragments, large and small.

One of the first clearly stated opinions that glaciers were more widespread in the past than they are today was made in 1821 by a Swiss civil engineer, Ignaz Venetz. At first he thought that glaciers had been more extensive only in the Alps, but by 1829 he concluded that they may have advanced across the northern European plain also. An associate of Venetz's, Jean de Charpentier, was skeptical, but after a field trip he, too, became convinced and wrote a paper in 1834 supporting his belief in the existence of a formerly greater expanse of ice.

This aroused the curiosity of one of the leading Swiss naturalists of the day, Louis Agassiz, and he persuaded his friend Charpentier to take him on an expedition in the Alps. Agassiz became a believer, and when in 1837 he came to America and to a professorship at Harvard, he spread the word far and wide of a "Great Ice Age" that had once refrigerated most of the Northern Hemisphere (Fig. 13-1).

A concept as novel as this aroused opposition, for some accepted the far more labored explanation that (1) the land sank, (2) the sea spread inland and boulders and other detritus were rafted by icebergs far and wide across its waters, and (3) the land rose, thus shedding

FIG. 13-1 *Extent of Pleistocene glaciation (white) in the Northern Hemisphere.*

its oceanic waters that left behind a residue of rocks and boulders scattered over the landscape.

Although Agassiz deserves full honor for carrying the word from Europe to America, as we have seen, he was not the first to believe that glaciers had once advanced across the European landscape. This problem of discovering who had the original idea is one of the manifold difficulties confronting the historian of science.

So it was with the glacial theory. A number of remarkably perceptive men had glimpsed the truth, and then were almost immediately forgotten—much the same fate as that of the patient monk, Gregor Mendel, with his pioneer discoveries in genetics. Among the trail breakers for the glacial hypothesis were two Scotsmen, James Hutton and his disciple John Playfair—whom we already encountered in Chapter XI through his early recognition of the basic principles of stream erosion. In 1802, Hutton and Playfair, through reading an account by the indefatigable alpine explorer, Benedict de Saussure, of the presence of erratic boulders on the uplands of the Jura Mountains, 50 miles from their source, recognized them for what they were—glacially transported rocks (Flint, 1957). This was a truly remarkable insight, because in Great Britain there were no accessible existing glaciers with which to make a comparison.

In Germany a professor of forestry, Bernhardi, employing the same reasoning, in 1832 wrote a paper stating his belief that the moraines and erratics that are significant terrain elements of the northern plain were evidence that glaciers had advanced southward from lands far to the north. He suffered the familiar fate of a prophet in his own country in that few people paid the slightest attention to him. Not until 1875 did the last German scientists accept the singular idea that their homeland had once been overridden by a sheet of ice.

Forward steps in science very often are the work of many men, rather than the brilliant inspiration of a single genius. Given a similar environment, or similar evidence, different people working quite independently of one another may come to the same general conclusion. The virtually simultaneous announcement of a mechanism of evolution by Darwin and Wallace is a classic example.

Little more than a century has elapsed since the glacial hypothesis won general acceptance in North America and Europe. An enormous amount of effort has been expended, chiefly in the last half-century, in the study of past and present glaciers. Today we know vastly more than our predecessors did of the extent of these vanished ice sheets, of the complexity of their major advances and withdrawals (there were at least four and possibly five), and something of the change of snow to ice and of the mechanics of glacier motion. Of the greatest mystery of all, the cause of the short-lived glaciation from which the world has been freed only since the beginning of historic time, little more is known than was a century ago. The riddle of glaciation is as challenging and inscrutable as many of the other more widely publicized problems of our day, such as the origin of the solar system or the mysteries of space.

DEVELOPMENT OF GLACIERS

Extent and Distribution

Glaciers were vastly more important in the very recent geologic past than they are today, but even today their extent is not insignificant. Almost all of Antarctica is ice covered, 5,000,-000 square miles or so, an area about equal to the United States and Mexico. The Greenland ice cap is much smaller, approximately 700,000 square miles, but like the Antarctic ice cap its surface rises to a surprisingly high altitude—around 10,000 feet, and the ice is more than 10,000 feet thick in places. This load of ice has succeeded in depressing the interior of the island below sea level. Thus, were the ice suddenly to be removed, Greenland would be a ring of islands enclosing a central sea.

A reasonable estimate of the frozen water piled up on land in glaciers and snow is that a land area of about 6,000,000 square miles is covered; of this total, around 96 per cent is in Antarctica and Greenland. Were all this frozen water to melt, the level of the sea would rise all over the world between 100 and 200 feet, with a devastating effect on property values in the world's seaports. In fact, the almost world-wide glacial recession that has occurred since the 1890's appears to be raising the sea level at a rate of approximately 4¾ inches per century.

Change of Snow to Ice

Without snow there would be no accumulation of extensive bodies of ice, and without ice there would be no glaciers. Hence glaciers are limited to those parts of the world where the temperature remains below freezing for a significant part of the year. This means that glaciers are active today in high mountains over much of the world, and in the farther reaches of the Northern and Southern Hemispheres. Thus, glaciers on the high upper slopes of such equatorial mountains as Kilimanjaro in Africa, the summits of the Andes in South America, and the Carstenz Toppenz Range in New Guinea are at altitudes of 16,000 to 18,000 feet. In middle latitudes, as in the Sierra Nevada of California and the Swiss Alps, the regional snowline has descended to perhaps 9,000 feet. Finally it reaches sea level in Antarctica (55°S), and stands at roughly 1,500 feet in lands bordering the Arctic Ocean.

More than cold temperature is needed for snow to accumulate and remain from year to year. There needs to be heavy snowfall as well. This explains the absence of permanent snow on Mount Whitney (14,495 feet) whose summit rises above what should be the theoretical regional snowline. The mountain is in a dry region with a high evaporation rate and generally high summer temperatures. Many of the arctic lands lack a permanent snow cover because, although they are cold, they are also dry.

The local environment also plays a significant role. Since north-facing slopes in the Northern Hemisphere are shadier than south-facing ones, their snowline is lower. In many American mountain ranges the western side may be the windward slope, as it is for the Sierra Nevada and the Cascades. On that slope the precipitation is greater, cloud cover is more persistent, and snowline commonly is lower than on the eastern side.

The next problem to consider is the relationship of snow to ice. Snow, strictly speaking, is not frozen water, as ice is, but is frozen water vapor. In other words, it is the solid phase of water that has crystallized directly from water vapor in the atmosphere. Since it is a crystalline substance, snowflakes grow in regular geometric patterns, as everyone knows from seeing photographs in books and designs on Christmas cards. Although they seem to show an infinite variety, it probably is not strictly true that no two are ever alike. Actually, crystalline H_2O behaves like other mineral crystals in that there is an established crystal form for the compound. In snowflakes it is some variant of the

hexagonal system—the same system of which quartz is a member.

When snowflakes settle to the ground, the individual crystals quickly interlock, and a dry, powdery, but surprisingly tough surface develops. The specific gravity of snow is much less than that of water, so that on the metric scale a centimeter of snow may be equal to a millimeter of rain water.

After snowflakes lie on the ground for a short while they ordinarily undergo a change. Individual flakes may sublime, or they may melt. But since the water freed by melting is in the presence of a large mass of ice, it may refreeze into granules of ice. This gritty, granular snow, with a texture much like coarse sand, is a familiar phenomenon in snow banks that survive for a fair share of the winter behind a building, in the shade of a forest, or in the lee of a cliff. Such granular recrystallized snow is called *firn* (from a German adjective meaning of last year) in the German-speaking parts of Switzerland. *Névé* (a word going back to the Latin stem of *nix* for snow) is used in French-speaking areas. Both are used in articles in English.

Firn, which typically accumulates on the upper slopes of alpine mountains, goes through a gradual transition into glacier ice. Firn is usually white or grayish white, and the spaces between the grains of ice are filled with trapped air. At a depth equivalent perhaps to an accumulation of three to five years of firn, the pore spaces become smaller, or even may be lacking, and the transition into blue glacier ice is completed. This is accompanied by an increase in the specific gravity from perhaps 0.1 in newly fallen snow up to 0.9 in solid ice.

The change from firn to ice is aided by the increase in pressure with depth. This brings the individual ice grains into closer contact with one another, and thus reduces the amount of air space. At the same time the individual ice grains are undergoing a process analogous to recrystallization. Glacier ice, then, is a mosaic of interlocking ice crystals. In general, as the ice descends from the firn field at the head of a glacier down to the terminus, the ice becomes denser as more and more air is excluded and the ice crystals increase in size. Finally, they may reach such imposing diameters as 3 to 4 inches.

Mechanism of Glacier Movement

Although the downslope motion of alpine glaciers has been known to scientists for nearly 150 years, we are still far from understanding its true nature. How is it that a solid substance, such as ice, can be said to flow, especially such a brittle solid as ice appears to be, judging from our own household experiences?

The problem is a perplexing one, for the surfaces of many glaciers are scored by cracks and fissures, known as *crevasses* (Fig. 13-2). As everyone is aware, fluids cannot fracture; whatever the mechanism of glacier advance may be, these bodies of ice do not move in the same way that the water does in a stream. When we speak of a river of ice, this is indeed using the language of metaphor. Yet to some degree there is an analogy between glacier and stream flow. We saw in Chapter XI that in a normal stream channel the central part of a river has a higher velocity than its margins. This is true also of glaciers.

There are no hard and fast values for rates of glacier advance. Different ones move at different rates, and within a single glacier different parts may have a range of velocities. Glaciers move with ponderous majesty. The Great Aletsch (Switzerland's largest) advances around 20 inches a day near the middle section and about 10 inches per day about a mile upstream from the terminus. The Rhone glacier moves at the rate of approximately 300 feet per year.

FIG. 13-2 *Crevasses in glacier ice, forming where the surface of the glacier steepens abruptly over a bedrock irregularity. Blue Glacier, Mount Olympus, Wash. (Photograph by Tom Ross.)*

FIG. 13-3 *A continental ice sheet with glaciers reaching the sea. Inglefieldland, northwest Greenland. (Courtesy of Geodetic Institute, Copenhagen.)*

This is slow when compared with Greenland ice that makes its way from the central ice cap down through a narrow fjord to the sea at the rate of 80 feet per day, or 5 miles per year (Kuenen, 1955).

Before discussing the actual mechanics of glacier motion, we might consider how it is that the ice may be advancing at rates such as these, and yet have the lower end remain stationary or, as in many glaciers, be receding. The position of the glacier terminus represents an uneasy equilibrium between the rate of ice advance and the rate of melting. The glacier continually moves ice forward to the point where the rate of melt-

ing triumphs. Or we might compare a glacier to a side of bacon being fed into a slicer. Although the bacon is continuously being shoved forward it never advances beyond a fixed point because it is always being cut off by the oscillating blade.

To return to the way in which ice moves, it obviously does not flow as a liquid does. The crevasses, or surface cracks, rule that possibility out. However, in another respect much resembling a liquid, a glacier does essentially take the shape of its container—in this case the configuration given it by the walls of the enclosing valley. Also, in very nearly the same fashion as a stream, the center of a glacier advances more rapidly than the sides, and presumably the surface moves more speedily than layers near the bottom.

Although far from being demonstrated with certainty, some of the flow that occurs in glaciers appears to be the sort that is characterized as *plastic*. This type of deformation is familiar in solid substances such as lead or aluminum when they are extruded as bars or rods. When such a solid is reshaped it does not spring back to its original, or nearly original, position once the stress is removed, as it would if the deformation had been elastic.

Water, as we have seen, differs from most other substances in that it expands upon freezing—actually by about 9 per cent. Pressure lowers the melting point of ice within a glacier, and the tendency is for ice to convert to water, which is more dense—in other words, it takes up less space. The chilled water, just freed, if it moves into an area of slightly reduced pressure, refreezes again. This whole process of freezing, unfreezing, and refreezing serves to provide by itself a measure of instability lacking in more orthodox solids.

Ice crystals themselves have a measure of built-in instability, too. They yield under pressure, and if the crystals are oriented properly this is easily accomplished. Ice is especially susceptible to slippage along planes parallel to the base of the typical hexagonal crystal. When enough of these are lined up, out of the millions present within a glacier, then a readjustment can occur through crystal gliding—a process akin to the multiple cleavage of minerals within a rock—and the whole solid substance makes a slight movement downslope. The cumulative effect of these individual slippages is enough partially to explain the downslope advance of the glacier as a series of minute readjustments under stress.

Another variety of glacial motion is actual slippage of the ice mass over the floor and margins of its trough. This mechanical sliding of the ice over its own bed is responsible for some of the familiar yet tremendously impressive end products of glaciation—grooves or scratches in the bedrock known as *striations* (Fig. 13-4), and broad expanses of smoothed, barren rock called *glacier polish* (Fig. 13-5). These phenomena nullify the belief held by some that the

FIG. 13-4 *Glacial grooves cut in crystalline bedrock, Val Camonica, southern Alps. The polished rocks here lay along the ancient amber trade route, and are inscribed with prehistoric figures and symbols.*

FIG. 13-5 *Glacial polish and striations on igneous rocks in the Sierra Nevada, Calif.* (*Photograph by Philip Hyde.*)

basal skin of a glacier does not move but is frozen tight to its foundation and that all the movement is within the layers of ice.

There is strong evidence that some motion of the ice, especially near the lower end of the glacier, is by shearing. This is displacement by fracture rather than by flow, and in some respects can be compared to the development of thrust faults in rocks of the Earth's crust. When such shear planes are visible in the side of a glacier near its terminus, they can be seen curving upward in crescentic sheets. How large a percentage these shears contribute to the total glacial advance is hard to say. Probably it is rather slight, and very likely is less than the effective flowage achieved within the glacier by melting and recrystallization under stress and by crystal gliding.

ALPINE GLACIATION

Although individual glaciers and ice fields are tremendously diverse, they can be placed in two broad categories: *alpine glaciers* and *continental glaciers*. Alpine glaciers typically are mountain glaciers that have their origin on mountain slopes and summits that rise above snowline. They advance downslope under the urging of gravity, and more often than not take the path of least resistance by following a pre-existing stream valley (Fig. 13-6).

Continental glaciers were much more important in the very recent geologic past than they are today. Then, North America as far south as the Ohio and Missouri rivers was buried under at least a mile-deep burden of ice, as was most of northern Europe (Fig. 13-1). Fortunately, such vast expanses of frozen water are gone, and the surviving relics, such as the Greenland and Antarctic ice caps, although of tremendous extent, are greatly subordinate to these vanished titans. Continental glaciers override the terrain and subdue many of the irregularities they encounter. Alpine glaciers are more likely to accentuate irregularities in the landscape, making bold peaks even more jagged and steepening the walls of already deep canyons.

Although alpine glaciers are conspicuous elements of the world's snow-capped mountain ranges, they, too, are much smaller than they were in the Pleistocene. Then, they advanced northward far beyond the foothills of the Alps onto the lowlands near Munich and southward into the low hills marginal to the Po Valley of Italy. Reduced though they may be, some of the surviving alpine glaciers are impressively large. Several of the Himalayan ice streams are 25 miles long, and the Great Aletsch in Switzerland has a length of 14 miles. The Seward gla-

cier in Alaska with its tributaries has a total length approaching 50 miles.

Glacial Erosion

There appear to be two leading ways in which alpine glaciers shape the land surface upon which they rest: *glacial quarrying* and *glacial abrasion*. In the first of these, rocks are sprung or pried out of place in much the same way they are in a commercial rock quarry, except, of course, at a far slower rate. In abrasion, the rock surface on which the ice rests is scoured or worn down in about the same way a wooden surface may be sandpapered. In general, quarrying seems to be most effective at the upper end of a glacier, essentially in the catchment area, while the effectiveness of abrasion is greater downstream.

FIG. 13-6 *An alpine-type glacier, showing the junction of tributaries. The glacial system occupies pre-existing stream valleys. Klinaklini Gla-* cier, Coast Ranges, British Columbia, Canada. (*Photograph by Austin S. Post, University of Washington.*)

Glacial Quarrying

The way in which this process operates is not completely understood. This is scarcely surprising because it is a process that takes place beneath the glacial ice in an environment inaccessible to us by any ordinary means.

The nearest access we have to this frigid, subglacial world is by crevasses that start at the surface and extend down through the ice to the bottom of the glacier. Such deeply penetrating fractures are rare, but are reasonably common in the catchment basin at the headward end of the glacier. A characteristically crescent-shaped crevasse at the head of a glacier is called a *bergschrund* (Fig. 13-7). As a rule it stands close to the boundary between the glacial ice which has started to move downslope and the stationary ice and firn frozen to the rocks at the upper end of the glacier.

In 1899 in the Sierra Nevada of California one of the leading topographers of that day, W. D. Johnson, had himself lowered on a line to a depth of 150 feet in such a bergschrund— certainly no venture for the faint-hearted—and what he saw there greatly impressed him. This was the ability of glacial ice to pry strongly jointed rocks loose from their foundations. Others have repeated such a descent, and many glaciologists have emerged equally convinced that the upper end of a glacier is a zone of active frost-riving.

The bergschrund and other crevasses provide an avenue by which meltwater supplied by melting of snow, névé, and surface layers of ice streams down into the inner recesses of the glacier. If such meltwater penetrates to the rocky headwall, or to the glacier floor, it percolates into cracks and joints of the bedrock. Then, when the water freezes it expands and, upon expanding, as we learned in Chapter X, it exerts a tremendous leverage against the enclosing rocks, which may then be pried loose.

Should these rocks be frozen into the glacier they are carried along with the glacial ice as it moves downslope, and a new surface is bared

FIG. 13-7 *The headwall of Palisade Glacier, in the Sierra Nevada, Calif., showing the well-developed bergschrund.* (*Photograph by Tom Ross.*)

FIG. 13-8 *Glacial polish formed on granitic rocks of the Sierra Nevada, Calif. (Photograph by Philip Hyde.)*

for the process to be repeated. The more that glacial meltwater freezes in these subglacial rock joints, the more effective the process of rock quarrying will be.

Differences of opinion center around whether or not any thawing takes place in the ice which is locked up in these crevasses in the rocks. Should freezing and thawing occur repeatedly, then a potent force is at hand to sunder the rocks as compared to what would occur were it to happen but once. According to many observers a considerable amount of melting does take place within and on the glacier surface. Anyone who has walked on a glacier on a windy day, or on a warm sunny day, will recall that a great amount of water is on the glacier surface, streams are everywhere, and water can be heard gurgling and roaring deep within the glacier's interior. Much of the surface meltwater makes its way down through crevasses, cracks, and other openings, large and small, all the way to the bottom. At night, when the air temperature drops below 32°F., the streams dwindle away and the sound of running water is stilled.

Glacial Abrasion

Rocks ranging from blocks the size of box-cars down to fragments of flour-like dimensions, are embedded in the ice as the result of glacial quarrying and mass wasting from higher slopes. These are dragged along with the glacier as it moves downslope.

This entrained rocky debris acts as an abrasive, much like the sand grains on a piece of sandpaper. Where the embedded rock fragments are large, they gouge out long grooves and scratches in the bedrock. Where the included rock fragments are fine-grained, they may polish the surface of the overridden rocks, much like the fine emery powder a lapidarist uses. Visitors to the higher parts of Yosemite National Park are impressed by the broad expanses of smoothly polished, shining granite, as fresh looking as though it had been given its bright sheen only yesterday (Fig. 13-8).

The process of abrasion works both ways, for the bedrock and the abrasive are both affected. Many of the fragments embedded in the ice develop scratches on their surfaces, or one side of a boulder may be worn away until it is flat and smooth. Such a rock is said to be *faceted,* and several such flat surfaces may be planed off if the rock shifts its position within the ice as the glacier moves along. This selective abrasion results in the production of angular rock fragments (Fig. 13-9) with a markedly different shape from those rounded by running water in streams.

As the debris-laden ice grinds away the surface over which it moves, it smooths most irregularities, so that a typically ice-abraded landscape consists of rounded-off rock knobs, and the lower ends of spurs and ridges are blunted or even worn away. Valleys are deepened, made more linear, and in the most striking examples

FIG. 13-9 *Glacial debris, showing typical faceted boulders and the large range in size of material. Sierra Nevada, Calif.*

their sides are steepened until they are almost vertical, as in Yosemite or the Lauterbrunnenthal, Switzerland (Fig. 13-10).

Landforms Produced by Glacial Erosion

The two major kinds of glacial erosion produce contrasting results. Quarrying makes for steepened higher slopes, spire-like peaks, and sharp ridge crests. Abrasion is more than likely to yield deep, trough-like, linear valleys, in which many of the exposed rock surfaces are rounded and smoothed off.

Of the features characteristically resulting from glacial quarrying, one of the more impressive is the *cirque* (Fig. 13-11). This is a horseshoe-shaped, steep-walled, glaciated valley head. Cirques are such distinctive landscape elements that there is a name for them in the language of every country in western Europe where they are found. Our ancestors were enough aware of their uniqueness to name them in that remote day when our various native tongues were being contrived. In the French Alps the term cirque is appropriate since it is a French word having the same meaning as the Latin word circus does in English-speaking countries. However, the term is not completely appropriate in this glacial connotation because a true circus is a fully round figure—such as the setting for the Ben-Hur chariot race. Actually, a glaciated valley head is a half-round feature and is more nearly comparable to the traditional form of a Greek theater.

To return to the other names for a cirque: in German-speaking lands it is a *kar;* in Wales, a *cwm;* in Scotland, a *corrie;* and in Scandinavia, a *botn* or a *kjedel.* This brief linguistic excursion also makes clear that geology is a truly international science; no single country has a monopoly on all the names for landforms. In fact, it would be an amazing thing if there were an English name for cirque because they are

not prominent in the originally English-speaking parts of the British Isles.

Cirques result from active plucking or quarrying in the bergschrund zone and throughout the catchment basin at the head of a glacier, probably as the result of the downward percolation of water and as a result of the frost-riving of the rocks in the headwall that towers above the glacier surface.

Should the glacier disappear, as so many of them have since the end of the Pleistocene, then the newly bared cirque is an impressive alpine sight. The rock wall at the upper end of such a titanic box canyon may be a cliff several thousand feet high, and at the same time the base of such a cliff may be nearly free of a long and sloping apron of talus blocks.

FIG. 13-10 *Lauterbrunnen, Switzerland, showing the glaciated valley and waterfalls plunging from hanging valleys. (Courtesy of Trans World Airlines.)*

Scores of clear, often dark blue, rock-basin lakes add immeasurably to the beauty of the alpine scene. These are *tarns* (Fig. 13-11), and many of them result from differential glacial scouring. Unlike a typical stream, a glacier digs deeply in some places and much less so in others. The floor of a glacial trough may consist of closed basins, in which water collects after the ice is gone, and of intervening barren, ice-smoothed ridges. Such an irregular floor, sometimes deep beneath the ice, sometimes shallow, can be excavated so long as there is a forward slope to the surface of the glacier. In the same way, lava flows are able to cross a corrugation of ridges and valleys athwart their path.

When two glaciers are in parallel valleys close to one another, then the divide separating them may become progressively narrowed through over-steepening until it is reduced to little more than a rock screen. To such an ice-sharpened ridge is given the appropriately descriptive name of *cleaver*.

FIG. 13-11 *Glacial cirques and rock-basin lakes (tarns) in the Wind River Mountains, Wyoming. (Photograph by Austin S. Post, University of Washington.)*

If two glaciers are on opposite sides of a divide, the headwalls of their cirques may intersect until only the narrowest sort of rock partition separates the two cirques. The top of such a rock screen may be almost razor-sharp, and commonly is surmounted by jagged pinnacles or spires. Such a septum is called an *arête,* which is an Old French word for fishbone or spine.

If glacial quarrying continues actively, in very little time the arête may be completely stripped away. When this happens, the two glacial troughs intersect, and a steep-sided and sometimes strategically important transmontane

FIG. 13-12 *Lower Aar Glacier, Switzerland, showing a well-developed medial moraine formed by the junction of two tributary glaciers. The ridgelines have been sharpened to arêtes, and a col has been formed (at the head of the right tributary glacier). (Courtesy of Swissair Photo A G.)*

pass may result. Some of the famous alpine passes, such as the St. Bernard, St. Gothard, and Simplon, are of this type, as are several in the summit region of the Rockies and the High Sierra. To such a glacially produced gap in a dividing ridge of a mountain range, the French word *col,* derived from the Latin *collum,* or neck, is often given (Fig. 13-12).

A mountain that rises above its fellows in a range, such as one of the Cascade volcanoes in the northwestern United States, may have glaciers radiating outward from the summit like the spokes in a colossal wheel. Should these glaciers continue to quarry actively at their upper ends, then the mountain may be whittled away by this concerted attack until only a jagged, saw-toothed pinnacle survives. The Matterhorn is the world's most familiar example of such a glacially accentuated peak. Similar occurrences around the world are spoken of as matterhorns (Fig. 13-13).

Down-valley, where abrasion is more likely to be the ruling glacial process, a primary result is the steepening of valley walls. Abrasion is not limited to the bottom of a glacier, but is effective along the sides as well. The part of an alpine valley occupied by a glacier resembles the

channel occupied by a river, but on a far grander scale, because the volume of water in the glacier is far greater and the velocity far less (Fig. 13-14).

The statement is commonly made that such a glacially occupied, ice-scoured valley has a

FIG. 13-13 *Mount Assiniboine, in the Canadian Rocky Mountains, is a typical glacial matterhorn. (Photograph by Austin S. Post, University of Washington.)*

FIG. 13-14 *Lake Tenaya and upper Yosemite Valley, in the Sierra Nevada, Calif. (Photograph by Ansel Adams.)*

U-shaped cross section in contrast to a V-shaped form for a stream valley. In reality, the cross-sectional outline of a glaciated valley more nearly approximates a catenary (a curve produced by a wire or chain hanging from two points, not in the same vertical line). This is the curve seen in the gracefully sweeping loops of the wire between the towers of a transmission

After W. M. Davis, "The Sculpture of Mountains by Glaciers," Scottish Geographical Magazine, vol. 22, 1906. By permission.

FIG. 13-15 *The transformation of a mature mountain landscape by glaciation. Note the development of cirques, cleavers and arêtes, U-shaped valleys, hanging valleys, and faceted spurs.*

line. If the points of suspension are close together, the curve is narrow and the slope is steep; if they are far apart, then the curve is open and the side slopes are gradual.

Among the more photogenic results of alpine glaciation are waterfalls that plunge over the rim of a glaciated valley and cascade in long streamers down the shining walls. Most renowned of these are the Yosemite Falls, which in three stages have a total drop of 2,565 feet. Falls such as this, as well as the Bridal Veil Fall (see p. 318), or the Straubach Falls in Switzerland (Fig. 13-10), are examples of falls that plunge into the main canyon from tributary *hanging valleys.* There are a number of explanations for the origin of these dramatically discordant side streams. A widely accepted view is that the side stream was unable to cut down rapidly enough to keep pace with the main canyon which was being deepened by the glacier.

Other waterfalls which interrupt the floor of a main canyon, such as Vernal and Nevada falls in Yosemite Valley, owe their existence to differential erosion by the ice. As we saw earlier, glaciers are by no means limited to eroding a continuously forward sloping channel, but can scour deeply where rocks are weaker or are closely fractured. The result may be the cutting of a series of cliffs, much like the risers of a gigantic stairway, over which the postglacial stream plunges in a succession of so-called staircase falls. An ice fall, where the glacier descends over a major irregularity in its path, aids the cutting of such a series of cliffs and pools. Where the ice is stretched, as it were, it cracks under this additional tension, and the resulting crevasses provide a channel for meltwater to reach the fractured rocks beneath the glacier. If freezing and thawing occur, quarrying may be effective at an intermediate point in the glacier's length. Such a process may be responsible in part for the so-called *cyclopean steps,* or great cliffs, that in effect are subsidiary cirques interrupting the longitudinal profile of a glacial valley.

Depositional Landforms

Much of the immense quantity of debris carried along by a glacier as it moves down its valley comes to rest when the downstream end, or terminus, is reached. The change from one mode of transport, ice, to another, water, is not achieved without a certain amount of lost motion and delay. The sheer volume of debris brought down by the ice, as well as the size of many fragments, is more than the meltwater streaming away from the glacier can remove—at least not as quickly as it is supplied. Consequently, the lower end of a glacier is nearly always smothered under its own rocky burden. This mass of ice-transported debris may accumulate as a hummocky, crescent-shaped, rocky ridge looped around the glacial snout, the *termi-* *nal moraine* or *end moraine* (from a Provençal French word *morena,* or heap of earth, derived ultimately from the pre-Latin *mourre,* meaning a projection of rock).

The terminal moraine may continue around the end of the glacial lobe until it outlines either side of the glacier. Such debris ridges around the flanks of the glacier are *lateral moraines.* As a rule they are higher and bulkier than terminal moraines and their crests slope forward with about the same inclination as the glacier surface (Fig. 13-16).

FIG. 13-16 *Terminal and lateral moraines and a moraine-dammed lake formed by the recession of the glacier. Mount Jacobson, Coast Ranges, British Columbia, Canada. (Photograph by Austin S. Post, University of Washington.)*

Should two glaciers join, then the lateral moraines that meet at their intersection may unite and continue together down the middle of the ice stream as a dark band of rocky debris known as a *medial moraine*. In fact, there may be as many bands as there are unions of trunk and tributary glaciers, resulting in a wonderfully banded, candy-cane effect of strips of white ice interspersed with darker morainal layers (Figs. 13-17, 13-12).

Downstream from the terminal moraine, the valley may be floored with an accumulation of stream-deposited but glacially supplied debris. This glacially eroded, meltwater-reworked detritus is the *valley train*. Because the streams responsible for the construction of this debris tail are almost all heavily burdened, deposition is rapid and their channels branch and join and branch again in a braided pattern. This same network of braiding channels is typical of the

FIG. 13-17 *Medial moraines formed by the junction of lateral moraines of tributary glaciers. Kaskawulsh Glacier, St. Elias Range, Yukon Territory, Canada. (Photograph by Austin S. Post, University of Washington.)*

streams of alluvial fans, and many of the same controls operate in their formation—a more than plentiful supply of debris, and streams that lose much of their volume through seepage into their own porous deposits.

Blocks of ice may be isolated on the valley train where they have been left behind through unequal retreat of the ice front, or where they may have been rafted by meltwater streams and later buried in the outwash gravels or the moraine itself. When this buried ice ultimately melts, and the covering layer of glacial debris collapses into the resulting cavity, such a depression is called a *kettle hole,* and may range in size from only a few feet across to several

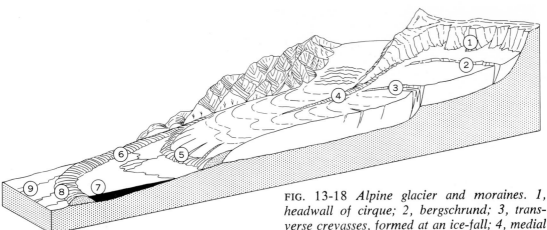

FIG. 13-18 *Alpine glacier and moraines. 1, headwall of cirque; 2, bergschrund; 3, transverse crevasses, formed at an ice-fall; 4, medial moraine; 5, end (recessional) moraine; 6, lateral moraine; 7, moraine-dammed lake; 8, end (terminal) moraine; 9, valley train.*

hundred. In glaciated regions, where there is likely to be a large supply of water available, these kettles appear as a multitude of small lakes dotting the surface of the valley train or even scattered along morainal ridges.

The combination of end moraines and lateral moraines that once looped in a semi-circular festoon around the terminus of a glacier often plays a scenically significant role after the ice has disappeared. These morainal embankments may serve for a time as natural earth-fill dams,

and quite successfully, even though in a sense they are pointed the wrong way. They are concave upstream, instead of being arched convexly against the reservoir as a well-designed dam is (Fig. 13-19). Nonetheless, such mo-

FIG. 13-19 *The system of lateral and terminal moraines and the moraine-dammed lake at Convict Lake, in the Sierra Nevada, Calif. (Photograph by John S. Shelton.)*

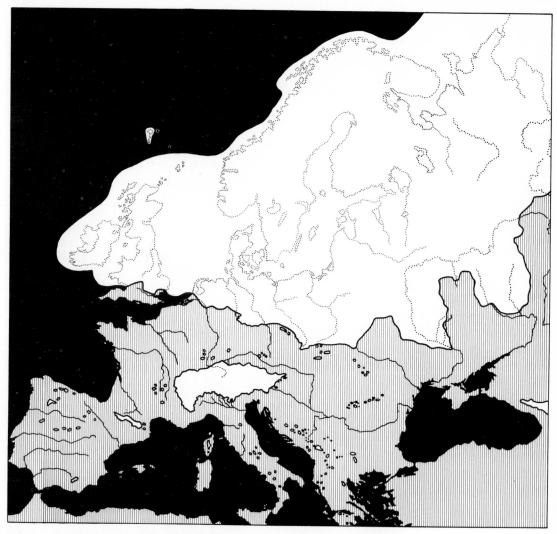

After R. F. Flint, *Glacial and Pleistocene Geology*, 1957. By permission of John Wiley & Sons, Inc.

FIG. 13-20 *The limits of Pleistocene glaciation (white) in Europe.*

rainal dams effectively impound the waters of some of the world's more scenic lakes. The best known probably are those bordering the Alps, such as Como, Maggiore, and Garda on the Italian side and Neuchâtel, Geneva, Luzerne, and Constance on the north. We have such moraine-blocked water bodies, too; Lakes Mary and MacDonald in Glacier National Park are two of the more striking American examples.

CONTINENTAL GLACIATION

Continental glaciers, unlike alpine glaciers, did not move under the impetus of gravity in tongue-like masses through pre-existing valleys countersunk in the flanks of mountain ranges. Instead, during the Pleistocene they sprawled broadly as great, disc-shaped masses of ice covering much of northern Europe and northern North America with a blanket spreading over 18,000,000 to 20,000,000 square miles of the land surface of the Earth (Figs. 13-20, 13-21).

This is a nearly unimaginable spectacle—an

almost 4,000-mile wall of ice extending across the whole width of Canada and far out into the North Atlantic. This frozen tide spread southward into the United States at least roughly to the line of the pendant loop marking the courses of the Ohio and Mississippi rivers today.

To find a partial replica of these vanished *ice sheets* we need to turn to the *ice caps* of Greenland and Antarctica (Figs. 13-22, 13-3). These are much smaller—the Greenland ice cap covers perhaps 700,000 square miles and Antarctica around 5,000,000. Each of these ice caps ends in the sea, so that the large accumulations of glacial debris that play such prominent roles in both the economy and the landscape of Europe and North America are lacking. Another unique feature of Greenland is that much of the ice from the central part of the island moves down through deep, narrow fjords to the sea. There the ice may break off, a process known as *calving,* and drift away as bergs into the sea lanes of the North Atlantic (Fig. 13-23). Such a berg

sank the *Titanic* in 1912 with a loss of 1,489 lives.

Much of the nature and behavior of continental glaciers remains in the realm of speculation. In contrast, alpine glaciers are with us today and can be investigated diligently, often in scenes of mountainous splendor. In North America most of the major centers of accumulation and dispersal of the ice sheets were in relatively remote regions, and then, too, the glaciers themselves are long gone. We can only reconstruct the event in our imagination. The generating centers for much of the North American ice appear to have been the Labrador Peninsula, the country west of Hudson Bay, and the islands north of the Canadian mainland. Ice from these various centers coalesced into one enormous inland sea of frozen water to

FIG. 13-21 *The limits of Pleistocene glaciation (white) in North America.*

After "Glacial Map of North America," 1949. By permission of Geological Society of America.

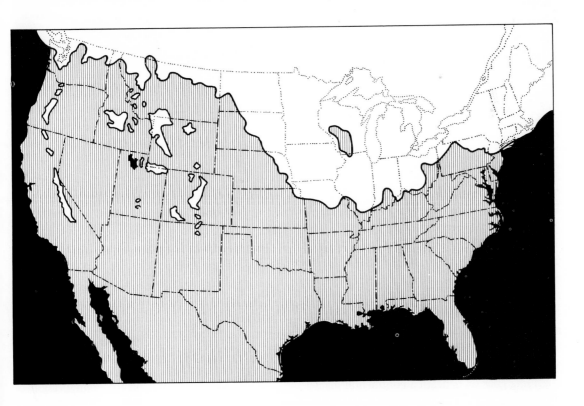

FIG. 13-22 *An ice cap and valley glaciers, at Evighedsfjord, west Greenland. (Courtesy of Geodetic Institute, Copenhagen.)*

make up the so-called Laurentide ice sheet. In Europe the ice sheets spread outward from the backbone of the Scandinavian Peninsula, and to a lesser degree from Britain and Ireland, until they traveled south beyond the present-day positions of Warsaw and Kiev and almost to the gates of Volgograd.

There are resemblances between the two major kinds of glaciers, alpine and continental, but there are significant differences, too. Chief among the differences is the fact that less quarrying goes on beneath a continental glacier,

at least when its thickness may be as much as a mile. Meltwater is not likely to penetrate a mile of ice in order to freeze and thaw and refreeze in the fractured bedrock far below. Since crevasses cannot extend to such profound depths, either, continental glaciers shape much of the land by abrasion. Near the margins, or where the ice has thinned sufficiently, quarrying may occur and in fact may be quantitatively several times greater in importance than abrasion. This is demonstrated by rock knobs and ridges in New England which have had much more granite plucked off their downstream slopes than has been abraded away from their upstream sides (Jahns, 1943).

How effective glacial abrasion may be is debatable. Much depends on the configuration of the ground over which the ice advances. There is a strong tendency for an ice sheet to scour deeply in a valley whose course approximately parallels the moving glacier and to fill with debris valleys whose trend is more nearly at right angles to the moving ice.

Hills and mountains overridden by ice are more likely to have their crests and ridges rounded off than to have them surmounted by spires, castellated divides, and matterhorns. Mountains of surprising height have been buried beneath the ice of continental glaciers. Among these in northeastern United States are the Catskills (4,200 feet), the Adirondacks (5,300 feet), and the Presidential Range of New England whose highest point is Mt. Washington with an altitude of 6,288 feet (Flint, 1957).

Glacial Landforms

The landforms produced by continental glaciation are complex, and since we are considering an area embracing almost all of northern Europe and northern North America, it is scarcely surprising that we are confronted by a great diversification of landscapes. In a simplified classification, a basic distinction is made between glacial landforms that primarily are the result of deposition and those that chiefly are the result of erosion. A further distinction is made between landforms produced under the ice and those that originated in an environment immediately adjacent to the glacier.

FIG. 13-23 *A birthplace of icebergs. Storströmmen, east Greenland. (Courtesy of Geodetic Institute, Copenhagen.)*

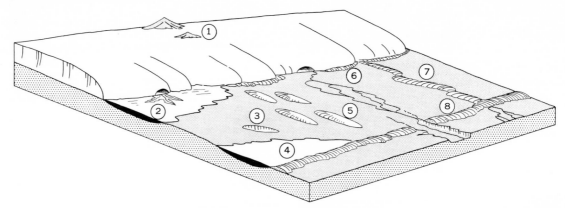

FIG. 13-24 *Continental glacial landforms. The fine stipple pattern in front of the glacial margin indicates the nearly flat surface of the outwash plain. Other features are: 1, nunatak; 2, ice marginal lake; 3, kettle; 4, moraine-dammed lake; 5, drumlins; 6, end (recessional) moraine; 7, esker; 8, end (terminal) moraine.*

The diagram (Fig. 13-24) shows two of the leading elements of landscapes of glaciated regions belonging to the outside-of-the-glacier category. These are the *outwash plain* and the *end moraine.* The outwash plain is about the same as a valley train, except that it is many times broader and may cover a large area instead of being confined to a single valley.

Outwash plains were spread widely as sheets of water-laid but glacially derived sediment. They are among the more level and featureless plains of the earth because the material beneath the plains has been graded and regraded endlessly by ever-shifting streams. Because this material is so fresh, so uniformly textured, and in the main so fine-grained, it makes fertile soil. Much of the better farm land in the Middle West has this origin, and on a hot, firefly-spangled midsummer's eve it strains credulity to believe that an ice sheet once stood over the site of Des Moines, Iowa, for instance.

Fertile as these plains are, they are extraordinarily flat, and even from a great distance one can see the grain elevators of a far-off town looming on the horizon—together with the ubiquitous water tank.

Because the glacial mill grinds so exceeding fine, much of the surface of the outwash plain is covered with rock flour which can readily be picked up and transported by the wind. Strong winds in turn are characteristic of many glacier fronts because of the great temperature differences in the vicinity of the ice margin—in this respect glaciers act meteorologically much like a permanent cold front. With strong winds sweeping across an open, unprotected, silt- and sand-covered plain, great clouds of dust are readily picked up and may be swept for scores of miles beyond the actual limits of glaciation.

Deposited, this fine, wind-transported glacial debris may blanket much of the neighboring countryside, sometimes to depths of tens of feet. This loess was broadcast over the length and breadth of the Mississippi Valley as well as across the lowlands of Central Europe and far down into the Danubian Plain of Hungary.

Where the ice front tarried for a time, as the result of a temporary attainment of equilibrium between the rate of ice advance and the rate of melting, a low ridge of glacially transported debris commonly accumulated. This end moraine is much lower as a rule than the alpine glacier's terminal moraine. It also is likely to have a far greater lateral extent, and a detailed glacial map of the United States shows festooned loops of them draped around the Great Lakes and westward across the north-central states.

Most of the rocks in such a glacial deposit are

locally derived; that is, they have been carried no great distance from their source. Thus, if the surrounding countryside is chiefly limestone, then the moraine will be mostly limestone fragments, large and small. Interspersed with them, however, may be a number of far-traveled rocks. If they have a distinctive composition, they may be traceable all the way back to their source, in which case they are called *indicators*. Many are known to have traveled 300 miles; none apparently can be traced more than 800 miles (Flint, 1957). Fragments of native copper from the southern shore of Lake Superior are found as far away from their origin as southern Iowa and southern Illinois. Other more challenging examples of glacial transport are the diamonds, some as large as small pebbles, found as far south as southern Ohio and Indiana, and having a presumed source north of the Great Lakes. The diamonds technically are not indicators because their actual source is not known, or if it is, it is a remarkably well-kept and presumably profitable secret.

An end moraine may include a great variety of rocks, not only with regard to their composition; these rocks may also be dumped more or less randomly, without being sorted according to size or specific gravity as they tend to be by wind and running water. This is in addition to the kettle holes characteristically left through the melting of blocks of stranded ice. These kettles and other depositional irregularities in such glacially produced ground make for a distinctive, hummocky sort of landscape (Fig. 13-25) to which the name of *knob-and-basin* topography is given.

Low, nested, crescentically looped morainal ridges are a characteristic landscape element of the north-central states. They may make for rougher ground than the surrounding prairie, and thus may be the site of surviving wood lots, or be the location of farm houses placed to gain the advantage of the little height available in such terrain. The height of such ridges seldom exceeds 100 feet, and in some places wide gaps may appear in the ridge, either because the ice at that point was not loaded with debris

FIG. 13-25 *Irregular morainal topography, on the west slope of Coteau des Prairies, South Dakota. (Photograph by John S. Shelton.)*

or perhaps because the moraine was eroded away. As a typical example, the largest end moraine in Britain, the Cromer Ridge, which is northeast of London, has a length of around 15 miles and reaches a height of 300 feet. Two conspicuous moraines extend the length of Long Island in the United States, and their extension eastward into the Atlantic beyond the main body of the island accounts for its distinctive whale-like pattern on the map.

The end moraine marks a line of comparative stability for the front of a continental glacier, where it may have stood its ground for many decades. When the ice wastes away so rapidly that such stability is lacking, the deposits blanketing the formerly ice-occupied area are the *ground moraine.* This is likely to be part of a region of low or of subdued relief which is a mixture of ice-scour and ice-depositional features, the whole resembling an especially poorly planned and dismally incomplete construction project.

Broad expanses throughout the ground moraine may be barren rock, scraped nearly clean by the ice; the more resistant rock ledges stand higher than more deeply abraded weaker zones. These, if gouged out, may hold lakes. Over hundreds of square miles of Labrador, because of this rasping effect of the ice, the ground as seen from the air looks like an immense engraved geologic map.

On the other hand, much of the ground moraine, especially near the margins, may be an uninterrupted mantle of glacial deposits whose surface may be quite level if there were not too much rock debris in the melting ice. If there were an abundant supply then the debris is likely to be dropped indiscriminately and blocks of ice entrapped, which upon melting would produce a pock-marked landscape of kettle holes. This jumbled subglacial topography, showing none of the effects of being shaped by moving ice, is called most appropriately a *dead-ice moraine,* and is clearly one formed under stagnant ice which had ceased to move, or, in

other words, had died on its feet before melting away.

Some glacial forms on the ground moraine do show a regular geometry, and are not random heaps of glacial till. Among the shaped features are swarms of curious elliptical, rounded, low hills, resembling the bowl of a teaspoon turned upside down. These are *drumlins,* from an Irish Gaelic word *druim,* which means the ridge of a hill (Flint, 1957). Of these curious features, certainly the most renowned is Bunker Hill, although there are many others in the Boston region, including some of the islands in the harbor. Other drumlins are in minnow-like clusters that from a distance look much like a school of fish all swimming upstream together. There are a number of famous swarms of these egg-shaped hills in various glaciated parts of the world, some of the best known being in upstate New York (Fig. 13-26), southeastern Wisconsin between Madison and Milwaukee, in Nova Scotia, the central lowland of Ireland, and in Scotland, adjacent to the Tweed River.

There is a wide range in the size and shape of these whale-like ridges, but few are more than half a mile long or more than 100 feet high. In general, they appear to have a higher percentage of clay in their make-up than is characteristic of most glacial deposits. Every gradation exists between drumlins that are 90 per cent bedrock to those that are 90 per cent or more debris.

Although details of their origin are uncertain (no one ever saw them being made), there is little doubt that drumlins originated beneath the ice. They obviously are streamlined, and also are oriented parallel to one another, as well as to the direction of ice advance as deduced from other lines of evidence. Because of this molded appearance, many geologists believe that during part of the time drumlins were being formed the ice above them was in motion. They may represent the scouring and reshaping of the ground surface beneath the ice; sometimes this

FIG. 13-26 *Well-developed drumlin field, east of Rochester, New York. (Photograph by John S. Shelton.)*

was dominantly bedrock, at other times it may have been an earlier deposited moraine. They may also represent accumulations made by sediment-laden and relatively slowly moving ice. As the excess load was being deposited, it also was being rounded off.

Eskers, from a Gaelic word used in Ireland, are elongate, narrow, sinuous ridges of glacial till which commonly show a measure of sorting, or rude stratification. They wander across the countryside, much like a canal levee or a railroad embankment laid out by a mildly inebriated surveyor. Their crests are rounded, their side slopes are moderately steep, and their longitudinal slope is gentle. They still march to-

day, quite imperturbably, across low hills and valleys, or even lakes, that may be in their path. Like drumlins, they, too, have a roughly parallel alignment; or, more properly speaking, they may radiate like the spokes of a wheel from a center of ice accumulation, such as Labrador. Unlike stream channels, they may have gaps or discontinuities in their courses. Like conventional streams they may meander, occasionally they are joined by tributaries, but unlike ordinary streams they may climb up hill slopes, especially where they cross low ridges through passes. Seldom do their crests stand much more than 100 feet above their surroundings. Some may be as much as 300 miles long, although most are a great deal less. The parts of the world where eskers have their prime development quite obviously are where the continental ice sheets were at their optimum. In the Western Hemisphere they are at their peak in Canada on either side of Hudson Bay—especially in Labrador—and in the Eastern Hemisphere in the lands bordering the Baltic, such as Sweden and Finland.

Once again we are confronted with an enigma because eskers are structures of uncertain origin. Small ones have been seen forming in the marginal zone of glaciers, but not the larger varieties. The consensus today is that eskers probably are deposits made by streams flowing in ice tunnels at the bottom of the glacier. Many glaciers have such tunnels at their termini, and presumably these passages continue back into the ice. That this should be true for hundreds of miles is what seems unlikely. Possibly such tunnels were continually extended as the ice front receded, and thus always reached back into the glacier by about the same distance. Countering this argument, however, is a large body of evidence which seemingly demonstrates that the ice stagnated or wasted away by thinning down long after it had ceased to move. Eskers clearly were formed under such a stationary glacier—had there been any motion, a structure as frail as an esker probably would have been obliterated.

Lakes abound in areas scoured by continental ice. Anyone caught in a traffic jam behind a Minnesota car can read on its license plate that back home there are 10,000 lakes. A casual inspection of a moderately detailed map of the part of Canada bordering Hudson Bay, or of the Finnish and Russian portions of the Scandinavian Peninsula, shows a multitude of lakes, some large, some small, some round, and many elongate. Because of their great number, it is not surprising that they have a great variety of origins. The three leading categories are (1) lakes resulting from differential erosion by the ice, (2) lakes impounded behind dams such as accumulations of morainal debris, and (3) lakes in kettle holes and other undrained depressions.

The Great Lakes are a good example of a system involving both origins. In part they are ice-gouged, and their floors lie far below sea level. The bottom of Lake Superior is 700 feet below sea level and that of Lake Michigan 343 feet. In part, they are blocked by moraines, especially around the south end of Lake Michigan, whose pendulous, lobate form is a close counterpart of the moraine-outlined glacial lobe whose place the lake has usurped. The Great Lakes had a different pattern during the last part of the ice age from what they do today; for one thing they were dammed to the north by the retreating wall of the receding ice sheet; for another, their levels were higher than those of the present-day lakes, and their outlets were quite unlike contemporary ones. One ice age outlet was via the Mohawk Valley and the Hudson, while another was down the course of the Illinois River to the Mississippi River, and thence to the Gulf of Mexico, rather than to the Atlantic by the Gulf of St. Lawrence, the present route.

Perhaps the outstanding Pleistocene lake was the one to which appropriately we give the name of glacial Lake Agassiz. Although it is long gone in its entirety, an impressive surviving remnant is Lake Winnipeg. In this part of Canada the regional slope is northward toward Hudson Bay. As the glacier receded it made a nearly continuous dam of ice behind which a lake about 700 miles long and covering perhaps 100,000 square miles was impounded. When the ice melted the lake drained away, leaving its nearly dead level bottom to form the extraordinarily bountiful wheatlands of southern Canada and the valley of the Red River of the North in Minnesota.

Glacial lakes have a great deal to tell us of the chronology of the latter part of the ice age. This is especially true of lakes whose surface was frozen in winter and open water in summer. In such strongly seasonal lakes, two distinctive sedimentary layers presumably accumulate each year; a thicker, light-colored band laid down in summer when streams are active, and a darker, thinner layer with a higher organic content that accumulated under the ice in winter when fine material, such as clay, has an opportunity to settle out through the still water. These rhythmic laminae are *varves,* from a Swedish word *varv,* meaning a periodic repetition. Although they are by no means restricted to glacial lakes (such seasonally controlled sediments also accumulate in favored environments in the sea), their occurrence seems to be favored in cold, fresh-water lakes.

A half-century of patient comparison by Baron de Geer and his associates of the varves in the glacial lake deposits of Sweden enabled them to establish a chronology extending back 17,000 years from A.D. 1900 (Flint, 1957). There are many assumptions in such a method, not the least being the one that each couplet, a light and a dark band of sediment, does represent a year's accumulation, and that these can be correlated from one lake to another. The process resembles the comparison of tree rings (these do not always represent annual layers, either) in the southwestern United States, not only to establish dates for the construction of pueblos but also to gain an insight into the nature of the climatic changes that have repeatedly vexed this region.

MULTIPLE NATURE OF GLACIATION

When the glacial hypothesis was proposed over a century ago, people spoke of a Great Ice Age. The idea was generally held that in some mysterious way the ice advanced across the northern lands, lingered a while, and then withdrew. Men of that distant frigid day, if indeed there were men at that time, were called upon to endure this affliction but once. Today we know that there were men on Earth during that actually not-so-distant day, and that the ice age was a vastly complex event, involving multiple advances and withdrawals of the continental ice sheets.

The map (Fig. 13-21) shows the maximum extent of the North American ice sheet. How do we really know, though, that there was more than one advance, and how do we determine how many there actually were?

Most geologists interpret the available evidence to indicate that there were at least four major advances of the ice, separated by three interglacial phases when the ice withdrew, perhaps completely. The evidence for this complex succession is based in part on (1) the way in which moraines and other deposits of a later glacial stage may overlap those of an earlier advance, and (2) the degree of weathering of these glacial and interglacial deposits. Older deposits may have a soil profile developed on them, younger ones almost surely will not. The original constructional pattern of older moraines and other glacial landforms will be blurred, or perhaps even obliterated, compared to younger ones. Weathering may have progressed to depths of 8 or 9 feet in older glacial deposits, and some boulders, even though they appear solid and intact, are so deeply decayed that they readily can be sliced through by a bulldozer blade. Such weathered glacial material is known by the eminently descriptive but etymologically unpleasant word, *gumbotil.* This was originally defined in 1916 as a gray, thoroughly leached clayey soil that characteristically is impassable when wet, hard and firm when dry.

The accompanying graph (Fig. 13-27) makes evident the unequal distribution in time of the four glacial stages. There were two earlier ones, Nebraskan and Kansan, separated by a long interglacial interval—the Yarmouth—from two later advances, the Illinoisan and Wisconsin. The years assigned to the various episodes are estimates. No one really knows whether or not the Pleistocene was 1,000,000 years long, but probably the order of magnitude of this estimate is about right, although a prevalent opinion, based on radioactive dating of volcanic rocks, is that it may have been as much as 3,-000,000 years.

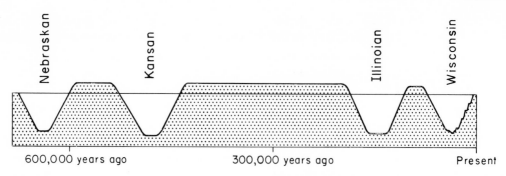

After A. Penck and E. Brückner, *Die Alpen im Eiszeitalter*, 1909.
C. H. Tauchnitz.

FIG. 13-27 *Estimated durations of glacial and interglacial stages of the Pleistocene.*

The names of the glacial stages also indicate the extent of the various glaciations—the earlier, Nebraskan and Kansan ice sheets spread farther south than the last, the Wisconsin. As mentioned before, the deposits and landforms produced by the Wisconsin glaciation appear so fresh that they look as though they were created only yesterday. It was thought that the ice age ended about 25,000 years ago, but since the announcement in 1947 of the time-keeping value of C^{14}, the estimated time-lapse since the withdrawal of the continental ice from the vicinity of the Great Lakes has decreased to around 11,000 years. We shall see how the principle of the C^{14} method works in Chapter XVI, but the effect of this telescoping of time on the thinking of archeologists, climatologists, geographers, geologists, and historians has been profound. In fact, some of them have not accepted it yet. The time available since the deglaciation of northern Europe in which to deploy many of the peoples of that wonderfully diverse population and to develop the various cultural patterns of both the Old and the New World seems much too short. This is especially true when one considers how stubbornly most primitive societies resist change, and to progress from a simple hunting and gathering existence to the development of agriculture, the domestication of animals and plants, and the erection of complex hierarchal social structures in the surprisingly short number of generations available is difficult to believe.

One of the more significant reference points in North America in dating the last phase of the Pleistocene is the Two Creeks forest bed near Manitowoc, Wisconsin. There, in a deposit of glacial till are the splintered logs of spruce, pine, and birch trees, all aligned in the direction of ice advance. Beneath the glacial debris, stumps of trees still stand in the positions they held before being overridden by this last short-lived advance of the ice. Since these logs have a radiocarbon age of 11,400 years, this gives us a date in this isotopic chronology for the close of the Pleistocene in the Great Lakes region (Hough, 1958).

The interglacial intervals, whose names are taken from Afton Junction, Iowa, Yarmouth, Iowa, and Sangamon County, Illinois, were times when the glaciers may have disappeared completely. In addition, there is strong evidence to suggest that during some of them the climate was warmer than it is now.

POSTGLACIAL CLIMATIC CHANGES

Determining the causes of the climatic fluctuations responsible for the waxing and waning of the ice sheets during the Pleistocene is a major scientific problem. We shall discuss some of the possible explanations, but before that we should consider the question of whether or not we are living in an interglacial time, or whether or not the whole chapter in Earth history built around the successive encroachments of the ice sheets ended with the Wisconsin glaciation.

The answer to this last question is simple—we do not know. For one thing, the length of time during which climatic observations have been made is far too short. Reliable instrumental records date only from the middle of the nineteenth century; in fact, the earliest rainfall record in the modern sense was made in Padua, starting in 1725 (Russell, 1941), and the earliest temperature record in Florence, in 1655 (Manley, 1962).

Enough is known from a mass of information of all kinds to tell us that the climate since the end of the ice age has not always been the same. Some of this scattered information seems authentic, some of it is interpretive, and some of it is frankly speculative. We are working in the realm of human history, though, and historic records have survived of many of life's bitter experiences which are reflections of climatic stringency, such as droughts, floods, crop failures, blocking of alpine passes by long-enduring accumulations of ice and snow, and successions of unusually savage winters. Many of these things were written down, others have to be inferred from such occurrences as finding village sites once built on a lake shoreline, now far up the slope laid bare through the evaporation of the lake waters. In an opposite sense, the original site of lake dwellings may now be concealed by a rising lake level.

A good example of a historical record encompassing a long span of time and one which reflects changing climatic patterns is the annual flooding of the Nile. Water levels were recorded almost continuously between A.D. 641 and 1480, and flood stages between the years 1480 and 1830 (Russell, 1941).

The doomed Norse colony in Greenland is an example of the impact of a climatic change. The colony was founded in A.D. 984 and perished around 1410. In its early history the Arctic seas were unvexed by ice and Viking ships could make a passage where today ice floes and stormy seas bar the way. The colonists raised cattle and hay, built permanent habitations, and the colony flourished to such a degree that it had its own bishop (Russell, 1941). With a climatic change that brought the Greenland ice southward again, with the pressure of the Eskimos at their gates, with a succession of crop failures, with the rise of permafrost in the ground—so that even such shallow excavations as graves were no longer possible—and with the perils of the ocean crossing too great for the frail vessels of that day, the colony and all its inhabitants perished.

Other examples, almost without number, might be cited of the impact of changing climates on the lives of men, and thus on the course of history. A powerful description of the effect of a climatic change of the magnitude of some of those that occurred in historic time on the early inhabitants of Europe is the following passage from Palle Lauring's *The Land of Tollund Man, The Pre-history and Archaeology of Denmark*.

The change which set in altered not only living conditions but the country itself. It became windy, rainy, and foggy, and there was a fall in temperature. The change is evident in the form of a clear stratum in bogs, which indicates that the rain turned to torrents. Grey mists swept like a veil across the land, the cattle congregating miserably round the houses. The winters set in with drifting snow, frost, and yet more snow. Wondering, men advanced through cold and death-like forests, where the snow stifled every sound and where oak tree branches were weighed down by it. Cattle froze to death; wolves failed to find food; belts and sounds were overlaid with ice, rendering navigation impossible for months on end; corn would often be destroyed by frost and water, and harvest would mean waiting for the air to dry while the ears blackened and rotted. Gone were the days when young women sang as they went about clad only in corded skirts, golden-brown from the sun. . . .

Piecing much of the fragmentary evidence together is a task yet unfinished, although a vast store of information has been accumulated, chiefly from Europe where a long and often turbulent record can be sifted. However, we know little of what postglacial climatic changes were like in lands that are more remote, or with radically different climates—such as the monsoonal tropics.

In western Europe and the Mediterranean region postglacial climates appear to have oscillated somewhat as follows (Ahlmann, 1953): From about 8000 to 5000 B.C. the glaciers of Europe receded, until a warmer climate than today's prevailed between 5000 and 1000 B.C. This happier time is the so-called *climatic optimum,* and during it many of the alpine glaciers disappeared and the higher passes were open. Temperatures were lower between 1000 B.C. and A.D. 1, then warmed until A.D. 400 (about the fall of Rome), cooled gradually, but were generally still warmer than they are today, until A.D. 1300. You may recall that North Europeans were prowling over parts of the northern world then that are completely inhospitable today. For example, it was roughly in this period that the Greenland colony flourished, and that Leif Ericson may have reached America by a northerly route (about A.D. 1000).

From A.D. 1300 on, glaciers readvanced, alpine passes were blocked, and living conditions in northern Europe were harsh. To some, the adversity of the northern winters may go a long way to explain the hardships that were accepted as part of ordinary living in that more brutal age.

By 1700 or 1750 alpine glaciers were at their maximum. From this peak they receded until 1800, and then readvanced to a second maximum about 1850. Since 1900 the rate of recession for most, although not all, Northern Hemisphere glaciers has been rapid. The last half-century has seen a significant warming of the atmosphere, accompanied by shifts of marine currents, fish populations, migration of land animals, and changes in annual temperatures and precipitation. As an example, according to Flint (1957), measurements of Swiss glaciers

show a reduction in area from 1,853 sq. km. in 1877 to 1,384 sq. km. in 1932, a loss of 25 per cent in fifty-five years.

Where this trend is leading, no man now living can say, but it will be interesting to watch the pattern unfold. Will the Earth's atmosphere continue to warm, will temperatures level off, or will the air chill once more and the glaciers start their march again?

CAUSES OF GLACIATION

This discussion of postglacial climatic changes has had a double purpose. First, to show that for all practical purposes we are still in an ice age. It exists today in Greenland and Antarctica and on the higher mountains of the Earth. Second, the record shows that there have been significant climatic fluctuations in the historic past. There have been times in recorded history when glaciers were more extensive than they are today, and there have been times when they were less.

Turning to the record of the rocks, the story is less clear. Of all the sediments which accumulate on the land surface, glacial deposits by their very nature might be considered least likely to survive. This is certainly true of deposits left by alpine glaciers high on mountain slopes, the most exposed of all locations to erosion. Continental glacial deposits are not too permanent either. These are likely to be a widely spread, thin veneer of boulders, sand, and clay. To convert this vulnerable sediment into rock, to bury it, and have it preserved as part of the geologic record calls for the working out of a whole battery of unique and interdependent events.

Because of this rarity of preservation, our knowledge of pre-Pleistocene glaciations is uncertain. There was a time, shortly after the multiple nature of glaciation was agreed on, when geologists were finding evidences of past glaciations in rocks of a great variety of ages from all over the world. This initial enthusiasm has cooled, and now the only generally accepted glaciation of great geological antiquity may have occurred near the close of the Paleozoic Era, perhaps 200,000,000 years ago. Oddly enough, the best evidence for, and seemingly the greatest extent of, this glaciation is in the Southern Hemisphere—chiefly from the Republic of South Africa, but from Brazil and central Australia as well. Another oddity in South Africa is that the direction of ice advance, judging from the orientation of striations and other linear elements, appears to have been from north to south. With the geography of South Africa of today, this has the ice moving from a warmer to a colder climate—quite the reverse of what would be expected logically.

Unfortunately, in part because of its remoteness, in part because of the necessarily fragmental nature of the evidence, no unanimity of opinion exists as to whether or not these South African deposits are of glacial origin—another example of the myriad fascinating problems of Earth history still awaiting solution.

Rather than embroiling ourselves in the controversy over the Late Paleozoic glaciation of the Southern Hemisphere, we shall attempt to unravel the tangled skeins of fact and speculation surrounding our near-contemporary, the Pleistocene glaciations. The purpose of the short discussion concerning the possibility of earlier glaciations in other times and other places is to point up the apparent circumstance that in the decipherable span of geologic time glaciation is a rare event.

Among the things to be kept in mind about the Pleistocene glacial record before attempting an explanation are the following:

1. Pleistocene glaciation was a multiple rather than a single event, and four major advances commonly are recognized in North America and Europe.
2. These advances were not of equal size, nor were the interglacial times of equal length. The record is bifurcated, with two earlier and more extensive glacial stages separated from two later and smaller episodes by the longest interglacial.
3. Glaciation appears to have been synchronous on both sides of the Atlantic. North American and European glaciers advanced or receded in harmony. The evidence is less clear for the Southern Hemisphere; but apparently when Northern Hemisphere glaciers advanced or receded, Southern Hemisphere glaciers did the same. In other words, the entire Earth seems to have responded to the same climatic pulses.
4. Although the evidence is not completely certain, nonetheless it strongly suggests that Pleistocene glaciation is a relatively unusual event, at least in the latter part of the Earth's history.
5. Times of glacial advance appear also to have been times of lowered temperature, as demonstrated by the nature and fossil content of cores recovered from sediments at the bottom of the sea, and by evidence of lowering of the regional snowline on higher mountains of the world.

Naturally, a phenomenon as challenging as an ice age has brought forth a host of attempts at explanation. No single explanation has won unanimous acclaim; each has its adherents and its detractors. At least fifty hypotheses must have been advanced over the years, but most of them contain some inconsistency that turns out to be a fatal flaw. Among these casualties are theories involving radical shifts in the Earth's axis of rotation, or of continents sliding around so that lands which now are warm were transferred to colder regions where they could then be refrigerated. The preponderance of available evidence tells us that during the Pleistocene the distribution and outline of the continents appear to have been essentially as they are today.

Other theories appeal to changes in the composition or character of the Earth's atmosphere. A surge in volcanic activity might result in a pall of volcanic dust lingering long enough to interpose a shield between the earth and radiation from the sun, thus decreasing the temperature of the lower atmosphere. Although the Pleistocene was a time of active volcanism, there have been times in the past when activity was greater, and these were unaccompanied by a notable advance of glaciers.

Perhaps the CO_2 content may have varied, and a marked increase of it in the atmosphere is believed by some to produce a so-called hothouse effect, or a general rise of temperature. In fact, the warming up that is generally recognized as having characterized the last fifty years is considered by some to result from the enormous quantities of CO_2 added to the atmosphere through the burning of coal and oil once the industrial revolution hit its stride. There is no compelling reason to believe that the atmospheric content of CO_2, or of H_2O for that matter, was much different from today, or that it varied systematically through the Pleistocene.

There appear to be two major possibilities that invite further investigation as possible mechanisms. These are (1) astronomical causes and (2) fluctuations in solar radiation.

Astronomical explanations make much of the fact that the eccentricity of the Earth's orbit changes slowly with respect to the sun; also the inclination of the Earth's axis with respect to the sun undergoes a slow change—part of the year the Earth is tipped toward the sun, part of the year away from it. The Northern Hemisphere is inclined away from the sun in the winter when the Earth and sun are a little closer to each other than they are in the summer. The effect is to give the Northern Hemisphere slightly warmer winter temperatures than the Southern. A third variable is that the amount of the Earth's inclination to the plane of its orbit may change slightly over millennia. These various eccentricities in the relation of the Earth to the sun do not combine in any systematic fashion, with the result that there will be variations over the years in the distribution of solar energy at any given place on the Earth's surface, but not in the total amount received from the sun.

Without carving our way through a bristling thicket of technicalities, among the leading objections to an astronomical cause for the ice ages is the strong possibility that glaciation in the Northern and Southern Hemispheres would be in opposite phase. All the accumulated evidence seems to indicate that when northern glaciers advance or recede, their southern counterparts do the same thing at the same time. Another critical point is that were such a repetitive and essentially geometric process to be effective in inducing climatic oscillations, then it would very likely have produced ice ages on a periodic schedule in the geologic past. We have already mentioned the uncertainties surrounding the existence of earlier glaciations, and should their validity be established some day, their extreme rarity through geologic time makes the rhythmic repetition of astronomically induced glacial and nonglacial cycles seem implausible.

Variations in the amount of solar radiation received on Earth appear to hold a leading position as a cause in the thinking of many geologists. What the nature of these variations may be is unknown at the moment, or even for that matter that they actually occurred. Whether the total solar energy output remained constant, or whether changes may have been selective, is debatable; for example, did the amount of ultraviolet light change while other parts of the spectrum remained constant?

Assuming that solar radiation did vary, then an ingeniously argued hypothesis is one advanced by Sir George Simpson, a British meteorologist. The accompanying diagram (Fig. 13-28) illustrates the steps in his argument, if we assume, first, that two marked increases in solar energy occurred in the Pleistocene, as shown by Curve 1, and that this would cause an increase in the Earth's atmospheric temperatures, as shown by Curve 2.

We know from our own experience that an increase in temperature will bring about an increase in evaporation, and this is reflected commonly by an increase in precipitation, as shown by Curve 3. Along with an increase in precipitation, very likely there would be a world-wide increase in cloud cover, and this would tend to keep the temperature at the ground surface lower than it might otherwise be.

Precipitation occurs as both rain and snow, and Curve 4 is concerned with snow accumulation since this is the crucial factor controlling the growth of glaciers. Snow must accumulate from year to year, and be converted to névé and into ice. Ice will accumulate, as shown by the curve, up to a point as the temperature increases, but there will come a time when the temperature rise is great enough that this no longer is possible. Then the snow accumulation curve drops off suddenly, as shown, although the precipitation curve continues on up, closely paralleling the temperature (2) and radiation (1) curves.

Translating snow accumulation into glacial terms, this means that two increases in the amount of solar energy received on the surface of the Earth would yield four glacial stages, which would be divided into doublets separated by a long interglacial interval. Incidentally,

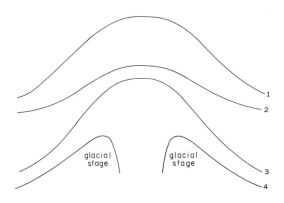

After G. C. Simpson, *Royal Meteorological Society Quarterly Journal*, vol. 60, 1934. By permission.

FIG. 13-28 *The effects of fluctuation of solar energy on temperature, precipitation, and snow accumulation as shown by curves: 1, solar energy; 2, atmospheric temperature; 3, precipitation; 4, snow accumulation. Two such increases in solar radiation would be required to account for the four Pleistocene glacial stages.*

should this hypothesis prove to be valid, then the long interglacial should be cool and dry relative to the two shorter, warmer, and more humid interglacials. Such a relationship has not been established, but this may be no more than an indication of our ignorance at this moment in the history of science.

Simpson's theory points up one of the great difficulties confronting scientists attempting to explain an occurrence as complex as the ice age. An understanding of its cause will come essentially through a knowledge of climatology and meteorology, but evidence for the existence of former widespread glaciations is geologic. Any valid theory of causes will have to fit the patiently worked out pattern of distribution of moraines and other glacial deposits.

Geologists are prone to criticize Simpson's theory on the grounds that glacial advances seem to be accompanied by lower temperatures, rather than increased ones, as is shown by the chilling of ocean waters revealed by cores of bottom sediments, by regional lowering of snowlines on mountains, by the broad southward displacement of taiga forest and tundra into more temperate lands, and by the southward migration of hordes of arctic animals, such as the musk ox and the extinct woolly mammoth.

A logical explanation appears to be one proposed by R. F. Flint of Yale University. He points out in his theory, which is admittedly tentative, that two factors may have been operative in the Pleistocene which may not have coincided so effectively in earlier geologic times. These were (1) an unusual prevalence of high mountain ranges and therefore of high, snow-accumulating uplands, and (2) fluctuations in the amount of solar energy great enough to produce an average annual lowering of temperature in the middle latitudes of 6° to 8°C.—the amount estimated as necessary to produce an ice age. Since there are two elements in this hypothesis that are essential for its operation—high, snowy uplands and fluctuations in solar energy—Flint (1957) gives it the dual name of *solar-topographic concept*.

Much needs to be done before the validity of the concept is firmly established, but these things seem reasonably certain. Fluctuations in solar energy appear to correlate with advances and retreats of glaciers today. The historical record also indicates that postglacial climate has not been constant; at times it has been warmer, and at others—notably the thirteenth century—it has been colder, almost cold enough to herald the onset of a glacial advance had it endured long enough.

However, pulsations of solar radiation very possibly may have occurred with about the same frequency in the remoteness of the geologic past as they have in modern times. The factor that sets the Pleistocene apart is its seeming prevalence of mountains and uplands. Most of the world's better known mountain ranges were elevated to their present heights then, including such lofty summits as those of the Himalayas, Andes, Caucasus, and Alps. Not only was the Pleistocene a time of unusual crustal activity, but the north-south pattern of such significant mountain ranges as those of North and South America became firmly established, and since these lie athwart the general planetary circulation of the atmosphere, they may have had a significant effect upon the growth and dispersal of glaciers.

An additional theory for the ice age was introduced recently by Maurice Ewing of Columbia University and William L. Donn of New York University (1956). Their theory involves two major elements: 1) the North Pole migrated from a position in the North Pacific to its present location at the beginning of the ice age, and 2) the Arctic Ocean alternated between ice-free and ice-covered phases during the Pleistocene.

Polar wandering is involved in this hypothesis to explain the sharp contrast between generally equable climates during the last million years of Earth history and the refrigerated episode, the ice age, immediately preceding the present.

A North Pole located in a large body of water such as the Pacific, with free circulation, would not cause the severe climatic stringencies of one located in a closed basin such as the Arctic—hence the abrupt break with climatic patterns of the past.

Alternations between ice-free and ice-covered phases of the Arctic Ocean are required to cause alternate advances and recessions of glaciers on land. An important consideration is the nearly landlocked status of the Arctic Ocean. A slight lowering of sea level would make it even more so; the connections with the Pacific would be severed, and the interchange of Atlantic and Arctic surface water between such islands as Svalbard, Iceland, and Greenland would be diminished.

The hypothesis states that, were the Arctic ice cover to melt, sea level would rise, and the Atlantic water could more readily penetrate the Arctic basin. This would result in a greater supply of moisture for arctic-generated storms and consequently increased precipitation over the Canadian barrens and northern Europe. Were this precipitation to be in the form of snow, ice sheets would grow and continental glaciation would be the consequence.

With the expansion of glaciers, sea level would be lowered, the interchange of water between the oceans would be impaired, the Arctic Ocean would freeze once more, and the source of moisture needed for continental glaciers would disappear. Thus, "temperature changes in the surface waters of the Arctic and Atlantic Oceans are the cause of, rather than the consequences of, the waxing and waning of continental glaciers."

Much additional work needs to be done to establish the validity of this or any other glacial hypothesis. The evidence for polar wandering is speculative, and cause and effect relationship between the cover of sea ice in the Arctic Ocean and continental glaciers is uncertain. Nor is the adequacy of such a mechanism demonstrated to explain glaciation on mountains far removed from northern lands, or the expansion of the Antarctic ice sheet. Nonetheless, such theories are important in provoking debate, in forcing scientists to marshal arguments pro and con, and encouraging them to seek new evidence.

Huntington (1922) pointed out long ago that the Pleistocene was not only a time of increased storminess, but that the paths taken by most storm centers were farther south than the routes they follow today across the northern United States and Europe.

This may also help explain a puzzle about which a prudent silence has been preserved thus far in this chapter, and that is the driving force that made the continental glaciers move. Clearly, it is not the relatively simple downslope gravitative pull that activates alpine glaciers. Continental glaciers advanced on fronts that were thousands of miles long and ice moved for hundreds of miles across low-lying terrain. In fact, these glaciers actually overrode hills and mountains in their path. How this was accomplished is not known, but part of the answer may be that much of the snow needed to nourish a continental glacier accumulated near its margin rather than at its center. The great temperature contrast between a glacier and its surroundings makes it operate meteorologically much like a permanent polar front. Here, with more rapid accumulation, ice domes (part of the ice sheet whose surface stands higher than adjacent areas) could accumulate, and from these the ice could spread out, rather than from some remotely northern center in far-off Canada. Thus continental ice advance may in part result from marginal accretion rather than outflow from a single point source.

OTHER EFFECTS OF GLACIATION

The ice age, just ended, provided one of the more stirring chapters in Earth history, and one whose effects to a greater or less degree have affected the lives of all of us. Soil was stripped from vast land areas, leaving them devoid of value for agriculture but enhanced as sources of minerals. The load of stripped soil and rocks was deposited elsewhere, notably in the Middle West in this country, thus making it a singularly productive land. Large lakes were created where none so extensive had existed before. Lake Agassiz is one of these, and its remnant, Lake Winnipeg, is a giant in its own right. The Great Lakes, also in large measure a product of glaciation, are still with us, and incidentally they flood thousands of acres of potential farm land.

Many of the areas blanketed by glacial ice were bowed down under its weight, and when this burden was lifted through the disappearance of the ice, the land rebounded. In Scandinavia, uplifted wave-cut features show that the central part of the peninsula has risen 800 feet or more. Historic records, and various shore line structures such as ancient landing places, show that this rise is still continuing. It reaches the unusually high rate of about 3 feet per century at the head of the Baltic and decreases to about zero in the vicinity of Copenhagen.

Sea level all over the world swung in rhythm with the waxing and waning of the ice sheets. When the ice sheets expanded, tens of millions of cubic miles of sea water were withdrawn to be locked up on land as ice. Sea level was lowered as a consequence, perhaps by 40 or 50 fathoms (240 to 300 feet). This may not seem like much, but it was enough to profoundly alter world geography. Land areas, now separated, were then connected, and with the climatic stringencies of the time not only were migrations of whole populations of animals stimulated but they were made possible by the appearance of *land bridges*. Among these natural causeways are such links as the ones that connected Tasmania and Australia, Ceylon and India, New Guinea and Australia, and others that united some of the islands of Indonesia. Most renowned of all was the land bridge joining

Alaska and Siberia, now separated by the 180-foot-deep waters of Bering Strait. In a way, this link must have been a veritable freeway, with all sorts of creatures, including human beings, pattering to and fro. Westbound from the New World, migrating into the Old, went the zebra, the camel, the tapir, and the horse. Eastbound immigrants to this hemisphere were elk, musk ox, bison, elephant, mountain sheep, and mountain goat. Not the least was man himself. Almost all archeologists agree that the ancestral stocks of the American Indians, great though their diversity, reached this continent across the Bering land bridge. One curious quirk of the ice age that made such a migration feasible was the fact that the interior of Alaska was ice free. This seems remarkable when we consider that ice advanced as far south in the normally much warmer continental interior of the United States as the present site of Cairo, Illinois.

In both Europe and North America men lived along the margins of the ice. Life was harsher then, but they endured. Not only was the climate more taxing than today's, and men less well endowed than we to cope with it, but the animals of that sterner time were larger and fiercer than those of today. According to Lauring (1957):

. . . The giant of all was the aurochs with its yard-long, superbly curved horns, a creature six feet tall at the haunches, powerful, deep-bellied, swift and agile; always aggressive, and as fierce as an African buffalo. The wolf howled on moonlit nights, and the bear padded through the thick undergrowth. Every animal was strong, alert, bigger than today, with one exception: the badger, strangely enough, was smaller. The aurochs was twice the size of a modern prize bull, the bear was rather like an Alaskan bear, the wild pig was more powerful, and not only was the red deer bigger than now but its antlers were enormous, with a stem as thick as a man's upper arm and strong, heavy branches, vastly different from the slender growths of stags today. . . .

Against such odds men had little to offer except a courageous determination to survive, the knowledge of fire, the skill to make and use stone tools, and the rudiments of co-operation and communication. Slight as these advantages may seem to us today, they were enough.

Suggested References

Ahlmann, H. Wilhelmsson, 1953, Glacier variations and climatic fluctuations, Bowman Memorial Lecture Series, Ser. 3, Amer. Geog. Soc., New York.

Brooks, C. E. P., 1949, Climate through the ages, Benn, London.

Charlesworth, J. K., 1957, The Quaternary Era with special reference to its glaciation, St. Martin's Press, London.

Cotton, C. A., 1942, Climatic accidents in landscape-making, Whitcombe and Tombs, Christchurch, N. Z.

Crary, A. P., and others, 1962, The Antarctic, Scientific American, v. 207, No. 3.

Daly, R. A., 1934, The changing world of the ice age, Yale Univ. Press, New Haven, Conn.

Dorf, Erling, 1960, Climatic changes of the past and present, Amer. Scientist, v. 48, p. 341-364.

Dyson, James L., 1962, The world of ice, Alfred A. Knopf, New York.

Ewing, M., and Donn, W. L., 1956, A theory of ice ages, Science, v. 123, p. 1061-1066.

Flint, R. F., 1957, Glacial and Pleistocene geology, John Wiley and Sons, Inc., New York.

Hough, J. L., 1958, Geology of the Great Lakes, Univ. of Illinois Press, Urbana, Ill.

Huntington, Ellsworth, and Visher, S. S., 1922, Climatic changes, Yale Univ. Press, New Haven, Conn.

Jahns, R. H., 1943, Sheet structure in granites; its origin and use as a measure of glacial erosion in New England, Jour. Geol., v. 51, p. 81-93.

Kuenen, Ph. H., 1955, Realms of water, John Wiley and Sons, Inc., New York.

Lauring, Palle, 1957, Land of the Tollund Man, Lutterworth Press, London.

Lewis, W. V., 1938, A melt-water hypothesis of cirque formation, Geol. Magazine, v. 75, p. 249-265.

MacGowan, Kenneth, 1950, Early man in the New World, Macmillan, New York.

Manley, Gordon, 1962, Early meteorological observations and the study of climatic fluctuation, Endeavour, v. 21, p. 43-50.

Matthes, F. E., 1942, Glaciers, in Physics of the Earth, IX, Hydrology, McGraw-Hill Book Co., Inc., New York.

Nye, J. F., 1952, The mechanics of glacier flow, Jour. Glaciology, v. 2, p. 81-93.

Russell, R. J., 1941, Climatic change through the ages, in Climate and man, Yearbook of agriculture, U. S. Dept. of Agriculture, Washington, D. C.

Shapley, Harlow, and others, 1953, Climatic change; evidence, causes, and effects, Harvard Univ. Press, Cambridge, Mass.

Sharp, R. P., 1954, Glacier flow; a review, Geol. Soc. Amer., Bull., v. 65, p. 821-838.

————, 1960, Glaciers, Condon Lectures, Oregon State System of Higher Education, Eugene, Ore.

Thorarinsson, Sigurdur, 1956, The thousand years struggle against ice and fire, Mus. of Natural Hist., Dept. of Geol. and Geog., Misc. Papers No. 14, Reykjavik, Iceland.

Woodbury, D. O., 1962, The great white mantle, The Viking Press, New York.

Zeuner, F. E., 1959, The Pleistocene Period; its climate, chronology, and faunal successions, Hutchinson and Co., Ltd., London.

The sea attacks a rocky coast at Shore Acres State Park, Oregon.
(Photograph by Ray Atkeson.)

The Sea

Most alien of all the world's environments, and therefore most mysterious, is the sea. In America, a country of virtually continental extent, our interests are largely directed inward upon the affairs of the land. The time when the sea played the role in American life that it did in the time of Richard Henry Dana or Herman Melville is long gone. For most of us today the sea is an obstacle, rather than a way of life, and at best is thought of chiefly as a source of diversion along its shore. Crossing the ocean now is a matter of hours rather than the weeks and months of unremitting toil and peril it was in the day of the wooden sailing ship.

Events taking place 30,000 feet below the surface are much less an intimate part of our lives than any seen from the deck of a small and heavily laboring vessel running before the dark seas of a mid-oceanic gale. Yet today the sea remains as almost the last great unexplored scientific frontier on Earth. There is no land area, however remote, about which we do not possess a hundredfold more knowledge than we do of the sea floor directly off our shores.

Any serious effort to explore the sea is staggeringly expensive. No one who has not seen the bills can believe the cost of maintaining and operating a ship, especially an oceanographic vessel which earns no profit for anyone. Because of its unique mission and specialized equipment it may be about the costliest thing for its tonnage afloat (Fig. 14-1). Oceanography is not a field for the lone-wolf scientist; only maritime countries or well-endowed institutions engage in this science. In this country there are few of the latter, and most university-connected oceanographic institutions are dependent on government grants to keep their ships at sea.

Today the United States and the Soviet Union appear to be the two nations most actively engaged in the study of the sea, with the Russians sending out an elaborately outfitted flotilla of large, seaworthy oceanographic vessels.

METHODS OF MARINE SURVEYING

All that men could learn of the sea floor in ancient days was insignificant. The longest lead lines in ordinary use on sailing ships as late as 1900 were only 120 fathoms. Even obtaining a sounding at such a modest depth as this required heaving a ship to and ranging the crew around the rail with each sailor holding 20 fathoms or so of line. At best all that could be collected from the sea floor was an imperfect sample stuck to a blob of tallow placed in a shallow recess in the base of a 50-pound lead.

Beyond the ordinary requirements of deep-water navigation there did exist some curiosity as to what the lightless depths of the sea concealed. According to Kuenen (1955), when Magellan ran out 2,300 feet of line in mid-Pacific he and his crew were convinced they were over the deepest spot on Earth.

FIG. 14-1 *Preparing to lower a piston corer from the Research Vessel* Atlantis. (*Courtesy of Woods Hole Oceanographic Institution.*)

For the next three centuries oceanographic technology made modest progress. The art of obtaining deep soundings advanced to where steel wire was substituted for hempen lines and a more sensitive quick-release mechanism was devised for getting rid of the weight once it touched bottom. One of the principal difficulties in taking deep sea soundings was knowing when the line had reached the sea floor. Without this knowledge, the line might be allowed to continue to pay out onto the sea floor in tangled spirals, thus giving an apparent depth of the ocean at that point that was truly record-breaking.

Among other difficulties were the problems of making certain that the line was actually vertical, and that the ship was holding its original plotted position and was not drifting away from a point directly over the lead. Even the fundamental problem of knowing where the ship was during the sounding could not be answered accurately a century or so ago. Positions at sea probably could be determined only within 5 miles of the true location. With electronic devices available today we can do much better, but accurate determination of position still remains a problem for deep-water oceanographic surveys.

The 69,000-mile, world-encircling voyage of H.M.S. *Challenger* in the years 1872-6 was one of the great forward strides in oceanography. Quantities of sediments were collected from the oceanic depths, and rocks, minerals, and fossils, and all manner of living things were collected from islands. The published reports of the expedition, which run to a score of volumes, were a scientific watershed of the time, and their exquisite illustrations and detailed descriptions of natural phenomena are unequalled. Perhaps they are a reflection of a more leisurely age, for scientific writings are indeed the losers in our less contemplative era.

Because *Challenger* and its successors, such as U.S.S. *Tuscarora,* moved at a sedate pace judged by modern standards, and very few such vessels were at sea, the collecting of oceanic soundings advanced with glacier-like progress. Until shortly after World War I only some 15,-000 soundings had been made. These were largely concentrated along the routes of submarine cables, with an average of only one sounding for every 6,000 square miles (Carson, 1950). Such a scattering missed several mountain ranges as high and rugged as the Rocky Mountains.

Challenger and other oceanographic ships built up a picture of the ocean floor as essentially a monotonous abyssal plain, covered with either a flour-like impalpable *ooze* made up of the microscopic skeletons of minute, surface-dwelling sea animals and plants whose tiny remains sifted down like an endlessly falling organic snow, or else in the deeper parts blanketed with an extraordinarily fine-grained inorganic sediment, the so-called *red clay*.

Not until after World War I did we gain the first rational picture of the irregularities of the ocean floor. The peacetime outgrowth of the anti-submarine effort then was the invention of the echo sounder around 1919. The principle

of the device is quite simple. A sound pulse sent out through the water from a ship's hull strikes the bottom and when reflected back is picked up by a microphone in the hull. Knowing the velocity of sound in water, roughly 4,800 feet per second, and the time between the sending of a signal and its reception back on board, it is possible to determine the depth. A great many improvements have been made through the years in echo-sounders. Some use ultrasonic waves which penetrate unconsolidated sediment, giving us a picture of its thickness and of the configuration of the rocky surface on which it rests. Recording devices have also been introduced that write a continuous profile of the ridges and troughs on the sea floor, thousands of feet below, on a slowly unwinding reel of recording paper in the chart room (Fig. 14-2).

The first major scientific application of the echo-sounding method was made by the German oceanographic vessel *Meteor* in 1925-7,

FIG. 14-2 *A fathometer record of a seamount in the Caribbean. (Courtesy of Woods Hole Oceanographic Institution.)*

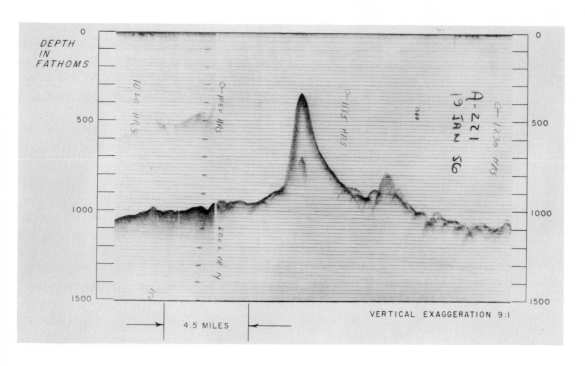

FIG. 14-3 *Geologists aboard ship examine cores taken from the floor of the Pacific. (Courtesy of University of California, San Diego.)*

and the results of its traverses across the depths of the South Atlantic were a revelation. For the first time the scientific world learned that the configuration of the sea floor was as diversified as the land—in some ways more so, in others, less. Perhaps it should not surprise us that there are volcanoes, fault scarps, lava flows of immense magnitude, and whole mountain ranges hidden from our view. These are counterparts of the same crustal features occurring on land, and the fact that they are covered by the water of the sea is entirely fortuitous. One of the great differences between submarine and the subaerial landscapes is that at the bottom of the sea there is no erosion in the sense familiar to us—no wind blows, no rain falls, no glaciers shoulder their way downslope. The only agent comparable to those on land that shapes some of the features of the sea floor is gravitative transfer, or mass movement. Rock falls and landslides occur there as they do on land, although probably less frequently since there is nothing comparable to the frost wedging found on high mountains.

Were the waters of the sea to be rolled away, we would see a landscape so alien to our experience that attempting to describe it would be a difficult if not impossible task. This is terrain completely invisible and inaccessible to us, except for what can be dimly seen by skin divers and by an occasional excursion to the black and silent depths by *bathyscaph*.

This extraordinary looking device might possibly be compared to an underwater free balloon since it rises or descends in the ocean water by unloading ballast or discharging the substance that gives it buoyancy—in this case, gasoline. The *Trieste,* developed by Auguste Piccard, was the first such manned submersible to reach the greatest depth in the sea, 35,800 feet, in the Mariana Trench about 200 miles from Guam, on January 23, 1960 (Piccard and Abercrombie, 1960). Here at the immense depth of roughly 7 miles, bottom-dwelling fish still live, demonstrating that oxygen is circulated downward by slow but massive transfers of water. The water temperature at this prodigious depth is 38°F., near the threshold of the freezing temperature of salt water.

Despite such direct approaches to the sea floor as the bathyscaph and the aqualung, our knowledge of its true appearance for the foreseeable future will be second hand. In visualizing the shape of the submarine world we are dependent upon indirect means as soundings obtained by lowering a weight to the bottom, or by receiving a sound echo bounced back through thousands of feet of water to a surface ship.

We gain a little further knowledge of the character of the material on the sea bottom from cores that have been recovered by devices lowered to the sea floor from a surface ship (Fig. 14-3). Some of the cores recovered are 70 feet or so in length, and these give us an extraordinary insight into the nature of these deep-sea deposits that are so alien to our world of sun and air. Not only do we gain some understanding of their physical and chemical nature when we bring them to the surface, but measurements of their radioactivity tell us their age, and thus we can make estimates of their rate of accumulation. The minute fossils of surface organisms trapped in the various layers tell us much of what the temperature of the sea may have been during the ice age, and thus we have here one of the most complete records obtainable of the extent and duration of the climatic pulsations that so profoundly affected the northern lands of the world. How strange a paradox that we should turn to the depths of the sea to look for help in answering one of the greatest riddles of the land.

Through the camera's eye we see increasingly more of this remote world. Technological improvements since World War II in lighting, in shielding the underwater camera and in its lenses, and in development of faster films enable oceanographers to photograph the floor and the inhabitants of the deep sea (Fig. 14-4).

FIG. 14-4 *A sea anemone and a shrimp, living in perpetual darkness on the sea floor in about 400 fathoms of water, are momentarily illuminated for photography. (Courtesy of Woods Hole Oceanographic Institution.)*

The results have been startling, giving a remarkable picture of the environment in which bottom-dwelling organisms live as well as the actual appearance of whole colonies of shell fish, brittle stars, and coral. Other features revealed on these photographs are a revelation for the marine geologist. Among these are well-developed ripple marks over much of the continental shelf and on the summits of submarine ridges and mountains. These corrugations almost certainly testify to the existence of currents at hitherto unexpected depths, which are capable of shifting sediment on the sea floor.

CHARACTERISTICS OF THE OCEAN FLOOR

Continental Shelf

One of the features of the ocean floor that would catch our eye is the shelf, sometimes broad, sometimes narrow, that rims nearly all the continents of the Earth. Off some coasts, as of those bordering the Mediterranean, the west coast of South America, Formosa, and parts of Indonesia, the continental shelf essentially may be lacking. On others, as the northern coast of Siberia, it is about 750 miles wide.

In many places the seaward edge of the continental shelf is at a depth of about 72 fathoms (432 feet), although it may be more or it may be less. In earlier descriptions of the sea floor it was usually placed at 100 fathoms (600 feet), but this was an arbitrary choice and appears to be deeper than the normal depth of the break in slope. Thus, most of the continental shelf is within reach of currents set in motion by waves and possibly tides.

Since sea level has risen about 240 to 300 feet in the very brief time since the close of the ice age, what are now the shallower parts of the continental shelf only recently were dry land. Naturally, this has had a profound effect upon the distribution of mankind. It was possible for men to make the crossing on foot from India to Ceylon; migrations throughout many of the islands of Indonesia were feasible; and the pre-Columbian Indians as well as a wide variety of animals could walk dry-shod into the Americas by the land bridge which preceded the modern Bering Straits between Siberia and the New World.

Along many coasts terrestrial features can be traced by soundings far out on the continental shelf. Among these are the shallow submerged upper parts of valleys cut by streams, such as the landward part of the Hudson submarine canyon. Other curious relics are the glacial features, such as the drumlins and terminal moraines on the continental shelf off the New England coast. Similar coastal features are also found on the North Sea floor and, like their American counterparts, form fishing banks.

In some places, as off the southern California coast, the English Channel, and the Formosa Strait, the sea floor may have broad expanses of barren rock cropping out of it—enough so that it is possible in the shallower parts for skin divers to construct a geologic map using about the same techniques that geologists employ on land.

In general, the continental shelf is a broad, sediment-veneered platform that to our eyes would appear to be a dreadfully monotonous expanse since its average inclination may be as slight as $0° 07'$. The sediment on its surface comes predominantly from the erosion of the land and has been redistributed by waves and currents in the sea. We are far from understanding how this sediment is spread across the sea floor. For one thing, there is not always a uniform gradation of sediment size from coarse detritus, such as gravel and sand, near the shore, to increasingly fine particles, such as silt and clay, in deeper water far from the coast line. Fine-grained sediment, such as mud consisting almost entirely of clay-sized particles, may cover the sea floor well landward of broad sand banks farther offshore. No one knows the reason for the capricious distribution of sediment on the continental shelves of the world. It may be a consequence of the migration of shore lines back and forth across their surface in the time of unstable sea levels of the ice age. Shore forms, as sandy islands and beach ridges, still survive in some places in fairly deep water where perhaps later sedimentation was too slow to bury them and currents in the rising sea were too feeble to erode them away. The rapid rise of sea level drowned some rivers, such as the Potomac and the Delaware, so that their sediments, which were once spread across the continental shelf, are now trapped in their own estuaries.

More problems confront us with respect to the continental shelves than there are answers. Many of the shelves may be underlain by the truncated edges of continental rocks which have been beveled by waves and in part mantled by sediment. The true nature of the continental shelf is unknown, other than that it appears to share its structural pattern with that of the adjacent land and thus is part of the continental foundation. It is clear that it has been flooded only very recently by the postglacial rise of sea level. High among the unresolved problems are (1) what are the factors responsible for the distribution of sediment over its surface, and (2) what is the explanation for its characteristically gentle gradient when compared to that of the immediately adjacent land?

Continental Slope

Among the more imposing features of the sea floor, in fact of the whole corrugated crust of the Earth, are the immense slopes that are the pedestals of the continents and that descend from the offshore margin of the continent down 12,000 to 18,000 feet into the silence of the abyss. Normally this slope is not a stupendous cliff rising from the abyssal plain but is more likely to be a slope that descends throughout a distance of 100 miles or more. In only a few places would it actually look like a slope to us, so gentle is its inclination, seldom exceeding 300 feet per mile.

Gentle and essentially constant as the inclina-tion of the continental slope may be, it is far from being a perfectly uniform sloping plane. Rather, along many coasts of the world it is apparent that much of the continental slope is furrowed by deep, canyon-like trenches incised far below its general surface, as well as by great numbers of closely spaced rills on such a slope as the one offshore from the mid-Atlantic seaboard of the United States. We shall say more about the origin of these canyons later; they are surely among the more mysterious features of the Earth.

Bare rock is frequently encountered by dredges when they are hauled up the sides of submarine canyons. How much of the intervening slope between such canyons is likely to be barren is uncertain, but along some continental margins quite extensive areas apparently are. Other segments of the continental slope are equally perplexing because they may be covered with surprisingly coarse material, ranging up to gravel or even boulders. These, according to Shepard (1959), together with areas of bare rock, may make up as much as 10 per cent of the surface. In waters marginal to the Arctic seas, gravel and boulders found so far from land can be explained as having been rafted out to sea by drifting ice. This explanation breaks down, however, when we speak of continental slope deposits off the coasts of temperate and tropical lands. There the presence of coarse sediments on the slope is a puzzle.

Much of the continental slope, 60 per cent of it in fact, is mud, according to Shepard (1959). Very commonly this flour-like mud has a strong greenish or bluish color. These *blue-green muds* are made of clay and other minute particles of sediment brought down to the sea by rivers or swept out over the ocean by winds. The particles are so small they remain in suspension for a very long time, once they are caught up by currents in the sea. Along with these air- and water-borne dust-sized mineral particles is a never-ceasing downward drift of the tiny remains of surface-dwelling microscopic animals and plants, among which calcareous single-celled organisms are important. In places the lime content of these slope-blanketing muds may run as high as 50 per cent.

The Abyss

At the bottom of the continental slope in the depths of the sea is the *abyss*. Its floor stretches for unimaginable miles from continental margin to continental margin. On it everywhere rests the stupendous burden of the sea. Pressure increases at the rate of one pound per square inch for each two feet of depth gained, until in the greater depths of the sea this may amount to 6 tons to the square inch, or 1,728,000 pounds to the square foot. Water is normally thought of as being incompressible, but under these pressures it is condensed to the point where average sea level would rise about 93 feet were this not true (Carson, 1950).

Beneath the cold waters of the open ocean, some parts of the floor of the abyss are a dead level plain and these so-called abyssal plains leave an unwaveringly smooth line on a fathometer for mile after mile. Some appear to be sediment covered, as is a broad expanse in the northwest Atlantic Ocean south of Newfoundland. Others, such as one in the Indian Ocean, seem to be the nearly level surfaces of vast sub-ocean floods of basalt, perhaps comparable to the Deccan lava plateau on land in nearby India.

Other parts of the sea floor are more varied, and include such diverse forms as broad *rises* and *plateaus* that may have quite gentle slopes. *Ridges* are narrower features with steeper marginal slopes and narrow crests. Many of them are submarine mountain ranges. Outstanding among these is the Mid-Atlantic Ridge, which stretches for 10,000 miles down the full length of the ocean and is practically equidistant from the continents on either side. Where the ridge pierces the surface of the sea its lofty peaks are the foundations of islands such as Ascension, the Azores, Iceland, St. Helena, and Tristan da Cunha. Highest of these is Pico in the Azores, which towers 7,600 feet above sea level and stands on a base that rises 20,000 feet above the ocean floor.

An interesting and completely enigmatic feature of the Mid-Atlantic Ridge appears to be an essentially continuous depression with a nearly level floor and steep sides that follows the crest in those parts that have been sounded in detail. In some ways this trough resembles the Rift Valleys of Africa. Locally, the mid-Atlantic crestal trough is a locus of volcanic activity where it intersects mid-oceanic islands, as in Iceland. According to Heezen (1960), this rift, whose walls average 6,000 feet in height and whose floor is 8 to 30 miles wide, has a nearly continuous distribution of earthquake epicenters throughout its length.

Almost equally mysterious are the great *trenches* countersunk below the general level of the ocean floor. The map in Chapter 15 (Fig. 15-7) shows the more significant ones in the Pacific, and these in general are clustered along the Asiatic margin. Except for the trenches off the coast of Chile and Peru, these troughs are associated with the chains of volcanic islands which lie betwen the trench and the adjacent mainland. The map shows, too, that these submarine wrinkles make roughly the same pattern as the adjacent land or island arc, and thus they, too, show a festooned pattern.

An interesting aspect of these trenches is that they are the deepest spots on Earth, although whether the greatest depth of all has been found is uncertain. Quite a number of contenders are on record. Among those reported in recent years are (1) 34,428 feet in the Mindanao Trench off the Philippines, (2) 35,800 feet for the Challenger Deep in the Mariana Trench, and (3) 34,000 feet for the Vityaz Deep off the Kurile Islands.

These long, narrow indentations on the sea floor, found not only in the Pacific Ocean but also in other places as the Indian Ocean along the southwest coast of Indonesia and in the Bartlett Deep in the Lesser Antilles, are of unknown origin. Many trenches are associated with chains of volcanoes, and earthquake centers are commonly clustered along a plane extending diagonally from them down into the Earth's crust. This plane acts as though it might be a fracture, or zone of shearing, possibly akin to the pattern associated with thrust faulting. Another curious phenomenon associated with these furrows is that over them the force of gravity is less than over the adjacent islands or the ocean floor. An explanation suggested for this is that these abyssal trenches are localized zones where lighter rocks or sediments have been downbuckled into the Earth's crust, thereby forcing an elongate wedge of lighter surface material down into the region of denser, subcrustal matter. As we shall see in Chapter XV, this is one of the possible mechanisms by which mountains made up of folded sedimentary rocks may get started.

The recognition of the extent and pattern of these deep, elongate trenches on the ocean floor is an outgrowth of World War II, especially in the Pacific. With naval vessels continually crossing its normally unfrequented waters, an enormous mass of fathometer records were accumulated. When these were compiled, the great system of trenches paralleling the Mariana Islands—one of the world's immense submarine mountain chains—was clearly apparent. The work of surveying these hidden features has continued to the present, and slowly our knowledge of their shape, if not their origin, is developing.

A surprising discovery in this world at the bottom of the sea was the isolated, individual peaks that rise above the abyssal plain. Their presence was scarcely suspected before the advent of the echo-sounder; now something like 500 have been found. These are called *seamounts,* and although little is known about them, many appear to be submarine volcanoes. Their distribution over the sea floor is not known because there still are extensive unsurveyed areas, but we do know that great numbers are concentrated in the far reaches of the Pacific Ocean, for example, south of the Aleutian Islands, and in the vicinity of the Caroline and Mariana Islands.

A much more puzzling feature than the seamount is the *guyot.* These are mountains, too, but their summits are a nearly level submarine plateau. Their strange name honors Arnold Guyot, a Swiss geographer and associate of Louis Agassiz, who came to America more than a century ago to teach at Princeton University. Guyots commonly rise to within 3,000 or 5,000 feet of the surface. Their surfaces typically consist of barren rock. Some of these platforms have been photographed and rock samples have been dredged from them. In addition to a summit of planed-off volcanic rock, many guyots also have a covering of rounded boulders. These may have been rounded when the guyot stood closer to sea level. Some guyots still have fossil coral attached to them, and some of these corals are identified as having lived in the Cretaceous Period (over 70 million years ago). One guyot in the Pacific near Bikini held the fossils of a species of *Globigerina,* a minute, single-celled, surface-dwelling organism that lived during the Eocene Epoch (about 50 million years ago). These fossils had sifted down into the cracks in the planed-off basalt summit.

How were guyots' summits truncated to such remarkable uniformity, and how did they reach the great depths at which we find them? If we argue that they were beveled by wave attack—which seems the most logical solution—then we are caught in the dilemma of believing either (1) that sea level has risen nearly a mile in the not-very-remote geologic past, or (2) that the guyots have been carried down to their present depth by regional subsidence. Although this latter explanation is plausible, it raises more questions than it answers, such as the sinking of great expanses of the ocean floor and the transfer of great quantities of material at subcrustal depths.

Many other perplexing features are only beginning to come to our notice as increasing numbers of oceanographic vessels cross the seas of the world, and as the technology of marine surveying improves. Great escarpments, several of them more than 1,000 miles long, interrupt the sea floor in places. Four of them, separated from one another by roughly equal spacing, strike almost due west from the coasts of California and Mexico into the Pacific, at least to the longitude of Hawaii. Their relationship to geologic structures on land is difficult to decipher. Rather than being a continuation of the prominent land fracture, the San Andreas fault, the two off the California coast intersect the fault very nearly at right angles. One of these escarpments off the coast of Mexico possibly may be a seaward continuation of the line of Mexican volcanoes aligned along the nineteenth parallel. This volcanic system includes not only the lofty cones of Popocatepetl and Ixtaccihuatl outside Mexico City but also the recently active volcanoes of Paricutin and of the island San Benedicto off the coast.

Abyssal Deposits

What of the material that covers the deep floor of the sea? Here again ignorance outstrips knowledge. Enormous stretches of the sea have never been visited. In fact, one whole ocean, the Indian, is virtually unexplored, and is only now (1962) the center of a combined oceanographic survey by the maritime nations of the Earth.

Many of the descriptions of sediments found on the floor of the abyss are taken from the reports of the *Challenger* expedition of nearly ninety years ago. Today we know that the pattern of the sea floor is more complex in detail, although in its broad outlines it may be something like the one worked out by the scientists of the *Challenger*.

In brief, the *Challenger* demonstrated that generally on the deep sea floor between the lower part of the continental slope and a depth of around 3 miles the most abundant sediment is *ooze*. This wonderfully descriptive term gives an impression of what this organic flour is like. Photographs of it, as well as verbal descriptions by bathyscaph divers, suggest that it looks like an ivory-colored blanket. The slightest disturbance sends a dust-like cloud swirling up through the dark water, making us realize what an impalpable powder it must be. Ooze does not form in place on the sea floor, but accumulates as the result of a gentle, unceasing "snowfall" of the remains of ornate, microscopic, free-floating surface organisms. When they die, their minute remains sift down from the sunlit surface to the lightless floor of the sea.

Much of the abyssal plain beneath tropical and warm-temperate seas, with depths of less than 15,000 feet, is drifted over with a carpet of microscopic shells of *Globigerina*. Like so many single-celled creatures, they do not die, but reproduce themselves by division. That is, one organism divides to make two, each of which grows a new shell, while the original shell, now vacated, is cast off to sink to the bottom of the sea. As it drifts downward the shell wastes away through solution. Its final disappearance occurs below depths of 15,000 feet or thereabouts, because these deeper waters are less saturated with lime in solution.

In deeper parts of the sea underlying warm-temperature surface waters, the chief organisms that survive to form ooze are the *Radiolaria*. The minute shells of these wonderfully ornamented animals, when seen under the microscope, are as intricately beautiful as snowflakes.

The delicate tracery of their myriad spines and protuberances has to be seen to be believed. In the immense depths of the sea where *Globigerina* shells melt away to gossamer thinness and ultimately disappear, *Radiolaria* shells may survive, perhaps because of their greater insolubility. *Radiolaria* shells are made of silica, a compound much less soluble than the calcium carbonate of the *Globigerina* shells.

In colder seas marginal to both the Arctic and Antarctic, a broad band of the sea floor is drifted over with the flour-like tests of *diatoms,* which are almost invisible to the unaided eye. These are single-celled, surface-dwelling, cold-water-inhabiting plants. They swarm in these frigid seas in uncountable multitudes, and in a sense compose the true pastures of the sea. How curious that the largest creatures of the Earth, the Arctic whales, should depend for sustenance upon these humble plants, among the smallest of living things.

Diatoms, like their floral counterparts on land, flourish during part of the year, reach a climax, and then decline. Often when they die, they appear to perish in hordes. The water in protected inlets, such as fjords, then becomes green and soupy looking, and oars and boats immersed in such a flood of organic matter grow green and slimy and acquire a distinctly fishy fragrance.

Where there is such a proliferation of diatoms, their tiny siliceous tests accumulate in such numbers that with the passage of centuries their remains may be consolidated into the unusual sedimentary rock, *diatomite.* Diatomites are common in the western United States, as well as in some of the lands bordering the Mediterranean. In fact, one of the earlier names for the rock was *tripoli.* Diatomites often are light enough that, like pumice, they will float in water. Their composition of nearly pure silica, together with their cellular nature, gives them attributes much like those of fiber glass. For this reason, diatomite is used for its heat- and cor-

rosion-resistant properties, for sound-proofing, for insulation, and as a filtering medium. Diatomites, such as the ones that underlie the California Coast Ranges, probably accumulated long ago in shallow bays or inlets, where diatoms drifted in great profusion, rather than in the depths of the open sea. In fact, some diatomites were not deposited on the ocean floor at all, but were laid down under the cool waters of desert lakes.

A unique sedimentary accumulation is the monotonous soft carpet of dark *red clay* that floors the deeper parts of the Pacific Basin as well as the Indian and Atlantic Oceans. In terms of square miles, it is the most widespread of all the deposits of the Earth. Curiously, it is almost wholly inorganic, save for such exotic souvenirs of marine life as the ear bones of whales and the teeth of sharks—both relatively insoluble in sea water. The fact that some of the sharks' teeth are those of species long dead, and known to us only as fossils, is evidence of the extraordinarily slow rate at which the red clay accumulates.

The red clay is deep reddish brown rather than a true red. It is extremely fine grained; 85 per cent or so of it consists of particles less than 0.05 mm. in diameter. Although there is no unanimity of opinion on how this clayey deposit originated, the fact that it is a true clay is now established. Some workers once thought the red clay consisted mostly of meteoritic dust —and thus in a sense was a product of outer space. Others believed it to be made of far-wandering volcanic debris, such as pumice, which might have drifted widely before it water-logged and sank. Now the evidence appears more convincing that the red clay has a land-derived origin, and that it consists for the most part of the very finest clay and related particles. These were transported to the sea by rivers, waves, or the wind, and were then carried far and wide by ocean currents. Gradually they sifted down, particle by particle, through the lightless depths to accumulate as an impalpable flour on the bottom of the sea.

An unusual deposit in some places on the deep ocean floor is large nodules—sometimes up to 3 inches in diameter—of manganese dioxide (MnO_2). Superficially these resemble cobbles or boulders, which they are not, since they grew by accretion with extreme slowness on the sea floor. The nodules may also contain appreciable amounts of cobalt and nickel, and are abundant enough in some parts of the deep ocean that, fanciful as it may sound, dredging them to the surface has been suggested as a possible means of obtaining these relatively scarce metals. No one knows exactly how these curious, lumpy masses of manganese accumulate. One opinion is that they are chemically precipitated, and are thus a further testimonial to the excessively slow rate at which the microscopic flakes of clay, volcanic ash, and cosmic dust that are the principal constituents of the red clay must accumulate around them.

MOVEMENTS OF SEA WATER

Almost all of us are aware of the endless parade of waves, both large and small, that disturbs the surface waters. However, we are less likely to know much of currents within the sea, unless we have lived along a coast where they run deep and strong.

Currents

Lieutenant Matthew Fontaine Maury, first in a long line of distinguished American oceanographers, aptly described the Gulf Stream in 1859 in his book, *The Physical Geography of the Sea:* "There is a river in the sea—the Gulf Stream." Maury's concern was to codify an immense mass of data from ships' logs, in order to make a coherent picture of the pattern of winds and currents in the sea. More than idle curiosity was involved, however. Using wind and weather charts prepared by Maury for the Hydrographic Office, the hard-driving masters of American clipper ships made record passages around Cape Horn and on other sea routes of the time that left their rivals far astern.

Maury was not the first to point out the advantages of picking a course to gain the thrust of such a current as the Gulf Stream. A pioneer in this regard was Benjamin Franklin. Since we often think of him in terms of Poor Richard's Almanack, or as one of the architects of the American Revolution, or of the figure he cut at the French Court, we lose sight of his remarkable sagacity. His ability to synthesize all sorts of natural phenomena placed him at the front rank of the pioneering scientists, or natural philosophers, of the eighteenth century. In fact, according to Carson (1950),

The first chart of the Gulf Stream was prepared about 1769 under the direction of Benjamin Franklin while he was Deputy Postmaster General of the Colonies. The Board of Customs in Boston had complained that the mail packets coming from England took two weeks longer to make the westward crossing than did the Rhode Island merchant ships. Franklin, perplexed, took the problem to a Nantucket sea captain, Timothy Folger, who told him this might very well be true because the Rhode Island captains were well acquainted with the Gulf Stream and avoided it on the westward crossing, whereas the English captains were not. Folger and other Nantucket whalers were personally familiar with the stream because, he explained, "in our pursuit of whales, which keep to the sides of it but are not met within it, we run along the side and frequently cross it to change our side, and in crossing it have sometimes met and spoke with those packets who were in the middle of it and stemming it. We have informed them that they were stemming a current that was against them to the value of three miles an hour and advised them to cross it, but they were too wise to be counselled by simple American fishermen."

From Franklin's day to this, the Gulf Stream has been a subject of intensive study. It follows a serpentine course from the Caribbean, skirting the Gulf of Mexico, thence through the Florida Strait, and across the Atlantic Ocean to warm the shores of Britain and Scandinavia. It moves an immense volume of water—perhaps as much as 26,000,000 cubic meters of water per second pour through the Florida Strait.

Intensive research, in large part by the British oceanographic vessel H.M.S. *Discovery* and the ships of the Woods Hole Institution of Oceanography in Massachusetts, make us aware of how complex the Gulf Stream is. It certainly is not the single, sharply defined river in the sea Maury described. For one thing, it appears to be much shallower than it was once thought. For another, it seems to consist of a number of narrow streams—perhaps as many as four— that not only constantly change position, and perhaps even meander, but also may throw off enormous spiraling eddies 100 miles or more across. Thus it is not a single current, but is an ever-shifting filament of warm water crossing the North Atlantic as a consequence, in part, of the eastward rotation of the Earth and, in part, of the westerly set of the prevailing winds. This forces water to the western part of the ocean, which then produces a hydraulic gradient toward the east. Part of the eastward flow of the stream may be due to temperature and salinity differences. Warm water flows northward in the Gulf Stream, and apparently this surface current yields at depth to a deep-water current of colder and denser water which flows southward out of the far northern seas. The discovery of this underflow was established by an ingenious electronic device perfected by the British oceanographer, John Swallow. It is a float which can be set to sink to a predetermined depth based on the salinity of the water. Once at this depth it gives off a chorus of beeps by which it may be tracked by a surface vessel.

Local differences in temperature and salinity are among the great driving mechanisms for ocean currents. A good example of how a subsurface current of denser water operates is the deep outflow of strongly saline water that pours into the Atlantic Ocean from the Mediterranean through the Strait of Gibraltar. This current results from the more rapid evaporation of the water of the land-locked Mediterranean than that of the open Atlantic. As a result of evaporation, the surface of the Mediterranean water becomes more concentrated and thus heavier. Lighter surface water from the Atlantic flows in through the strait in an effort to equalize the level of the two water bodies, and at the same time the saltier Mediterranean water flows seaward across the Gibraltar sill and out into the Atlantic.

So pronounced is the inflowing surface current, that in the days of sail hundreds of vessels at a time waited behind the strait for a wind strong enough for them to beat their way out into the Atlantic against the current. In 1805 the combined French and Spanish fleet was delayed behind Gibraltar by this current, a delay which gave Lord Nelson time enough to assemble his fleet and place it in line of battle opposite Trafalgar on the Spanish coast outside the strait.

Winds, in addition to differences in temperature and salinity within the ocean, are a powerful driving force in setting great masses of water in motion. Nowhere is this more pronounced than in the great stream of chilled water circling Antarctica, driven before the strong prevailing western winds. These sweep almost unceasingly and uninterruptedly around the world, across the unbroken reaches of the sea south of Cape Horn and the Cape of Good Hope.

In friendlier seas, the planetary wind circulation sets in motion great drifts of surface water, and these may eddy in enormous clockwise *gyrals,* such as those of the North Atlantic and North Pacific. The prevailing westerlies, around latitude 40°, marshal water ahead of them and thus produce a general easterly drift. Below 30°N the circulation of surface water is westward before the trade winds. A knowledge of these winds and currents dates back to the time of Columbus; and they long controlled the routes of sailing vessels in either sea, including the path taken for 250 years by such a legendary ship as the Manila Galleon (Fig. 14-5).

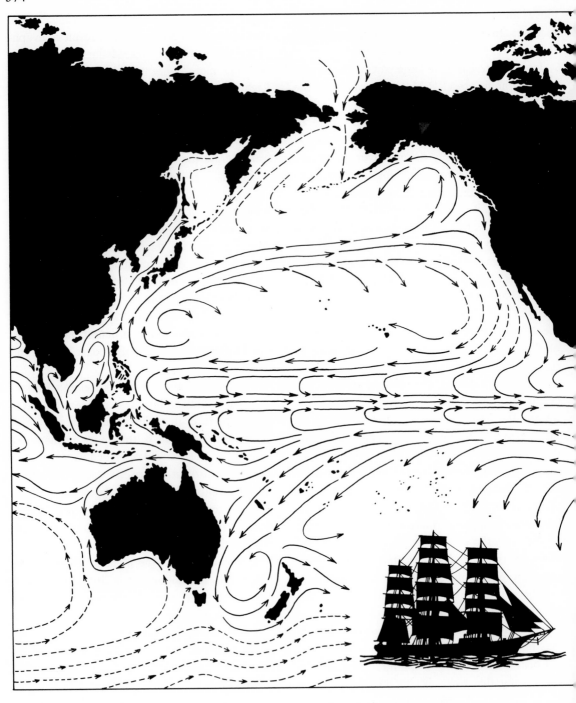

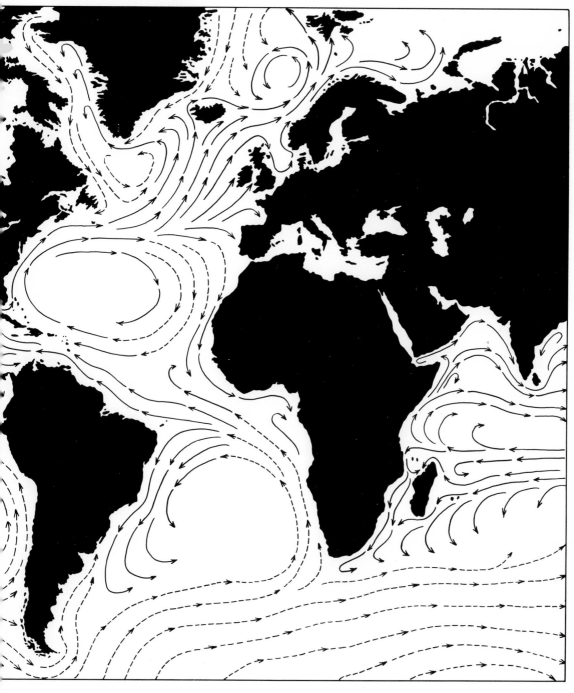

FIG. 14-5 *The major oceanic currents. (Courtesy of U. S. Navy Hydrographic Office.)*

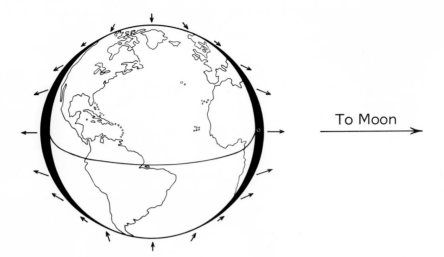

Tides

Although a relationship between the passage of the moon across the skies and the rhythmic rise and fall of the sea that we call the tides was known before the beginning of the Christian Era, we are still far from having a satisfactory theory of their origin. What seems at first a simple relationship between the Earth, the moon, and the sea becomes complex when an attempt is made to explain it in detail. For example, some coasts have tides of 20 feet or more, while on others, as those of much of the Mediterranean, the tide is negligible. Then, too, some coasts may have two high and two low tides a day—probably this might be regarded as the average pattern—while others may have one high tide and one low tide in every lunar day.

The fundamental cause of the tides is the gravitative attraction of the moon. Its pull is slight, however, compared to that of the Earth —only 1/300,000 as much. Slight as this is, it is enough to raise the level of the sea on the side of the Earth nearest the moon (Fig. 14-6), for the attractive force of the moon is greater than the centrifugal force set up by the Earth's spin. Conversely, on the opposite side of the Earth, away from the moon, the Earth's centrifugal force is the greater of the two. The result is shown diagrammatically in Fig. 14-6. The

FIG. 14-6 *The tidal bulge is shown diagrammatically by the black areas. The relative direction and strength of the tide-producing forces at various places on the Earth is shown by the inclination and length of the arrows.*

two bulges, corresponding to high tides, are on opposite sides of the Earth, and the arrows show by their length and inclination the relative direction and strength of the tide-producing forces at intermediate places on the Earth's surface.

This means that twice each lunar day two of these tidal bulges may pass a given point. These passages occur twice in every 24 hours and 50 minutes, because the forward motion of the moon carries it eastward in its orbit by about 50 minutes each day. In addition to this variable, the inclination of the Earth with respect to the plane of the moon's orbit makes for strong seasonal variations.

Possibly the most conspicuous vagary in the tidal range at many places is the occurrence twice each month of tides whose range (difference between high and low tide) is great, and twice a month another set whose range is slight. The tides with the maximum range are called *spring tides,* although the name has nothing to do with the season of the year. They occur when the moon, in its circuit around the Earth every 28 days, falls in line with the sun. The sun's attraction, although much slighter than the moon's because of its enormous distance, is added to the moon's, and this creates a more effective pull. We, on the Earth, are conscious that this relationship is operating when the moon appears as either a thin crescent, the new moon, or in its most resplendent nocturnal glory as the full moon.

Tides with minimal range, the *neap tides,* occur twice each month when the moon is in its first and third quarters. Then the Earth, sun, and moon all occupy the separate points of a right triangle and their attractive forces tend to cancel one another.

In addition to these astronomical factors, the configuration of the water basin affects the pattern and the range of the tide, possibly as much as any other single cause. Modern tidal theory holds that the tide is more of an oscillatory effect of water in an enclosed basin, and that this water has been set in motion by the pull of the sun and moon. Thus, the characteristics of the tide are related to a *seiche,* or standing wave, rather than to a tidal bulge loping endlessly across the sea in pursuit of the elusive moon. The tides should be considered as enormous shallow-water waves that behave like a giant see-saw. That is, the greatest tidal range is at either end of the basin; the least is likely to be near the central point. How great the tidal range will be depends very largely on the period of oscillation of the particular basin. Sometimes this range can be very great, as in the upper part of the Bay of Fundy where it may be as much as 40 to 50 feet. In other parts of the world where the oscillatory effect is slight, the range may be as little as one foot, or even less.

Occasionally, when circumstances conspire such as a combination of a strong wind, a decrease in atmospheric pressure, and a high spring tide, then a tidal surge may be set in motion. Most destructive of these in modern times was one in the North Sea in the middle of the winter of 1953. During this particular surge—

caused in part by a pattern of lowered atmospheric pressure over the North Sea, accompanied by gale force winds from the North Atlantic—an estimated 15 billion cubic feet of water or more poured into the North Sea between Scotland and Norway. On some bordering coasts the peak of the surge coincided with the crest of high tide, especially along the low-lying shores of the Netherlands. There the level of the sea rose 9 to 10 feet above normal. In many places there, as well as along the coast of Britain, dikes failed, broad expanses of coastal lands were flooded, and hundreds of lives were lost. In the Netherlands a total of 67 dikes were overrun, 375,000 acres of farm land were inundated, and at least 1,800 people drowned.

To return to the origin of the tides, the attractive force of the sun and the moon appears to be basically the triggering effect; the shape and depth of the basin—including large segments of the oceans as individual basins—determine the number and range of the tides.

An important aspect of the tides for the geologist is that they are a means by which enormous volumes of water are transferred from one place to another in short intervals of time. As a single example, something like 100 billion tons of water have been shifted by the flood tide into the Bay of Fundy day in and day out through thousands of years (Carson, 1950).

Where the tide flows through a narrow channel it can produce a swiftly moving current in which even the more powerful ships of today are hard put to hold their own. Fortunately, a tidal current is not a steady stream, but is one that slacks off as the tidal flood passes and then reverses its direction with the ebb. One of the more redoubtable examples of such a tidal current is the one that pours through the Pentland Firth off the northernmost tip of Scotland. When the tidal current streaming through the narrows separating Scotland from the Orkney Islands flows against the wind, a wildly tempestuous sea results to which the picturesque name of the Merry Men of Mey is given. With an ebb tide running and a westerly wind driving against it, in the laconic words of the *North Sea Pilot,* "a sea is raised which cannot be imagined by those who never experienced it" (Carson, 1950).

Tidal currents in such a confined space as a channel between islands, or in a narrow strait, such as the Golden Gate at the entrance to San Francisco Bay, commonly extend all the way from the surface to the bottom. In this respect they are unlike surface currents which may be the product of temperature or salinity differences. The channel at the bottom of the Golden Gate at a depth of 380 feet is bare rock and is scoured clean by the outpouring current of the ebb tide to which is added the outflowing waters of the San Joaquin and Sacramento rivers. In 1904 the steamer *City of Rio de Janeiro* struck a rock just inside the Gate, sank, and many years later parts of its wheelhouse were recovered from the San Francisco Bar, around 8 miles away, where they had been swept by the outflowing current.

Incidentally, the San Francisco Bar, which is made of sand and has an average depth of 24 feet, provides an interesting illustration of how man's activities can affect natural processes. In 1851 the bar started to migrate landward, and by 1900 it had shifted nearly 1,000 feet, at a rate of around 20 to 25 feet per year. The bar owes its position (Fig. 14-7) and its unique crescent shape to the strength of the current flowing seaward through the Golden Gate. The force of this current was diminished after 1851 as a result of the immense volume of debris dumped into the Sacramento and San Joaquin rivers, and ultimately into San Francisco Bay, by hydraulic miners in the Sierra Nevada in the years following the 1849 Gold Rush. This amounted to 1,675,000,000 cubic yards of debris transported into the drainage basin tributary to Suisun Bay (the easternmost arm of San Francisco Bay) in the years between 1850 and 1914. The addition of this vast quantity of sediment (at least eight times as much material as

excavated in the building of the Panama Canal) had the effect of reducing the volume of water in the outflowing current. This was because the place of much of the water in the bay was taken by the hydraulic tailings; therefore, less water flowed out through the Golden Gate on the ebb tide than did in the centuries before we appeared to disrupt the natural scene. With the outflowing current diminished, the force that held the bar offshore was reduced. The waves and currents of the sea gained the ascendancy and were able to drive the bar shoreward to the point where temporary equilibrium re-established it in its present position.

Turbidity Currents

One of the more intriguing mysteries of the oceanic depths, and one that has been the subject of an immense amount of investigation, exploration, and speculation during the past quarter-century, are currents of dense, muddy water

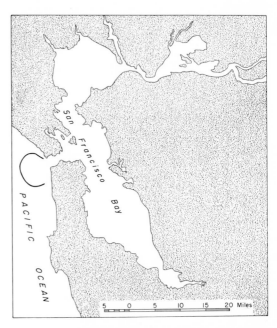

After G. K. Gilbert, by permission of U.S. Geological Survey.

FIG. 14-7 *The bar outside the Golden Gate, California.*

that course down slopes on the sea floor—with perhaps their greatest effectiveness on the continental slope.

Turbidity currents, as the name implies, are clouded or muddy streams of moving water. They were first described scientifically in 1840 by a Swiss engineer, Forel. He noticed that the muddy waters of the Rhone disappeared where the river flowed into the clear waters of Lake Geneva. He reasoned, quite correctly, that the colder water of the Rhone laden with glacial silt was heavier than the water of the lake. Therefore, the river sank through the lake water and flowed as an undercurrent along the bottom.

Much the same thing happens where the muddy Colorado River flows into Lake Mead, whose water is backed up for miles behind Hoover Dam. A muddy current makes its way along the bottom of the lake to deposit sediment all the way to the powerhouse intake towers. The surprising effectiveness of such a current apparently was not anticipated at the time the dam was designed. The working assumption made then was that much of the river sediment would be deposited in more or less conventional fashion in a delta at the upper end of the lake.

Two major problems are present: (1) the abrasive effect of the sediment particles on the turbines, and (2) sediment transport for the entire length of the lake might seriously shorten its life expectancy by having it fill more rapidly than planned. A model of the lake was prepared in order to study the circulation of the silt-laden bottom current, and photographs show how this turbidity current glides along the reservoir floor below the less dense and clearer water of the upper levels of the lake.

That turbidity currents may exist in the sea was suggested strongly on the afternoon of November 18, 1929, when a severe earthquake shook the Grand Banks off the Newfoundland coast. Apparently the shock was violent enough to trigger what may have been a submarine landslide or slump, which was soon converted into a roiled cloud of suspended sediment that swirled away down the continental slope. Such an event normally would go unnoticed were it not for the unique circumstance that the path followed by the earthquake-induced current was directly across one of the greatest concentrations of submarine cables in the world. This is the communication network linking North America with Europe, and in this nexus Newfoundland is the easternmost land station in the New World.

One after another the cables were broken that afternoon and night, and since the instant of time as well as the point of rupture could be determined electrically, the pattern of their failure was worked out. It turned out that the cables broke progressively downslope. When the cables were fished up for splicing, many of them were found to be chaotically snarled and jumbled, as though they had been thrust aside by a giant hand.

From the distance separating the individual breaks and from the time of failure it was estimated that in the early part of the current's life it had a velocity of about 60 miles per hour, but that this gradually decreased to approximately 25 miles per hour when the last cable broke, nearly 300 miles seaward from the epicenter.

Whether the cable-breaking pulse traveling across the sea floor was a turbidity current or not probably never will be known. About all we do know from this isolated episode, and a few other kindred occurrences, is that occasionally currents are set in motion in the depths of the sea that for short periods are capable of doing an immense amount of work and of shifting great volumes of sediment.

Another line of evidence strengthens the argument that sediment-charged currents may be operative over wide reaches of the sea floor. This is the presence of broad, fan-like expanses of sand spreading out across the abyssal plains from the continental margins. They are best known in the North Atlantic, probably because this is the most thoroughly surveyed of all the seas. These sands carpet the ocean floor in regions where ooze normally would be found. In addition, many such sand deposits contain the remains of organisms which to the best of our knowledge live in shallow waters near the margin of the ocean basin. This is a different problem than the presence in these bottom deposits of surface-dwelling animals and plants—these latter simply sank from the uppermost levels of the open sea down to the floor. In contrast, the shallow-water organisms found in the deep sea sands appear to have been swept to their final resting place by currents flowing down the continental slope and carrying the sand to the abyss.

Such sediments, supposedly deposited by turbidity currents, commonly show a distinctive kind of stratification when samples of them are examined from cores. This stratification is called *graded bedding,* with the coarser particles typically concentrated at the base of a layer, the finer near the top. This is interpreted to mean that, if the whole load of sediment now making up a single layer had been swept across the sea floor in a turbulent cloud, the coarser particles would settle out first and the finer particles would be deposited later when the disturbed water had calmed down.

That such a mechanism may exist in the real world appears to be a possibility. The evidence for this is a result of an extended series of experiments made by Ph. H. Kuenen of the University of Groningen in the Netherlands.

He was able to produce a great range of turbidity currents in a long trough, using many mixtures of sediment and also varying the velocities of transporting currents. Then he compared their artificially produced graded bedding with the real thing. He found (1950) that dense turbidity currents can reach high velocities on gentle slopes. Because of their high density, the transporting ability of these currents was increased enormously; in the experimental trough they were able to move such things as cobblestones, which were several thousand times heav-

ier than objects that an equivalent stream of clear water would be able to transport. This ability of turbidity currents to transport large objects may explain the anomaly that coarse grains of sand in the bottom of one sedimentary layer may rest directly on the top of the particles—say of silt—in the layer immediately underlying, without there being any significant amount of scouring of the lower bed.

Turbidity currents appear to be a plausible mechanism by which sediments that normally might be found at shallow depths, possibly on the continental shelf, are transported in enormous quantities down to the abyss, there to be spread far and wide in a fan-shaped sheet of sand.

Waves

No single attribute of the sea so intimately affects us as do the waves that add such diversity to its surface. Without them life at the beach would be dull indeed; with them an ocean voyage on occasion may be altogether too stimulating.

Waves are intriguing, and can be almost hypnotically fascinating. Although one wave may look like any other, no two are ever the same. Their rhythmic beat depends not only upon the local wind for perhaps the shorter, steeper waves, but also upon far distant fiercer winds that may have set the long, even-spaced ridges of the ground swell moving outward from a storm center half a world away.

As we watch the endless procession of waves march past, it is difficult for us to believe that it is the form of the wave that moves forward through the water and not the water itself. This statement may not appear to make sense at first, but watch a bottle bobbing on the surface of a bay. Waves pass under it repeatedly, but other than a slow drifting with the current the bottle holds its position remarkably well. An analogy for waves in the sea is the waves the wind makes when it blows across a field of grain. Ripples follow one another across the stalks of wheat, and yet the wheat does not pile up in a heap on the far side of the field. Instead, the wave motion in the grain results from the up and down nodding of the individual stalks each time a wave passes through them.

As long ago as 1802 it was known that water particles within a wave do not move forward with the advancing wave itself but follow a circular orbit (Fig. 14-8). Detailed studies have been made in the 160 years since, but the basic principles of water motion in a *wave of oscillation* are the same as those discovered then.

Some of the effects of this orbital motion are familiar to every surfboarder. For example, when a person is standing in the ocean a short distance out from the beach, he is very conscious that the water is running strongly seaward toward the next oncoming wave. When the next wave surges shoreward past the swimmer, then the water sweeps him strongly toward the beach. All of us are fully aware of

FIG. 14-8 *The circles show the paths followed by water particles in a wave. Wave profiles and positions of water particles are shown at two moments which are one-quarter of a period apart in time. The nearly vertical lines show how grass would be bent as the wave form passes. The stalks are vertical beneath a crest or trough.*

From Misc. Pub. 11,275, by permission of U.S. Naval Oceanographic Office.

this backward and forward pulse of the sea in the breaker zone, but not too many people realize that this is only part of the orbital path described by water particles within a wave.

The diagram (Fig. 14-8) is intended to show (ideally) the paths followed by water particles within a wave of oscillation. The wave is traveling in the direction shown by the horizontal arrow. As the wave crest approaches, the water in the immediately preceding trough moves toward the approaching crest. Then, progressively, the particles move upward, then forward with the crest, then downward, and then seaward again in preparation for the passage of the next wave crest.

The same diagram also shows how rapidly wave motion diminishes with depth. The diameter of the circles decreases in a geometric ratio with increasing depth. For practical purposes wave motion ceases to be effective when the water depth is approximately equal to the wave length.

Thus far a few terms have been introduced that need some clarification. *Wave length* is the horizontal distance separating two equivalent wave phases (Fig. 14-8), such as two crests or two troughs, but not a crest from the adjacent trough. The direction as well as the speed with which a wave travels is called its *velocity,* and this can be related to its other physical properties by a number of simple relationships. The

Direction of progress

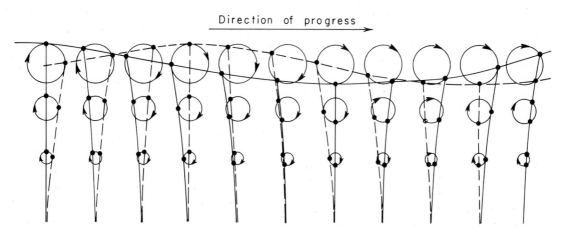

period of a wave is the length of time required for two crests or two troughs to pass a fixed point. The *frequency* is the number of periods that occur within a set interval of time—say a minute.

There appear to be finite limits to the size that waves can reach. Among the larger waves whose dimensions have been reasonably well established was one that was 112 feet high when it was sighted off the stern of U.S.S. *Ramapo* in 1933 during a gale in the North Pacific. Incidentally, wave heights are difficult to determine at sea, for they are extremely uncertain objects to estimate from the bridge of a laboring ship (Fig. 14-9). It is difficult for even a hardened mariner not to overestimate them if he feels some measure of emotional involvement in what is going on around him in a storm.

Wave lengths are likely to be less than most people imagine, but they are impressively large at times. According to Bascom (1959) one of the largest swells reported had a wave length of 2,600 feet (about half a mile), which would give it a period of 22.5 seconds and a velocity of 78 miles per hour. These are formidable figures when one considers the enormous masses of water involved.

How such volumes of water are set in motion is a fair question. Almost everyone knows that the wind driving across the surface of the sea is the primary cause. If this is true, though, how is it that on completely windless days a tremendous surf may belabor some exposed coast? Or that in a violent gale the wind may hammer the sea flat into a wildly turbulent mass of dark, malevolent-looking water streaked to the horizon with foam?

Such a mood as this is conjured up by Joseph Conrad in the *Mirror of the Sea:*

If you would know the age of the earth, look upon the sea in a storm. The greyness of the whole immense surface, the wind furrows upon the face of the waves, the great masses of foam, tossed about and waving, like matted white locks, give to the sea in a gale an appearance of hoary age, lustreless, dull, without gleams, as though it had been created before light itself.

Beyond the general agreement that the wind blowing across the sea sets waves in motion, there is not yet a consensus on how they form. For large waves in deep water at least the following requirements must be met: First, there must be a strong wind in order to set large masses of water to moving. Second, it must have a fairly long duration—more than just a sudden gust of wind is needed. Third, the water must be deep, at least deep enough to round out the full orbital pattern—100-foot waves are not likely to grow in a water basin only 10 feet deep. Fourth, the distance wind friction can operate on waves—called their *fetch*—is important for their growth, too. When waves have a long, uninterrupted run they have an opportunity to reinforce one another. The ripples crossing a small pond are a good example. They are small on the upwind side of the pond, yet they may have grown to fair dimensions by the time they reach the downwind shore.

It is not surprising, then, that some of the largest seas are those driven before the strong westerly winds which rule south of Cape Horn. Around the margins of Antarctica is an unbroken sweep of ocean which encircles the Earth.

To return to an earlier question: how, if waves are formed by the wind, can they march shoreward in an endlessly rhythmically advancing succession on a dead calm day? The answer is that such waves, to which the name of *swell* is given, may have originated in gales thousands of miles away. Waves that break on the exposed coast of Cornwall may have had their start in the far-distant reaches of the South Atlantic.

The swell is made up of so-called *long-period waves,* and these outrun the more mixed-up, randomly distributed, *short-period waves* which are characteristic of a storm. These short-period waves are left behind, and the more uniformly spaced swell far outdistances the gale winds localized around some cyclonic center.

Wave Refraction and Surf

As deep water waves move shoreward they begin to feel bottom when the depth of water becomes about equivalent to one half the wave length. As deep water waves move into shallower water near shore their length is shortened

FIG. 14-9 *The Coast Guard Cutter* Pontchar-train *wallows in the trough of a following sea in the North Atlantic. (Official U. S. Coast Guard photograph.)*

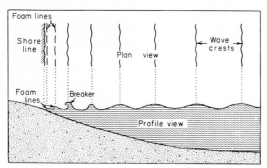

From Publication No. 234, by permission of U.S. Naval Oceanographic Office.

FIG. 14-10 *How waves shorten, steepen, and break as they advance into shallow water.*

and their height is increased relatively (Fig. 14-10). Their velocity is also reduced, and if one looks at their crests along a pier or breakwater, they do indeed seem to rise up out of the sea. This shallowing of the water at the shore has two major effects on waves of oscillation as they move landward; first, they may be *refracted,* and second, when they reach shoal water close to the beach, they break.

The effect of refraction is shown in the accompanying diagram (Fig. 14-11). Two things are especially important. First, waves approaching an irregular coast adjust themselves to the irregularities until they achieve a near-parallelism to the shore throughout all of its indentations. Second, wave attack is concentrated on the headlands, and thus these promontories are gradually beaten back while the deposition of sand, for example, is concentrated in the bay heads. The fact that wave energy is focused on the headlands is demonstrated by the lines in the diagram (Fig. 14-11), which are drawn so they are everywhere at right angles to the advancing wave fronts. These lines are called *orthogonals,* a term borrowed from ship builders, and we may consider their equal spacing on the outermost wave front as indicating equal amounts of available wave energy. Then it is apparent on the diagram that most of the energy in an advancing wave is concentrated on

the projecting salients along a coast and is diffused in re-entrants, such as a small bay.

As we have seen, when waves approach the shore and encounter shallower water, their length is shortened and their height increased. Finally, they become unstable and break. Without breakers most coasts of the world would lack their most picturesque element.

The formation of surf is a complex, and not yet fully comprehended, phenomenon. The endlessly changing pattern of breaking waves—and their variations with the tide, with wind and calm, with storm, and with the lulls between—have been an inspiration to generations of painters, photographers, writers, and ordinary daydreamers. Few manifestations of the natural world are more dynamic, or make us more conscious of the force of moving water, than to be caught in the surging mass of a strongly running surf.

Although much remains to be learned about how waves of oscillation break, a good deal is

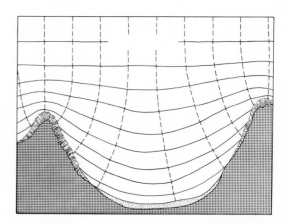

FIG. 14-11 *How waves are refracted. The solid lines are wave crests, which crowd together as they move into the shallow water around the rocky headlands but stay more widely spaced in the deeper waters of the bay. Wave energy, equally distributed between the parallel dashed orthogonal lines in deep water, is concentrated where the orthogonals converge on the headlands, and is diminished in the bay.*

known as a result of observations, model studies, and the application of hydrodynamic theory. In a general way, waves of oscillation break when the stillwater depth is roughly equal to 1.3 times the height of the wave. At least two major causes appear to lead to the formation of breakers. The first of these is a speed-up of the orbital velocity of particles in a wave that has moved into shallowing water, which makes the velocity of such particles at the wave crest exceed the decreasing velocity of the wave form. The second is the decrease in the shallow depths near shore of the amount of water needed to complete the wave form. This is especially conspic-

uous in the so-called *plunging breaker,* in which a wave curls over in a beautifully molded half cylinder, topples, and crashes with a thunderous roar. The entrained air is violently compressed, and in its efforts to escape converts the entire roller into a froth of foam-whitened water.

Spilling breakers (Fig. 14-12) are those in which the crest foams over and cascades down the front of the advancing wave without actually toppling over. Such breakers ordinarily diminish in height as they move landward, and they

FIG. 14-12 *Spilling breakers. (Courtesy of Humble Oil and Refining Company.)*

may advance in rows simultaneously over a broad stretch of beach. The two types of breakers grade into one another, although one may be dominant at one time, the other at another. For example, plunging breakers are especially likely to form when the tide is high, the beach gradient is steep, and the approaching wave fronts are steep also. Spilling breakers are perhaps more characteristic of broad, gently sloping beaches at low tide.

COASTAL LANDFORMS

Wave Erosion

It is in the shore zone, where breakers are able to bring their full force to bear against the land, that most of the erosive work of the sea is concentrated. Since there is an upper and lower limit to such attack, the work of waves might be likened to that of an enormous horizontal saw. The upper limit of their effectiveness is the maximum height that waves can reach at high tide during a storm. This will differ among coasts depending on how boldly the land faces the sea and how strongly gales drive waves before them. On the more rugged coasts, storm-driven waves have been known to reach heights of 200 feet or so.

The tsunami at Hilo, Hawaii, on May 23, 1960, provides an excellent example of the power concentrated in a moving mass of sea water. There, a series of waves, the largest reaching a maximum height of 35 feet, devastated the waterfront section of the town, taking 61 lives and causing $20 million worth of damage. Geologically, an impressive result was a demonstration of the transporting ability of moving water. Automobiles were swept for whole blocks, and in some cases were piled three-high; in others they were wrapped like limp fish around the bases of coco palms. These waves, which were not far from storm waves in their dimensions, moved generators and sugar mill

rolls and ripped up whole slabs of asphalt paving. Boulders from the sea wall, weighing 22 tons or so, were transported inland 500 to 600 feet.

Many of the waves that caused the damage were approximately 20 feet high and, according to wave theory, moved through the shallow water of the harbor at 45 miles per hour. This means they were capable of exerting pressures of nearly 2 tons to the square foot against objects placed in their path (Eaton, 1961).

The lower limit of wave erosion is much less certainly known. Estimates vary widely, possibly reflecting the prejudices of the estimator. Observational evidence seems to indicate that ordinary waves can generate currents capable of moving sand at depths of not much more than 40 feet—although ripples and other signs of disturbance of the sea floor are often seen at depths of 100 to 200 feet below sea level. Average wave currents alone are seldom strong enough to move gravel and cobbles below depths of 20 feet (King, 1959). The lower effective limit of wave transportation and erosion is called *wave base;* obviously its depth differs on different coasts just as the upper limit does.

Wave and current erosion and transport make some portions of a coast retreat and others advance, a complicated pattern of trading, as it were, along a coast line. Material that is eroded from a point or headland may be deposited by a longshore current in a nearby bay or marsh. In the long run, erosion and deposition may attain a rough equilibrium; or one may outpace the other. In Britain, for example, in the 35 years immediately preceding 1911 it is estimated that 4,692 acres were lost to the sea while 35,444 acres were gained. The latter were chiefly salt marshes, sand spits, beaches, and bars. On the other hand, the island of Heligoland in the North Sea off the German coast in A.D. 800 had a 120-mile shoreline, and was a much fought-over piece of terrain in the Viking era. By 1900, this one-time independent dukedom had been reduced to a strongly fortified rock only 3 miles around, encircled by sea walls, breakwaters, and other artificial defenses.

Profile of Shore Zone

Since wave erosion has an upper and lower limit, and works horizontally, it produces landforms differing from those made by downward cutting streams and glaciers.

The most noticeable of coastal landforms is the *sea cliff*. Its height depends upon a variety of factors, including the power of the attacking waves, the slope of the land surface, and the resistance of its rocks. Obviously, a headland of granite is likely to be much tougher than one made of chalk. The imposing height of the chalk cliffs near Dover results from the erosional weakness of this rock, as well as the fury of the sea's attack in a North Atlantic gale.

As a sea cliff recedes before the onslaught of the waves, a planed-off rock bench is cut at its base, called a *wave-cut platform*. Sometimes it will be bare, abraded rock, interrupted, perhaps, by tide pools, and occasionally by un-

reduced remnants of the cliff, known as *stacks* (Fig. 14-13). Where the platform is mantled with sand, it is the *beach*. Seaward of the platform there may be an accumulation of wave- and current-transported material which constitutes the *marine-built terrace*. Whether or not this last feature will exist or not depends in part on the strength of waves and currents, especially the longshore current. Should the current be strong enough, it may sweep the sediment into the mouth of the next bay down the coast instead of accumulating it at the base of the cliff from which it came.

The minor subdivisions of the shore zone are named on the accompanying diagram (Fig. 14-15), and the relationship of one to the other is indicated there. Remembering the subtleties of these various subdivisions is not half so impor-

FIG. 14-13 *Sea cliffs near San Simeon, Calif. An isolated stack stands at the left. Landward from the cliff the elevated wave-cut platform, which skirts an old sea cliff, is surmounted by an old stack. (Photograph by John S. Shelton.)*

tant, however, as recognizing that the shore zone is one of the more dynamically active erosional theaters on Earth. This is a zone whose characteristics are shared between land and sea. When the tide is in it is submerged. When the tide is out, and if the range is great, then a broad expanse of the shore zone may be exposed to the air where it can be acted upon by agencies such as the wind and the rain, and in the Arctic it may be modified by shore ice.

Parts of the profile of the shore zone are particularly well displayed on those coasts that have been uplifted by crustal movements in the comparatively recent geologic past. Some of the more striking examples are the coasts of much of Peru and Chile, California and Oregon, New Zealand, Scandinavia, and the Arctic islands. These coasts may be bordered by a whole flight of *terraces,* which are elevated wave-cut plat-

FIG. 14-14 *A wave-cut platform cut across Tertiary sedimentary strata, at Seal Rocks, Oregon. A sill of basalt forms the row of stacks. (Photograph by Parke Snavely.)*

forms. On some coasts these may resemble a gigantic stairway with the former sea cliffs acting as risers. On the Palos Verdes Hills in southern California, there are at least thirteen of these former shorelines, rising to almost 1,400 feet (Fig. 6-4).

Shoreline Classification

Though the problem of classifying shorelines may appear simple, it is complex enough that no system devised in the last century has won universal acclaim. Even the proponents of some of the proposed classifications have grown disenchanted with their own creations. Among the manifold reasons for this difficulty is the fact that shorelines range through all the climatic environments of the world, from Antarctica where for thousands of miles the shore is an unbroken cliff of ice, to coasts in the tropics which may be fronted by mile-wide forests of sea-dwelling trees such as the mangrove.

Controlling to some degree the pattern of landforms that may develop along a particular coast are the different kinds of rocks that crop

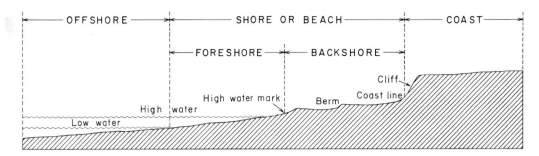

FIG. 14-15 *Subdivisions of the shore zone.*

out, their attitudes, and their relative resistance to erosion. As if this milieu were not complex enough, two other factors are also of great importance: (1) crustal instability which has caused some coastal areas to be uplifted or depressed relative to sea level, and (2) actual changes in sea level itself. By their very nature these latter will be world-wide in their effect, and to them the name of *eustatic* change of sea level is given. Crustal changes, on the other hand, are purely local.

That sea level is inconstant may surprise some people; it has certainly fluctuated widely through quite a vertical distance in late and postglacial times, or within the last 17,000 years. As we have already learned, during the latter part of the ice age sea level was 240 to 300 feet lower than it is today. Then sea level apparently rose at a fairly constant rate up to about 6,000 years ago (Fig. 14-16). In these last 6,000 years it has fluctuated through a narrow range of 10 or 12 feet above or below present sea level (Fairbridge, 1960). Interestingly enough, this world-wide relative stability coincides roughly with the appearance of the maritime civilizations around the shores of the Mediterranean Sea and the Persian Gulf, so that ancient harbors of the Egyptians, Persians, Phoenicians, and Minoans correspond roughly to the sea level of today.

Today's sea level is far from stationary, however. Beginning around 1850 it started to rise, as shown by a careful comparison of tide gauges from seaports all over the world. This rise, which now amounts to about 4.5 inches per century, almost certainly correlates with the virtually world-wide recession of glaciers and is a result of the return of their water to the sea.

On some coasts the effects of this eustatic change are augmented or diminished by movements of the Earth's crust. In areas such as northern North America and Scandinavia, which were burdened under a load of ice in the Pleistocene, the land is now rebounding. Perhaps the greatest rate measured at the present time is along the shores of the Gulf of Bothnia where the rise

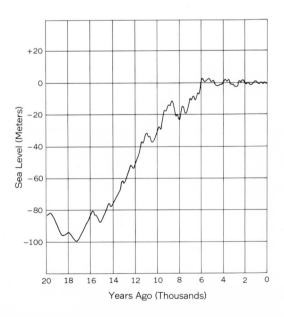

FIG. 14-16 *Recent changes in sea level.*

amounts to 11 mm. per year (slightly less than 0.5 inch).

Other coasts such as those of the Netherlands, which are in a deltaic area of rapid subsidence, are sinking, in this case at the rate of nearly 4 inches per century. No wonder that with a total rate of sinking of around 8 inches per century—4 inches from subsidence and 4.5 from rising sea level—that, beginning with the great floods of medieval times, the Dutch have been compelled to resort to the construction of an extraordinary complex of dikes and coastal defenses upon which their national survival depends.

The significant thing to remember is that the last major postglacial change to affect the shorelines of the world has been the rise of sea level by something like 300 feet, thus making nearly all the coasts of the world show the effects of submergence. This may take the form of long incursions of the sea into former river valleys, such as those of the Delaware, the Hudson, and the Potomac, or the invasion of coastal valleys such as those forming the arms of San Francisco and Sydney harbors, or the flooding of ice-deepened valleys, such as the fjords of Norway, Scotland, Labrador, Alaska, or New Zealand.

It is a rare coast where recent uplift has overcome the 300 feet of submergence, so that the effects of elevation are dominant over those of subsidence. Even in those parts of Scandinavia where postglacial uplift amounts to nearly 1,000 feet, this has not been enough to drive the sea from the fjords, some of which extend 50 or more miles inland.

Recognizing, then, the extraordinarily complicated nature of the coastal environment and the lack of any satisfactory classification of the

FIG. 14-17 *The embayed coastline north of San Francisco, Calif., showing the Pacific Ocean at the left and part of San Francisco Bay at the right. (Photograph by Aero Photographers.)*

FIG. 14-18 *The sea has flooded the ice-sculptured valleys along the coast of Maine. (Photograph by John S. Shelton.)*

world's shorelines, the discussion here is limited to only two representative types out of the myriad possibilities. The two selected, the *embayed coasts* and *plains coasts,* are typical of many of the coasts of the temperate parts of North America and Europe. The same principles that are developed in the description of these two types can be applied to other shorelines in other lands and in other environments.

Embayed Coasts

Typically these are coasts in which the sea extends inland, sometimes for long distances, in embayments such as those shown in Figs. 14-17, 14-18. Should these indentations have been shaped by stream erosion before their invasion by salt water, such an embayed coast is known as a *ria coast,* from the name applied to the southern shore of the Bay of Biscay.

Deep trough-like arms of the sea penetrating far inland and shaped by glaciers are known as *fjords.* Such ice-modified coasts are grandly picturesque, and because of the unflagging zeal of the tourist agencies in many of the countries where they are located, they are familiar to virtually every TV-viewer, movie-goer, or reader of travel ads. Prominent among fjord coasts are those of Norway, Scotland, Iceland, Greenland, Labrador, British Columbia and Alaska, New Zealand, and southern Chile. In general, fjord coasts are likely to be encountered along hilly or mountainous coasts in higher latitudes north or south of the equator.

How a particular coast may have become embayed may be difficult to determine. Perhaps the land subsided, in which case the sea invaded or "drowned" pre-existing river valleys. Or the land may have remained stationary and the postglacial rise of sea level flooded low-lying parts of it. In fjord coasts it is possible that neither of these circumstances alone gave such distinctive coasts their unusual attributes. The deep, narrow, sea-penetrated fjords may well have been excavated in large part below the sea level of the time by glacial ice. This ice would not have floated off until at least eight-ninths of its thickness was submerged. When the ice melted at the close of the Pleistocene the sea moved in to occupy the space it once occupied.

Something of the progressive changes that the relatively more commonplace ria coast is likely to undergo as a result of its modification by the waves and currents of the sea are shown in the set of diagrams (Fig. 14-19).

In the first stage the sea has come to rest, either through subsidence of the land or a rise of sea level, upon a land mass whose surface has been shaped by stream erosion. Former ridges now extend seaward as headlands, and the sea may reach inland as an embayment or estuary, perhaps much as Chesapeake Bay does.

The second diagram shows some of the changes that might be anticipated with time. Since most of the fury of the sea is concentrated on the headlands, they are soon made to terminate in sea cliffs. If there is a longshore current in the sea, then debris supplied by wave erosion of the cliff tails off downstream to be deposited in a submarine embankment called a *spit*, which may partially enclose the entrance to the bay (Fig. 14-20). Streams entering the bay deposit their sediment when their velocity is abruptly checked and thus build deltas out into the relatively still water.

In the later history of such a coast the headlands may retreat inland until a time comes when they have receded as far as the innermost bay head. Then the coast will have lost its original indented character and will be cliffed throughout much of its length. What irregularities there are will very largely reflect the relative resistance of the rocks cropping out along the cliff face.

Few coasts have advanced to this last stage because of the brief span of time that has elapsed since sea level reached its present height. Among those that have just about reached this stage are the cliffed coasts near Dover in southern England or near Dunkerque in northern France. These cliffs are cut in exceptionally

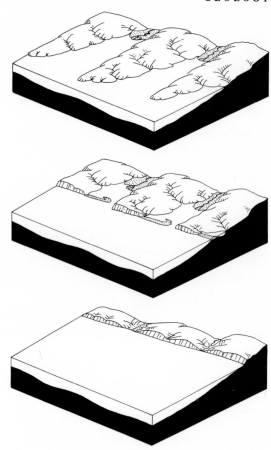

After D. W. Johnson, *Shore Processes and Shoreline Development*, 1919. By permission of John Wiley & Sons, Inc.

FIG. 14-19 *Development of ria coast. In the top diagram, the embayments are as yet unmodified by waves and currents. In the center block, cliffs front the headlands and spits partly block the bays, into which streams are building deltas. In the lower diagram, the coast has been straightened to a line of cliffs.*

weak rock, chalk, and are exposed to the full brunt of wave attack in the Channel.

What happens after a coast achieves this pattern of a nearly continuous cliff fronted by a wave-cut platform is hard to say. Although no one has seen such a coast, this does not prevent us from speculating about it. Possibly, with the passage of time the wave-cut platform may become immensely broad, assuming that wave attack continues to be effective and that sea level remains constant. Probably, too, a sea cliff would mark the inner margin, although it would lose height in time as the land mass behind it was gradually worn away by mass movement, by erosion of streams, glaciers, or the wind.

Plains Coasts

Some coasts of the world are fringed by long, narrow sand bars—in some places in contact with the land and in others standing far offshore. Perhaps the extreme example in our country is the nearly continuous sand bar forming Capes Hatteras, Lookout, and Fear, and standing as much as 30 miles offshore from the Carolina coast.

A map of the United States shows that sand bars similar to these make long chains, like linked sausages, extending from Long Island,

New York, around Florida and the Gulf of Mexico, to the southern end of Texas. A comparable chain of sandy islands stretches along the low coasts of the Netherlands, Friesland, and Denmark around the southeastern margin of the North Sea.

Many articles have been written about the origin of these distinctive features. They are conspicuous elements along the coasts where they occur and in fact have played quite a role in history. The ill-fated Roanoke Island colonists of 1587 settled on one of these, and when they vanished into the unknown interior of the continent they took with them to her death the first-born English child in America, Virginia Dare.

In the Civil War these sandy bars and islands were the locale of scores of amphibious landings and minor naval operations. Gaining control of the offshore islands and the passes between them was of the utmost importance to the Union Navy and proved to be a formidable task. The shallow, unlighted passes (or openings) through the barrier islands, with their endlessly shifting channels, were a boon to the blockade runners

FIG. 14-20 *A curved spit nearly closes the opening into Bolinas lagoon, north of San Francisco, Calif. Tidal channels meander across the mud flats. (Photograph by Aero Photographers.)*

FIG. 14-21 *A plains coast, bordered by an off-shore bar on which are sand dunes. The bar shelters a lagoon.*

with their shallow draft and greater maneuverability than the vessels of the blockading fleet.

Unpromising as such low, and often unstable, islands may be, on occasion they may be the sites of large and flourishing communities—including such metropolitan concentrations as Galveston and Atlantic City, as well as scores of beach and resort centers.

The diagram (Fig. 14-21) of a coast bordered by these sandy islands shows that it has about the same pattern as the coast where cities such as these are built. To reach such a city one must cross a broad stretch of shallow water, a *lagoon,* separating the island from the mainland. The island itself is commonly only a few feet higher than sea level, and the most conspicuous natural objects on its surface are sand dunes (Fig. 14-22), which are much overshadowed at Atlantic City by the resplendent towers of beach hotels.

The origin of these offshore bars is still unresolved. One theory is that they probably start in

water at about the depth where the larger waves break. As these waves break, they scour the sea floor and heap sand up in a low ridge landward of their so-called plunge point. In time the sand piled up in such a bar reaches the surface. Then the portion exposed to the air is vulnerable to having its loose sand picked up by the wind to be dumped in the lagoon.

As waves continually undermine the seaward base of the sand island and wind transports sand exposed above sea level toward the land, the whole structure migrates shoreward.

Ultimately, a day will come when the offshore bar migrates all the way to the mainland and the coastal swamp is overwhelmed and destroyed. Much of the sand in the bar then may be driven up on land to construct a belt of coastal dunes. The coast itself, now exposed to the full onslaught of ocean waves and denied the protection once afforded by the offshore islands, is likely to become cliffed throughout its length. In this way it will be virtually identical with the later stages of the sequence described for an embayed coast.

Among the problems concerning these curious sandy barriers are, first of all, where did the sand come from? There are two leading possibilities: either the sand was shifted by longshore currents running parallel to the coast and was reworked by waves, or it was picked up off the sea floor by waves scouring the bottom and carried forward by them to be piled up in an embankment. Because the sea floor appears to be deeper outside the bar than inside the lagoon (Fig. 14-21), Johnson (1919) concluded that the sea bottom had indeed been scoured, and thus may have been the major source of material.

Another problem has to do with the nature of the coast along which offshore bars develop. Johnson (1919), whose description of them is still the classic work, believed them to be characteristic of coasts newly emerged from the sea. This seems a strange belief today, since some of the better known examples in the world, as those bordering the mid-Atlantic states, are in the immediate vicinity of splendid specimens of sub

FIG. 14-22 *Moriches Inlet, Long Island, N. Y. Currents carry great quantities of sand into the lagoon through the pass that cuts the offshore bar. (Photograph by Fairchild Aerial Surveys, Inc.)*

mergence such as Chesapeake and Delaware bays. The consensus today probably would be that offshore bars are not by themselves indicators of emergence or submergence at all. Apparently they form where the right environment of a gently sloping, shallow, sand-surfaced sea floor, and waves of generally constant direction and magnitude are available. True, an uplifted sea floor may provide this setting, but a glacial outwash plain encroached upon by an advancing sea will serve the purpose equally well. In fact, this latter appears to be the state of affairs on the southern shore of Long Island.

SPECIAL PROBLEMS

Origin of Submarine Canyons

To return briefly to the depths of the sea, one of their many intriguing features whose explanation eludes our understanding are the deep, steep-walled, canyon-like furrows that are incised in the submarine slopes bordering most of the continents of the world. Some of these "valleys" beneath the sea have been known since the

eighteenth century, especially the shallow inner portions of ones marginal to the North Sea, because these could be reached by the lead lines of sailing ships of that day. Canyons on the Atlantic coast of the United States were first described about the time of the Civil War, and by the beginning of this century their presence was known on both coasts of the United States. When these canyons were discovered a dispute broke out over their origin, and it has continued with varying degrees of intensity ever since. At times, however, the more candid oceanographers will admit that we are not much closer to an understanding of their origin than we were a generation ago.

Roughly thirty years ago the echo-sounder, or fathometer, was introduced into general use on merchant ships, naval vessels, and hydrographic ships of the principal maritime countries. At the same time enormous strides were being made in the improvement of navigational devices, and now a ship's position in coastal waters can be determined within a few hundred yards.

There are limitations, however, to what is actually known about the configuration of these canyons. The echo-sounder sends out a pulse which might be thought of as a spherical shell continuously expanding outward through the water from a transducer on a ship's hull. When such a wave encounters a narrow steep-sided depression on the sea floor, echoes may result which distort the true picture. Also, the pattern of such canyons as recorded on a fathometer becomes increasingly blurred with depth.

Before reviewing some of the explanations offered for submarine canyons we might briefly consider some of the things now known about them:

1. Canyons are known to exist off nearly all the coasts of the world. The fact that the greatest number of them appear to be off the coasts of Europe and the United States possibly is a reflection of the greater number of detailed surveys there.
2. Canyons occur not only on continental slopes

facing the open sea, but are incised in slopes bordering closed submarine basins, such as those off southern California, or in nearly enclosed seas, such as the Mediterranean.

3. Their relationship to rivers on land is ambiguous. Some canyons have no streams opposite their heads, others do. Some canyons extend across the continental shelf, others do not. Few extend as far as the mouths of actual rivers, or penetrate into the continental interior, but the largest of all, the Congo submarine valley, does, since it heads at least 25 miles into the Congo estuary.
4. Many of these canyons are imposing affairs, ranking among the grander topographic features of the Earth. The Congo canyon, for example, is 130 miles long and descends to a depth of at least 10,000 feet. Its floor is 5,000 feet deeper in some places than the continental shelf in which it is cut.
5. From the information furnished from both the lead- and echo-sounding of these canyons, their walls flare outward much like a giant V, and thus they resemble the walls of stream canyons on land. Their floors also appear to slope continuously forward and to be concave upwards in their longitudinal profile, in this respect also resembling land canyons. The gradients of submarine canyons appear to be steeper than their nearest counterparts on land. The submarine canyon opposite the mouth of the Salinas River in central California has an average slope of 4°, while the river has a declivity of only 0.1° near its mouth.
6. Submarine canyons are cut in a great variety of rocks, including granite, and the rocks they penetrate appear to range from ones of great geologic antiquity to strata deposited as recently as the Pleistocene. The last are important in any theory of canyon origin because such a theory will have to account for the recency of some canyon-cutting.
7. Some canyons head almost in the modern surf zone, and this appears to be true of many of the California examples. Others, such as those bordering the Atlantic coastal states, are confined chiefly to the continental slope and barely nick the continental shelf. Since the shelf is broad, their heads are as much as 80 miles offshore.
8. The great depths to which many of these canyons descend is one of their more difficult

attributes to explain. How far down some of them go is unknown because of the uncertainties inherent in echo-sounding, but the evidence is strong that the mouths of many of the larger ones are at least 12,000 feet below sea level. Incidentally, many of these canyons appear to have fan-like accumulations on the sea floor beyond their mouths. Some of these fans consist of sand and other inshore detritus much more characteristic of shallower depths than where they are found today. Also, within the limits of accuracy attainable at present, the evidence is strong that some of the fans are scored by outward-radiating furrows.

9. Lastly, as is true for so many natural phenomena, more than one kind of canyon is known, and therefore no single cause can be appealed to to explain them. There appear to be at least three major types: (a) relatively shallow trenches on the continental shelf—in many cases extensions of streams on land, such as the Hudson; (b) deep and narrow canyons cut in the continental slopes; and (c) broad, level-floored shallower troughs in the greater depths of the open ocean. These last have only recently been described, but one of them discovered east of Newfoundland by scientists from Columbia University may be over 1,000 miles long.

As mentioned earlier, there has been no dearth of hypotheses to explain these submarine canyons. The theories can conveniently be grouped into two major categories. The first explanation is that the canyon-cutting had been done essentially by surface streams with later submergence of their valleys. The second theory is that the canyons have been carved by some submarine agency, that is, by some process operating wholly within the sea.

The world-wide occurrence of these puzzling troughs, the fact that some are opposite the mouths of rivers on land, the continuous forward slope of the submarine canyon floor, their sinuous pattern, and the existence of tributaries, naturally led many workers to the conclusion that the canyons might have been cut by rivers at a time when sea level was lower than it is today. At first it was thought that the eustatic lowering of sea level during the ice age when perhaps 20,000,000 cubic miles of water were locked up in glaciers on land might have done the trick. However, the consensus among oceanographers is that the sea level lowering amounted to only 50 fathoms or so, leaving us far short of the 2,000 fathoms needed for the cutting of the deeper canyons.

An amendment to this fundamental idea is that perhaps the canyons were cut to a less forbiddingly great depth as a result of a moderate lowering of sea level, and then were warped downwards as a result of a relative sinking of the ocean basins or an elevation of the continental landmass. This alternative has the virtue of explaining the steeper gradient of the submarine canyons than that of equivalent streams on land, but it runs into difficulties geologically. There is little evidence to support the concept of a world-wide downwarping of continental coasts, and this becomes especially unlikely in enclosed water bodies such as the Mediterranean or the Caribbean. Furthermore, we cannot explain the canyons which have no counterpart on land.

An alternative proposal is that the canyons may be very old geologically, and thus might well have been cut at a time in the remote geologic past when sea level had a different relationship to the land than it has today. This alternative also states that they have been kept free of deposits laid down in more recent geologic time through being flushed out by turbidity currents, while their heads were steepened and perhaps even enlarged by submarine landsliding.

The second of the two leading theories—that the canyons are the result of submarine processes—centers largely around the efficacy of turbidity currents. These, as we have already seen, consist of denser muddy water. They appear to be fully capable of transporting large volumes of sediment from shallow water down the continental slopes to the abyssal depths.

Many geologists and oceanographers appeal to turbidity currents as a means not only of

FIG. 14-23 *Sand spilling over a "fall" about 30 feet high in the Cape San Lucas Submarine Canyon, Baja California, Mexico. (Courtesy of University of California, San Diego.)*

moving sediment but of excavating canyons as well. The advocates of turbidity-current erosion point out that these currents may have been more effective during the ice age than they are today, for (1) sea level was lower then, (2) waves were breaking on the continental shelf whose readily eroded surface was a prolific source of mud, and (3) because this was generally a time of increased storminess and colder oceanic waters, dense, cold, turbidity currents were more common and were more effective than they are today in eroding canyons in the submerged slopes of the continental foundations.

Few will deny the seeming effectiveness of turbidity currents in transporting sediment (Fig. 14-23). Not all geologists are prepared to accept the idea that currents moving through water

of only slightly lower density are capable of eroding great defiles, fully comparable to the Grand Canyon. Some of these are in rocks as resistant as granite.

Actually, the case for the erosional effectiveness of turbidity currents rests largely on Kuenen's model studies in the Netherlands, and the relatively few reported incidents of submarine cable failures, such as the Grand Bank episode, and some sizable submarine slumps triggered off by earthquakes.

There the matter stands at the moment. An appeal to a world-wide lowering of sea level encounters insuperable difficulties as an explanation by itself. Other alternatives operating in conjunction with sea level changes do not seem capable of accomplishing all they are called upon to achieve. Perhaps largely by default or an imperfect understanding on our part, turbidity currents presently hold the center of the stage as the mechanism favored by the majority of marine geologists. The final answer still eludes us. This is no cause for dismay, however, when we reflect on how little we know of the internal workings of the sea, and yet how far we have advanced toward understanding in the past half-century. It is a real stimulus to creative scientific thinking to have a problem as vast, as unknown, and as intriguing as the origin of these canyons in the sea still awaiting a solution.

Origin of Coral Reefs

Among the more romantic aspects of the natural world, few features usurp the position held by coral reefs in the imagination of mankind (Fig. 14-24). Their appeal reaches back across the centuries, since the first Western European seafarers made their way into the distant reaches of the tropical seas. This is the world made famous by Herman Melville, by Robert Louis Stevenson, by the stirring events arising out of the contentious voyage of H.M.S. *Bounty,* and, in our time, by the naval conflict that surged back and forth across the vast domain of the

Pacific in the years 1942-5. For those who are interested, the modern world of these far-distant islands is described in a most effective fashion in the novels and essays of James Michener.

Probably only a relatively few people realize that coral reefs once excited the scientific world as greatly as they fired the thoughts of the more romantically inclined literary figures of the nineteenth century. Few environments provide a setting more unlike that of the western world than this, nor a way of life more different from ours than that of the sea-roving Polynesians.

Early in the nineteenth century the more expansionist powers fitted out a number of exploring expeditions, and in many cases these included a naturalist among the ship's company. His status in this nautical world was never high, but we can be grateful today that a few such dedicated men broke the scientific trail for us.

FIG. 14-24 *A barrier reef encircling a volcanic island (Office of Naval Research.)*

Charles Darwin will always stand chief among these. As a young man of twenty-two he was assigned as a naturalist to H.M.S. *Beagle*. He sailed on this 10-gun brig of only 235 tons, scarcely 100 feet long, carrying 74 persons, on a voyage that circumnavigated the world. His zoological observations when sifted through, compiled, and analyzed contributed to the conclusions stated in the *Origin of Species* and are known to almost every literate person as the theory of evolution.

Few people are aware that Darwin's scientific training had been in geology as much as in any other branch of science, and that on the voyage of the *Beagle* he made great numbers of observations on rocks, volcanic features, fossils, etc. Among the many wonders he beheld, few aroused his interest more than the fairyland world below the sea that was created by the corals. Though he actually saw only a few reefs, Darwin had the insight to recognize that there were three major kinds: (1) fringing, (2) barrier reefs, and (3) *atolls;* and that these were

related to each other in a logical and gradational sequence.

Darwin believed that this succession from one reef type to another could be achieved by the upgrowth of coral from a sinking foundation, such as a subsiding volcano. So long as the rate of coral growth was more rapid than the rate of sinking, Darwin argued that the progression would be from a fringing reef through the barrier stage, and with the disappearance through subsidence of the central island, only a reef-enclosed lagoon, or atoll, would survive (Fig. 14-25).

Although at first Darwin's theory, which he set forth in detail in 1842 in a book, *The Structure and Distribution of Coral Reefs,* was widely acclaimed, it was not long before firm opposition developed. However, before we launch into the details of the coral reef controversy, there

are a few facts about coral organisms and coral reefs that should be kept in mind.

Corals are animals, although to most people they look much more like plants, especially those that form elaborately branching and re-branching structures. They belong in the same general group of spineless animals as the sea anemones and jellyfish. After a brief free-floating stage in their infancy, corals settle down, and having anchored themselves on a firm foundation, which very commonly may be the skeleton of one of their predecessors, they proceed to secrete a limy exterior wall which encloses their fragile, jelly-like bodies. Since the same site will prove attractive to many corals, if it is a favorable one, they may aggregate to form large colonies of closely-packed individual coral organisms—resembling in many ways the cells in a beehive. That creatures as frail as these can construct the calcareous edifices they do in the face of the full onslaught of the waves of the open ocean is a seeming miracle. Few can watch the long Pacific swell hurl itself in a thunderous fury of foam at so delicate a structure as this rampart built of the bodies, living

FIG. 14-25 *Block diagram of the succession of reef types around a sinking volcanic island, from a fringing reef (front block) to a barrier reef (middle block) to an atoll (rear block).*

After W. M. Davis, *The Coral Reef Problem,* Spec. Pub. No. 9, 1928. By permission of American Geographical Society.

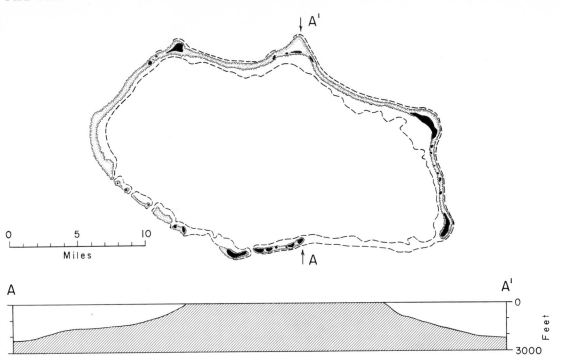

After K. O. Emery, J. I. Tracey, Jr., and H. S. Ladd, 1954. By permission of U.S. Geological Survey.

FIG. 14-26 *A map and cross section of Bikini Atoll.*

and dead, of these minute, flower-like creatures and not be left with a feeling of awe.

For reef corals to flourish, a number of requirements must be fulfilled, and the limitations they impose are important in devising a theory to explain such an inscrutable structure as an atoll. Corals require warm water; it must be at least above 68°F. for them to prosper, and they do best in the range between 77° and 86°F.

In addition to being warm, the sea water should be clear, of normal salinity, and it should be stirred continuously. These last factors explain why reefs do best on the windward side of tropical islands, and why many of the passes, or channels, in a reef are likely to be opposite the mouth of a stream in the central island—this is where the salt water, diluted by fresh, is less favorable for growth.

Sunlight is helpful for reef corals to flourish, and is essential for the growth of the algae (marine plants). The latter are part of the whole reef complex and may contribute as much to its growth as coral. The coral animals supply the algae with CO_2, and the algae in turn supply the O_2 the corals need for life. Since photosynthesis is necessary for the algal life cycle, this, together with the temperature requirement, puts a lower limit on the growth of most reef-building corals of somewhere between 200 and 300 feet.

This necessity of fairly shallow water creates the coral reef problem. How can organisms, whose margin of survival is so slender, build such miraculous structures in the open ocean in water tens of thousands of feet deep?

Fringing and barrier reefs are not as difficult to explain—even such imposing ones as the Great Barrier Reef of Australia, which is 1,260 miles long—as are the atolls. These are made entirely of coral, according to Cloud (1958), and their lagoons lack any central, pre-existing land mass (Fig. 14-26). Some atolls are very

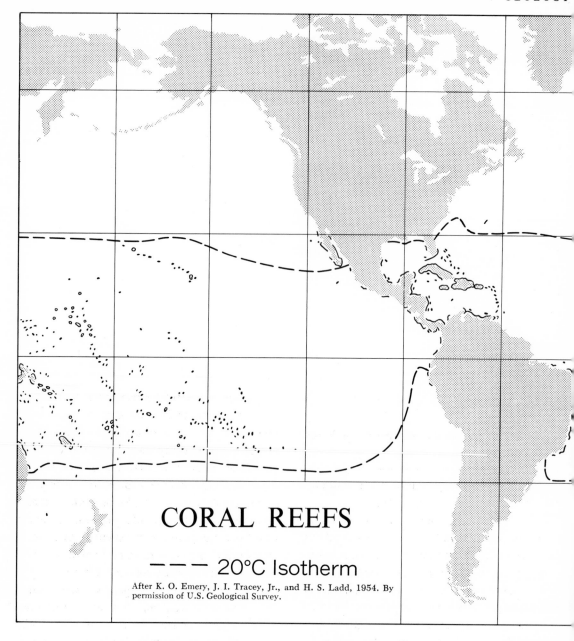

CORAL REEFS

- - - 20°C Isotherm

After K. O. Emery, J. I. Tracey, Jr., and H. S. Ladd, 1954. By
permission of U.S. Geological Survey.

FIG. 14-27 *Coral reefs of the world.*

large—Kwajelein in the Marshall Islands of the South Pacific is 75 miles long and averages as much as 15 miles across. Most are far smaller, some are little more than dots. Incidentally, according to Preston Cloud (1958), there are approximately 330 atolls in the tropical seas of the world, and these are almost exclusively in the Indian and Pacific Oceans (Fig. 14-27).

Nearly all true atolls are low—few have a freeboard of much more than 10 feet. The reef ring consists of solid coral and over it the sea sweeps freely at high tide, and with telling effect during storms. The rest of the time the reef may be just barely awash. In the reef ring are the *reef is-*

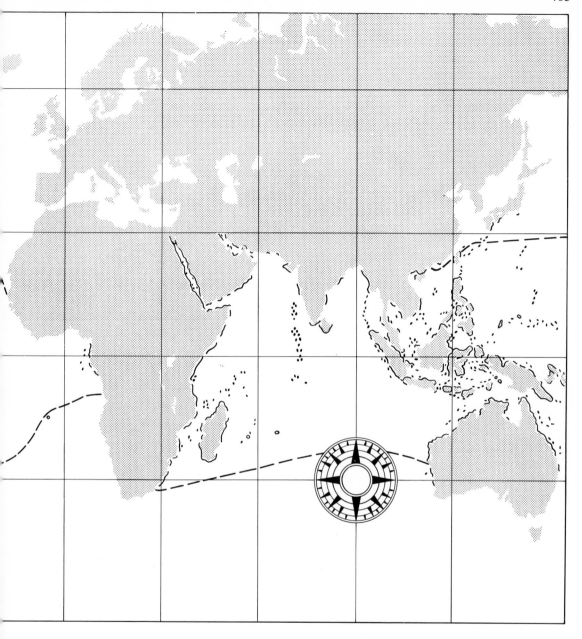

lands—in a sense they are like sand dunes—which are composed of thousands upon thousands of small fragments of ground-up coral, algae, pieces of shell, and the like (Fig. 14-28). On them are rooted the pandanus and the coco palm—lifegivers of the Polynesian world. It is on these tiny specks, in the world's largest oceans, that the whole panorama of one of the world's more challenging ways of life unfolds. In this two-dimensional world one is eternally aware of the encircling sea. No place on Earth could be more vulnerable to the unbridled savagery of a hurricane, whose impact on such a defenseless world is vividly described by Nordhoff and Hall in their novel *Hurricane*. During one of these gales the sea rises with the fall of barometric pressure, and storm-driven waves can strip off the patiently accumulated reef islands like so much bark off a tree—together with all the people and their coco palms, taro patches, boats, villages, and their graves.

During the century since Darwin stated his belief that atolls are the culmination of a progression of upward-building fringing and barrier reefs standing on a subsiding foundation, another theory arose in opposition. This is one that largely bears the stamp of Reginald A. Daly, now dead, but for many years one of the more creative thinkers in North American geology. Daly argued that possibly the foundation upon which an atoll was built stood firm, but sea level oscillated up and down. Since we know that such eustatic changes of sea level did indeed occur during the ice age, the term *Glacial-Control Theory* came to be applied to Daly's hypothesis.

Briefly, his theory runs as follows (Fig. 14-29): typically an open-ocean island, such as a former volcano, might have been planed off by waves to make a broad and nearly level platform. Perhaps a reef may have flourished on this pedestal in interglacial times and have been accompanied by its lagoon, much as atolls are in our day. During a glacial stage, such as the one just ended, sea level was lowered by 300 feet. Daly believed that in this colder, stormier sea most of the corals may have perished; not only because of the more hostile environment but because of exposure to the air as well. The platform was planed off by the waves of the lowered sea, and what reefs there may have been were stripped away.

With the rise of sea level upon the disappearance of the ice sheets, and a consequent warming of the seas, coral reefs were reinstated and grew up to the general level we see today.

One consequence of Daly's hypothesis is that most lagoons should be fairly shallow, and they are when compared to the abyssal depths beyond the reef. Most lagoons appear to be less than 35 fathoms deep, and only a few reach 50—depths quite consistent with the accepted figure for glacial lowering of sea level.

The real test, however, is the depth of the reef foundation. If subsidence operated, it may very well be great; if glacial control has been the mechanism, it should be shallow. Darwin realized that drilling a hole through a reef would be the surest test of his theory, as he suggested in 1881 in a letter to Alexander Agassiz, an American oceanographer and the son of Louis Agassiz.

The first such effort to drill through a reef

FIG. 14-28 *Cross section of a typical reef island.*   *The dashed line is the high tide line.*

By permission of U.S. Geological Survey.

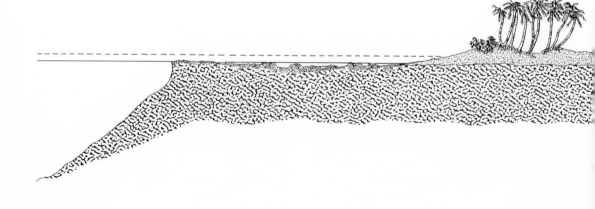

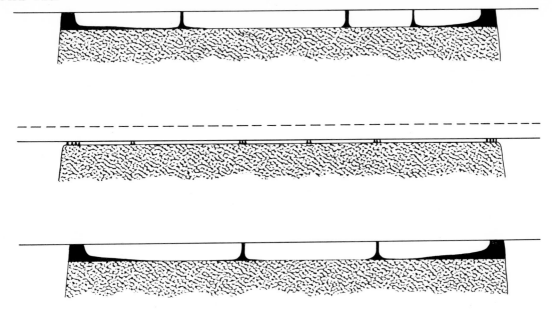

After R. A. Daly, *Changing World of the Ice Age*, 1934. By permission of Yale University Press.

FIG. 14-29 *The Glacial-Control Theory of atolls. Top: cross section of an atoll during an interglacial time.* Middle: *sea level falls during glaciation from its former position (dashed line), the corals die, and the old reefs are stripped away by waves.* Bottom: *with renewed warming the corals re-establish themselves. As sea level rises in post-glacial times, the corals build upward.*

to test the nature of its origin was made by the Royal Society of London in 1896-8, when they drilled a 1,114-foot hole on Funafuti atoll (one of the Ellice Islands, close to the equator in the western Pacific). The Japanese made a similar effort in 1934-6, and reached a depth of 1,416 feet on an island near Okinawa. Although both these holes remained in shallow-water reef material all the way, the interpretation of the cores recovered from them was inconclusive. Advo-

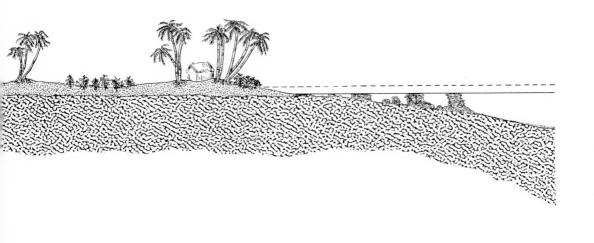

cates of subsidence could claim that this great thickness of reef material represented an upgrowth of shallow-water organisms on a slowly subsiding base. Disbelievers in subsidence could say that since the boreholes were located close to the outer edge of the reef, most of the coral specimens recovered were actually part of a submarine talus slope on the outer margin of the atoll and had slid or rolled to their final resting place from a point of origin close to the surface of the sea.

There the matter stood until shortly after World War II. Fortunately, as part of the environmental studies made in the Marshall Islands in connection with atom-bomb testing, the U. S. Navy drilled a series of deep holes. A total of five were put down on Bikini in 1947, three shallow and two deep, the latter to 1,346 and 2,558 feet. The drill holes remained in coralline material all the way. Three deep holes drilled in 1951 and 1952 on nearby Eniwetok were more decisive. The two deepest, 4,222 and 4,630 feet, went completely through a 4,000-foot cap of shallow-water reef limestone and bottomed in a typical mid-Pacific volcanic rock, basalt. The age of the fossils in the basal limestone was Eocene, which meant that Eniwetok atoll is at the top of a coralline accumulation that has grown upward during the last 60,000,-000 years of Earth history. The rate of subsidence does not appear to have been constant, but ranged between perhaps 50 feet and 170 feet per million years, with the rate slowing down in the later compared with the earlier history of the reef.

Thus some of the events ushering in the nuclear age, a little over a century after Darwin saw his first atoll, serve to vindicate his altogether remarkable insight. There can be little doubt that at least two of the great atolls of the western Pacific in the Caroline and Marshall Islands resulted from the upgrowth of reef organisms on a slowly sinking foundation.

This is not to say, however, that *all* reefs are the result of subsidence. In fact, the more they are studied in detail, the more apparent it becomes that this is a complex subject—not quite as bad as the old saying, "every reef its own story," would imply, but certainly not far from it. We know today that Darwin's original concept is too great a simplification, and that Daly's emphasis on the role of the glacial control of sea level is an element of major importance, but one that Darwin can well be pardoned for overlooking since he was unaware of the profound influence of glaciation on the level of the sea.

There the problem rests. Certainly it is one of the more fascinating ones in the whole realm of geology—a most complex one, too, involving zoology, oceanography, and climatology, as well as geology. It was once thought to be much simpler and was considered in relatively absolute terms, subsidence versus glacial control, for example. Since most workers today are willing to acknowledge that at least three major possibilities exist, it then becomes a problem in studying an individual atoll to determine which one, or combination of several ones, may have operated. The three leading possibilities essentially would appear to be (according to Cloud, 1958):

1. Slow subsidence below a growing reef which may have been a barrier or fringing reef to begin with, or which may have been some other kind of bank or rimmed structure from which coral might have built a reef upward.
2. A slow eustatic rise of sea level from some kind of pre-atoll structure. This might have been an earlier reef on which a later one is superimposed—or a broad, wave-planed platform brought to a favorable depth for coral growth through lowered sea level.
3. Upward growth of reefs from any favorable anchorage, such as a bank or rimmed structure, regardless of its origin, providing it lies at a depth of probably not more than 300 feet.

Perhaps we have tarried overlong on an intriguing byway, but it is one of extraordinary interest, and with air travel what it is today, more people are likely to see and enjoy these organic marvels of the ocean than the hardy few of a century ago who were cut off from their fellowmen for years at a time on an arduous exploring expedition or, like Herman Melville, had to endure the perils and hardships of a voyage on a New England whaling ship in order to reach the distant shores of Polynesia.

Suggested References

Bailey, H. S., Jr., 1953, The voyage of the "Challenger," Scientific American, May.

Bascom, Willard, 1959, Ocean waves, Scientific American, v. 201, p. 74-84.

———, 1961, The hole in the bottom of the sea, Doubleday and Co., Garden City, N. Y.

Bruun, Anton, and others, 1956, The *Galathea* deep sea expedition, Macmillan, New York.

Carson, Rachel, 1950, The sea around us, Oxford Univ. Press, New York.

Cloud, Preston E., Jr., 1958, Nature and origin of atolls, Eighth Pac. Science Congress, v. III-A, p. 1009-1035.

Cornish, Vaughn, 1912, Waves of the sea and other water waves, Open Court Publ. Co., Chicago, Ill.

Cowen, Robert C., 1960, Frontiers of the sea, Doubleday and Co., Garden City, N. Y.

Daly, R. A., 1934, The changing world of the ice age, Yale Univ. Press, New Haven, Conn.

———, 1942, The floor of the ocean, Univ. of North Carolina Press, Chapel Hill, N. C.

Darwin, G. H., 1962, The tides and kindred phenomena in the solar system, W. H. Freeman and Co., San Francisco, Calif.

Davis, W. M., 1928, The coral reef problem, Amer. Geog. Soc., Special Publ. 9.

Defant, Albert, 1958, Ebb and flow; the tides of earth, air, and water, Univ. of Michigan Press, Ann Arbor, Mich.

Eaton, J. P., Richter, D. H., and Ault, W. V., 1961, The tsunami of May 23, 1960, on the Island of Hawaii, Seismological Soc. of Amer., Bull., v. 51, p. 135-157.

Emery, K. O., Tracey, J. I., Ladd, H. S., and others, (1945-1959), Bikini and nearby atolls, U. S. Geol. Survey, Prof. Paper 260 (a-w).

Engel, Leonard, 1961, The sea, Life Nature Library, Time, Inc., New York.

Fairbridge, R. W., 1960, The changing level of the sea, Scientific American, v. 2020, p. 70-79.

Guilcher, Andre, 1958, Coastal and submarine morphology, Methuen and Co., Ltd., London.

Hamilton, E. L., 1956, Sunken islands of the mid-Pacific mountains, Geol. Soc. Amer., Memoir 64.

Hedgpeth, J. W., and others, 1957, Treatise on marine ecology and paleoecology, Geol. Soc. Amer., Memoir 67.

Johnson, D. W., 1919, Shore processes and shoreline development, John Wiley and Sons, Inc., New York.

King, C. A. M., 1959, Beaches and coasts, Edward Arnold, London.

Kuenen, Ph. H., 1950, Marine geology, John Wiley and Sons, Inc., New York.

Ladd, H. S., 1961, Reef building, Science, v. 134, p. 703-715.

Newell, N. D., 1959, Questions of the coral reefs, Natural History, v. LXVIII, nos. 3 and 4.

Piccard, Jacques, and Abercrombie, T. J., 1960, Man's deepest dive, Natl. Geographic, v. 118, p. 224-239.

Shepard, Francis P., 1959, The earth beneath the sea, Johns Hopkins Press, Baltimore, Md.

Steers, J. A., 1946, The coast of England and Wales, Cambridge Univ. Press, London.

Stewart, J. Q., 1945, Coast, waves, and weather for navigators, Ginn and Co., Boston, Mass.

Stommel, Henry, 1958, The Gulf Stream, Univ. Calif. Press, Berkeley.

Sverdrup, H. U., Johnson, M. W., and Fleming, R. H., 1942, The oceans, their physics, chemistry, and general biology, Prentice-Hall, Inc., Englewood Cliffs, N. J.

Wiens, H. J., 1962, Atoll environment and ecology, Yale Univ. Press, New Haven, Conn.

XV

Mountains

Of all the landforms on the Earth's surface, none, surely, is closer to the heart of geology than mountains. The greatest variety of rocks is visible in their valleys and on their ridges and peaks. Many of the more dramatic aspects of erosion are concentrated in them. Landslides and other kinds of mass movement have their maximum development; streams are more powerful in mountains where their gradients are steeper; frost-riving efficiently subdues the higher alpine summits; lastly, it is in high mountains that glaciers add the final touch to make montane scenery a source of joy and inspiration to many of us dwellers of the lowlands.

That mountains can be a place of solace and of beauty is a relatively new point of view. Mountains were greatly feared by travelers in medieval times, and rightly so. Roads crossing them were few, and almost all were rough and tedious. Inns were incredibly crude by our standards and distances between them in terms of travel time were great. Dangers from landslides, cold, snow, and armed robbers were very real. Certainly few people would have been deranged enough to climb a mountain just for the sake of climbing it.

By the eighteenth century a change set in. Not only had climbers started Alpine ascents, but there was an awakening intellectual curiosity as to the nature of the mountain world. One of the leaders in this emerging inquiry was a Swiss, Horace Benedict de Saussure (1740-99), who, in addition to making a first ascent of Mont Blanc, wrote a four-volume work, *Voyages dans les Alpes,* in which, among descriptions of birds, flowers, trees, etc., is a first account of the complex structure of the rocks within these famous mountains.

Mountains have been explored scientifically through the years since the middle of the eighteenth century, until today we know vastly more than our predecessors about the rocks and structures found within them. We still are far from understanding how mountains are formed, and what processes operate within the Earth's crust to raise some of them, such as the Andes and Himalayas, to their imposing heights.

Fortunately, some mountains are relatively simple compared with others; these we shall dispose of first. Like many other natural phenomena mountains are difficult to divide into classifications that have real meaning in the natural world. We are prone to make rigid, pigeonhole categories into which to fit features that may have had more than one kind of origin, or that tend to merge with one another rather than to have sharp boundaries. The very abbreviated classification below serves to differ-

---

Mount Gardner, Ellsworth Mountains, Antarctica. (Courtesy of Science.)

entiate the more distinctive types and yet not be so arbitrary as to be inflexible.

VOLCANIC MOUNTAINS

These are built up of an accumulation of magmatic material, such as ash, pumice, bombs, and lava flows.

BLOCK MOUNTAINS

These owe their elevation to differential movement along faults, so that some parts of the crust are raised and others lowered relative to one another.

FOLDED MOUNTAINS

These commonly are made up of folded sedimentary rocks.

COMPLEX MOUNTAINS

This composite class consists generally of igneous and strongly deformed sedimentary and metamorphic rocks, but commonly this category grades into the preceding class of folded mountains.

Volcanic Mountains

Some of the world's best-loved and most scenic peaks are volcanoes. Among the more familiar are Fujiyama, Mt. Rainier, Mt. Etna, Mauna Loa, and the lofty Andean summits, such as El Misti and Aconcagua. Volcanic mountains may range in size from cinder cones to such a monolithic edifice as Mauna Loa, which, counting the submerged as well as the visible part, rises 30,000 feet from a base 90 miles in diameter on the sea floor; it is the world's largest isolated mountain mass.

Volcanoes constitute a fairly high percentage of the world's mountains; this is apparent on the map showing the distribution of active craters (Fig. 3-1). Add to these the extinct centers, such as the Cascade volcanoes of the western United States (Fig. 15-1), and the total number is large. Could the waters of the sea be rolled away, we should be doubly impressed, because then the peaks of many of the volcanic

FIG. 15-1 *A chain of volcanic mountains surmounts the Cascade Range in Oregon and Washington. Mount Jefferson is the closest, and in the background, from left to right, are Mounts St. Helens, Rainier, Hood, and Adams. (Photograph by John S. Shelton.)*

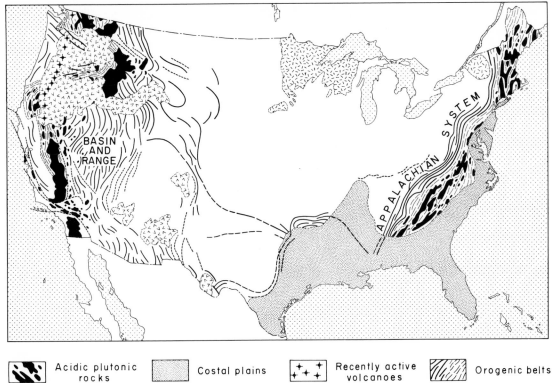

Acidic plutonic rocks

Post-orogenic volcanic rocks

Costal plains

Shield

Recently active volcanoes

High-angle faults

Orogenic belts

After P. B. King, *The Evolution of North America*, Copyright ©
1959 Princeton University Press. By permission.

0   500   1000

MILES

FIG. 15-2 *Tectonic map of the United States.*

islands would loom above the surrounding abyssal plain, and we should also see for the first time the hidden slopes of seamounts, many of which must be volcanic.

However, volcanic mountains differ fundamentally from all the others in our classification since they are accumulations of material piled up on the Earth's surface. In Chapter III we discussed the great diversity of form that volcanic mountains may show; there is no need to repeat the description here. The chief point to be emphasized is that volcanoes are heaps of pyroclastic material or of lava or of both. Although they may be grouped in clusters, or even chains, they do not form the long and nearly continuous ridges so characteristic of folded or complex mountains, such as the Alps,

the Himalayas, or the Cordillera de los Andes. Characteristically, volcanoes rise as conical, or dome-like, mountains above their surroundings.

Block Mountains

To the emigrants making their way with immense travail westward in the Gold Rush days, as well as during the post-Civil War expansion, few elements of the landscape of the arid West were more taxing than the succession of isolated mountain ranges separated from one another by broad and desolate basins, many of which contained saline playas surrounded by gravel-carpeted wastes. This region, now known as the Basin and Range Province, is shown in Fig. 15-2.

To the geologists who accompanied the early exploring expeditions these mountains were a challenge. Obviously their structure was wholly unlike that of the central Appalachians (Fig. 15-2), with nearly continuous ridges broken at long intervals by water gaps such as those of the Cumberland, Potomac, and Susquehanna rivers (Fig. 15-5). By the 1840's the outlines of the geologic structure of the Pennsylvania portion of the Appalachians had been deciphered through the geological surveys of the Rogers brothers, who pointed out that the internal arrangement of the mountains was a succession of synclines and anticlines whose crests and troughs much resembled a train of waves.

Although men looked for a similar geometry in the Great Basin, its discovery eluded the nineteenth century geologists who were attached to the various railway surveying parties or to military expeditions. Instead of the relative simplicity of the central Appalachians, the internal structure of many of the Great Basin ranges is wonderfully complicated with intricate patterns of thrust faults, folded stratified rocks, and complex hierarchies of igneous intrusions. Certainly there was no wave-like progression of rhythmically folded strata.

It remained for one of America's greatest geologists, Grove Karl Gilbert (1843-1918), to solve the riddle of the origin of these mountain ranges. This was a difficult scientific feat indeed, for scientifically next to nothing was

FIG. 15-3 *The base of the straight steep escarpment of these block mountains near Lakeview,* *Oregon, is marked out by a fault. (Courtesy of Oregon State Highway Dept.)*

FIG. 15-4 *East side of the Sierra Nevada and the floor of Owens Valley. (Photograph by Roland von Huene.)*

known of the remote and arid Southwest. No adequate maps existed to even show the location and extent of many of the desert ranges. As a young man of twenty-eight, Gilbert accompanied an exploring party of the Corps of Engineers, U. S. Army. In addition to the difficulties imposed by the hostile terrain, Gilbert, a civilian, had to contend with the arbitrary decisions governing the movements and route of a militarily oriented topographic surveying detachment. That he accomplished so much in so short a time, while still an untried and largely self-taught geologist, earned him an enduring place among the pioneers of scientific exploration.

In simplified terms, Gilbert saw that the unusual topographic form of these generally straight-margined mountains, separated from one another by broad, gravel-floored basins, was most plausibly explained by their having one or more faults along their margins by which they had been uplifted. For its time (1872) this was a bold generalization, but investigations of these and other mountains of the Far West, as well as of comparable ones around the globe in the years since then, support Gilbert's prescience in making a sound generalization from the limited data available to him.

As is often true with scientific discoveries, later work demonstrates that an originally simple concept becomes increasingly complex as more and more information comes to light. No one as yet has devised an explanation for these fault-bordered mountain ranges that is completely satisfactory to geologists. There appears to be a general consensus on the nature of the boundary faults—they are relatively straight along their strike; their dip is steep, perhaps 60-70°; and they appear to be more akin to normal faults than to other types. Very possibly the same general kind of deformation is responsible for long, down-dropped wedges of the Earth's crust such as the Owens Valley, east of the Sierra Nevada in California (Fig. 15-4), the Rhine graben of western Germany, and the system of Rift Valleys of eastern Africa.

Clearly, vertical movements in the Earth's crust have been responsible for the origin of these fault-bordered mountains and troughs. There is no evidence here of compression, or shortening of the Earth's crust, the process that commonly is believed necessary for the formation of structures such as anticlines, synclines, and thrust faults, among others. Whatever the cause may be, its discovery eludes us but remains a challenge for some future generation to solve. From our limited understanding, the forces operating to uplift or depress these blocks of the Earth's crust appear to be unlike the ones responsible for the elevation of complex mountain chains such as the Himalayas, the Andes, the Rockies, and the Alps. Such cordilleras as these belong in the next two categories of folded and complex mountains, which are combined in order to simplify their discussion.

Folded and Complex Mountains

Geologists knew long ago that in many of the world's mountain chains the leading kinds of rocks were sedimentary, or if metamorphosed, were once sedimentary. Even for some of the highest ranges, such as the Himalayas, this generalization seems to hold, for on the upper slopes of Mount Everest, which rises more than 29,000 feet above the sea, there are Tertiary rocks containing fossils that once accumulated on the ocean floor.

Not only are sedimentary rocks likely to be one of the leading components of a mountain range, they commonly are much thicker than their counterparts underlying the neighboring lowlands. This paradoxical relationship was commented on in 1859 by James Hall (1811-98), a young and energetic member of the pioneering New York Geological Survey, at a time when much of upstate New York was still a frontier. He found that Paleozoic strata underlying the Mississippi Valley states, such as Iowa and Illinois, were much thinner than those of identical age underlying the Allegheny Plateau of New York and Pennsylvania. From this observation, as well as from the knowledge he acquired through reading, he reasoned that many of the world's mountains had somehow been formed in regions with abnormal thicknesses of sedimentary rocks.

A contemporary of his, James Dwight Dana (1813-95), had done his stint of wandering as a geologist attached to the vessels of the U. S. Exploring Expedition (1838-42). This was a round-the-world investigation that has disappeared into unmerited oblivion in the scientific memory of this country but deserves to stand

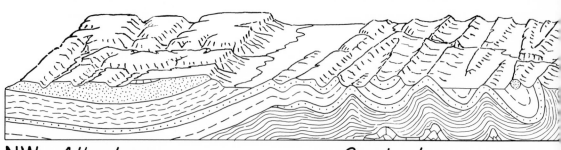

NW *Allegheny
Plateau*

*Central
Appalachians*

with the much better known voyages of the *Beagle* and the *Challenger*. Dana was greatly impressed by Hall's discovery of the abnormal thickness of sedimentary rocks exposed in the Appalachians, and, recognizing the rather unusual circumstances under which such sediments accumulated, coined the name *geosynclinal,* now shortened to *geosyncline,* for the trough in which they were laid down.

Although the two men agreed upon the physical relationships of the rocks and structures in the Appalachians, they differed strongly on how they got that way. Hall believed that the Earth's crust was bowed down as a consequence of the load imposed upon it by a localized accumulation of sediment. The more sediment that was deposited in such a wedge, the deeper the crust would be arched downward. Obviously this made for a rather uncertain equilibrium. The comparatively weak material of these sediments could be crumpled readily and thrown into contorted folds by inward movement of the vise-like margins of the trough. Fracturing of these infolded sediments also provided a means by

---

FIG. 15-5 *A section across the Appalachian Mountains from the Allegheny Plateau on the northwest to the Coastal Plain on the southeast. Narrow water gaps are shown where a river cuts through the ridges formed of resistant rocks in the central Appalachians.*

which magma could invade shallower zones in the Earth's crust, or possibly even reach the surface.

Dana did not believe the weight of such accumulated sediments was capable by itself of bending the crust downward. Without the knowledge that seismology has given us today of varying densities of the material in the Earth's crust and in the mantle, he recognized the difficulty of having relatively light, water-soaked, and unconsolidated or only recently consolidated sediments displace subcrustal material whose density was higher. Dana was one of the earlier geologists to voice the opinion that the Earth was slowly contracting through time, and this contraction of the interior (very likely, he believed, through loss of heat) caused the crust to be thrown into folds, or mountains, much like the wrinkles on the skin of a drying apple.

In the century since then, both points of view have continued to find their adherents, and we still are far from achieving a theory of mountain building which has universal acceptance. Fortunately, we have learned a number of additional facts since the days of Hall and Dana, and as a consequence competing theories nowadays are more sophisticated.

There is general agreement that the Appalachians (Fig. 15-5), for example, progressed

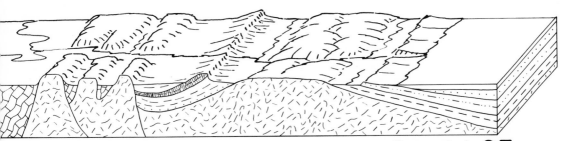

After D. Johnson, *Stream Sculpture on the Atlantic Slope*, 1931.
By permission of Columbia University Press.

Coastal SE
Plain

through an evolutionary sequence somewhat as follows:

(1) A lens of sediment perhaps 30,000 to 40,000 feet thick and 2,000 miles long and 300 miles broad, accumulated slowly through the Paleozoic Era—roughly from around 500 million to about 185 million years ago. From all the evidence contained in the rocks, the source of most of these sediments was east of the modern Appalachians. Sometimes this source land stood relatively high, and streams emptying into the geosynclinal sea carried coarse material such as boulders, gravel, and sand. At other times the source land may have stood lower, and in fact, the source area itself may have been a more easterly parallel and more active geosynclinal trough. One certainty from the record of the rocks that mark its former site, is that it was a region where considerable volcanic activity was concentrated.

Such a thick accumulation of sediments does not mean that the first grain of sand to accumulate settled down through water 6 or 7 miles deep, to be followed by other grains until the geosyncline filled to the brim. In fact, the evidence of the physical and paleontological record is that the water probably was fairly shallow during the 300,000,000 years the trough was in existence. During part of its history, the time the coal beds of West Virginia and Pennsylvania were being laid down, some of the geosyncline was a broad marshland above sea level. At other times it may have been an expansive delta surface, perhaps much resembling the Mississippi Delta of today.

During the long passage of years, much more happened than a peaceful, well-nigh imperceptible sinking of the geosynclinal floor. Times of deformation were interspersed with times of slow subsidence. The disturbed intervals are recorded in the rocks by unconformities, and by structures such as anticlines, synclines, and faults. There were occasional volcanic episodes, and a succession of alternating incursions and retreats of the sea.

(2) Finally this long depositional episode in Earth history, in what is now the eastern United States, ended at the close of the Paleozoic Era. Then, the thousands of feet of patiently accumulated strata were thrown into folds, or were broken by great, low-angle thrust faults—the latter chiefly in the southern part of the range.

(3) Omitting some minor episodes of deformation and volcanism, the mountain range created by this disturbance of the Earth's crust was worn away, and in its place a wide-spread peneplain beveled the upturned edges of the rocks which had been folded and faulted in the late-Paleozoic deformation.

(4) Later still, the barricade of the Appalachians from New England to Alabama was upwarped to its present altitude. As a consequence of this elevation, streams which had wandered sluggishly over a gentle terrain of low relief were rejuvenated and became entrenched in such deep defiles as those now forming the ridge-crossing segments of the Susquehanna, Delaware, and Potomac rivers.

This highly condensed version of the history of the Appalachians embodies what might be regarded as the life cycle of the typical mountain range. From the paragraphs immediately preceding, we have learned that this cycle reduced to its simplest terms consists of: (1) a period of *geosynclinal deposition,* (2) a time of intense *deformation* involving folding, faulting, and possibly igneous activity, (3) an interval of quiescence and widespread *erosion,* and (4) a final episode of vertical *uplift* to carry the range to the height that it now stands. All these steps required something like 500 million years.

In science it often seems that no sooner is a generalization advanced than exceptions leap to the fore. An opponent to the universal applicability of the stages described for the Appalachians does not have to look far to find departures from the rule. One of the more striking exceptions in the United States is the Colorado Plateau. Here an immense pile—more than a mile thick—of nearly horizontal strata has been uplifted bodily more than 7,000 feet above the sea. In its most visited section, the Grand Canyon, this uplift was responsible for the rejuvenation of the Colorado River, that enabled it to excavate its deep canyon.

Essentially the same sequence of events that typifies the Appalachians occurred in other mountains, but was enormously compressed in time. The southern Coast Ranges of California are a good illustration. There, within the short limits of the Pleistocene Epoch strata a mile thick were deposited; then they, as well as the older rocks of the region, were intensely deformed, eroded to make a landscape of moderate relief, and finally were uplifted at least a quarter of a mile above the sea—the last episode is demonstrated by a flight of marine terraces which marches like a cyclopean stairway up the seaward slope of some parts of the range.

EVIDENCE REGARDING ORIGIN

Before constructing a theory to explain the building of mountains, we should remember that such a theory must include the basic elements of geosynclinal deposition, deformation, erosion, and final vertical uplift. The time required for these events may range from roughly 1 million up to 500 million years. Furthermore, not all the stages need be present for an imposing mountain range to be raised above its surroundings.

A major tenet of geology is the assumption that processes active in the world today were also active in the world of the past, and that very likely they operated at rates not greatly different from their present-day ones. While geologists recognize that in the main the principle appears to be a valid one, they are aware that there are also exceptions, not the least being the ice age from which we so recently have emerged. Counterparts of this awesome event fortunately are meager in the contemporary world.

Nonetheless, for a theory of mountain building to have validity, we should be able to recognize some of its stages on the Earth now. Otherwise, we are in the philosophically insecure position of arguing that once all the mountains of the Earth had been constructed, the mechanism responsible for their fabrication might then be dismantled, and they would stand for all time as a thing once accomplished and perhaps never to be repeated. To discount such an extreme view, we have already learned that the hills are somewhat less than everlasting—no sooner do they rise above the level of the sea than the forces of erosion set to work to tear them down. The record of the rocks, deformed as they are by folds and faults, tells us, too, that lofty mountains once stood where broad plains now stretch to the far horizon. We know also from the recurrence of earthquakes and the record of earth movements, as revealed by precise surveying, that mountain-making forces are still active in the Earth's crust. It takes only a little foresight, then, to realize that in some distant day other mountains will tower skyward above landscapes in a world unimagined by us.

Modern Geosynclines

First among the many features to look for are geosynclines, because they are so central an element in any theory of the origin of complex mountains. Are there any geosynclines in the world that are comparable to the one responsible for the deposition of the rocks in the heart of the Appalachians?

The answer is a cautiously guarded yes. There appears to be no unequivocal example of a geosyncline, as we imagine one might look from interpreting the rock record of the Appalachians, but there are examples of partial geosynclines, or of depressions that might be considered as stages of geosynclinal growth.

A leading example of such a partial geosyncline in the United States is the region bordering the Mississippi Delta in the Gulf of Mexico (Fig. 15-6). There a thick pile of sediments, perhaps 40,000 or 50,000 feet, has accumulated, thickest on the northern side of the Gulf, approximately under the present shoreline (Murray, 1961). The net result of this gradual accretion of sediment into the Gulf is to extend a lens of land-derived debris seaward over a submarine terrain of oceanic materials.

From the evidence of thousands of oil well cores, including some of the world's deepest, we know that this thick wedge of sediment accumulated in shallow water—certainly not 30,-000 or even 10,000 feet deep. For the layers to reach their present depth, slow subsidence of the sedimentary prism is required. That subsidence has occurred—and for that matter is still occurring—is something on which most Gulf Coast geologists are agreed. However, what caused the subsidence is another matter, and is a strongly debated question. Was it the load of sediment gradually piling up on the crust that caused it to buckle downward? Should this be the case, then material such as water-soaked clay whose density may be as low as 1.8 is displacing subcrustal material whose density may be as great as 3.3 grams per cubic centimeter. In support of this hypothesis, its adherents point out that this happened under the continental ice sheets, whose specific gravity is only 0.9, and that Scandinavia and Canada only now are rebounding upon the removal of this excess load.

Dissenters from the belief that load causes subsidence take the view that the Gulf Coast is a region where downbuckling of the Earth's crust is occurring anyhow, and that while the load of sediment unquestionably aids the process of downwarping, it is not the primary cause. The primary cause is within the Earth, and to find an answer we shall have to turn elsewhere than to mere surface transfers of load. In the Mississippi embayment where both processes of sedimentary loading and crustal downwarping are in operation, it would be difficult to determine the relative importance of either.

Oceanic Trenches and Island Arcs

Fortunately, there are segments of the Earth's crust which appear to have been downbuckled without being burdened with an unusually thick accumulation of sediment. The most striking are in distant parts of the world, and are largely inaccessible to direct observation. Chiefly, they are long, narrow trenches on the sea floor. These are conspicuously developed among the islands of Indonesia, the islands bordering the far western Pacific Ocean, including Japan, in

FIG. 15-6 *A section across the Gulf Coast Geosyncline.*

After P. B. King, *The Evolution of North America,* Copyright ©
1959 Princeton University Press. By permission.

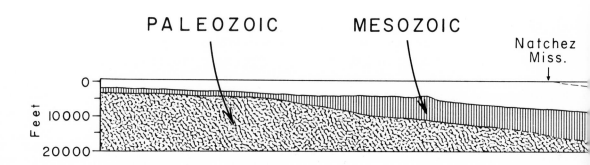

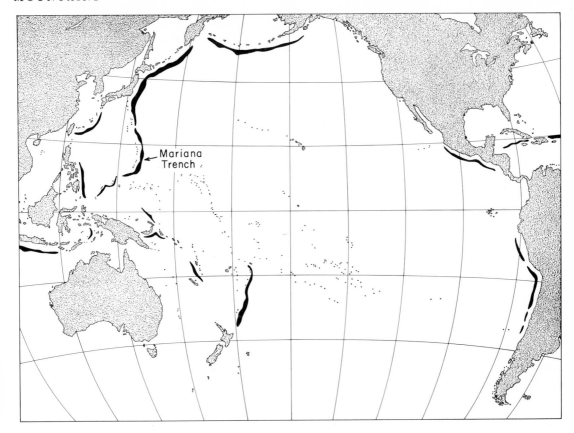

the eastern Pacific marginal to the coasts of South America and Alaska, and in the Caribbean (Fig. 15-7). Incidentally, the greatest known depth in the sea, 35,800 feet, is in one of these troughs, the Mariana Trench of the western Pacific.

FIG. 15-7 *Deep trenches, shown in black, on the sea floor.*

From Chart No. 1262A. By permission of U.S. Naval Oceanographic Office.

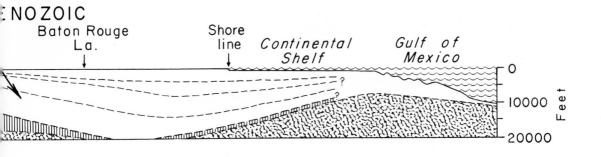

Around thirty years ago the discovery was made that in the vicinity of some of these oceanic trenches the value of gravity was less than it properly should be for the latitude of the place. How this deficiency was determined is an intriguing illustration of the overcoming of a seemingly insuperable observational difficulty. You may remember from Chapter I that the force of gravity can be measured by repeated observations of a swinging pendulum. Few more incompatible objects can be imagined than a swinging pendulum and a rolling ship, and thus it seemed a hopeless task to ever measure gravitative values over these wrinkles in the sea floor from the heaving deck of a vessel laboring across the trade wind seas.

A stable platform for measuring gravity at sea was made by mounting a specially designed gravimeter in a submarine and taking the readings when submerged below the lower limit of wave action. The pioneer work was done by the Dutch geodesist, F. A. Vening Meinesz, aboard submarines of the Royal Netherlands Navy. The

map (Fig. 15-8) shows the arcuate belt of lower than normal gravity which he discovered curving through the East Indian Archipelago.

The relationship of the band of the so-called *negative gravity anomaly* and the deep trenches in the sea adjacent to the islands is not immediately apparent. Sometimes the belt of lower gravity is on one side of the trough, sometimes on the other. In fact, rather than being confined solely to the ocean floor, it swings northward near the eastern end of Indonesia and crosses the islands of Timor and Ceram. Nonetheless, the relationship between island arcs, belts of deficient gravity, and oceanic deeps, here and elsewhere, is too close to be merely fortuitous.

Another significant relationship that exists in the curious world of arc-like chains of volcanic islands in the western Pacific fronted by abyssal trenches is the distribution of earthquake foci. When they are plotted in their proper relationship for depth and location, they line up along an inclined plane whose dip from the surface down to approximately 180 miles averages 30° to 35°, after which it steepens to perhaps 60° down to a depth of 400 to 450 miles.

Such a relationship may indicate the presence of a fracture of some kind. The surprising thing is the great depth to which these earthquake

FIG. 15-8 *The belt of negative gravity anomalies, East Indian Archipelago.*

After F. A. Vening-Meinesz, J. H. F. Umbgrove, and Ph. D. Kuenen, *Gravity Expeditions at Sea*, 1923-1932, 1934. By permission of The Netherlands Geodetic Commission.

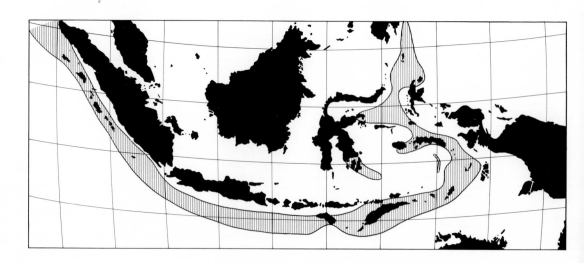

centers go—they are far down in the mantle below the Mohorovičić discontinuity, and thus are in a realm where rocks presumably yield plastically rather than failing by fracture. At any rate, if this plane of earthquake centers is a fracture, it seemingly indicates that forces within the Earth are at work to push an arcuate ridge, such as the one defined by the Mariana Islands, upward and at the same time toward the abyssal trench at its base. Should this be true, continued deformation may operate to buckle the trench down deeper still, to compress the sediments already in the trench, and to hold these lighter sediments down, as it were, even though they have in a sense displaced rocks heavier than themselves.

The relative lightness of the rocks that presumably are buckled down into the Earth's crust is stressed because their presence is the most generally accepted explanation for the long belt-like bands of deficient gravity associated with the island arcs and their bordering trenches. The lower gravitational attraction must be related to a deficiency of mass, and the most logical assumption is that this represents a concentration of lighter material that has taken the place of the denser subcrustal material by being forced downward into it.

Experimental Models

Such a relationship has been reproduced experimentally by two investigators, D. T. Griggs of the University of California and Ph. H. Kuenen of the University of Groningen, Netherlands. Both men constructed models of the Earth's crust scaled down in all proportions so that the model behaved structurally in the same way as its prototype, the Earth. In this scaling down, surprisingly weak materials must be used to simulate what appear to us to be very strong substances, such as rocks. Griggs, for example, used glycerine to represent subcrustal layers,

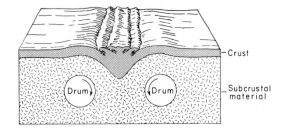

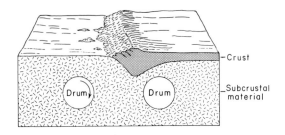

After D. Griggs, *American Journal of Science*, vol. 237, 1939. By permission.

FIG. 15-9 *Downbuckle of the crust resulting from two opposing currents in subcrustal material (upper diagram) and from a single current (lower diagram).*

and the crust was represented by a mixture of cylinder oil and sawdust (Fig. 15-9). In Kuenen's experiment a downbuckle of the crust resulted from compressing a model consisting of a layer of paraffin floating on water. At first very weak undulations appeared—perhaps to be compared with the geosynclinal stage in nature —then quite suddenly the "crust" folded downward into the watery substratum, producing a pattern much resembling the one that Vening Meinesz believed to exist beneath the Indonesian islands.

Griggs produced essentially the same geometry by immersing two drums in a glycerine subcrustal layer and rotating them toward each other. By doing this he succeeded in producing a downward bending of the crust closely resembling the one Kuenen made by simple compression. In each case, lighter crustal layers were dragged down into a denser subcrustal zone. When the rotating drums were stopped, the crumpled lens of lighter material was buoyed up to form a low ridge.

How does an artificial approach such as this relate to the real world? It does, perhaps, if we make some assumptions, one of them being that currents resembling convection currents in air or water may be active within the crust. These are currents set in motion by temperature differences—a familiar example is the rise of heated air above a stove.

Convection is difficult to conceive of in such materials as rocks. We know from experience that the process works best in substances of low viscosity—liquids and gases—and rocks certainly are not in either of these categories. A saving factor for the theory of convective overturn is the immensity of geologic time, during which slow processes can accomplish prodigies of change. In addition, rocks can be deformed plastically if temperatures and pressures are high enough, as we surmise, for example, from the contorted bands we see in some metamorphic rocks.

The other essential needed to make slow-moving transfers of material possible is differential heating within the mantle. It was once believed that heat lost from within the Earth came from the slow cooling of an originally molten globe. We know now that the length of time that the Earth has been in existence is far too great, and that the temperature does not increase at a uniform rate with depth in the Earth, but that the greatest rate increase apparently is nearer the surface than the center.

The discovery of radioactivity within rocks provides us with a mechanism that makes it possible for heat to be supplied continuously through time, instead of coming from a source which is slowly running down. Also, heat may be unevenly distributed in the Earth's mantle, as the result of local concentrations of radioactivity. This means that slow-moving currents

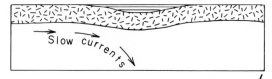

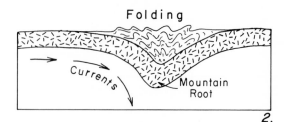

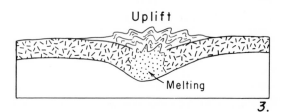

After D. Griggs, *American Journal of Science*, vol. 237, 1939. By permission.

FIG. 15-10 *Stages of mountain-building, according to the convection current theory: 1, period of slowly accelerating currents; 2, folding of geosynclinal sediments and formation of the mountain root; 3, buoyant rise of thickened crust aided by melting of mountain root.*

of subcrustal material may be set in motion between cooler and warmer parts of the mantle. If such currents actually are present, they undoubtedly do not flow as steadily as currents do in fluids, because the rocky material probably will always possess some shear strength which must be overcome if flowage is to occur. If it is not exceeded, then transfer of material is stopped until additional heat is gained, viscosity is lowered, and convection is renewed. This may help to explain the pulsatory nature of the growth that seems so characteristic of mountain building.

Dragging crustal material down in an infold, such as was done in the models, may help to explain two phenomena that must be accounted for in any theory of mountain building (Fig. 15-10). The first is the essentially vertical uplift of the belt of crumpled and faulted rocks that form mountains such as the Appalachians, Alps, and Himalayas. The second is the presence of sizeable intrusive bodies of granite and related rocks included in the contorted rocks of the range.

Crustal rocks may have a lower melting point than subcrustal ones, and thus they should melt if forced down into a zone of higher temperature than their original environment. This melting and possible conversion to granite will be greatly aided if the pressure is reduced temporarily, possibly by sudden fracturing, for then molten material which originated in the root area of the downbuckled rocks can make its way upward through these contorted rocks to crystallize in granitic batholiths and related intrusives.

Vertical uplift of the whole mass of downfolded, contorted, and injected rocks may occur when convection currents cease to flow. Then, because there is an excess of lighter material in the root compared to the denser subcrustal material on either side as well as below, the root tends to rise, much as a ship is buoyed up by the denser water in which it floats.

As we saw in Chapter I, men recognized a century ago that the Himalayas consist of lighter material than the normal crustal rocks. To this property of lighter masses in the Earth's crust tending to stand higher than their denser surroundings, Captain C. E. Dutton, a career army officer and contemporary of G. K. Gilbert's, gave the name *isostasy* (from a Greek word for equal standing) in 1871.

A rise of lighter, downfolded material occurred in Griggs's model when the drums stopped rotating, and it may be reasoned by analogy that this is what occurs in nature when convection currents cease to flow.

PROBLEMS OF ORIGIN

Our inquiry into the origin of mountains has taken us on a long journey, including stops along the way at the Gulf Coast and among the island arcs of Indonesia and the Pacific. These areas of local crustal sinking may or may not be counterparts of geosynclinal troughs of the past. It is difficult to tell, because in the strongly folded rocks of a mountain range we see only the end product of geosynclinal deposition, and have to reconstruct in our imagination the stages that led to the pattern of the present.

Although experimental models produce results resembling the crustal geometry that may exist beneath the island arcs, there still remain tremendous unsolved problems. Among these major uncertainties are whether or not convection currents actually exist within the Earth. They are a convenient, and indeed logical, explanation for much of what we surmise has happened, but their actual presence has yet to be proved.

Another problem is the enormous span of time required for such a depositional cycle as that of the Appalachian geosyncline to run its course—something like 300 million years. This requirement is not readily reconciled with the comparatively rapid flow of convection currents. On the other hand, we are confronted with the fact that the entire evolutionary history of a complex mountain range, from geosynclinal deposition through the folding and faulting of these basin sediments, their wide-scale peneplanation, and final vertical uplift, was achieved within the last few million years in southern California.

The list of paradoxes and exceptions might be prolonged indefinitely, but one of the more striking ones in North America might well serve to close the discussion. This is the Colorado Plateau in the southwestern United States—the region bordering the Grand Canyon—which has been elevated bodily for at least a mile in comparatively recent geologic time without greatly disturbing the horizontality of the strata every tourist sees in the canyon walls. How could such an immense block of the Earth's crust be lifted with so little evidence of crumpling or contortion of the rocks? Frankly, it remains as great a mystery to us as it did to Major Powell and his companions when they climbed the canyon rim shortly after the Civil War and gazed across the brooding landscape of the high plateaus.

All that we know is that at times enormous forces appear to be freed within the Earth's crust, and that these are capable of crumpling and shearing rocks into the involved and contorted pattern of folds and faults we see bared in the canyons and on the high peaks of mountain ranges. At other times sections of the crust are elevated bodily, without significant compression, to the impressive heights attained by the Tibetan, Andean, and Colorado plateaus. Are the two kinds of deformation related, or are they independent? No one knows for certain, although it does appear that they are related.

THEORIES OF MOUNTAIN BUILDING

When it comes to theories to explain the origin of complex mountains, there is no lack of suggestions or of ingenuity. Many are of historic interest only. None of the current hypotheses have achieved universal acceptance.

Contraction

A venerable theory, and one that has followers even now, is that mountains are wrinkles in the crust of a contracting Earth—an Earth whose shrinking probably resulted from the loss of its original heat.

Among the reasons for discounting this theory are:

(1) All great circles measured on the Earth should contract about equally, with the result that mountain ranges should be distributed more uniformly than they are. Certainly they would not be separated by the enormous distances found between some ranges. It is also difficult to reconcile such great differences in trend as the essentially east-west line followed by the Alpine-Himalaya chain with the generally north-south line followed by the American cordillera.

(2) The Earth's crust appears to be too weak to transmit for long distances the thrusts required to build such mountains. A corollary of this is that once the Earth's crust was buckled through contraction, mountain ranges should tend always to be in the same place because contraction would be an essentially continuous process. Nothing known of the Earth's past history supports this belief. Mountain ranges have been elevated in former times, only to waste away into oblivion as complete as Babylon's, then to be supplanted by other ranges in other lands and times. Sometimes a range may be built upon the wreckage of its predecessor, but at other times areas that formerly were mountainous now are worn down to broad lowlands which have remained quiescent and undisturbed through eons of geologic time.

(3) With the discovery of radioactivity in rocks, the old idea of the Earth's slowly cooling from a molten beginning went into eclipse. Today we know that much of the Earth's radioactivity is concentrated in fairly shallow depths, and that there probably has been no great decrease with time. In fact, in some areas there may be local increases from time to time, and it may be that the resulting build-up in temperature causes localized melting and starts the thermal cycle that is so essential for convection currents to operate.

Convection Currents

At the moment convection currents appear to be a logical mechanism. Their possible existence can be demonstrated experimentally, and assumptions about their behavior fit many of the requirements imposed by the nature of the rocks in the crust. Although no one has successfully demonstrated the actuality of convection currents in the Earth, some of the evidence does strongly suggest their existence.

Convection currents appear to be a logical means for explaining the dragging down of lighter crustal material into the denser subcrustal layers, and this may be the explanation for the deficiency of gravity under the island arcs of the Pacific and the Caribbean. The cessation of these currents also appears to be a reasonable explanation, coupled with the theory of isostasy, to account for the vertical uplift of a belt of the intruded, complexly deformed, lighter rocks that constitute the heart of an alpine range.

Questions of imposing magnitude remain to be resolved, however. For one thing, we cannot be certain that the oceanic trenches or the Gulf of Mexico are fully comparable to the geosynclines of the past.

Aside from the uncertainty as to the existence or nonexistence of convection currents, it is difficult to explain how subsidence should have persisted for 300 million years in the Appalachians, to be followed by a pause of perhaps another 200 million years or so before the vertical uplift began that is responsible for the elevation of the mountains of today.

Phase Changes

A contrasting theory of mountain building has been proposed recently by George C. Kennedy (1959) of the University of California and by others. A fundamental tenet of this theory is an explanation of the pronounced difference in density of the material above and below the Mohorovičić discontinuity (Chapter IX). This difference is believed to be an expression not of a difference in composition, but of a *phase change*. Under high pressures some substances may be converted from one crystalline pattern to another, an effect known as *polymorphism*. Such a phase change without change in composition occurs when graphite is converted to diamond at pressures in the neighborhood of 100,000 atmospheres and a temperature of 1500 K. (0 on the Kelvin scale = −459.4°F.). Thus rocks which have undergone a phase change may have wholly unlike mineralogy, but have very nearly identical chemical compositions. A good example is the dense intrusive rock, *eclogite,* whose specific gravity is 3.3, compared to basalt or gabbro with a specific gravity of 2.95, yet with nearly the same chemical constituents. Eclogites are rare on the Earth's surface, but are known in volcanic necks and other intrusives. They contain no feldspar, and since they are denser rocks than basalt or gabbro, they must exist at higher pressures.

With local heating, dense rocks such as eclogite may undergo a polymorphic inversion to a less dense form. In geologic terms this means an increase in volume will take place, amounting to as much as 10 per cent. With an increase in volume of a large body of material within the Earth, vertical uplift of the surface will occur and at the same time the Mohorovičić discontinuity will migrate downward.

The phase change theory provides a plausible explanation for the vertical rise of broad regions as the Colorado Plateau to altitudes of 7,000 feet or more without crumpling or drastically deforming the rocks. The theory also explains the presence of roots of lighter, less dense rocks beneath the high-standing Himalayas and Tibetan Plateau. As Kennedy (1959) points out, to accumulate roots of lighter material under these elevated regions through transfer by convection currents requires the emplacement of 2,500,000 cubic miles of light rock for the Colorado Plateau and about 25,000,000 for the Tibetan. Not only is the problem of moving such prodigious volumes by subcrustal flow troublesome, but finding a source from which they came is equally vexing.

Polymorphism also can be appealed to as the mechanism responsible for the subsidence of geosynclinal troughs in which sediment accumulates. The problem is to explain how unconsolidated sediment whose gravity may be no more than 2.5 can, by downwarping, displace rocks whose density is 2.9. By appealing to polymorphism, an argument can be advanced that the increased load of sediment on the crust will bring about an increase in pressure. The effect of this will be the promotion of phase changes at subcrustal depths and an upward migration of the Mohorovičić discontinuity. Because of the reduction in volume accompanying this phase change, the accumulating sediment will continue to sink.

If we assume that geosynclinal sediments are relatively high in radioactive material, then a gradual increase in temperature will occur. If we also consider this sedimentary blanket to be a poor conductor of heat, then the rise of temperature in the crust will cause the phase change to reverse and will cause subcrustal rocks to invert from more dense to less dense forms. The effect of this will be a downward migration of the Mohorovičić discontinuity and a rise of the formerly subsiding sediments.

This theory of polymorphism goes far toward explaining the rise of large segments of the crust such as the Colorado and Tibetan plateaus, the existence of roots of lighter material under mountain ranges, and the geological antiquity of mountains and of continents. The presumed reversal of direction of motion of the boundary between crust and mantle in geosynclines perhaps requires amplification. Objections have been raised that the theory does not adequately explain large-scale compression or horizontal movement in the crust, but here we are arguing without adequate proof. Polymorphism seems inadequate to explain the downbuckling of long furrows such as the deeps bordering the island arcs; for these, convection currents are an appealing mechanism.

We are uncertain that an absolute relationship exists between folded rocks and mountain ranges. The first of these appears to be the result of horizontal compression; the latter, of vertical uplift. In fact, as we have seen from the Colorado Plateau, vertical uplift can occur without compression, or even without large-scale faulting. In the final analysis, the principal mountain ranges of the world are primarily the result of uplift. Here we cannot explain what force it is that operates within the crust to enable a linear element, such as a mountain range, to rise against the force of gravity.

The origin of mountains remains as one of the great, certainly one of the most challenging problems confronting the geologist. Our patiently won store of knowledge tells us much more than our predecessors knew, but perhaps we can count ourselves fortunate that the final answer still eludes us.

Suggested References

Belousov, V. V., 1961, Experimental geology, Scientific American, v. 237, p. 611-650.

Billings, M. P., 1960, Diastrophism and mountain building, Geol. Soc. Amer., Bull., v. 71, p. 363-398.

Bucher, W. H., 1933, The deformation of the earth's crust, Princeton Univ. Press, Princeton, N. J.

Collett, L. W., 1927, The structure of the Alps, Edw. Arnold and Co., London.

Daly, R. A., 1940, Strength and structure of the earth, Prentice-Hall, Inc., Englewood Cliffs, N. J.

de Sitter, L. U., 1956, Structural geology, McGraw-Hill Book Co., Inc., New York.

Eardley, A. J., 1951, Structural geology of North America, Harper and Bros., New York.

Gilluly, James, 1949, The distribution of mountain building in geologic time, Geol. Soc. Amer., Bull., v. 60, p. 561-590.

Griggs, D. T., 1939, A theory of mountain building, Amer. Jour. Science, v. 237, p. 611-650.

Howell, B. F., Jr., 1959, Introduction to geophysics, McGraw-Hill Book Co., Inc., New York.

Hsu, K. J., 1958, Isostasy and a theory for the origin of geosynclines, Amer. Jour. Science, v. 256, p. 305-327.

Kay, Marshall, 1951, North American geosynclines, Geol. Soc. Amer., Memoir 48.

Kelley, V. C., 1955, Regional tectonics of the Colorado Plateau and relationship to the origin and distribution of uranium, Univ. of New Mexico, Publ. Geol. No. 5, Albuquerque, N. M.

Kennedy, G. C., 1959, The origin of continents, mountain ranges, and ocean basins, Amer. Scientist, v. 47, p. 491-504.

King, L. C., 1962, Morphology of the earth, Oliver and Boyd, Edinburgh and London.

King, P. B., 1959, The evolution of North America, Princeton Univ. Press, Princeton, N. J.

Kuenen, Ph. H., 1950, Marine geology, John Wiley and Sons, Inc., New York.

Joly, John, 1930, The surface-history of the earth, Oxford Univ. Press, London.

Moore, Ruth, 1956, The earth we live on, Alfred A. Knopf, New York.

Murray, G. E., 1961, Geology of the Atlantic and Gulf Coastal province of North America, Harper and Bros., New York.

Poldervaart, Arie, and others, Crust of the earth, Geol. Soc. Amer., Spec. Paper 62.

Umbgrove, J. H. F., 1947, The pulse of the earth, Martinus Nijhoff, The Hague, Netherlands.

XVI

Geologic Time and Life of the Past

High up in the land of Svithjod, there stands a rock. It is a hundred miles high and a hundred miles wide. Once every thousand years a little bird comes to sharpen its beak.

When the rock has thus been worn away, then a single day of eternity will have gone by.

—Hendrik van Loon: THE STORY OF MANKIND

The concept of the enormity of geologic time is a relatively new one in the western world. In fact, if one were to ask a geologist what has been the unique contribution of his science to our understanding of the universe, he might find it difficult to give a single answer. It would be a great temptation to select the facet of the science which is his chief concern, and to say that his specialty outshines the others. Viewed dispassionately, however, a consensus probably could be reached that perhaps the distinctive contribution of geology is an appreciation of the enormous length of the river of time that recedes into the darkness of the past. Unfortunately—or perhaps it is just as well—we have so limited a consciousness of how vast this parade of years is that it is as incomprehensible to us as are the limitless dimensions of space.

Some of our ancestors worried about the duration of past ages; others apparently were not at all concerned. The Hindus thought the world had an age of 2 billion years (this was the seventh part of a great cycle of 4.32 billion years, which was to be the entire universe—or one "day" in the life of Brahma)—quite a commendable effort in estimating the length of past time, especially when compared with early opinions in western Europe. There, even as late as the seventeenth century, a widely accepted belief was that the Earth was created in the year 4004 B.C. This was a figure worked out by Archbishop Ussher (1581-1656) of the Irish Protestant Church who arrived at this value by adding up the genealogies recorded in the Old Testament and setting up a system of dates based on the length of each generation.

With the emergence of geology as a science, men became aware that a tremendous length of time was needed to accomplish the changes they recognized as having occurred. The deposition of sedimentary rocks is an example. When it was acknowledged that these strata were layers that had accumulated one by one, then if we know the rate at which such sediments were deposited, as well as their total thickness, we would then have an approximate measure of the length of time erosion and deposition had operated on the surface of the Earth.

Unfortunately, there are a number of things wrong with such a direct approach. No one knew then—or now, for that matter—the rate at which sediments are deposited. Obviously, it must be different for a conglomerate made of

Fremontia fremonti (Walcott), a trilobite from the Lower Cambrian Latham Shale, Marble Mountains, Cadiz, California. Length, 4½ inches. (Photograph by Takeo Susuki.)

boulders which are several feet across than it is for a limestone consisting of the remains of microscopic marine organisms. Furthermore, few, if any, sediments are deposited uninterruptedly. There may be times of accumulation interspersed with intervals of no deposition at all. To add to these difficulties, no place is known on the land surface of the Earth where strata of all the geologic ages are laid in one continuous succession. Actually, if the maximum known thickness of strata for each of the various ages deposited since the start of the Paleozoic were to be combined in such a column, it would be very nearly 400,000 feet thick.

An early estimate of how long such a pile would take to accumulate was made by W. J. Solas, in 1905, who estimated 26 million years. With the better knowledge of today, a generous calculation would be 600 million years for the rocks deposited since the beginning of the Cambrian, which turns out to be nearly the same as the age determined more precisely by radioactive methods.

An ingenious attempt to relate processes active now to the age of the world was an estimate made in 1899 by the Irish scientist, John Joly, based on the amount of salt added yearly to the sea. The quantity of salt dissolved in the oceans has been determined fairly accurately, and if a reasonable estimate can be made for the amount contributed each year by rivers, then we can establish a value for the age of the sea. Joly's best estimate turned out to be about 100 million years, which is far short of what we consider to be the real age.

There are many sources of error in this method which cannot properly be evaluated. Among these are the immense quantities of salt that have accumulated from the evaporation of sea water in ages past, and are now deposited as salt beds along with other sedimentary rocks. Another uncertainty is whether or not the amount of salt added to the sea each year remained constant throughout geologic time. Probably it has not, because the evidence seemingly indicates that there have been times, such as the present, of relatively high mountains and rapid erosion, which have alternated with times of low relief and correspondingly lesser additions of salt to the sea. Many other factors operate to introduce further errors, not the least being the constant loss of salt from the sea through winds blowing across its surface and carrying salt far inland. When all these factors were weighted carefully by another scientist, Conway, in 1934, he estimated the age of the sea to be somewhere between 800 million and 2,350 million years.

Thus far we have been talking about time measured in years, and this understandably is the goal of all age-dating methods. It is the sort of figure we speak of as *absolute age,* and its determination depends upon our having some time scale or measure. Customarily we measure time in years, which is really an arbitrary way of dividing up something which has no discernible beginning or foreseeable end, since it is based on the circling of what is essentially a flake of dust—our Earth—in the immensity of space around a very minor star—the sun—lost in the midst of an infinitude of galaxies.

Not only do we need an age scale, but we need a beginning point from which units of time can be measured. Most of us are conditioned to thinking in terms of the Christian chronology, in which we are familiar with such dates as Anno Domini 1963. This, however, is far from the only chronology in general use. The same year in the Moslem world is A.H. 1341, in the Jewish calendar it is 5724, and were Rome still to rule it would be the year 2716.

The other time we commonly employ is the kind we call *relative age.* This is what people often prefer to use, and is the kind employed when we speak of such an event as having happened before or after the war. (Unfortunately, there have been so many wars in the past century that a person finds it difficult to decide which one is meant.) The geologist in the field is chiefly concerned with relative age.

In the section to follow, we shall describe something of the way in which absolute dates for various kinds of rocks are being determined today. This is the branch of Earth history which is receiving an immense amount of attention in laboratories all over the scientific world, and which gives the greatest promise of enabling us to place events in the geologic past in a chronologic sequence that will be the same in all parts of the earth.

ABSOLUTE AGE

Few people alive in 1895 were aware of the immense forces that were to be loosed on an unready world as an outgrowth of a seemingly innocuous experiment by Professor Henri Becquerel in Paris. He had been intrigued by Röntgen's discovery within the same year of the X-ray, and wondered whether or not the phenomenon of phosphorescence bore any relationship to these strange emanations. He thought that perhaps various substances might pick up energy from the sun, and because of this he exposed a number of them to the sun's rays with no discernible effect. By chance he observed that when some uranium salts were placed on photographic paper, the paper darkened as though subjected to some kind of radiation, and this was true whether the uranium had been placed in the sun's rays or not.

It was in the same period that the Curies, Marie and Pierre, were engaged in their prodigious labor of isolating radium, and the scientific world was scarcely prepared for the upset of so many strongly cherished beliefs that the advent of radioactivity brought about.

Among the first to recognize the potentiality of radioactivity as a geologic clock was one of the distinguished physicists of this century, Lord Rutherford, born Ernest Rutherford in New Zealand. In 1902 he discovered that in effect radioactivity was the disintegration of radioactive atoms and their transformation into completely different elements. By 1904, such was

the rapid advance of this revolutionary concept, he was able to announce the existence of the radioactive clock. This was based on the assumption that each radioactive substance disintegrates at its own rate, and that for many of them the rate of change is extremely slow. That of uranium is such that by 4,500 million years only one-half of the original radioactivity is left (for this reason we speak of this length of time as the half-life). At the end of another 4,500 million years one-half of the remaining radioactivity is gone, and so on (Fig. 16-1).

The breakdown of uranium is as follows:

$$\text{uranium} \longrightarrow \text{lead} + \text{helium} + \text{energy}.$$

As uranium slowly disintegrates, it changes into lead; a gas, helium, is freed; and energy, which we may be aware of as heat, is liberated. Thus, in theory, if we could determine the ratio of unchanged uranium to lead, then, knowing the rate of disintegration, we could establish the age of the host mineral or rock. Unfortunately, things turn out to be not quite so simple as they first appeared. We now know that there are three isotopes (chemical elements that differ in

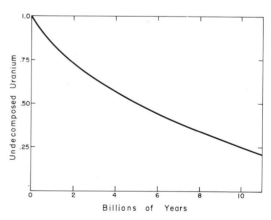

After C. G. Croneis and W. C. Krumbein, *Down to Earth*, 1936. By permission of the University of Chicago Press.

FIG. 16-1 *Exponential curve of uranium decay to show the proportion of undisintegrated uranium remaining from some original amount (1.0) for any time (in billions of years). Half of the original uranium remains at 5 billion years, and one-fourth at 10 billion years.*

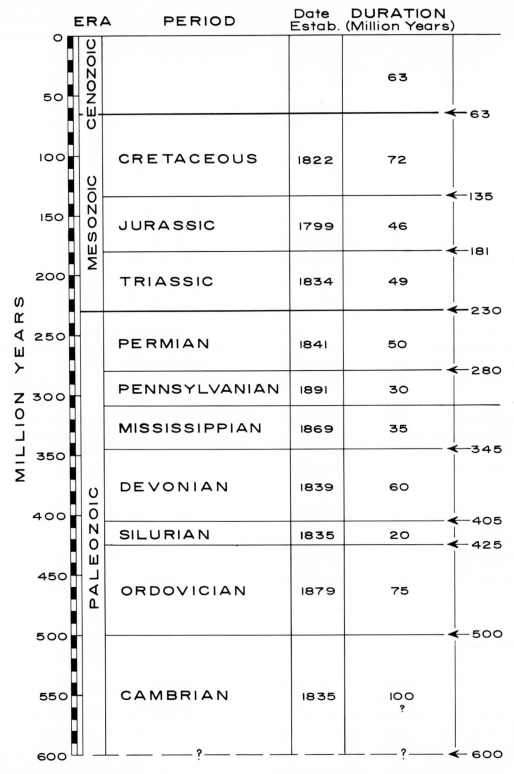

FIG. 16-2 *Geologic time scale.*   After J. L. Kulp, *Science*, vol. 132, 1961. By permission.

atomic weights because of the different numbers of neutrons in the nucleus, but which otherwise are alike) of lead derived from radioactive substances, and one, lead 204, that is not. The relationships that hold after a complex series of transformations are:

$$\text{uranium } 238 \longrightarrow \text{lead } 206$$
$$\text{uranium } 235 \longrightarrow \text{lead } 207$$
$$\text{thorium } 232 \longrightarrow \text{lead } 208$$

Through a series of chemical procedures of great complexity, the relative proportion of these isotopes can be determined, and if we assume the rates of decay have been constant, an internal check is provided by comparing the ages of the three. Another essential is that the minerals being tested must have remained in a closed chemical system throughout the eons of time we are attempting to measure. This simply means that the sample cannot be contaminated if it is to yield a meaningful date. Other errors are introduced if we are not sure of the position of our sample in the geologic succession of events in any region, and lastly, errors may be made in the actual laboratory procedure. Gradually, through constant checks and counterchecks, a generally acceptable time scale has been built up (Kulp, 1961), and the dates given in years on the table are based on it (Fig. 16-2).

Fortunately, there are other isotopes that give us dates for later parts of the geologic time scale which are closer to us than the remote ones recorded by the lead-uranium ratio. These are the ratios between potassium 40 which disintegrates to the gas argon 40, and between rubidium 87 which alters to strontium 87. Although more work needs to be done on these, they are proving invaluable in dating rocks.

As the table shows, the beginning of the Cambrian, or the time when fossils first became abundant in the geologic record, was approximately 600 million years ago. Backward beyond this date stretches a seeming eternity to the oldest dates determined thus far, which are in the neighborhood of 3,000 million years. Some me-

teorites are even more ancient, and have an age of 4,500 million years, which still falls short of a current opinion of an age of the universe of 9,000 million years.

According to Ruth Moore (1956), if we want to bring this immensity of time down to comprehensible dimensions, we might think of the age of 4.5 billion years of the older meteorites as being represented by a single year. Then the fossil record extends back a scant 40 days or so; man has been on Earth 2 hours (equal to 1 million years), and a generous span of 50,000 years for modern man allots him 5 minutes out of the entire year. A further illustration of the great length of geologic time is shown in Fig. 16-3.

FIG. 16-3 *Spiral graph representing geologic time. The numbers indicate millions of years since the beginning of each major subdivision of geologic time. From the graph it is seen that more than 85 per cent of geologic time transpired before the Paleozoic, and that the Cenozoic Era—the age of mammals—represents only about 1 per cent of geologic time.*

Carbon 14

An exciting scientific achievement of the post-World War II period has been the identification of radioactive carbon, and the awareness not only of the role it plays in living organisms, but an appreciation of its extraordinary value in dating events in this last five minutes of Earth history, as it were.

The recognition of the existence of radio-carbon goes back to research in 1939 on cosmic rays in the upper atmosphere by Serge Korff of New York University. He noted that cosmic rays produce secondary neutrons on their initial collision with nitrogen in the higher levels of the atmosphere. These neutrons, he predicted, when they collided with the abundant isotope nitrogen 14 would react to free a proton and to form carbon 14. The radioactive carbon then combines with oxygen to form $C^{14}O_2$, which is absorbed by plants and ultimately by all living things. New carbon 14 is added to the total supply on land, in the sea, and in the atmosphere about as rapidly as the old disappears.

Research on the problem of carbon 14 and its relationship to cosmic radiation was continued by Willard F. Libby, then at the University of Chicago and now at the University of California.

One of the basic premises in this method of age-dating is the assumption that when an organism dies, it no longer assimilates carbon 14, and the radiocarbon present in it decays without any new carbon 14 replacing the old. A sample of just-dead wood placed in a geiger counter yields about 15.3 disintegrations per minute per gram.

The number of disintegrations per minute decreases with increasing age of the sample, with only one half the original number occurring when the carbon 14 is $5,568 \pm 30$ years old, which is the half-life. With so short a half-life, it is obvious that here is a radioactive clock that is of tremendous value to archeologists and pre-historians, but one that is of limited significance to the geologist, because dates can be determined back with decreasing confidence to only 50,000 years or so.

The curve shown in Fig. 16-4 is one developed by Libby and his associates, and is the first effort to fit the predicted decay curve for carbon 14 to materials whose ages were known. Among those objects whose ages had been established by other means, and which were checked against the radioactive carbon curve, are part of a funeral barge of the Pharaoh Sesostris II, a charred loaf of bread from Pompeii, a redwood log from California, and a linen wrapping from the Book of Isaiah in one of the Dead Sea Scrolls.

A number of interesting dates have been established as a result of a veritable flood of determinations made in the past decade or so. In fact, there is scarcely a museum relic or mummy that is safe from being plugged, or having a couple of corners snipped off to be used as a sample in a geiger counter.

The Book of Isaiah in the Dead Sea Scrolls is $2,050 \pm 100$ years old. A specimen from one of the ritual pits at the imposing prehistoric ruin of Stonehenge proved to be $3,798 \pm 275$ years old. Charcoal from the Lascaux Cave in France, the site of the extraordinarily subtle and imaginative wall paintings of Cro-Magnon man, has an age of $15,516 \pm 900$ years (Bowen, 1958). This is truly an amazing date when we consider, as we shall in a moment, that the ice age ended only about 11,000 years ago. That men could have achieved such a level of artistic excellence so long ago in the face of such adversity as the late-glacial climate of Europe is one of the marvelous achievements of all humanity.

To return to the problem of when the ice age ended. This is a crucial event in the pre-history of western Europe and of the Americas, because until the ice once shrouding the northern lands of the world had melted away it was not possible for the wonderful diversity of modern

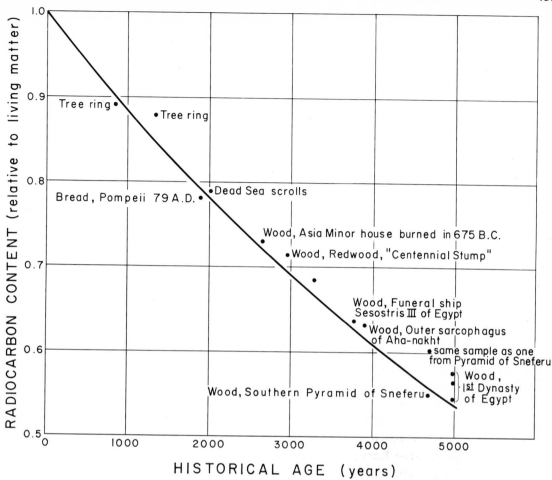

After William F. Libby, *Science*, vol. 133, 1961. By permission.

FIG. 16-4 *The heavy line is the calculated decay curve for carbon 14, using a half-life value of 5568 ± 30 years, and the dots show the radiocarbon content of certain materials of known historical age.*

peoples with all their differing languages and cultures to be deployed across Siberia, the European mainland, Scandinavia, Great Britain and Ireland, as well as the two Americas.

Before radiocarbon dating, the commonly accepted estimate for the length of time since the end of the ice age was approximately 25,000 years. This is an educated guess, based in large part on counting the annually layered sediments in glacial lakes, estimating rates of ice recession, and so on. This number of years seems a reasonably adequate time span for the postglacial landscape to evolve, and for men to invent such attributes of modern living as languages, agriculture, social grouping, religions, trade, and organized warfare.

The discovery of spruce trees at Two Creeks, Wisconsin, many of which were broken and their stumps splintered by a last advance of the ice, was an impressive indication of the effectiveness of the last and final push of the glacier in overriding the forest blocking its path. The find was doubly significant when radiocarbon dating showed that these trunks were shattered 11,400 ± 200 years ago. This date corresponds with similar ones obtained in Europe, which means that the time once thought to be available for western civilization to evolve since the close of the ice age was cut in half.

Understandably, a compression as drastic as this has had a revolutionary impact upon the thinking of geologists, prehistorians, and archeologists. The problem is how to accommodate all the events we know occurred in Europe and elsewhere in the remarkably short span of a little over 10,000 years.

Whether or not radiocarbon dates are true dates has stirred a controversy. There is a rather general agreement that dates well this side of the 5,568-year half-life probably are true. The disputes arise over the more distant ones, for there are a number of unresolved problems still awaiting an answer. For example, in older samples the level of radioactivity is very weak; the difference between one or two counts per minute means a long difference in time. Despite elaborate shielding, with this low level of radioactivity it becomes increasingly difficult to separate the few authentic counts from the background noise of cosmic rays.

Another uncertainty arises from the assumption that the level of cosmic radiation has remained essentially constant through time. A further error requiring constant vigilance to correct is the danger of contamination of buried organic material, through the introduction of more recent carbon carried to it by ground water, by burrowing animals and roots, and by increased exposure to radioactive carbon through nuclear explosions. All these have the effect of making the measured age less than the actual age.

Despite these possibilities for error, which are being attacked as vigorously as possible, the method of radiocarbon dating holds great promise for the future in archeology, geography, geology, meteorology, and oceanography. Results have already accumulated which are little short of miraculous in establishing a chronology within various cultures or within sequences of postglacial geologic events, and relating these to

one another, even across such barriers as thousands of miles of open sea.

RELATIVE AGE

We are accustomed not only to thinking of time in absolute terms such as years but also in terms of the relationship of one event to another. Thus we speak of the Reconstruction, which would be the period following a particular event, in this case the Civil War.

One of the unfortunate outgrowths of the way in which we are exposed to history is our habit of thinking of it in unrelated, compartmented units. The majority of us are likely to have encountered only U. S. history, and thus to have little understanding of events in America in relation to those of the rest of the world. For example, few people think of the American Revolution in its context as a skirmish in the world-wide struggle between France and Britain for supremacy.

The following passage from Palle Lauring's *Land of the Tollund Man,* which describes the prehistory of Denmark, expresses with great eloquence the contemporaneity of remote, and what at first might appear to be unrelated, events:

But the Scandinavian Bronze Age lasted from about 1500 B.C. to 500 B.C.

During this period the New Kingdom of Egypt came and went, Tutankhamen was laid to rest in his golden coffin, and in 525 B.C. Egypt fell to the Persians. The totalitarian military state of Assyria had arisen and spread death and destruction around it, crushed cultures, and perished in turn. In Greece a civilization had arisen that was to shed its lustre over centuries to come, moulding the destiny of untold generations in Europe, shaping Western thoughts and ideas, art, and architecture; the Greek states, having passed through their Archaic youth, were well on the way into the Classical period and a temple had already appeared on the Acropolis. At the Tiber ford, where an island divided the river in two, Rome had been founded and had already worsted its rival Alba Longa, and kings were reigning over the city between the hills. In Jerusalem centuries had passed since Solomon begot children with the Queen of Sheba, and David sang psalms and seduced the wives of his officers. None of them suspected that, thousands of miles to the west, Indians were creating strange civilizations in Yucatan and Mexico and Peru. Equally far to the east the Chinese Empire was ruled by the Chou dynasty and was in the middle of the remarkable period known as the Spring and Autumn Annals. Towards the south the wise King Asoka had been buried in his Indian empire and Prince Siddhartha, called Buddha, was dead, while his thoughts were alive and spreading. The world had not stood still while the North was experiencing its Age of Bronze.

This historical analogy has a direct relevance to the second major problem we are confronted with in deciphering past geologic events, and that is how to *correlate* a succession of them in one part of the world with those in another. In human history we have the immense advantage of written records, in spite of the ravages of time, war, pillaging, fires, and floods; there are also workable calendrical systems for some parts of the world extending back for 4,000 or 5,000 years.

Before the advent of isotopic methods of age dating, how were the rocks of Cornwall, England, for example, to be correlated with those of upstate New York? They happen to be of the same geologic age, and this has been known for over a century. By what method did our predecessors determine this contemporaneity? It certainly was not on the physical resemblance of the two kinds of rocks. At first they had believed this kind of evidence might be used; that all the reddish-colored sandstones of Britain were the same age, for example. It took effort and argument to establish the fact that there were several sets of red sandstone, some of which were the same geologic age, while others were separated from one another by hundreds of millions of years.

Where different kinds of rocks are in direct physical contact with one another, then by constructing a geologic map showing their mutual relationships and drawing geologic cross sec-

tions, it is possible to work out their three-dimensional geometry, and from this to determine their relative ages. Two major principles are employed in doing this. These are: (1) *superposition* of the rocks—that is, younger rocks normally rest on top of older, and (2) *cross-cutting relationships.* The latter are characteristic of igneous intrusions, such as dikes and sills. The intrusive rocks which do the invading, or the cutting across of others, are the younger.

The problem becomes more acute when the effort is made to compare rocks and the sequence of events they represent in one region, with another succession of rocks or events in a region hundreds, or even thousands, of miles away with no direct contact between the two.

Fossils

The method our predecessors employed was to use the fossils contained in the rocks. In fact, working out the evolutionary succession of fossil forms and understanding their time significance is a major creative achievement of the human mind. Fossils have excited men's interest and have been collected since before historic time. They are shown in ancient drawings; some have been employed in heraldry, and for centuries they have been cherished because of the interestingly decorative effect they give to cut and polished stone. The word itself, a Latin one from *fossilus,* meaning something dug up, shows an awareness almost since the beginnings of language that these were things of the Earth.

Although such an awareness may have existed, it was accompanied by an abysmal ignorance of the true meaning of these testimonials to the existence of life in the remote past. To some, fossils were the creation of Satan, placed in the world to confuse mortal men. To others, such as Avicenna (A.D. 980-1037), the Arab philosopher responsible for the revival of interest in the works of Aristotle, they were inorganic petrifactions that grew within the rocks as a result of the workings of a creative force, the *vis plastica*. Only by chance did they come to resemble bones or shells of living creatures. This ignorance extended to the discovery of the remains of prehistoric man, such as the Cro-Magnons and Neanderthalers, whose bones were sometimes carted to the village churchyard for a proper interment. It remained for the age of discovery, with the contact it gave Europeans with primitive societies, before the idea was accepted that the western world itself had passed through a primitive stage before it became civilized.

Others, however, did recognize fossils in the rocks for what they really were—the remains of organisms long dead. Leonardo da Vinci was such a pioneer, and the fossil shells he found entombed in the rocky hills of Tuscany told him that the sea had once extended far inland from the Italian coast.

For those who accepted fossils as the remains of organisms, Noah's flood provided a ready answer. Logically, these were the relics of creatures who had perished once and for all in this catastrophic event. In fact, one of the first fossils to be illustrated scientifically was that of a giant salamander (an amphibian, thus belonging to the same group of animals as frogs and toads) which Johann Scheuchzer in 1726 named *Homo diluvii testis,* meaning: Man a witness of the flood.

Some fossils proved difficult to accept because their bones resembled those of no known creature, or none of those living in the region where they were found. In western Europe this is especially true of such once common adornments of the ice age landscape as the woolly rhinoceros, the mammoth, the mastodon, and the great Irish elk.

The bones of such formidable creatures, as well as those of an occasional dinosaur, gave rise to legends and interpretations. Many such fossils were believed to be the skeletons of unicorns—a favorite medieval animal since it was supposed to have an unerring instinct for determining the presence or absence of maidenly

virtue. Dragons were also a preferred interpretation. One of the best examples is a splendid monster, the Lindwurm, a statue fully 40 feet long in the town square of Klagenfurt, Austria. It was carved in 1590, but the concept is based on the discovery of the skull of a woolly rhinoceros found nearby in A.D. 1335—seemingly it took quite a time to decide how a dragon looked.

It remained for a singularly devoted, untutored, and eminently practical canal-builder, William Smith (1769-1839), to establish the existence of a relationship between stratified rocks and the fossils they contain. Fortunately for him, and for us, he lived and worked in the right time and place, during the period when canal building was active in England. The advent of the Industrial Revolution, coupled with the post-Napoleonic prosperity of Britain, placed a premium on the construction of such relatively cheap and modestly efficient transportation as canals. In this boom, Smith was a willing participant.

Not only is the structure of midland and eastern Britain relatively simple, but the rocks themselves are distinctive. For example, the Cretaceous strata include the white chalk of the Dover cliffs; the Carboniferous, the black coal of the midlands upon which Victorian England was to base a century of prosperity for some, grinding labor for others, and the denudation of whole countrysides as a by-product.

In the construction of canals, the recognition of various rocks and an understanding of their physical properties are matters of prime importance. If the rocks are harder than expected, or if they slump and cave readily, or if, like the chalk, they allow water to drain away, then with very little difficulty a contractor on a canal project can go broke.

Smith's approach was entirely empirical, and considering the rate at which canals were dug by hand, he was in no hurry. As a single example, he ran surveys on the Somersetshire Coal Canal for six years. All told, he tramped up and down the English countryside for twenty-four years making observations. When he was done he had made the great fundamental discoveries that (1) the distribution of sedimentary rocks in southeastern England made a logical pattern that could be represented on a map, (2) the strata occurred in the same order—that is, the chalk beds were always found above the coal, unless disturbed structurally, and never vice versa, and (3) different layers contained assemblages of distinctive fossils. The practical result of this was that, given a representative collection of fossils, he could determine from which layer of rock they came.

Smith had no awareness of the evolutionary significance of the fossils he collected so patiently over the years. To him they were little more than uniquely shaped objects. Yet, unknown to him, he had found the key by which strata could be correlated with one another, not only in a local region but with rocks whole continents apart.

This type of correlation is no simple matter, however, because we are dealing with the remains of organisms that lived in environments as varied as those of today. Furthermore, during the long span of geologic time some groups of animals and plants gradually evolved into more complex creatures, while others, having achieved perhaps an uneasy balance with their environment and their enemies, remained essentially unchanged. Still others, such as the dinosaurs, vanished completely.

This brings us to an important contribution that *paleontology* (the study of ancient life) makes to the whole realm of contemporary thought. This is the demonstration—from the fossils preserved in the thousands of feet of stratified rocks in many lands—that many creatures have evolved from relatively simple forms to complex hierarchies of plants and animals. In fact, the fossil record was one of the stronger bodies of evidence advanced by Darwin and his followers in support of the theory of evolution.

For some lines of descent the record appears

to be reasonably clear—this is true, for example, of the family tree of the higher vertebrates. The lineage of the horse family, to pick a familiar illustration, is fairly well known. The developmental route followed by such organisms as the invertebrates is less well known. No one can say which large grouping (*phyla*) of these is descended from which other—or, in some cases, which is related to which.

Along with the discovery made by Smith, that different layers of rock very commonly contained different assemblages of fossils, it became apparent that many of these are the remains of organisms for which there are no living counterparts. Because such fossils were found in strata separated not only by hundreds of feet of barren rock but by unconformities as well, it did not occur at first to naturalists that there might be an unbroken continuity in the fossil record. Remember, too, this was a time preceding Darwin, and although some elements of evolutionary theory were suspected, nothing resembling a consistent hypothesis had been worked out.

Also, a knowledge of rocks and their contained fossils was limited very largely to western Europe in the post-Napoleonic period. Thus, it is not surprising that the idea gained wide acceptance that each of the various assemblages of extinct animals or plants had been separately created, and that each of these had perished in some cataclysm. The preference seemed to run to volcanic activity and to great overwhelming floods—the Noachian deluge was much favored as being a representative catastrophe.

In fact, according to Eiseley (1959) in his perceptive biography of Sir Charles Lyell,

The catastrophic school had a powerful religious appeal. It retained both the creative excess and fury of an Old Testament Jehovah. "At succeeding periods," wrote Adam Sedgwick, one of Darwin's geological teachers at Cambridge, "new tribes of beings were called into existence, not merely as the progeny of those that had appeared before them, but as new and living proofs of creative interference; and though formed on the same plan, and bearing the marks of wise contrivance, oftentimes unlike those creatures which preceded them, as if they had been matured in a different portion of the universe and cast upon the earth by the collision of another planet."

People thought in terms of a geotheological drama, a prologue to the emergence of man on the planet, after which no further organic developments were contemplated. The theory predicted a finished world which, in some eyes at least could be compressed into the figurative week of the Book of Genesis. "Never," commented Lyell, "was there a dogma more calculated to foster indolence, and to blunt the keen edge of curiosity, than this assumption of the discordance between the former and the existing causes of change."

In this half-supernatural atmosphere Sir Charles Lyell in 1830 published the first volume of his *Principles of Geology.* Like most great ideas it was not totally original with its author. But to Sir Charles belongs the unquestioned credit of documenting a then unpalatable truth so effectively and formidably that it could no longer be ignored. In this respect again his career supplies a surprising parallel to that of Darwin. For Darwin too, at a later time, was the resurrector and documentor of forgotten and ill-used truths.

Lyell's principal precursor, James Hutton, died in intellectual eclipse in 1797, the very year that saw the birth of the man who was to revive his views—so tenuous and yet so persistent is the slow growth of scientific ideas. In the 1780's Hutton made the first organized and comprehensive attempt to demonstrate that the forces that had shaped the planet—its mountains, boulders, and continents—are the same forces that can be observed in action around us today. Hutton had an ear for the work of raindrops, an eye for frost crystals splitting stones, a feel for the leaf fall of innumerable autumns. Wind and frost and running water, given time enough, can erode continents, ran his argument. Peering into the depths of the past, he could see, "no vestige of a beginning, no prospects of an end."

GEOLOGIC TIME SCALE

As knowledge accumulated of strata in different parts of the world, as well as in a single region, they could be compared with one another, or correlated, on the basis of their fossil content. It was necessary first to determine the order of deposition in one region, and when this had been done, the succession of rocks there might be compared with a different succession of rocks—perhaps a whole continent away, and not necessarily the same kinds of rocks at all, but containing fossils of the same geologic age.

The other step to be taken—and in many places the two were made simultaneously—was to determine which fossils were older than others. This is where evolutionary theory and paleontology have complemented or supported each other through the past century.

Although some organisms have shown little significant change with the passage of whole millennia, some have progressively advanced in the direction of increased complexity. Sometimes organisms became too inflexible, or too specialized, and thus, unable to adapt to a changing environment, or for other reasons, vanished from the Earth. Most spectacular of these failures was that of the dinosaurs. None survived the Mesozoic.

Other geologically important groups that failed to make good are: (1) *trilobites,* curious segmented marine arthropods, distantly related to such creatures as shrimps and crabs, and superficially resembling the sow bugs that lurk under stones and logs, and (2) *ammonites,* complexly partitioned, marine mollusks, related to the chambered nautilus, and more distantly to the squid and octopus.

Conversely, some families of animals and plants have not lived throughout the entire span of Post-Cambrian time. For example, fish were not common before the early Paleozoic (Silurian), amphibians before the middle Paleozoic (Devonian), reptiles before the late Paleozoic, mammals and flowering plants before the very late Mesozoic (Cretaceous).

By determining the appearance, or the culmination, or the disappearance, of many thousands of fossil animals and plants throughout the thick accumulation of stratified rocks that has been deposited since the Cambrian, it is sometimes possible to determine the relative geologic age of a fossiliferous layer with confidence. Not all fossils are of equal value in such an age determination. The least valuable are those that settled on one design and never had a model change through most of the sweep of Post-Cambrian time.

The most valuable fossils for correlating rocks in one region with those of another are ones that had comparatively short racial histories geologically speaking—and yet which in their limited span on Earth achieved a wide geographic range and underwent rapid evolutionary changes. Such chronologically ideal examples are called *index fossils*.

Geologic time is divided into units by using much the same philosophy we employ in subdividing historic time. To take a single example, in the western world one of the longer time intervals is the Christian Era. True, there is a measure of unity within this nearly 2,000-year chapter of history, but were we to find ourselves transported to ancient Palestine or Rome, very likely we should be more impressed by the differences than by the resemblances.

It is a rare one-semester history course that, in attempting to cover such a broad panorama, succeeds in making it appear more lasting than the fleeting, multicolored patterns of a kaleidoscope. Fortunately, most history courses break this enormous block of time with all its crowded events into smaller units; sometimes they become very short indeed, and a semester may be devoted to a five- or ten-year period.

To carry the analogy with human history a bit further, these intensely studied parts of the record are more likely to be the later rather than the earlier part. For example, 2,000 years of Egyptian history may be sketched in with broad strokes, while a large fraction of a semester may be devoted to the decades following the treaty of Versailles.

This same distortion colors our view of geologic time. Events closer to us leave more complete and decipherable records than those grown increasingly fragmentary over a long lapse of time and through the repeated deformation rocks undergo in such processes as mountain building. The result is that more is known about events in the later parts of Earth history than in the earlier, and this is reflected in the larger number of divisions of the last part of the geologic time scale.

If we consider the names of the scale, the grand divisions, comparable in significance to such human episodes as the Stone Age, are the Eras. They take their names from our concept of the dominant aspect of life during each Era; thus a free translation, beginning with the oldest, would be ancient life for the Paleozoic, medieval life for the Mesozoic, and modern life for the Cenozoic. In very broad terms, the Paleozoic was a time in which invertebrates, and relatively simple vertebrates, such as fish, amphibians, and primitive reptiles were ascendant. The Mesozoic was high noon for the reptiles, and this is the chapter in Earth history when the hegemony of the dinosaurs was complete. The Cenozoic, which is the contemporary Era, is a time of mammalian dominance.

The Eras are divided into lesser units called Periods. From their names, it obviously is hard to find a common pattern. Two have a familiar aspect to Americans—the Pennsylvanian and Mississippian—and we can use them to illustrate the philosophy behind the naming of these time units. Most are named for regions where rocks containing fossils characteristic of their segment of geologic time were found. This means that strata deposited in the later Paleozoic in an inland sea covering much of the eastern United States were named for their occurrence in Pennsylvania, just as strata approximately 20 million years older were named for their occurrence in the Mississippi valley—not the state. Incidentally, neither of these time terms is used in Europe; there the two periods are treated as a single unit, the Carboniferous, which acquired its name from the coal-bearing strata of England.

Another time term whose place of origin can

be recognized readily is the Devonian, named for the rocks that crop out along the southwestern tip of Great Britain in Devonshire and Cornwall. A less familiar period is the Permian —named after the ancient Kingdom of Permia in Russia.

Only the small number of persons with a knowledge of Latin may recognize the ancient name of Wales, Cambria, as the basis for the naming of the Cambrian. Two closely related periods, the Ordovician and Silurian, perpetuate the memory of Stone Age tribes whose homes had been in Wales, the Ordovices in the north and the Silures in the south.

Some of the other periods are named, not for places, but for physical characteristics of their rocks. The Cretaceous is a good example, since it is derived from the Latin word *creta*, chalk, for the exposures of these rocks in the cliffed coast of southern England. Incidentally, this by no means is a characteristic rock type for this age. In the United States, Cretaceous rocks run the gamut from conglomerate through sandstone and shale to limestone and coal; or, as in the Sierra Nevada, may include the enormous bodies of granite intruded during this period. The Triassic takes its name from the fact that in Germany the rocks of this age are divided into three distinctive layers—a limestone in the middle, with reddish sandstones and shales above and below.

The table lists the periods in their proper order, and gives the date at which each was established. It is immediately apparent that most of them were named in the first half of the nineteenth century, and nearly all from areas in western Europe. This parochial approach—an inevitable result of the way the system was created—has led to repeated difficulties ever since. Geological events that happened in Europe very often did not happen elsewhere, and thus a system once thought to be of world-wide applicability has had to be patched up and tinkered with continuously as more and more of the world is explored geologically.

The subdivisions of the Cenozoic are called Epochs, and their rather strange names are a special case. They were established for the most part by Sir Charles Lyell on the percentage of extinction of marine molluscan fossils. Thus in Eocene (Greek *eos,* dawn + *kainos,* recent) strata about 1 to 5 per cent of the species found are still living. In the Miocene (Greek *meion,* less + *kainos,* recent) 20 to 40 per cent of the fossil species are still alive. In the Pleistocene (Greek *pleistos,* most + *kainos,* recent) 90 to 100 per cent of the fossil shells are those of species living in the seaways of the world today. Without perhaps fully realizing it, Lyell had divided this later segment of geologic time on a statistical basis—one of the earlier applications of statistics to a natural science.

The Pleistocene, the latest subdivision of the time scale, is regarded by many geologists as being coincident with the ice age, and although the length of time represented by the multiple advance and retreat of the ice sheets is unknown, it probably is between 1 and 3 million years.

The entire Cenozoic is divided by some geologists into two parts: the Tertiary (meaning third)—which includes all but the Pleistocene and postglacial time—and Quaternary (meaning fourth). This represents a sort of cultural lag, since we no longer speak of the Primary and Secondary rocks as our forebears did. With the first and second of a series gone, it seems strange to speak of a third and fourth, but you will see these terms employed consistently in much geologic writing today; such is the force of habit.

LIFE OF THE PAST

As we near the end of this survey of our physical world, there is an opportunity now for a hurried glance at the diverse patterns life took as it evolved through ages past. This brief survey of the history of life is included to give an insight into this record, which should be part of any thoughtful person's background. This is the story of our shared heritage and of our kinship with all living things. If the lesson that all men are brothers is ever to be learned, it is to be learned from this story in the rocks of the origins of our common humanity.

The Origins of Life

No one knows where, or when, or under what circumstances life originated on Earth. We do know that it is immensely old. We know, too, that for the greater part of the record the pages are blank. In the more than 3,900 million years represented by Precambrian rocks, the fossil record is so meager as to be nonexistent, or questionable at best. Mostly the evidence consists of indirect clues, such as the traces of burrows, tracks, and trails, although the remains of such simple plants as lime-secreting algae have been identified in some of these ancient rocks. Another indirect line of evidence is the thick deposits of metamorphosed limestone and of graphite in some Precambrian terranes. Both these rocks contain carbon—in fact, graphite is nothing else—and much carbon is interpreted as having had an organic origin.

The probability is very strong that life originated in water, rather than on land. Very likely it started in shallow water—perhaps in tidal inlets and estuaries. This is an environment where water is well aerated, sunlight penetrates to the bottom, and from such an estuarine environment various forms of life can disperse into the deep waters of the open sea, or inland by rivers, and ultimately up onto the land.

Because deposits made in the shore zone are so readily destroyed by erosion, and because the first forms of life may have been microscopic and fragile, it should not surprise us that they were erased so completely from the record that we might well think that they never lived (Axelrod, 1958).

A remarkable thing is that with the start of the Cambrian (Fig. 16-5), the great difference

FIG. 16-5 *Reconstruction of a Middle Cambrian sea floor. At lower right and far left are colonies of tube-like sponges. A jellyfish floats just left of center. Swimming in the foreground and center are two kinds of trilobites, and several trilobite-like forms. Burrowing worms crawl on the sea floor in the lower front. (Courtesy of the Smithsonian Institution.)*

FIG. 16-6 ZYGOSPIRA modesta *Say. Brachiopod shells in a rock slab of the Ordovician Maysville Formation, Cincinnati, Ohio. (Courtesy of the Smithsonian Institution.)*

Why shelled animals should suddenly appear, however, remains a riddle. Perhaps the concentration of lime in the sea became great enough to be available for use in making shells. Possibly competition became severe enough to place a premium on the development of protective devices.

Paleozoic Life

In the beginning of this long era, the only life we know of lived in the sea. The continents of that remote time stretched inland incredibly bleak and barren from the coast, with no vestige whatever of green plants. Assuming the Earth had a global climatic pattern then, not too unlike today's, very likely there were places where the rainfall was 100 inches or more. How vastly different such a barren, deeply rilled landscape would be from the verdure-blanketed slopes of the recent tropical rain forest.

The life swarming in the early Paleozoic seas would have appeared modest to us, but nonetheless it represented a prodigious step forward from its humble beginnings. Typical creatures of that time were the *trilobites*. Most were less than 3 inches long, although some did attain a length of 2 feet. These curious animals, distantly related to such things as hermit crabs, were very highly organized to have existed at the dawn of recorded life. They had complex, multilensed eyes (like those of flies and other insects), segmented bodies, elaborate sensory antennae, multiple legs, bodies differentiated into head, thorax, and tail, and a central nervous system. In their heyday they successfully exploited the available environments in the sea. Some swam freely on the surface, some dwelt in shallow waters near the shore, others scavenged and burrowed in the mud at the bottom.

More abundant than trilobite remains in early Paleozoic rocks, especially throughout the strata of the Atlantic and Middle Western states, are fossil *brachiopods* (Fig. 16-6). A common

between rocks above this time boundary and those below is that the strata above are often richly fossiliferous while those below are not. All that we know is that at the beginning of the Cambrian representatives of all the principal *phyla* into which we divide the animal kingdom had appeared, with the exception of the vertebrates, and in the plant world none as yet grew on land.

A factor sometimes cited for the lack of fossils in Precambrian rocks is that the humble animals of that day, if they were akin to modern flagellates, protozoans, and jelly fish, were animals without shells. Only when external hard parts, such as the shells of mollusks and the chitinous protective carapace of arthropods, appeared could fossils be preserved in quantity. Very likely it is this essentially world-wide appearance of shelled organisms at the beginning of the Cambrian that is the fundamental difference between the Precambrian and the Paleozoic.

name for some of these is lamp shells, a name based on their fancied resemblance to the ancient olive-oil lamps of Mediterranean lands—the symbol we use for scholarship. Brachiopods apparently had roughly the same habitat that mollusks do today.

Gradually, through the Paleozoic, the seas began to be thronged with animals and plants, which, though extinct now, have living relatives. Among these were the forerunners of *sponges,* and they lived in great profusion at the start of the era. Abundant, too, were *corals, sea scorpions,* some of gigantic size, 9 feet or so long, *mollusks,* including varieties related to the squid and octopus, but encased in shells with a maximum length of 15 feet, and *crinoids.* These last, the so-called sea lilies, are animals that grow upward from the sea floor on long, segmented, limy stalks. There they wave to and fro in submarine currents like forests of flowering plants.

A great step forward is recorded in the Ordovician with the appearance of fragmentary *fish* remains. Fish were well established by the Silurian (Fig. 16-7), and their evolution and dispersal throughout the seas, rivers, and lakes was rapid. The first varieties appear strange to us. They were small sluggish creatures without true fins and the bodies of some were encased in bony plates, rather than being covered with scales as most modern fish are. A leading survivor of the ancient fish of the past are the sharks, and these arose in the Devonian. Look closely at a representative of this remorseless clan some day and you will be impressed with the fact that its tough, leathery skin is studded with thousands of teethlike denticles, rather than scales, and these give the whole animal a rough, sandpapery surface.

Presumably at some time in the Devonian, a revolutionary step occurred, and this was the advance of the vertebrates from the sea onto the land. Credit for this achievement goes to the animals which appropriately enough we call the *amphibians.* A typical amphibian leads a life

FIG. 16-7 Pteraspis. *One of the several ostracoderms, which were jawless vertebrates that lived during the Silurian and Devonian Periods. The posterior part of the body was covered with a pattern of small scales while on the anterior part there was an unjointed armor shield. The ostracoderms were mostly less than one foot long. (From the film "The Dinosaur Age," courtesy of Film Associates of California; art work by A. D. Nellis.)*

reminiscent of an amphibious operation—involving a move from water onto the land. Most amphibians are born in water from eggs laid and fertilized in water. Many go through a phase—tadpoles are an example—in which they fundamentally are fish, without legs and breathing by means of gills. Then, like toads and frogs, they develop legs and learn to breathe with lungs. Henceforth, in the case of toads and salamanders, they are land creatures.

Very possibly the amphibian's ancestry is from one of the lobe-finned Paleozoic fish, the *crossopterygians,* whose fins are muscular and have a central bony axis. Amphibian evolution may have gone through a phase like the living lung fish of the Southern Hemisphere. These curious, in-between creatures survive drought by gulping air into their swim bladders, rather than by circulating oxygenated water across their gills, and by going into a long hibernation sealed off in mud burrows along dried-up stream courses.

Vertebrates were not the only animals to make the transition from sea to land. Even such obscure beings as snails crossed the barrier, and the arthropods were notably successful. Not only are we afflicted by such things as scorpions and spiders in this group, but their close relatives, the insects, contest with us for supremacy. They outnumber all other land dwellers many times, including as they do perhaps as many as 800,000 species.

Plants, too, gained a foothold on the land and were established by the Devonian. These earliest varieties lacked true roots and leaves. Most reconstructions of the Carboniferous landscape show a swampy scene, much like the tropical rain forest of today, peopled by sluggish, squatty amphibians, ranging up to 10 or 15 feet long, being bothered by enormous insects, including "dragonflies" with wing spreads of 29 inches or so, droning through the trees. To many people the forest probably would look tropical, because it would present such a dark green wall, as the forests of New Guinea do today. There

were no flowering plants in the Carboniferous, nor deciduous trees whose foliage changes with the march of the seasons, especially with the brilliant coloring of fall so cherished by dwellers in cool-temperate lands.

Some of the coal-making trees were large. *Lepidodendron,* with a narrow, tapered trunk and paired branches, grew to heights of perhaps 150 feet. *Sigillaria* had no lower branches and sported feather-dusterlike ones on top. Both trees had curious eye-like patterns on their trunks which really were scars left by the branches which they shed. *Cordaites,* the forerunner of today's conifers, was a tree that would look moderately familiar to us. It had a narrow trunk surmounted by a crown of narrow, straplike leaves up to several feet long.

This is the forest whose dead branches, trunks, leaves, and spores accumulated in the swamps of the Carboniferous, and in the course of centuries was converted into the coal of western Europe, the Atlantic states, and the Mississippi valley. Coal of the western states, such as Alaska, Utah, Colorado, and New Mexico, was deposited much later—a great deal of it in the Cretaceous.

Coal of Carboniferous age is found in latitudes far north and south of where forests even remotely resembling the ones of that period grow today. Examples are the productive coal mines of Svalbard (Spitzbergen), and the visible coal seams of Antarctica. A look at an economic geography map of commercial coal fields shows that most of them are in temperate rather than tropical lands. A further suggestive factor is that the present-day environment where peat accumulates is in boggy ground in such cool, rainy regions as Ireland, Scotland, and Scandinavia.

The coal forest was not necessarily tropical. However, it almost surely grew in an equable climate to judge from the lack of growth rings and of deciduous trees, and from the presence of large insects and amphibians, both of whose sensitivity to cold temperatures is pronounced.

FIG. 16-8 *A landscape of the Permian Period.* DIMETRODON, *the large fin-backed reptile with a blunt head, was carnivorous. Note the mammal-like differentiation of the teeth. A single* EDAPHOSAURUS, *an herbivorous fin-back with a smaller, more pointed nose, stands in the center. The smaller lizard-like reptiles to the left are* CASEA; *the two small specimens with boomerang-shaped heads at extreme lower right are* DIPLOCAULUS, *an amphibian. A clump of horsetails is at the middle right; in the left background is a group of primitive conifers. (Courtesy of Chicago Natural History Museum; Charles R. Knight, artist.)*

Toward the close of the Paleozoic the climate became more rigorous. In the American Southwest where Texas, New Mexico, and Oklahoma are today, it was arid enough that thick beds of evaporites, such as salt, gypsum, and potash, accumulated. In the Southern Hemisphere, wide areas, such as a large part of the Republic of South Africa, are considered by many to have been glaciated.

From the evolutionary point of view the most noteworthy innovation of the Permian was the ascendancy of the *reptiles,* who appeared in the Pennsylvanian. In a time of aridity, the advantage is distinctly with the reptiles, in contrast to the amphibians. Reptilian eggs are laid directly on land; there is no necessity for an infantile stage spent in water; and finally, as adults, a dry scaly surface is an enormous advantage over a skin that has to be kept moist much of the time, as with amphibians.

The Permian reptiles were wide-ranging—great numbers are known from the Southern Hemisphere, including some with skeletal traits that are prophetically mammalian. Chief among these attributes are differentiated teeth, such as we have in our molars, incisors, and bicuspids. Permian reptiles included the strange-looking *Dimetrodon* (Fig. 16-8) from Texas, with a grotesque, sail-like spine running the length of its back. More familiar to us would have been turtles, which had appeared even at this distant date. How remarkable it is that such seemingly obtuse creatures as turtles and tortoises could have survived so many arrows of fate, while apparently far more gifted creatures vanished into oblivion.

Mesozoic Life

This was a truly medieval time in the long history of life on Earth. It was a time when the emphasis for survival was placed upon brute force, limited intellect, and the development of

FIG. 16-9 TYRANNOSAURUS, *a giant Cretaceous carnivorous reptile, attacking the horned dinosaur,* TRICERATOPS. TYRANNOSAURUS, *one of the last of the dinosaurs, was the greatest land-living flesh-eater known. Standing 20 feet high, it had jaws armed with large saber-like teeth. The plant-eating* TRICERATOPS *was protected by its three horns and by the bony frill covering its neck. Both of these dinosaurs lived in North America at the end of the Cretaceous Period, 60 to 70 million years ago. (Courtesy of Chicago Natural History Museum; Charles R. Knight, artist.)*

---

armor to a degree never to be repeated in the vertebrate world.

This was the era of the *dinosaurs,* and nearly all of us have seen pictures, movies, or outdoor statuary of them—as at Rapid City, South Dakota. Their skeletons are impressive when we see them mounted in the United States National Museum in Washington, D. C., the American Museum of Natural History in New York, the Carnegie Museum of Pittsburgh, the Chicago Museum of Natural History (Fig. 16-9), and the Denver Municipal Museum. Probably one of the more exciting opportunities to witness something of this life of the past is to visit the museum area in Dinosaur National Monument in northeastern Utah. Their bones can be seen in place in the rocks, and much of their story can be learned from displays in the Park Service museum as well as in the museum in the nearby town of Vernal.

The dinosaurs (from the Greek words *deinos sauros,* meaning terrible lizard) were the dominant vertebrates of the Mesozoic. The name is more than a century old and no one would advocate changing it, but many of them bear no resemblance to lizards and many were far from terrible. In the beginning of their reign, in the Triassic, some were very small, scarcely larger than chickens. Typically, in this early part of the Mesozoic, some varieties scurried around on their hind legs; like kangaroos, they had long tails for balancing. Many of the early dinosaurs had three toes, which we know because scores of their tracks, looking for all the world like ones left by an enormous flock of running turkeys, are preserved in the red Triassic sandstones of the Connecticut Valley.

The golden age of the dinosaurs was the Jurassic and the early Cretaceous. In these periods they reached their greatest size and achieved an astounding diversity of forms and adaptations. Largest and most ponderous were the four-legged, swamp-dwelling, herbivorous dinosaurs, such as *Diplodocus.* These weighed up to 50 tons, and with their long necks and tails were as much as 80 feet long. Their stumpy, pillar-like legs and general build suggest that they were swamp dwellers, possibly spending much of their time immersed in water as the hippopotamus does today.

In any natural population a balance is quickly struck between herbivorous animals and the carnivores preying upon them. Among meat-eating animals few could be guaranteed to strike more terror than *Tyrannosaurus rex*. This fearsome beast was perhaps 20 feet high and had an overall length of 50 feet. Since it stood on enormously powerful clawed hind legs it needed a heavy tail for balancing. The front legs were dwarfed; in fact, they were far out of scale with the rest of the animal. The ferocious head was nearly four feet long and large and powerful jaws were sown with what to its prey must have appeared like a forest of dragon's teeth.

One of the more obvious means of survival for the less bloodthirsty land-dwelling dinosaurs was the typical medieval solution of retiring inside a defensive redoubt to resist a siege. This took the form among the dinosaurs of the addition of bony plates, spines, spiked tails, and so on, until some outdid the noble knight in the age of chivalry with their weight of armor.

Stegosaurus (Fig. 16-10) was an imposing exemplar of this philosophy. This ponderous animal had curiously mismatched legs, with the rear pair much longer than the front; the result was that the beast must have presented a strangely humpbacked appearance with its head forced down to ground level. This probably did not matter too much since there was so little in it. Although stegosaurs weighed about 10 tons,

FIG. 16-10 STEGOSAURUS. *This plated dinosaur is among the earliest of the known ornitischians (reptiles with a bird-like pelvic-girdle) and comes from the upper Jurassic. The edges of the peculiar vertical plates on the back were thin; the bases were thickened and embedded in the animal's back. What function these plates had is not known; perhaps they were protective, or they may have served some physiological function. (Courtesy of Chicago Natural History Museum; Charles R. Knight, artist.)*

their brains weighed little more than 2½ ounces —about the size of a walnut. To protect this dwarfed intellect, as well as the spinal cord, a double palisade of large triangular plates extended the length of the back, and the tail ended in a set of four fierce-looking spines.

Ankylosaurus, a squatty, four-legged dinosaur superficially resembling the modern armadillo, carried this defensive approach for survival to the ultimate degree. It clanked along furbished with studs, spines, and bony plates, culminating in a knobby lump of bone at the end of the tail, which could be wielded as a club, much like the medieval warrior's "morning star."

Triceratops, a Cretaceous dinosaur, combined both offensive and defensive elements in its anatomy. They were stocky animals, rather like a modern rhinoceros, but with three long and sharply pointed horns. Unlike rhinoceros horns, which are made of felted hair, these horns were solid bone. They were fused at the base into a solid shield of bone, much like an Elizabethan ruff, which protected the upper spine, heart, and lungs from a frontal assault. No triceratopsian outlived the end of the Cretaceous; and this might mean that hardware alone is not enough to guarantee survival— some brainpower is needed, too.

The Mesozoic reptiles are an excellent example of adaptive radiation, because they successfully invaded some part of every available environment; land, sea, and air. In this last regard they equalled, if not surpassed, the achievements of the mammals, because the only representative of our class in the aerial world is the bat. Flying reptiles collectively go under the name of *pterosaurs* (winged lizards), and their wings resemble those of bats more than they do those of birds. The leading edge of their wing for nearly half its length is made up of an enormously extended little finger. Just as birds do, pterosaurs differed greatly in size, ranging from small ones the size of sparrows up to veritable gliders, with wing spreads of 27 feet,

that ranged far out over the shallow, chalk-accumulating seas covering Kansas in the Cretaceous.

Seagoing reptiles achieved an extraordinary degree of success, considering the very real limitations of their physiology. Mesozoic turtles reached lengths of 12 feet, which is quite a contrast to their diminished successors of today. The *ichthyosaurs* (Fig. 16-11) (fish lizards), perhaps 25 feet or so long, were as fully adapted to life at sea as their mammalian counterparts, the modern porpoises. Ichthyosaurs had streamlined, fish-shaped bodies, although their legs were rounded out into flippers rather than fins. Unlike whales, but like fish, their tails were vertical. The backbone ran along the lower edge, and thus differed from fish whose backbone spreads out in a fan. Ichthyosaurs had narrow, teeth-studded jaws that from a distance made them look like swordfish. Their eyes were large and were encircled by a bony ring made up of wedge-shaped plates.

A remarkable adaptation was in the birth of their young. Since ichthyosaurs were fish-shaped they could not lay their eggs on land, as turtles do. Rather the eggs were hatched internally, as is demonstrated by embryonic ichthyosaurs found preserved as fossils inside their mother's rib cage. Possibly the baby ichthyosaur was born tail first, and slowly enough that it learned to swim before being released to make its way in the world. Unlike mammals there was no umbilical cord, nor were they nursed. A characteristic distinguishing the reptilian from the mammalian world is the total lack of any parental interest in the offspring.

Other maritime reptiles, such as the *plesiosaurs,* played a role approximately equivalent to that of seals and sea lions. They had barrel-shaped bodies, long necks and flippers, and only slightly modified front legs. Still others looked like mythological sea monsters—or perhaps even medieval dragons *sans* wings. *Elasmosaurus* was such a one, with a spiny back and long tail. Its remains are found in the former sea

FIG. 16-11 *Skeleton of* ICHTHYOSAURUS, *a common marine reptile of the middle Mesozoic era. These marine reptiles were similar to modern porpoises in size and habits. They had no neck, nor any caudal fin. The four legs were modified to become like paddles. The numerous teeth had a labyrinthine structure characteristic of the labyrinthodont amphibians and the primitive colylosaurian reptiles—a possible clue to the ancestry of these highly specialized marine reptiles. (Courtesy of the Smithsonian Institution.)*

floor deposits of Kansas that are also the final resting place of the giant-winged pterosaurs.

Naturally there has been speculation as to why so diversified and seemingly successful animals as the Mesozoic reptiles perished. The odd thing is that not all did. Quite sizable reptiles survived to our day; among them are crocodiles and alligators, turtles and tortoises—including the immense ones of the Galapagos Islands—and pythons, lizards, and iguanas.

Possibly climatic changes at the end of the Cretaceous may have contributed to dinosaurian extinction. Certainly it appears more than coincidental that two great groups of organisms dominant in the world today—flowering plants and mammals—should have achieved hegemony during the time the dinosaurs vanished.

The earliest mammals, whose remains date back to the late Triassic, were an unprepossess-

ing lot. The majority were rodent-like creatures, perhaps the size of small rats. They are difficult to tell from reptiles when only skulls are available. Teeth, as we have seen, are a diagnostic skeletal element; reptilian teeth are not differentiated according to function, while mammalian ones are. The number of mammalian teeth is fixed—the typical number is 44 in placental mammals, and since we have only 36, we have moved quite a distance along an evolutionary path in this regard.

Other differences between reptiles and mammals are well known. Mammals do not have scales, and have varying amounts of bodily hair. Their body cavity is divided by a diaphragm, and they have a four-chambered heart. Most significantly, they can maintain a constant body temperature—ours centers around 98.6°F. This is an enormous advantage in severe climates—reptiles are immobilized when temperatures drop too low and suffer from heat strokes when it is too hot since they do not perspire. This means that the geographic range of reptiles is sharply restricted when compared to the mammals. There are a number of large mammals that can tolerate cold temperature and whose range extends far into arctic regions, such as the blue whale, walrus, polar bear, musk ox, reindeer, and caribou.

Another significant difference is that reptiles are hatched from eggs, while mammals are born alive. Among the more primitive mammals, such as the *marsupials,* which include the opossum and the Australian kangaroo, the young are born prematurely and then placed in a pouch until they are fully formed. In *placental mammals* the embryo is carried full term in the womb.

Since new-born mammals are nursed and there is a degree of interest and solicitude shown in their welfare—an aspect of life totally lacking in the reptilian world—mammals have an immensely greater advantage for survival during their most vulnerable period. Incidentally, there is a correlation between the degree of intelligence and the length of parental care— the more intelligent mammals taking the longer time to mature.

The flowering plants, or *angiosperms,* appeared early in the Cretaceous. Their advent provided a wholly new source of food, a wide variety of nuts, fruits, seeds, and cones, which were possibly seized upon by the emerging mammals and neglected by the rather inflexible dinosaurs. With the ascendancy of the angiosperms the world took on an increasingly familiar aspect. The forerunners of the *sequoia,* the giant tree of the western forest, were widely distributed around the Northern Hemisphere. Another holdover from the Cretaceous is the *ginkgo,* a native of the Orient, but a tree whose rounded, pale greenish leaves enliven many a city park. *Cycads,* stumpy, palm-like, extraordinarily slow-growing trees, flourished widely. Other plants which diversified the formerly somber green forest were the forerunners of such familiar things as magnolia, willow, oak, laurel, and a wide variety of palms and conifers.

The angiosperms very possibly originated in the tropical uplands of the Earth and spread outward into temperate lands. Their appearance had a profound effect upon the insects, whose role in plant fertilization—the bees are an example—is widely known.

Birds, too, gained their ascendancy during the Mesozoic. A remarkable fossil find was made at Solenhofen, Bavaria, in 1877, when the bones and feathers of a wonderfully preserved bird, *Archaeopteryx,* which was the size of a pigeon, were recovered (Fig. 16-12). The fact that *Archaeopteryx* had feathers, and thus was not a pterosaur, was established beyond doubt; yet its anatomy still preserved many reptilian characteristics, including teeth along the beak, claws on the wings, and a long nonbird-like tail.

Evolutionary changes had not ceased in the sea while these developments were occurring on land. They were far too numerous to detail here, but many familiar forms of marine life gained a foothold in the Mesozoic. The bony, flexible-scale-covered fish, the *teleosts,* the dominant kind today in rivers, lakes, and shallow seas, achieved the ascendancy they now hold.

Distinctive among Mesozoic marine invertebrates were the *ammonites.* Ammonites are coil-shelled mollusks, and resemble the chambered nautilus of the tropical seas. The name comes from the ram-headed god Ammon, in the ancient Egyptian pantheon, and at first glance typical ammonite shells resemble the coiled horn of a mountain sheep. The animal lived in the outermost of the chambers, and when it outgrew this last one a new one was added. The distinctive difference between a nautilid shell and an ammonite's is in the intersection of the partition wall with the outer shell. In a nautilus the junction is smooth, in an ammonite it is extremely complex; much as though the partition were too large for the shell and had crumpled along the junction line. The result is the development of a pattern at the intersection, as involved as the intricately sutured way the bones in our skull are joined. The animal resembled a squid or octopus because it had imposingly large eyes, a mouth like a parrot-beak, and a collection of tentacles with suction discs— ten as contrasted to the customary eight for an octopus.

Near the end of their geologic life span some ammonite shells have the most aberrant form imaginable. Some are partially straight, then coiled; others were coiled so that finally the animal was turned back on itself and died. Still others, the *Baculites,* developed nearly straight, long, tapered shells, much like an old-time dunce cap (except for a tiny coil at the very end), and thus reverted to nearly the same pattern as the original nautiloids of the early Paleozoic. By the close of the Mesozoic all ammonites were gone.

Cenozoic Life

The climate in the beginning of the Cenozoic over much of the Earth seems to have been warmer and more humid than today. Broad expanses of North America were cloaked with a subtropical forest that included trees such as figs, breadfruit, magnolias, sassafras, palms, and palmettos.

Gradually through the Cenozoic this humid, subtropical aspect diminished, and the landscape acquired an increasingly modern appearance. In what now are temperate North America

FIG. 16-12 *A Jurassic landscape. The primitive toothed bird,* ARCHAEOPTERYX, *is in the middle foreground. Two individuals perch on a cycad frond, and two others swoop down toward two midget dinosaurs inspecting a primitive crustacean. Note the claws on the front of the wings of* ARCHAEOPTERYX. *Above, and in the background, are several flying reptiles,* RHAMPHORHYNCHUS. (*Courtesy of Chicago Natural History Museum; Charles R. Knight, artist.*)

and Europe, oak, beech, maple, chestnut, spruce, fir, and pine succeeded the original forest. An important floral event in the mid-Cenozoic was the appearance and proliferation of the grasses. Although grass seeds have been recovered as fossils from Cretaceous rocks, grasses did not reach their peak until much later.

It would be nearly impossible to describe our debt to this humble plant. Grasses are the most widely distributed of the flowering plants, and include at least 5,000 species. It would be hard to think of a region so desolate that no grass will grow. Not only is grass directly valuable as the food for nearly all grazing animals, but from wild grasses were derived a host of domesticated grains, such as wheat, rice, barley, and corn. Two other grasses play so vital a role in the tropics that it would be difficult to imagine this part of the world without them; these are bamboo and sugar cane.

Geologically, grass is enormously significant in controlling erosion. Grasslands are virtually impregnable to ordinary erosional processes, but when the sod is stripped away the resultant gullying may be spectacular. There was a time when the western prairies were truly a sea of grass, and our literature—as well as movies and TV—has been telling for decades of conflicts between cattlemen and sodbusters.

In retrospect, it is interesting to speculate on what erosional processes were like, and what the appearance of the world may have been before the grasses evolved. This is much the same problem we were confronted with in reconstructing a mental image of the Pre-Cambrian terrain without land plants.

The yielding of forest to grassland in the mid-Cenozoic had a profound effect upon the evolution of the land mammals. This gave an advantage to the plains dwellers and to grazing animals as the horse, camel, and bison, as well as scores of cursorial animals, much like the ones we see in photographs of the African savannah.

In North America and in Europe the climate became cooler, with some oscillations back and forth, and many of the prominent deserts of the world began to develop in the later Cenozoic. This was especially true of the western United States, where the growth of intermontane deserts correlates closely with the rise of the Sierra Nevada and the blocking of rain-bearing winds from the west.

Near the end of the Cenozoic, in the Pleistocene, the climate of the world underwent one of its more stringent modifications, the ice age. As we learned in Chapter XIII there were at least four major advances of continental ice sheets and the most drastically affected areas were in northwestern Eurasia and the northern part of North America. This was also a time of crustal disturbance—there very possibly is a causal relationship between the two events—and the world's higher mountain ranges, such as those of Canada and the United States, the Cordillera de los Andes, and the Himalayas, were elevated to their present heights.

Sea level rose and fell in rhythm with the retreat and advance of glaciers on land. This rising and falling of the sea was vastly important in the distribution of land animals, including the wanderings of our prehistoric ancestors. When sea level stood low, Britain and Ireland were joined to Europe, Ceylon to India, and many of the islands of Indonesia were connected to one another as well as to the Asiatic mainland. Perhaps the most important of these land bridges was the one across Bering Strait which connected the New with the Old World. Across this isthmus between Siberia and Alaska trooped a parade of creatures. Migrating from North America westward marched the zebra, the camel, and the horse; eastbound came the elephant (at least four kinds), the bison, the mountain goat and sheep, the moose, the elk, and the musk ox, and lastly the ancestors of the diverse races of people we call American Indians.

Any attempt to describe the panorama of Cenozoic mammalian evolution in so brief a span as remains in this chapter would be fool-hardy. It is nearly as hopeless a task as trying to describe the contents of the world's largest zoo in words, and at the same time make it interesting. Fortunately, because of the proximity to us in time of the evolution of the Cenozoic mammals, their fossil record is more complete than for animals of earlier eras.

In the beginning of the Cenozoic most of the mammals were small and the majority of them were forest dwellers. It almost appears that the death of the dinosaurs left a temporary vacuum the mammals at first were reluctant to fill. The earliest mammals included insect eaters, small hedgehog-like creatures, shrews, raccoon-like animals, and opossums.

Very quickly a number of distinctive lines appeared. The first unquestioned member of the horse family lived in the Eocene, *Eohippus* (meaning dawn horse), a graceful, slender-legged animal with short, even teeth, and a small head. A distinctive difference from the modern horse was the feet; the front had four toes, the back, three.

Rodents flourished in the Eocene forest, and were perhaps more common then than they are today. Carnivores prospered, too, and in this early age appeared the precursors of such later types as the cat and dog families.

In the Eocene the two landmasses of North and South America were separated, and in the Southern Hemisphere the evolution of distinctive animals such as the sloth, the armadillo, and the anteater went on quite independent of the rest of the world. Another curious world apart was Australia, where, through early isolation, the vastly more primitive marsupials did not have to contest with more advanced placental mammals for survival. Marsupials filled most of the available ecological niches, even producing a dog-like carnivore, the so-called Tasmanian wolf.

Two bizarre forms in the early Cenozoic fauna were (1) the archaic mammals and (2) the giant birds. The first were hoofed animals, with stump-like legs, large ungainly bodies much resembling those of the rhinoceros, and heavy, low-browed skulls supporting a variety of knobby horns (Fig. 16-13). A typical archaic

---

FIG. 16-13 BRONTOTHERIUM, *a large Oligocene titanothere, in the middle and background; at right foreground,* HYAENODON, *a primitive carnivore; and in the left foreground, giant tortoises.* BRONTOTHERIUM, *distantly related to the horse, was the largest (8 feet at the shoulder) of the titanotheres, a group whose evolutionary history was marked by an increase in size and the development of horns; the titanotheres nevertheless remained primitive in other respects, particularly in the dentition and feet.* (Courtesy of Chicago Natural History Museum; Charles R. Knight, artist.)

mammal was *Uintatherium* (beast of the Uintas —which are mountains in northeastern Utah), and, judging from the brain case, his I.Q. did not exceed that of the recently extinguished dinosaurs by very much. Like the dinosaurs, the early Cenozoic uintatheres were an unsuccessful experiment in which brute strength and feeble intellect lost out to more agile, aggressive, and intelligent competition. The birds were an uncanny element in the landscape of the early Cenozoic. With no effective carnivores preying on them, some reached enormous size and at the same time were wingless. *Diatryma* was one of these monster birds in the Eocene, and reconstructions of it are like something remembered dimly from a childhood nightmare. This appalling bird stood about 7 feet high, its large skull and beak measured approximately 1½ feet long, and it had tremendously powerful scaly lower legs and claws. It must have been a frightful thing for an early mammal to encounter. *Phororhacus,* with a great hooked beak, was another utterly savage looking individual from the middle Cenozoic of South America. In the later Cenozoic and on into modern days, flightless birds characterize the Southern Hemisphere, where they are relatively free from carnivores. Among them are ostriches in South Africa, rheas in Argentina, emus and cassowaries in Australia, and penguins in Antarctica and the South American coastal islands. Most remarkable of all were the moas of New Zealand—13-foot giants which were exterminated by the Maoris as recently as the sixteenth century.

Beginning in the Oligocene and continuing into the Miocene, the animals of North America and Europe acquired an increasingly modern aspect. Some of the more bizarre and primitively organized earlier mammals died out, and with the thinning out of the primeval forest and the spread of grassland, grazing herbivores came into their own.

Merychippus, a typical horse of this time, was the size of a small pony. It ran on graceful, nimble legs which terminated in a three-toed foot. Only the middle toe was functional, and the nail had already evolved into a hoof. Incidentally, the atrophied trace of the useless second and third toes can still be identified in the modern horse as the splint-like cannon bones on either side of the hoof. In response to the plains environment, *Merychippus'* teeth grew high-crowned and developed elaborately enameled surfaces to cope with the harsh prairie grasses—grass is a plant that has silica in its composition. In harmony with the lengthening of legs, there was a corresponding lengthening of *Merychippus'* neck and muzzle. In fact, the jaw had lengthened and the gap that is such a characteristic feature of the modern horse appeared between the incisors and the rest of the teeth.

The camels, also a distinctively North American animal, were undergoing a parallel evolution. Two varieties were *Procamelus,* without a hump and about the size of a sheep, and *Alticamelus,* a strange-looking version with a long, giraffe-like neck which enabled it to browse on the branches of trees.

Other mid-Cenozoic mammals displayed the variety we associate with these, our distant relatives, today. The ancestors of the whales started on a way of life that would take them to the most distant seas of the Earth. Forerunners of the deer, antelope, and bison emerged and were preyed on, then as now, by carnivores—clearly differentiated in this distant day into members of the cat (lions and tigers) and the dog (wolves, coyotes, bears) clans.

One of the most appealing of animals is the elephant—perhaps because of our nostalgic recollections of circus parades—although mid-Cenozoic elephants would look unfamiliar to our eyes. Some had tusks only on their lower jaws, and these curved sharply downward at right angles to the jaw. No one knows their function, but possibly they were used for gouging out roots. Others had four tusks; two above and two below.

No one knows where the lineage of elephants

had its start, but there is some evidence it may have been in the vicinity of the valley of the Nile. Should this be true, they started from here on an immense journey that was ultimately to take them under such alien skies as those of Alaska, Siberia, Europe, and North America. Two great families emerged: the *mastodons* and the *mammoths*. The mastodons are the smaller of the two, and became extinct during the Pleistocene. The living elephants are related to the mammoths.

The Pliocene Epoch, which merged with the Pleistocene, saw the rise of the living, or only very recently exterminated, animals of the Earth. The nature of the boundary between the Pliocene and Pleistocene is still being argued, but the beginning of the general advance of the continental glaciers southward across the prairies of the Middle West and radially outward from the Scandinavian highlands somewhere between 1 and 3 million years ago is a logical event to separate the two epochs.

To return to the history of the horse, the Pliocene form, *Pliohippus,* was larger than his Miocene progenitor, and only slightly smaller than his Pleistocene descendant, *Equus.* Both varieties had single hoofs, and the vestigial remnants of the second and third toes essentially had vanished. The main difference is in the teeth, with those of *Pliohippus* being smaller and with less intricately involuted enamel partitions within the tooth than those of *Equus.* Horse teeth grow upward during the modern horse's life until it is about 34 years old. Then, with no further growth, the teeth rapidly disappear and death is likely to result from starvation. The ability to estimate a horse's age from his teeth is a knack that stood the old-time horse trader in good stead.

From the Pleistocene on, the story of the horse takes on a truly epic character. The evolutionary development from a small, multitoed, browsing animal the size of a sheep, up to a single-toed grazing creature the size of an Indian pony took place largely within the Western Hemisphere. Then for no reason now known, the horse vanished from its former home, crossed the Bering land bridge, and appeared in Eurasia.

Where the horse was first domesticated is uncertain, but its impact on the slowly emerging Eurasian world was profound. For one thing, it gave Eurasian man a beast of burden—something the American Indian sorely lacked. For another, the horse added a completely new dimension to warfare, with perhaps the greatest mobility being realized by the Tartars when they swept everything before them from Korea to the gates of Warsaw.

Although the Golden Horde achieved amazing mobility, the Tartars lacked the ability to make a stand and fight from horseback. This "achievement" awaited the invention of such a simple device as the stirrup. With the stirrup it was possible to strike a sweeping blow with a sword, and with the sword came the knight in armor, and with him came not only the Age of Chivalry (from Old French, *Chevalier,* one who rides a horse) but the social pattern of the medieval world.

The horse's wanderings were not ended, for, brought to the New World by Hernando Cortes, some escaped and re-established themselves in what had been their ancestral home. The impact of the feral horse on the life of the Indian—especially the plains tribes—can only be described as explosive. Some tribes accepted the horse; others did not—and quickly came to rue the day. Among the more successful horsemen were the Comanches, who were the scourge of the frontier in the Civil War era. They ranged in pillaging bands all the way from Durango in Mexico north into central Kansas. The Sioux and other northern tribes were equally redoubtable foes on horseback, as General Custer, for one, learned on a bitter day in June, 1876.

Other animals evolved rapidly in the Pliocene and into the Pleistocene—many of them were vastly more numerous than now, as well as being far larger and more formidable. An impressive example is the elephant. In addition to the mastodon, at least four major varieties of mammoth roamed the northern continents of the world. In the far north, or in lands marginal to the Pleistocene ice sheets, both the mammoth and the mastodon were covered with thick, coarse hair. They lived and died in Siberia in such vast herds that for centuries their tusks, dug out of the tundra, constituted one of the world's sources of ivory.

We know very clearly how the woolly mammoth looked (Fig. 16-14). For one thing, his curious hump-backed profile was drawn repeatedly on the walls of caves by his contemporary, stone-age man. For another, his remains, frozen in permafrost, complete even to his last meal, undigested in his stomach, have been recovered in Siberia and Alaska. The strange, dome-like top of his head and the hump on his back were reservoirs of fat, which, together with his covering of hair, helped him survive the arctic chill.

The southwestern United States was the domain of the imperial elephant—a creature that would have gladdened the heart of the departed Barnum—standing 12 to 14 feet high, with enormous recurving tusks. He, too, was a contemporary of early man in the New World.

Other animals of the latest Cenozoic were the woolly rhinoceros, the bison—larger than the ones which darkened the western plains in pioneer days—the ubiquitous musk ox, reindeer and deer in great profusion, and their inevitable predators, wolves, lions, tigers, and bears. The cave bear, an exceptionally large and powerful animal, contended with our ancestors for occupancy of caves and shelters in Europe during the ice age.

A paradox of our generation is that one of the more revealing insights we have into this savage world of the ice age is in the heart of a major American metropolis. To someone driving down Wilshire Boulevard in Los Angeles, attempting to survive the hurtling traffic dimly seen through smog, the glittering façade of

FIG. 16-14 *Woolly mammoth and woolly rhinoceros in a Pleistocene glacial landscape. Both of these animals have been recorded in the cave paintings of southern Europe and were hunted by early man. The woolly mammoth, a member of the same family as the modern-day elephant and more distantly related to the mastodon, is known to have been covered by a dense coat of hair because frozen carcasses of this beast have been found in the tundra of Siberia and Alaska. (Courtesy of Chicago Natural History Museum; Charles R. Knight, artist.)*

nearly identical, "international" style buildings is an insipid vista when compared with the once more colorful scene on the same site.

Tarry for a moment a few blocks west of La Brea Avenue; there, in a small park surrounded by the ziggurats of today, some memories of this bolder past are recalled for us. Dotted through the park are concrete statues of some of the vanished animals of the Pleistocene (Fig. 16-15). These are reconstructions of animals whose skeletons were recovered from tar seeps once interrupting the surface of the then barren plain where Hollywood now sprawls.

The La Brea tar pits were active in 1769, when the first white men, members of the Portola expedition on their way northward to find a harbor of refuge for the Manila Galleon, passed by them in their search for a way out of the Los Angeles basin. Later, when tar was first spread on the dusty streets of the "City" of Our Lady, Queen of the Angels, enormous numbers of bones were sifted out of the pits excavated on Rancho la Brea (Brea means tar in Spanish), and they still remain as dank, scum-filled depressions—perhaps not notably different from their appearance in the late Pleistocene. Then, scores of animals were lured to their death when they sought to drink the water that formed a thin film over the deadly tar beneath.

Most intriguing of the animals recovered were sabre-tooth tigers. These were stocky, powerfully built cats with broad and heavy shoulders. Their lower jaws were hinged to drop far back, which enabled them to strike a deadly stabbing blow with their long, sharp-edged incisors.

Other exotic denizens of southern California a few tens of thousands of years ago were the sloths (Fig. 16-16). These outlandish-looking, witless creatures evolved quite independently in South America, and when the two continents were rejoined in the late Cenozoic, they wandered northward to North America.

The skeleton of one of them that was found in a cave in Virginia was described by no less

FIG. 16-15 SMILODON, *the great saber-tooth cat, attacking a bison mired in the tar seeps of La Brea tar pits, Los Angeles, California.*

The acme of the saber-tooth evolution, that began in the Oligocene, was attained in SMILODON *during the Pleistocene. This saber-tooth cat was as large as a modern lion and preyed upon slow-moving animals. His powerful neck and long sabers were completely specialized for destroying his prey, but when his supply of slow animals became scarce in the late Pleistocene he was unable to compete with his swifter cousins in the chase of the remaining more speedy game animals, and he became extinct. (Courtesy of Film Associates of California.)*

a personage than President Jefferson, who had the bones spread around the White House when he was studying them. Few Presidents since then have had the inclination, or found the time, to carry on an independent paleontological investigation. Jefferson believed the sloth remains were the skeleton of an immense lion, probably living somewhere in the wilds of the Louisiana Purchase, because, in his own words, "Such is the economy of nature, that no instance can be produced of her permitting any one race of animals to become extinct. . . ."

The ground sloths resembled great clumsy bears with long recurving claws. Their coarse, shaggy hair covered a tough hide studded with little bony pellets, or scutes. Sloths lived in the southwestern United States contemporaneously with the early Indians, and may have survived almost into our day, since a settler in the Cape Horn region in the early 1890's found a sloth hide together with signs of human occupancy in a cave bordering the appropriately named Inlet of the Ultima Esperanza, or Last Hope Inlet.

Another distinctive member of the Pleistocene of Rancho La Brea was *Teretornis,* an enormous, carrion-eating bird with a wing spread of 12 feet, the largest flying bird ever found. The California condor, its diminished successor, even now is an unforgettable sight soaring on motionless wings thousands of feet aloft in the summer sky.

Thus, evidence from the La Brea pits, as well as other Pleistocene graveyards around the world, poses an unanswered problem similar to the great dying out of the dinosaurs at the end of the Cretaceous. In the case of the Cenozoic mammals it must not have been the rigors of glaciation; most of them survived these, only to perish with the advent of the modern climate.

The wanton destructiveness of mankind is sometimes named as a cause. Although men are remorseless destroyers of wild life, and even within recent generations a sobering list of man-induced exterminations can be compiled, it is extremely doubtful that stone-age man was that

---

FIG. 16-16 *Statues of the giant ground sloth in Hancock Park, Los Angeles. These animals, which are represented by many remains in the La Brea tar pits, were common in the southwestern United States in late Quaternary time, and were contemporaneous with early man.*

Their closest relatives are the armadillos and *the giant anteaters, and they are characterized by peg-like teeth with which they chewed leaves of trees and bushes. They grew to the size of a small elephant and lumbered along on the sides of the hind feet and upon the knuckles of the front feet. (Courtesy of Film Associates of California.)*

effective. The Indian, for example, had little impact on the buffalo population compared with the deadly slaughter accomplished by white hunters in the decades following the Civil War.

ORIGIN OF MAN

When the men of western Europe, having gained momentary technical ascendancy with gunpowder and the sailing ship, set out to explore the rest of the world they brought back animals, plants, and people as samples of the wonders they beheld on distant shores. With increasing knowledge of the diversity of the plant and animal kingdoms, attempts were made to create an orderly biological classification. Then the problem arose: where do we fit in? There was not only the question posed by the great diversity of the living races of men, but that of our relationship to the anthropoids, such as chimpanzees, gorillas, orangutans, and the like. Awareness of this resemblance goes back to the beginnings of recorded history. According to Greene (1959), Ennius, who lived from 240 to 169 B.C., wrote, "How much doth the hideous monkey resemble us!"

Linnaeus (1707-78), founder of the binomial classification of organisms that biologists employ today, recognized this kinship and placed man in the same order with the apes and, of all things, sloths.

Throughout this same period in the formative years in the growth of natural science, increasing numbers of finds were made of human remains and of stone-age implements throughout western Europe. Oddly enough, there was no general appreciation of the significance of these artifacts up to the beginnings of the nineteenth century. This seems strange, because as far back as the Renaissance the knowledge was widely shared that the Romans, for example, had subjugated people far more primitive than they. Furthermore, in the Age of Discovery, explorers in distant parts of the Earth encountered people using stone weapons and tools. This was some-

times explained on the basis that they were degenerate tribes who had wandered far from the center of civilization, perhaps even before the flood.

The beginnings of a stratigraphic sequence of the relics of ancient man were worked out first in Denmark. This clasification, familiar to educated people—the Old Stone Age, the New Stone Age, the Bronze Age, and the Iron Age—was established by Christian Jürgensen Thomsen in the 1830's when he was director of the Royal Museum in Copenhagen. No one visiting Copenhagen today, after taking in the sights of Tivoli, should fail to see the amazing collection of implements, clothes, people, and so on in the museum. Denmark in prehistoric time was unusually favored because of the immense supply of amber from the Baltic—which was traded the length of Europe, even to the Mediterranean, across well-established Alpine routes—and also for its supply of flint which was used for spear and arrow heads.

However, cultural relics and chronologies erected on them pose the same problems fossils do when we attempt to use them in correlating sequences of events in distant areas. Similarities between the methods and philosophy of paleontology and archeology are close, and each of these sciences can learn much from the other.

While such a relative succession as stone, bronze, and iron has local validity in Europe, it is not of universal application. The American Indians, with few exceptions, never left the stone age until they were suddenly brought in contact with relatively advanced forms of the iron age in A.D. 1492. Even in Europe, one age did not end abruptly and another begin; stone implements were still handy to have around the house, and were far less expensive than bronze when it was first introduced. The same holds true for iron; it was used as long ago as 3000 B.C., but did not really reach central Europe until about 800 B.C. Such, however, was the conservative nature of the military mind that long afterward the legions were still fighting with the traditional Roman short bronze sword while the barbarians were equipped with weapons of iron. An enormous advantage of an iron sword is that a man can strike with it, whereas with bronze he can only stab.

Puzzling as his cultural remains were to our ancestors, the actual skeletons of early man were even more so. In the first place, very few of them were found, or are very likely even to be discovered for that matter. Above all else the founders of our race must have had a certain amount of sly cunning. They were not likely to be trapped in great numbers on the sandy flood plains of large rivers, as happened repeatedly to grazing animals. Also, the number of prehistoric peoples, to judge from the estimated pre-Columbian population of North America, was insignificant compared with the dense agglomerations we find in parts of the world today. Then, too, it is a rare environment in temperate climates where bones do not quickly decay. Fortunately for us, early man was a contemporary of the ice age in Europe. Storm, cold, and driving rain were no strangers to him, with the result that caves were a highly prized refuge—even if title to them had to be disputed with the cave bear.

Since limestone is a relatively common rock in many parts of Europe, caves are fairly abundant there, the most renowned being in the Spanish Pyrenees and the Dordogne Valley of France. Fortunately, the cave people were not compulsive tidiers. They would not have been the best of all possible roommates, and any notion on their part of sanitation was nonexistent. In some caves which were more or less continuously inhabited, debris on the floor may be 70 feet or so deep. Such piles of litter yield records of people and their possessions extending back tens of thousands of years.

Apparently among the first unquestioned representatives of the now-vanished Neanderthal race to be described was a skeleton recovered from a quarry in the Rock of Gibraltar in 1848. Like the first of almost everything it was ignored

and forgotten until more publicized remains of the same race were discovered in the Neander Valley near Düsseldorf in West Germany. Since the description of this find was published in 1858, only one year before Darwin's *Origin of Species* appeared, the possibility of this being some kind of extinct prehuman was recognized almost immediately.

A debate soon broke out between those who were persuaded that here indeed was a subhuman type, and those who believed this was no more than the skeleton of some unfortunate, imbecilic victim of an advanced case of rickets.

Today we know this unkind interpretation was not true. More than thirty sites, some including a fair number of individuals, have been found from Iran to the coast of Britain. We also have an idea of how Neanderthal man looked. He looked tough. Perhaps many of the reconstructions made have not dealt charitably with him, but he did lack a certain amount of grace. He was short, with long arms, and he had a barrel-like chest with powerful shoulders. He was bent forward more than we are because his backbone lacked the four curvatures that give spring to our backs and allow us to hold our heads upright. Neanderthal man had a low forehead, a broad and rather flattish face, a powerful jaw and yet a receding chin. Whether or not he was as furry as reconstructions often show him to be is unknown. In spite of the fact that this description may remind you of some of your acquaintances, he was not of our race, but vanished somewhere between 30,000 and 50,000 years ago. Despite his rugged appearance, he was far from a cretin—his brain size was about the same as ours, 1,200 to 1,600 cubic centimeters. He had learned to make fire, to make stone axes and spears, and to bury his dead.

For a brief while Neanderthal man lived contemporaneously with his successor, Cro-Magnon man, and then vanished as completely as the great creatures—the cave bear, the aurochs, the great elk, the mammoth, and the mastodon—

who had been his companions and his adversaries in this shadowy world before the dawn of ours.

The first recorded discovery of the Cro-Magnon people was at Aurignac, France, in 1852. There seventeen skeletons were found, carefully collected, and buried in the village cemetery, thus becoming lost to science. A later find, in 1868, of five skeletons in a rock shelter known as Cro-Magnon in France was recognized for what it was, and this discovery gives its name to this remarkable race.

They would have been regarded as a handsome people by our standards. They were tall and powerfully built—taller, for example, than the Celts or other modern European races that followed them—and their cranial capacity averaged larger than ours. As an identifiable race they lived from 35,000 to around 5,000 B.C., and are deserving of our lasting admiration for the extraordinary level of their artistic achievement.

As we learned earlier, the cultures associated with the vibrantly life-like paintings in the caves at Altamira, Spain, and Lascaux, France, have a carbon 14 age of 15,000 years, and this makes them very likely the handiwork of the Cro-Magnon people who also developed the technique of fashioning stone tools and weapons to a degree of perfection never equaled since.

What happened to the Cro-Magnon race remains a mystery. They apparently went into a decline in the closing days of their history, and may well have been overrun by the Mediterranean and round-headed Alpine races that invaded Europe at the beginning of historic time. Some traces of the Cro-Magnon physique are said to survive in the people of southwestern France, in Brittany, and perhaps among the Basques.

However, both the Neanderthal and the Cro-Magnon people were enough like ourselves to leave little doubt of our kinship. What of their predecessors? What connection is there between our first human ancestors, and the higher primates, such as gorillas, chimpanzees, and baboons?

Here we may become lost in a maze of fact, of fancy, of speculation, and of special pleading. Several things, however, do appear to be reasonably certain. First, we are physically related to the animals of the world. Zoologically, we are classified as primates; we are mammals; and we belong to the great group of vertebrates, or animals with backbones.

Second, we have unique specializations that distinguish us physically from our closest relatives, the anthropoid apes. Among these distinctive features are our upright posture, which is related to the four curvatures of the spine, our basin-shaped pelvis, and our relatively short arms—quite different from the gorilla, for example, whose arms dangle as far as his knees.

Loss of bodily hair is a distinctive feature and a puzzle since it has disappeared chiefly from the back, whereas in animals that have lost hair as an adaptation to a hot climate, it disappears on the underside first. In northern races the loss of skin pigmentation is a specialization, too.

Our facial angle is much greater than that of the anthropoids. This means that a line drawn touching most of our face is nearly vertical, around 85°, while for a chimpanzee, whose jaw is longer and forehead lower than ours, it is only about one half as great, or 43°. The anthropoid jaw moves more nearly transversely, while ours has a much greater rotary capability. Watch a dedicated gum chewer some time to see this attribute displayed. Our reduction in the number of teeth, from the normal mammalian 44 down to as low as 32, is a primate rather than a human characteristic. However, the reduction in use, or in size, of premolars, and occasionally incisors, is an indication of a continuing trend.

Our opposable thumb is not a uniquely human attribute, but it is an extraordinarily important trait. It gives us an ability to pick up and handle objects, ultimately to shape them to our needs, and thus with weapons and tools in our hands to achieve supremacy over our fellow creatures, as well as over much of our physical environment.

The physical characteristic most significantly separating us from our distant cousins is articulate speech. This ability to communicate with one another, to convey ideas, to express emotion, to achieve the co-operation that only human beings can, is the tangible attribute that most clearly sets us apart. No other single attainment of the organic world compares with it, because through this medium our common humanity has been achieved and the world of the spirit is made possible. Our nearest relatives, the apes, may seem remarkably human at times, but the difference between anthropoid behavior and that of the most primitive men is wide and fundamental.

Should one look for a driving force responsible for the acquisition of these social traits differentiating the anthropoid from the human way of life, it probably came from the development of hunting as a mechanism for survival. As soon as men learned to hunt, a social organization was essential, and a means of communication became necessary. That these lessons were learned long ago is demonstrated by the association of the skeletons of early man with the fire-charred remains of Pleistocene mammals. Fully 50,000 years ago, men were skilled and deadly hunters.

With the background of the discoveries of cave people of Europe and with the growing interest of nineteenth-century naturalists in Darwin's theory, it is not surprising that a search began for the so-called missing link. One of the searchers was a young doctor, Eugene DuBois, whose conviction was that the remains of the progenitor of the human race would be found in a warm climate, much like the habitat of the larger anthropoids today. His urge to visit the tropics was strong enough for him to join the Netherlands Army as a surgeon and be shipped out to Sumatra. He had no success in his search there, but when word reached him of fossil dis-

coveries on Java he journeyed there, and after the customary disappointments he made a series of remarkable discoveries near Trinil in the years 1890-93. He found the top of a primitive man-like skull, a jaw bone, a number of teeth, and a femur. To these he gave the name of *Pithecanthropus erectus* (erect ape-man), and although he was correct in reasoning that he had found the remains of a primitive man-like creature, he was subjected to so much ridicule that he locked his finds away until as recently as 1923. Fortunately, DuBois's work was continued by a German paleontologist, G. H. R. von Koenigswald, from 1930 to the beginning of World War II, when he was interned by the Japanese. Von Koenigswald found enough more partial remains of *Pithecanthropus* to enable us to know what this primitive man-like being looked like. He walked upright; he was shorter than most of us; his brain case was low and flat, with a capacity of only 700 or 800 cubic centimeters; and he had very large and beetling eyebrows. His teeth were large, his lower jaw was powerful and extended forward; yet, like Neanderthal man, he lacked a chin. The animals and plants associated with his remains indicate a cool and relatively rainy climate, and this is generally correlated with the second interglacial stage. How long ago this actually was depends on what the length of the Pleistocene may have been.

In 1941, very shortly before his internment, von Koenigswald made an amazing discovery —the true significance of which has never been evaluated. This was the finding of fragments of an immense lower jaw—at least one inch thick near the base—and several enormous teeth. The same sort of human teeth, many times larger than ours, also showed up in apothecaries' shops in Hong Kong and elsewhere as "dragon's bones." Ground up, they were much prized as a cure-all for a broad spectrum of ailments.

Some day we may know the significance of these massive molars. To some archeologists they were puzzling traces of a vanished race of giants. Were the same proportions to hold with these teeth as do with ours, these people would have been 11 feet tall. To counter this argument it has been pointed out that the teeth of orangutans are larger than ours, yet their body size is much less.

The bones of a much better known race of ancient people were recovered from cave deposits at Chou-k'ou-tien about 35 miles southwest of Peking. There, in a low range of limestone hills honeycombed with caverns, an immense quantity of fossil bones has accumulated. In 1923 some human teeth were recovered by two paleontologists, J. G. Anderson of Sweden and Otto Zdansky of Austria. Through the years, with the support of the Rockefeller Foundation and others, and under the devoted leadership of Davidson Black, a young professor of anatomy at Peking Union Medical College, an immense amount of material was recovered. When Black died in 1934 the work went on under the direction of Franz Weidenreich, from the University of Chicago, and Weng Chung Pei, a Chinese paleontologist.

The bones of the primitive people found there are now assigned to the same general race as Java man, but put in a slightly different species, *Pithecanthropus pekinensis* (Black). They had the same massive jaws, strong teeth, low-crowned brain cases, and exceptionally prominent brow ridges. All told, parts of more than forty people were recovered, so that a convincing record was available of this early Pleistocene race. Primitive as they were, they possessed weapons and tools and used fire. They may have been either head hunters or cannibals since much of the material consists of fire-burned skulls with the basal part broken open.

This remarkable collection appears to have vanished forever. On December 5, 1941, when the threat of a Japanese advance on Peking appeared imminent, the fossils were turned over to the legation guard of U. S. Marines for safekeeping. On December 8 the men of the detachment on their way to the coast at Ch'ingtao were captured by the Japanese. To this day no record has come to light of the unhappy fate of Peking man.

In recent years the most challenging finds of early man have come from South Africa. The first discovery, that of a child's skull, was made in 1924 by Professor R. A. Dart of the University of Witwatersrand. This ape-like fossil was recovered from a filled-in limestone cavern. Its discovery was greeted with disbelief tinged with derision, but when the authenticity of the so-called Taungs child, or "Dart's Baby," was certified by the leading South African anthropologist, Robert Broom, it was recognized as a distinctly different prehuman, *Australopithecus africanus* (Dart), which means African southern ape. Since then, through the devoted labors of Dr. Broom, a number of discoveries have been made in caves and quarries in the Transvaal; at Swartkrans in 1949, Sterkfontein in 1947, Makapansgat in 1947 and 1949, and Komdraii in 1958.

Even more ancient hominid remains were discovered in 1960 at Olduvai Gorge in Tanganyika by the archeological team of Dr. and Mrs. L. S. B. Leakey (1961), and to these earliest tool-makers they gave the name of *Zinjanthropus*. Fortunately, the fossil remains are buried in volcanic ash layers whose age is determinable by the potassium-argon method. A provisional age of 1,750,000 years was assigned to them by G. H. Curtis and J. F. Evernden of the University of California.

Although a variety of names have been given the various hominids in this South African assemblage, they do show enough resemblance to one another that collectively they are called the *Australopithecines,* or southern apes. What they really were has not been determined satisfactorily. They were short, perhaps around five feet tall; they walked upright and their skulls were well balanced. They had large and powerful jaws and teeth and low and receding foreheads. Their teeth were man-like, but their brain capacity was more akin to the apes, averaging only around 600 cubic centimeters. Whether they knew anything of fire, or how to shape implements or weapons has not been established completely. Although these ancient beings of South Africa were far removed from us, nonetheless the resemblances to us turn out to be greater than the differences.

There are many other kinds of primitive men in addition to these, but the study of their peculiarities and the relationships of one to the other, and possibly to us, properly belongs in the domain of archeology. The essential purpose of this brief discussion has been to demonstrate that physically we appear to be related to ancestors more primitive than ourselves. That the evolution of the modern races of mankind required a long time also seems certain. We do know that men lived during the ice age, and were contemporaries of many of the Pleistocene mammals, now vanished from the Earth.

What is uncertain is the actual evolutionary path our forebears walked. No one knows where mankind originated, except that it was almost certainly in the Old World; but as to whether it was in Africa or Asia, the record is silent. Our relationship to the other primates is equally beclouded, although the agreement is general that we are not descended from the apes. Whether or not we share a common ancestor at some distant time is something about which we can only speculate. It would be a rash person indeed who would claim knowledge of the shape of man's family tree.

This, then, brings us to the end of the story. The Earth and the sea are part of our being, just as surely as we shall some day return to them. My hope in writing this book is that, through the description of the physical attributes of Earth as well as something of the processes operating on and within it, you may acquire the beginning of understanding of this wonderful ancient sphere which is our home, as well as some knowledge of how we came to be what we are. I am sorry at the end of the tale not to be able to answer so many of the questions still vexing us. Some of them will be answered in your lifetime, just as others will remain to challenge us in years ahead.

Many of these questions have been with us a long time—in essence they are the same as those asked millennia ago by God speaking out of the whirlwind to Job:

38:4 "Where wast thou when I laid the foundations of the earth?

38:16 "Hast thou entered into the springs of the sea?
Or hast thou walked in the recesses of the deep?

38:18 "Hast thou comprehended the earth in its breadth?
Declare, if thou knowest it all.

38:25 "Who hath cleft a channel for the waterflood,
Or a way for the lightning of the thunder;

38:28 "Hath the rain a father?
Or who hath begotten the drops of dew?

38:29 "Out of whose womb came the ice?
And the hoary frost of heaven, who hath gendered it?"

And perhaps the answer given then is equally valid today:

"Speak to the earth, and it shall teach thee."
(Job 12:8)

Suggested References

Augusta, J., and Burian, Zdenek, 1956, Prehistoric animals, Spring Books, London.

——, 1960, Prehistoric man, Paul Hamlyn, Spring House, Spring Place, London, N.W.5.

Axelrod, D. I., 1958, Early Cambrian marine fauna, Science, v. 128, p. 7-9.

——, 1961, How old are the angiosperms?, Amer. Jour. Science, v. 259, p. 447-459.

Barnett, Lincoln, 1955, The world we live in, Time, Inc., New York.

Bibby, Geoffrey, 1956, The testimony of the spade, The Fontana Library, Collins, London.

Beerbower, J. R., 1960, Search for the past, McGraw-Hill Book Co., Inc., New York.

Blum, H. F., 1951, Time's arrow and evolution, Princeton Univ. Press, Princeton, N. J.

Bowen, R. N. C., 1958, The exploration of time, George Newnes, Ltd., London.

Clark, Grahame, 1960, World prehistory, Cambridge Univ. Press, London.

Clark, W. E. L., 1955, The fossil evidence of human evolution, Univ. of Chicago Press, Chicago, Ill.

Colbert, E. H., 1955, Evolution of the vertebrates, John Wiley and Sons, Inc., New York.

Coon, C. S., 1962, The story of man, Alfred A. Knopf, Inc., New York.

Dobzhansky, Theodosius, 1962, Mankind emerging, the evolution of the human species, Yale Univ. Press, New Haven, Conn.

Dunbar, C. O., 1960, Historical geology, John Wiley and Sons, Inc., New York.

Eiseley, L. G., 1957, The immense journey, Random House, New York.

——, 1958, Darwin's century, Doubleday and Co., Garden City, New York.

——, 1959, Charles Lyell, Scientific American, v. 201, p. 98-106.

——, 1960, An evolutionist looks at modern man, from Adventures of the mind, Vintage Books, New York.

Ericson, D. G., and Goesta, William, 1962, Micropaleontology, Scientific American, v. 207, p. 96-106.

Flint, R. F., 1957, Glacial and Pleistocene geology, John Wiley and Sons, Inc., New York.

Gillespie, C. C., 1959, Genesis and geology, Harper Torchbooks, New York.

Greene, J. C., 1959, The death of Adam, Iowa State Univ. Press, Ames, Iowa.

Gregory, W. K., 1951, Evolution emerging, McGraw-Hill Book Co., Inc., New York.

Haber, F. C., 1959, The age of the world—Moses to Darwin, Johns Hopkins Press, Baltimore, Md.

Holmes, Arthur, 1959, A revised geological time-scale, Edinburgh Geol. Soc., Trans., v. 17, p. 183-216.

Hurley, P. M., 1959, How old is the earth?, Anchor Books, Doubleday and Co., Garden City, N. Y.

Kluckhohn, Clyde, 1949, Mirror for man, McGraw-Hill Book Co., Inc., New York.

Knight, C. W., 1935, Before the dawn of history, McGraw-Hill Book Co., Inc., New York.

Kummel, Bernhard, 1961, History of the earth, W. H. Freeman and Co., San Francisco, Calif.

Kulp, J. L., 1961, Geologic time scale, Science, v. 133, p. 1105-1114.

Lauring, Palle, 1957, Land of the Tollund Man, Lutterworth Press, London.

Leakey, L. S. B., and Sisson, R. F., 1961, Exploring 1,750,000 years into man's past, National Geographic, v. 120, p. 564-589.

Ley, Willy, 1941, The lungfish and the unicorn, Modern Age Books, New York.

——, 1951, Dragons in amber, The Viking Press, New York.

Libby, W. F., 1961, Radiocarbon dating, Science, v. 133, p. 621-629.

Lull, R. S., 1929, Organic evolution, The Macmillan Co., New York.

Macgowan, Kenneth, 1950, Early man in the new world, The Macmillan Co., New York.

Moore, R. C., 1958, Introduction to historical geology, McGraw-Hill Book Co., Inc., New York.

Moore, Ruth, 1953, Man, time, and fossils, Alfred A. Knopf, Inc., New York.

——, 1956, The earth we live on, Alfred A. Knopf, Inc., New York.

Oakley, K. P., 1952, Man the tool-maker, British Museum (Natural History), London.

Oparin, A. I., 1953, The origin of life, Dover Publishing Co., New York.

Romer, A. S., 1945, Vertebrate paleontology, Univ. of Chicago Press, Chicago, Ill.

Schrock, R. R., and Twenhofel, W. H., 1953, Principles of invertebrate paleontology, McGraw-Hill Book Co., Inc., New York.

Scott, W. B., 1937, A history of the land mammals of the Western Hemisphere, The Macmillan Co., New York.

Simpson, G. G., 1953, Life of the past, Yale Univ. Press, New Haven, Conn.

——, 1953, The major features of evolution, Columbia Univ. Press, New York.

——, 1961, Horses, Doubleday-Anchor Books, New York.

Stirton, R. A., 1959, Time, life, and man; the fossil record, John Wiley and Sons, Inc., New York.

Stock, Chester, 1949, Rancho la Brea, Los Angeles County Museum, Los Angeles, Calif.

Stokes, W. L., 1960, An introduction to earth history, Prentice-Hall, Inc., Englewood Cliffs, N. J.

Tax, Sol, and others, 1960, The evolution of man, Univ. of Chicago Press, Chicago, Ill.

Washburn, S. L., 1960, Tools and human evolution, Scientific American, v. 203, p. 62-75.

Washburn, S. L., and De Vore, Irven, 1961, The social life of baboons, Scientific American, v. 204, p. 62-71.

Wendt, Herbert, 1956, In search of Adam, Houghton Mifflin Co., Boston, Mass.

——, 1959, The road to man, Doubleday and Co., Garden City, New York.

Zeuner, F. E., 1950, Dating the past, Methuen and Co., London.

Index